Modern

METALWORKING

MATERIALS, TOOLS AND PROCEDURES

by

JOHN R. WALKER

Supervisor, Industrial Education
Harford County, Maryland

Homewood, Illinois

THE GOODHEART-WILLCOX COMPANY, INC.
Publishers

INTRODUCTION

MODERN METALWORKING supplies basic information on tools, materials, and procedures used in metalworking occupations. It covers both hand and machine-tool operations, and supplies background knowledge on industrial equipment and processes.

Metal is used for many different purposes. It is used to manufacture such items as jet and rocket engines where the material must withstand terrific heat. It is used to make buckets for mammoth earth movers where toughness is a must, and modern aircraft where light weight combined with great strength are required.

Metals are used to make things of beauty such as jewelry, tableware, furniture, and works of art. Fuel that powers the nuclear submarine is a metal; only a few pounds being needed to generate power required to propel the submarine around the world. Still another combination of metals has the unique ability to convert sunlight to electrical energy. A thin layer of metal only a microinch (1/1,000,000 in.) thick makes it possible for a computer to make split-second computations.

Just about every man-made thing we eat, see, feel, hear, smell and touch, has used metal in its manufacture.

With so much of our daily living depending upon metals, it is essential that we learn something about them; how they are worked, and the industry that uses them. The following paragraphs may answer your question, "Why study about metals?"

1. The metalworking industries in the United States employ more workers than any of the other industries. There is a great possibility that you will be employed in this area of our economy. This course will increase your understanding of the occupational requirements and opportunities in this field.

2. By studying and participating in the metalworking areas you have the opportunity to develop and practice basic skills necessary for vocational competence.

3. If you are a potential engineering student, you will have the opportunity to acquire information and develop skills that are considered basic to many engineering programs. These same skills may enable you to secure a better-than-average paying job during your summer vacation.

4. The technical knowledge you acquire may help you to advance more rapidly in the Armed Forces, should you decide to make this your career.

5. Many of the major items you will purchase during your lifetime will be made from metal. This course will help you develop an appreciation of good design and the ability to select, care for, and use industrial products wisely.

6. You will learn and practice safe work habits.

7. The problem-solving situations you encounter will give you opportunities to make practical applications of the math and science you have studied.

8. Perhaps you just like to work with your hands. If so, this will give you a chance to satisfy this desire.

CONTENTS

Contents

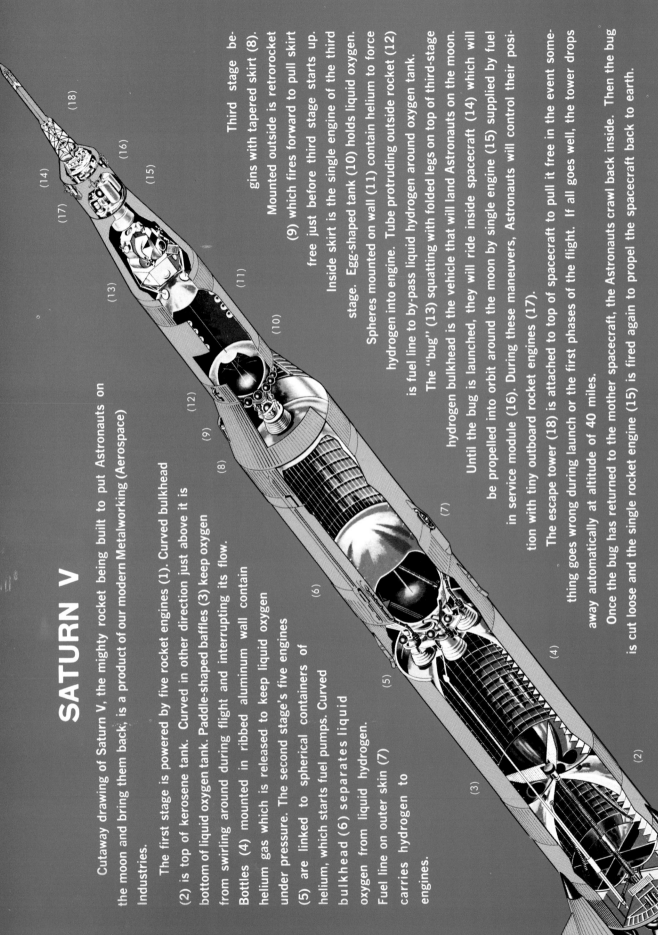

SATURN V

Cutaway drawing of Saturn V, the mighty rocket being built to put Astronauts on the moon and bring them back, is a product of our modern Metalworking (Aerospace) Industries.

The first stage is powered by five rocket engines (1). Curved bulkhead (2) is top of kerosene tank. Curved in other direction just above it is bottom of liquid oxygen tank. Paddle-shaped baffles (3) keep oxygen from swirling around during flight and interrupting its flow. Bottles (4) mounted in ribbed aluminum wall contain helium gas which is released to keep liquid oxygen under pressure. The second stage's five engines (5) are linked to spherical containers of helium, which starts fuel pumps. Curved bulkhead (6) separates liquid oxygen from liquid hydrogen. Fuel line on outer skin (7) carries hydrogen to engines.

Third stage begins with tapered skirt (8). Mounted outside is retrorocket (9) which fires forward to pull skirt free just before third stage starts up. Inside skirt is the single engine of the third stage. Egg-shaped tank (10) holds liquid oxygen. Spheres mounted on wall (11) contain helium to force hydrogen into engine. Tube protruding outside rocket (12) is fuel line to by-pass liquid hydrogen around oxygen tank. The "bug" (13) squatting with folded legs on top of third-stage hydrogen bulkhead is the vehicle that will land Astronauts on the moon. Until the bug is launched, they will ride inside spacecraft (14) which will be propelled into orbit around the moon by single engine (15) supplied by fuel in service module (16). During these maneuvers, Astronauts will control their position with tiny outboard rocket engines (17).

The escape tower (18) is attached to top of spacecraft to pull it free in the event something goes wrong during launch or the first phases of the flight. If all goes well, the tower drops away automatically at altitude of 40 miles. Once the bug has returned to the mother spacecraft, the Astronauts crawl back inside. Then the bug is cut loose and the single rocket engine (15) is fired again to propel the spacecraft back to earth.

(c) *Life Magazine, Time, Inc.*

Unit 1

METALS WE USE

At first thought, it would appear that everyone knows about metal. But do we know as much about it as we think we do? Metal is usually thought of as a material that is hard, strong, tough and withstands heat without melting. However, there are metals that have characteristics which are very unusual. For example: MERCURY is fluid at room temperature; body heat will melt

When you consider it realistically, it is impossible to tell all about a piece of metal by just looking at it. To help us better understand the properties of metals, industry has developed the science of METALLURGY. The person who does this work is called a METALLURGIST. One of his more important duties is to develop metals with special properties that will do a better job

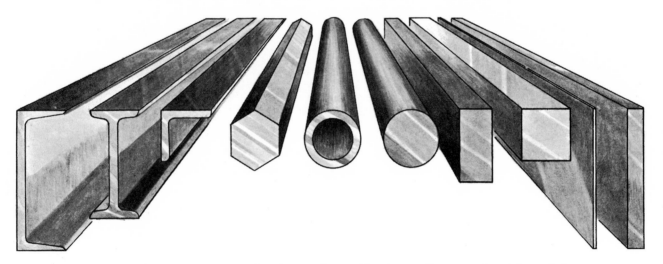

Fig. 1-1. Metal is available in a myriad of shapes and sizes. This drawing illustrates a few of the stock shapes.

GALLIUM in the palm of your hand; LITHIUM is so soft that it can be scratched by your finger nail. One thing we do know is that metals are available in a large range of sizes and shapes, Fig. 1-1.

Can you tell by looking at a piece of metal whether it is a FERROUS metal - a metal containing iron, or a NONFERROUS metal - a metal containing no iron? Is it an ALLOY - a mixture of two or more metals? Could it be a BASE metal - a pure metal like tin, copper, zinc, etc.? Then again, it might be a PRECIOUS metal - gold, silver, platinum, etc.

more economically. The metal being poured in Fig. 1-2, is the result of careful studies made by the metallurgist.

In making projects in the shop, or in industry, it is important to know which metal is best suited for the particular project. Must the metal be tough and hold an edge? Does it have to resist corrosion? Is weight an important factor? Does it have to be polished or will its natural finish be satisfactory? These are only a few of the many questions that must be considered when designing a project. The characteristics of a few of the most commonly used metals are included

Fig. 1-2. Making a "pour" of alloy steel from an electric arc furnace. (Steel Founders' Society of America)

on the following pages. Many of these can be found in the school shop.

FERROUS METALS

CAST IRON

Cast iron is a commonly used material in industry. It is a hard brittle metal but it machines well and is low in cost. It contains 3.0 to 4.0 percent carbon which is responsible for the brittleness and hardness. Several varieties of cast iron have been developed. WHITE CAST IRON is very hard and brittle. It is not too useful in this form and is converted to MALLEABLE IRON by an annealing process that involves heat-ing white cast iron and slowly cooling it under carefully controlled conditions of temperature and time. This annealing process can require several days. Malleable iron is a great deal stronger and tougher but more expensive than GRAY IRON, another form of cast iron, that is widely used by industry. Gray iron is used in great quantities because of its ability to flow readily into intricate mold passages, and form complex shapes such as engine blocks for automotive and diesel engines.

WROUGHT IRON

Wrought iron is iron with most of the carbon removed. It is tough and bends easily whether it is cold or heated. Wrought iron rusts very slowly and is readily welded. It is used to make such items as ornamental iron work, rivets, nails, wire, etc.

STEEL

Steel is an alloy of iron and carbon or some other alloying elements. The alloying elements impart to iron, the basic ingredient of all ferrous metals, certain desirable characteristics which are necessary if the metal is to perform certain jobs. When carbon is the alloying element, the steel is called CARBON STEEL. Carbon steels are classified by the percentage of carbon in "points" or hundredths of 1 percent they contain. LOW CARBON STEELS contain less than 0.30 percent carbon. These steels are easy to work, Fig. 1-3, can be welded, but cannot be hardened. Low carbon steel is available as band iron, black iron sheet, and many different shapes and sizes of bars and rods. MEDIUM CARBON STEELS contain 0.30 to 0.60 percent carbon. They are used for making such items as clamps, hammer heads, etc. HIGH CARBON STEELS contain 0.60 to 1.50 percent carbon. They are used for products that must be hardened and heat treated.

ALLOY STEELS

When elements other than carbon, such as CHROMIUM, MANGANESE, MOLYBDENUM, NICKEL, TUNGSTEN and VANADIUM are used to make steel harder, tougher and stronger, the resulting metals are called ALLOY STEELS.

CHROMIUM is added when toughness, hardness and wear resistance are desired. It is the basis of STAINLESS STEEL. Chromium

steel. Nickel steel does not rust easily. It also enables the metal to withstand shock. Much armor plate is nickel steel.

TUNGSTEN added in the proper amount makes steel self-hardening. Tools made from tungsten steel need no special hardening treatment and will withstand heat. It is used extensively for making cutting tools.

VANADIUM as an alloying element makes steel that has a fine grain and is very tough. Vanadium steel is used when a tough, strong but not brittle metal is needed.

TOOL STEELS

Tool steels by their nature are dense steels containing either a high percentage of carbon, or a high alloy content, or a combination of both. These steels are tough and are used when the tool must hold a cutting edge.

HIGH SPEED STEEL

High speed steel is a self-hardening steel alloy that withstands high temperatures without becoming soft. These characteristics make this alloy ideal as a cutting tool which can take deeper cuts at a higher speed than regular tool steels.

TUNGSTEN CARBIDE

Tungsten carbide is the hardest man-made metal. It is almost as hard as a diamond. The metal is molded from tungsten and carbon powders under heat and pressure. Tools made from this metal can cut metals many times faster than high speed steel.

Fig. 1-3. A step-by-step diagram of how steel angles are rolled. The forming rolls shape the stock gradually from a rectangular bar.

steel is used extensively for automobile and aircraft parts.

MANGANESE purifies steel and adds strength and toughness. Manganese steel is used for parts that must stand shock and hard wear.

MOLYBDENUM is used as the alloying element when the steel must remain tough at high temperatures.

NICKEL imparts toughness and strength to

GETTING ACQUAINTED WITH METALS

Rods, bars, sheets, plates and structural steel shapes are produced by passing the metal through a series of forming rolls that gradually form the billet of steel to the desired shape and size. When the metal is shaped while "red-hot" it is called HOT-ROLLED STEEL. See Fig. 1-4. Hot-rolled steel is characterized by the blue-black oxide that forms during the rolling process.

Selected hot-rolled steel shapes are PICK-LED, or treated with a dilute acid to remove the oxide coating. The metal is then rolled cold to

Steel sheet can be made more rigid by having designs embossed in its surface, Fig. 1-5. Economy is gained in some applications by slitting and expanding the metal sheet, Fig. 1-6.

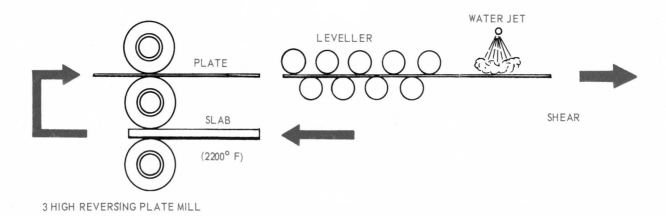

Fig. 1-4. Steel plate rolling mill.

the final shape and size. The steel that is shaped cold is known as COLD-FINISHED STEEL. Cold-finished steels are used where a fine finish is required; where a uniformity of temper is essential for best machinability; and where accuracy of shape and size are necessary without additional machining.

Hot-rolled and cold-finished steels sometimes receive additional treatment to shape them to final size and shape. Steel treated in this manner has a smooth bright surface and is very accurate in shape and size. This steel is called COLD DRAWN STEEL because it is pulled or "drawn" through a series of smooth holes in a

IDENTIFYING STEELS

Because the different kinds of steel look so much alike, several methods of identification have been developed. The American Iron and Steel Institute (AISI) has devised the PREFIX and NUMERICAL DESIGNATION to identify steels. A prefix letter A, B, C, D, or E, is used to designate the manufacturing process:

A - Denotes basic open hearth alloy steel.
B - Acid Bessemer carbon steel.
C - Basic open hearth carbon steel.
D - Acid open hearth steel.
E - Electric furnace steel.

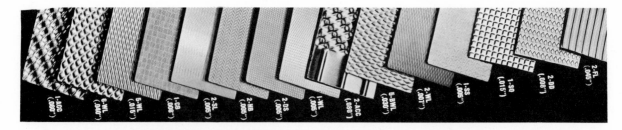

Fig. 1-5. A few of the many surface finishes and decorations available on metal sheet. These finishes enhance the appearance of the metal and make it more rigid. (Rigidized Metals Corp.)

hardened steel block called a DIE. This gradually reduces the bars or rods until they are the desired size. Hot-rolled steel must be cooled and pickled before it can be drawn. Wire is made by this process.

A four-numeral series identifies carbon steel or alloy steel specified to chemical composition ranges. The first number indicates the kind of steel: 1 is carbon steel; 2 is a nickel steel; 3 is a nickel-chromium steel; 4 is a molybdenum

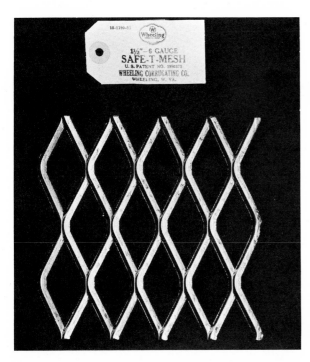

Fig. 1-6. Expanded metal is made by piercing or cutting slits in a piece of sheet metal. The edges of the sheet are gripped in a special machine and pressure is applied to pull or expand the sheet to many times its original width. There is no lost or waste metal when manufacturing this kind of metal sheet.
(Wheeling Corrugating Co.)

steel; etc. The second number indicates the approximate percentages of alloy element in the steel. The last two digits of the four-numeral series are intended to indicate the approximate middle of the carbon content range. For example: 20 represents a range of 0.18 to 0.23 percent carbon. AISI C-1020 indicates a carbon steel with 20 points or 0.20 percent carbon.

COLOR CODING

Color coding, Fig. 1-7, is another method used to identify steel. Each different kind of commonly-used steel is identified by a certain color. The color coding is painted on the end of the bar, if it is 1 in. or larger. On bars that are less than 1 in. the color may be applied to the ends of the bar or on an attached tag.

SPARK TEST

The spark test, Fig. 1-8, is also used to determine the grade of steel. It has proved successful as a practical shop test. The material should touch the grinding wheel lightly and the resulting sparks carefully observed.

NONFERROUS METALS

There are many metals that do not have iron as their basic ingredient. These metals are known as nonferrous metals. Several nonferrous metals are used in the school shop because of their desirable characteristics. They are easy to machine, can be joined (soldered, brazed, riveted, etc.) with little difficulty, and take an excellent polish or finish. Nonferrous metals are often used with other metals in the finished product, Fig. 1-9.

ALUMINUM

Aluminum has come to mean a large family of metals and not just a single metal. The various alloys are classified by the Aluminum Association Alloy Designation System. Pure aluminum is somewhat soft and weak. Increased strength is accomplished by adding small amounts of other elements such as copper, manganese, zinc, and magnesium. Some of the alloys that have been developed are, pound for pound, stronger than structural steel.

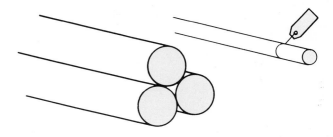

Fig. 1-7. Color coding steel rods.

Aluminum alloys have a number of desirable qualities. They are lighter than most other commercially available metals. They do not rust or corrode; can be shaped and formed easily; are strong; and are readily available in a wide assortment of shapes, sizes, and alloys, at moderate cost.

ALUMINUM ALLOYS 1100 and 3003 are almost pure aluminum (about 99 percent and 98 percent respectively) and are used where strength is secondary, but where workability and finish are important, and cost must be kept to a minimum.

5052 is an alloy containing about 2.5 percent magnesium. It is about twice as strong as 3003 and is a general-purpose alloy used for sheet

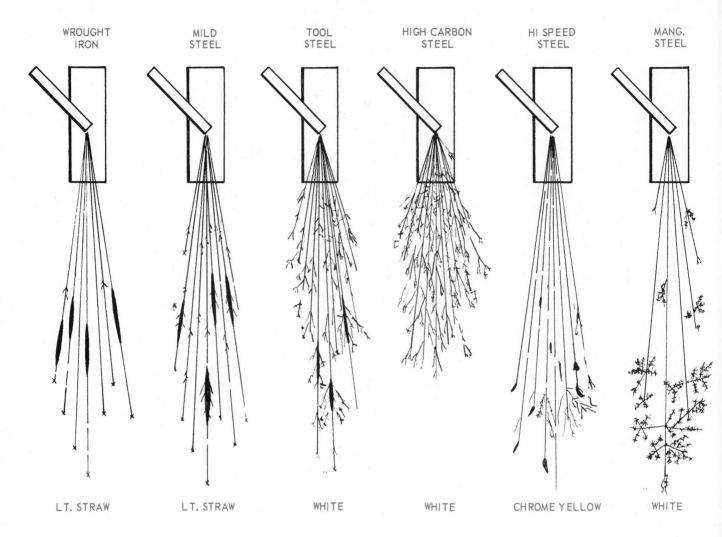

WROUGHT IRON	MILD STEEL	TOOL STEEL	HIGH CARBON STEEL	HI SPEED STEEL	MANG. STEEL
LT. STRAW	LT. STRAW	WHITE	WHITE	CHROME YELLOW	WHITE

Fig. 1-8. Spark tests used to determine grades of steel.

metal work. The alloy has excellent resistance to corrosion, and in this respect is superior to most other aluminum alloys. It is used in applications that are subject to abuse.

6061 is another general-purpose aluminum alloy. It is readily joined by all methods of welding. 6061-T4 (tempered) is widely used for such items as bus and truck trailer construction, shipping containers, and small boats and canoes.

2024 is a high-strength aluminum alloy that has wide application in the aircraft industry.

7075-T6 aluminum alloy is the highest strength aluminum alloy that is commercially available. Because of this higher strength, it is rapidly replacing 2024 in many applications of aircraft construction, Fig. 1-10.

Many alloys in sheet form are CLAD with pure aluminum to make them more resistant to corrosion. This covering is only a few thousandths of an inch thick, and is bonded to the sheet when it is rolled to the desired thickness.

Fig. 1-9. This model aircraft engine uses more than a dozen different metals and alloys in its construction.
(L. M. Cox Mfg. Co.)

Fig. 1-10. The aircraft industry uses tremendous quantities of aluminum and other metals in the construction of modern aircraft. (Cessna Aircraft Corp.)

ALLOY DESIGNATIONS

Besides being available in a multitude of shapes and sizes, alloys can be purchased in varying deg. of hardness. The designations are indicated by suffixes to the alloy number. Designations for all heat-treated alloys are as follows:

-F as fabricated (condition as cast or extruded, Fig. 1-11)

-0 annealed (soft)

In addition to -F and -0 temper, the alloys can be had in a number of higher strength tempers which are obtained by heat treatment. This series is designated by the letter -T followed by one or more numbers which indicates how the metal was treated - 7075-T6, 6061-T4, etc.

Non-heat treatable alloys are also available in -F and -0 condition. Non-heat treatable alloy sheet and wire are manufactured in several additional tempers. These are designated by the letter -H followed by two numbers. The first number denotes the process involved in producing the temper. The second number indicates the actual temper (deg. of hardness):

2 1/4 hard (2/8) - 3003-H12

OPERATION 1

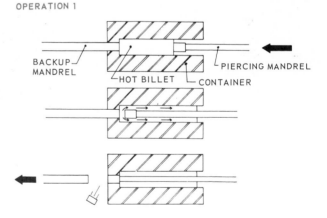

BILLET IS REMOVED AND PUT IN NEW PRESS FOR OPERATION 2

OPERATION 2

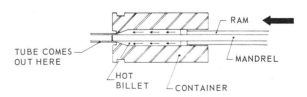

Fig. 1-11. Diagrams showing how tubing is extruded.

4   1/2 hard (4/8) - 3003-H14
6   3/4 hard (6/8) - 3003-H36
8   full hard (8/8) - 5052-H38

Like other metals in sheet form, aluminum can be secured with virtually dozens of different surface patterns and finishes, Fig. 1-12.

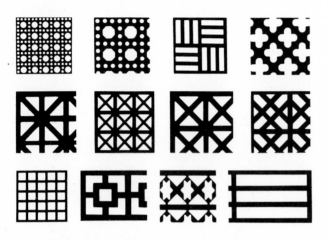

Fig. 1-12. Typical perforated metal sheet patterns.

MAGNESIUM

Magnesium is the lightest of our structural metals. It is obtained from the inexhaustible waters of the oceans and is silvery white in color. Magnesium has many desirable characteristics - high strength to weight; unexcelled machinability; and the ability to be worked by all common methods. For higher strength, magnesium is alloyed with aluminum, zinc, manganese, zirconium, thorium or combinations of these metals.

COPPER

Copper, which is a base metal, is the oldest metal known to man. It is easily identified by its rich reddish-brown color. The metal is a good conductor of electricity, second only to silver. Much copper is used for art metalwork because of its easy-to-work qualities. It can be shaped easily but becomes hard when it is worked and must be softened or annealed. This is done by heating it to a cherry-red color and quenching or cooling it in water. Copper can be readily joined with rivets, and both soft and hard solders.

When copper is exposed to the air for a period of time a greenish tinge called PATINA develops. This can be removed by polishing. However, on certain copper articles, a fine natural patina is desirable.

Copper can be purchased in a large variety of shapes and sizes. Sheet copper is measured by either of two methods:

THICKNESS BY GAUGE (Brown & Sharp and American Standard).

WEIGHT IN OUNCES PER SQUARE FOOT.

BRASS

Brass is an alloy of copper and zinc. It is bright yellow and one of the more important alloys of copper. The proportion of copper to zinc varies according to the use of the metal. Commercial brass contains about 90 percent copper and 10 percent zinc. The working characteristics are almost identical to those of copper.

BRONZE

Bronze is another alloy with copper as the chief ingredient. It is composed of copper and tin, and is reddish-gold in color. Bronze is harder than brass and is also more expensive.

ZINC

Zinc is familiar as a protective coating on steel and iron. This coating is called GALVANIZING, and is done by dipping the metal into molten zinc. Zinc is alloyed with copper to make brass. Zinc is a bluish-white crystalline metal that is brittle.

TIN

Tin is a soft, shiny silvery metal that is rarely used except as an alloying agent. Tin is familiar as the shiny exterior surface of the "tin can" because it provides excellent protection against corrosion and is non-toxic. When alloyed with copper it forms bronze. Tin is also the chief ingredient of pewter.

PEWTER

Modern pewter or Britannia metal is an alloy of tin (91 percent), copper (1-1/2 percent) and antimony (7-1/2 percent). When polished, it has a fine silvery white sheen. Modern pewter DOES NOT CONTAIN LEAD and can be used to serve food and drink. However, old pewter may contain lead and should not be used for this purpose. Pewter is a pleasant metal to work, but skill is required to join it properly. Because a soldered joint will eventually oxidize and become noticeable, all joints should be fused.

GAR-ALLOY

Gar-alloy is a zinc-base alloy with small amounts of copper and silver being used to impart strength. It is used as a substitute for

GERMAN SILVER

German or nickel silver is used as a substitute for silver in the manufacture of inexpensive jewelry. It is another copper-base alloy with varying quantities of nickel and zinc. It has working characteristics that are very similar to those of brass, with the exception that it is rather brittle, and cannot be hammered

MATERIAL	HOW MEASURED	HOW PURCHASED	CHARACTERISTICS
Sheet (less than 1/4" thick)			
COPPER	Gauge number (Brown & Sharp & Amer. Std.)	24 x 96" sheet or 12 or 18" by lineal feet on roll	Pure metal
BRASS	Gauge number (B & S and Amer. Std.)	24 x 76" sheet or 12 or 18" by lineal feet on roll	Alloy of copper & zinc
ALUMINUM	Decimal	24 x 72" sheet or 12 or 18" by lineal feet on roll	Available as commercially pure metal or alloyed for strength, hardness, & ductility
GALVANIZED STEEL	Gauge number (U. S. Std.)	24 x 96" sheet	Mild steel sheet with zinc plating, also available with zinc coating that is part of sheet
BLACK ANNEALED STEEL SHEET	Gauge number (U. S. Std.)	24 x 96" sheet	Mild steel with oxide coating-hot rolled
COLD ROLLED STEEL SHEET	Gauge number (U. S. Std.)	24 x 96" sheet	Oxide removed and cold rolled to final thickness
TIN PLATE	Gauge number (U. S. Std.)	20 x 28" sheet 56 or 112 to pkg	Mild steel with tin coating
NICKEL SILVER	Gauge number (Brown & Sharp)	6 or 12" wide by lineal sheet	Copper 50%, zinc 30%, nickel 20%
EXPANDED	Gauge number (U. S. Std.)	36 x 96"	Metal is pierced and expanded (stretched) to diamond shape; also available rolled to thickness after it has been expanded
PERFORATED	Gauge number (U. S. Std.)	30 x 36" 36 x 48"	Design is cut in sheet; many designs available.

Fig. 1-13. Metals we use--how measured, how purchased, characteristics.

pewter because it is not as costly, and does have several of the qualities of pewter. Gar-alloy is a bluish-gray metal that works well cold, and can be buffed to a high polish.

into shape. Nickel silver, with a composition of 64 percent copper, 18 percent nickel and 18 percent zinc, is widely used as the base for most silver-plated ware.

STERLING SILVER

Silver combined with a small amount of copper (7-1/2 percent) is known as sterling silver.

When polished, it has a very shiny silvery-white color. Sterling silver has outstanding working characteristics. It can be readily shaped and formed, and it hard solders well.

SHAPES		LENGTH	HOW MEASURED	*HOW PURCHASED	OTHER
 Sheet less than 1/4" thick		to 144"	Thickness x width widths to 72"	Weight, foot or piece	Available in coils of much longer lengths
 Plate more than 1/4" thick		to 20'	Thickness x width	Weight, foot or piece	
 Band		to 20'	Thickness x width	Weight, or piece	Mild steel with oxide coating
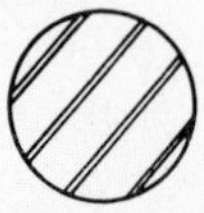 Rod		12 to 20'	Diameter	Weight, foot or piece	Hot rolled steel to 20' length - cold finished steel to 12' length - steel drill rod 36"
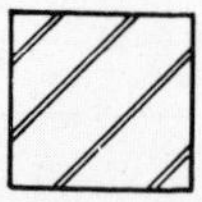 Square		12 to 20'	Width	Weight, foot or piece	
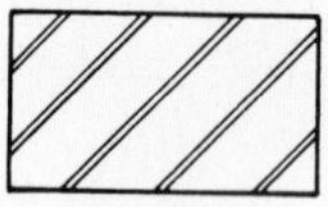 Flats		Hot rolled 20-22' Cold finished	Thickness x width	Weight, foot or piece	
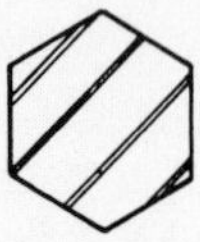 Hexagon		12 to 20'	Distance across flats	Weight, foot or piece	
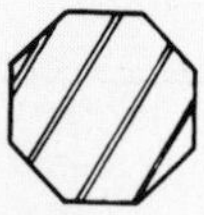 Octagon		12 to 20'	Distance across flats	Weight, foot or piece	
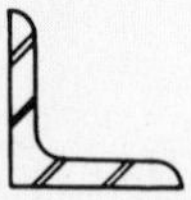 Angle		Lengths to 40'	Leg length x leg length x thickness of legs	Weight, foot or piece	
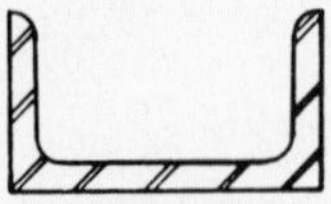 Channel		Lengths to 60'	Depth x web thickness x flange width	Weight, foot or piece	
 I-beam		Lengths to 60'	Height x web thickness x flange width	Weight, foot or piece	

* Charge made for cutting to other than standard lengths.

Fig. 1-14. Metals we use -- shapes available, how measured, purchased, characteristics.

SPACE AGE METALS

The advent of the missile and high-speed aircraft has required the development of metals with great strength and rigidity at high temperatures. At the same time, these metals must be reasonable in weight. Many metals that were originally used only as alloying elements - manganese, molybdenum, nickel, etc., are finding importance as the base metal because of their desirable characteristics at elevated temperatures. A few of the more widely used space metals are described below.

TITANIUM

Titanium will be an important airframe structure material of the future. It compares to low alloy steel in strength but weighs only about half as much. Many titanium alloys are heat treatable and retain high strength up to 1100 deg. F.

BERYLLIUM

Beryllium is easily worked, light in weight, has good elevated temperature properties, but its brittleness creates problems in many forming operations. It is currently used in nuclear reactors and some missile components.

COLUMBIUM

Columbium is of interest to the manufacturers of space vehicles because of its high melting point - 4380 deg. F. It has good strength at 1800-2000 deg. F.

It is under study for nuclear reactor application because of its resistance to radiation damage.

OTHER METALS

Into this category fall the many metals that are still in the development stage. Metallurgists know their properties, but machining, forming and fabricating them involves problems which have not yet been solved. Metals like tantalum and tungsten alloys that can be used in the 2500-4000 deg. F. range are being developed. You may be the metallurgist that makes the breakthrough that will make these metals as widely used as aluminum is today.

SHAPES OF METALS WE USE

The chart, Fig. 1-13, lists several commonly used metals and how they are measured and purchased. Fig. 1-14, indicates shapes in which a number of metals are commonly manufactured, measured, and purchased.

TEST YOUR KNOWLEDGE, Unit 1

Write your answers to these questions on a separate sheet of paper. Do not write in this book.

1. A metal is considered a ferrous metal when it
   a. Contains a large portion of iron.
   b. Contains no iron.
   c. Is a mixture of two or more metals.
   d. None of the above.
2. A metal is called an alloy when
   a. Contains a large portion of iron.
   b. Contains no iron.
   c. Is a mixture of two or more metals.
   d. None of the above.
3. A nonferrous metal
   a. Contains a large portion of iron.
   b. Is a mixture of two or more metals.
   c. Contains only a little iron.
   d. None of the above.

4. Brass is an alloy of _____ and _____.
5. _____ is formed when tin and copper is alloyed.
6. Carefully examine the following list of metals. Which does not belong?
   a. Copper.
   b. Aluminum.
   c. Bronze.
   d. Brass.
7. Which metal does not belong?
   a. Copper.
   b. Tin.
   c. Steel.
   d. Zinc.
8. Chromium, manganese, molybdenum, nickel, tungsten and vanadium are used to make steel _____, _____ and _____.
9. _____ _____ is the hardest man-made metal.

Unit 2

UNDERSTANDING DRAWINGS

Drawings, made mechanically with drafting instruments or sketched free hand, are used by industry to tell the craftsman what to make and how to make it. Symbols, lines and special fig-

ures are employed to give drawings meaning. See Fig. 2-1. They have been standardized to mean the same thing wherever drawings are made and used. Frequently these symbols are

VISIBLE OBJECT LINES *are used to outline edges of the object that can be seen.*

HIDDEN OBJECT LINES *represent edges of the object that are hidden from view.*

DIMENSION LINES *are capped at each end with an arrowhead. It is used to indicate distances.*

EXTENSION LINES *indicate points from which the dimensions are given.*

CENTER LINES *are light lines that locate centers of symmetrical objects, like circles, holes, etc.*

CUTTING PLANE LINES *are used to show where an object has been cut in order to show the interior features more clearly.*

SECTION LINES *indicate the area or section cut by the cutting plane line. They also indicate the general classification of the material from which the object is to be made.*

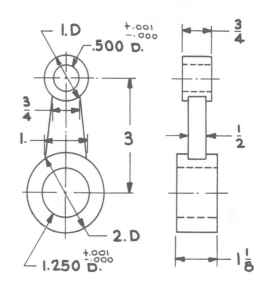

SAMPLE DRAWING

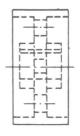

NOT SECTIONED

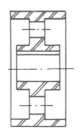

SECTIONAL VIEW

Fig. 2-1. Lines and what they mean.

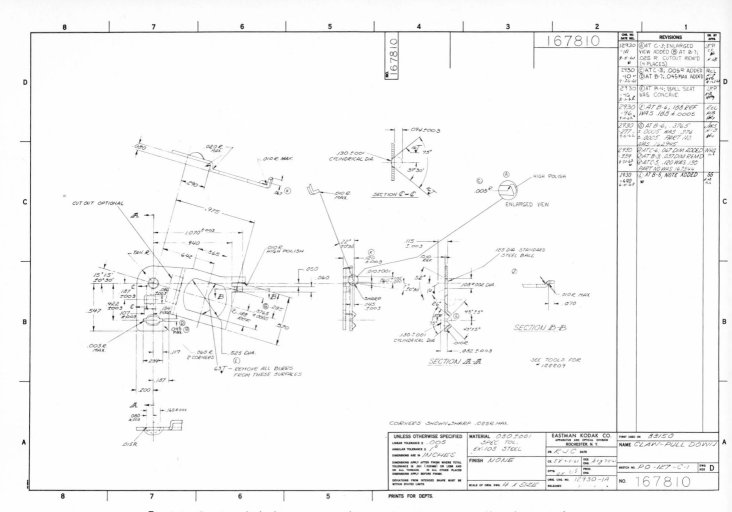

Fig. 2-2a. Drawing which shows a part used in a motion picture camera. Note the required accuracy.
All information necessary to manufacture the part is included. (Eastman Kodak Co.)

called THE LANGUAGE OF INDUSTRY.

The lines are used to draw the views that are necessary to fully describe the object, Fig. 2-2a. In addition to this, the drawing also includes other pertinent information needed to manufacture the object.

NECESSARY DIMENSIONS IN PROPER RELATION

Drawings are dimensioned in inches and common fractions when the object does not require a high degree of accuracy. Greater precision is indicated when the dimensions are given in inches and decimal parts of the inch. A properly executed drawing includes all dimensions, in proper relation to one another, that are required to manufacture the piece.

MATERIALS TO BE USED

The general classification of materials to be used in the manufacture of an object is indicated by the type of section line shown on the plan. The exact metal specification is included in the notes or in a section of the title block.

FINISHES REQUIRED

In the past symbols were used to indicate how the surfaces were to be finished (machined). With so many machining techniques in use now, symbols are no longer used because they do not indicate the quality of the surface finish required. A new method has been developed that gives more complete surface finish information. Numbers are used to indicate the surface roughness in MICRO-INCHES (a micro-inch is one-millionth of an inch - 0.000001 in.). The machinist can compare the surface of the work by using a set of SURFACE ROUGHNESS COMPARISON STANDARDS, Fig. 2-3, as a guide. If the surface finish is critical, as it is in some missile components, the finish is measured electronically with a device called a PROFILOMETER.

TOLERANCES TO BE ALLOWED

Tolerances are allowances in either oversize or undersize the machinist is permitted to take when making an object. Acceptable tolerances may be shown on drawings in several different ways.

When the dimension is given in inches and fractions of an inch, UNLESS OTHERWISE INDICATED, the permissible tolerances can be assumed to be $\pm$ 1/64 in. The symbol $\pm$ means that the machined surface can be PLUS (larger) or MINUS (smaller) by 1/64 in. The dimension can be larger or smaller by 1/64 in. and still be acceptable. When the tolerance is plus AND minus, it is called a BILATERAL TOLERANCE. If it is permissible to make the dimension larger, but not smaller, the dimension on the plan would read $2\text{-}1/2\ ^{+1/64}$. If only a minus tolerance is permitted, the dimension would read $2\text{-}1/2\ ^{-1/64}$. When the tolerance is plus OR minus (one direction), it is called a UNILATERAL DIMENSION.

Dimensions shown as inches and decimals indicate that the work must be made more accurately. Two methods of showing these tolerances are in general use. Under normal conditions, UNLESS OTHERWISE INDICATED, the tolerances can be assumed to be $\pm$ 0.010 in. A PLUS tolerance would be shown as $2.500\ ^{+.001}$ or $\dfrac{2.501}{2.500}$ while a MINUS tolerance would be shown as $2.500\ ^{-.001}$ or $\dfrac{2.500}{2.499}$. The dimensions show that the part could be used as long as the machined dimensions measure within these limits.

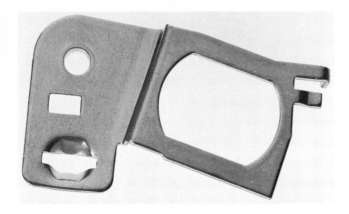

Fig. 2-2b. A photograph of the part shown on the drawing 2a. (Eastman Kodak Co.)

QUANTITY OF UNITS

The plans show the number of units required. This facilitates ordering the necessary materials, and will help to determine the way the pieces can be manufactured most economically.

SCALE OF DRAWING

When drawings are made other than actual size they are called SCALE DRAWINGS. The scale is usually shown in a section of the title

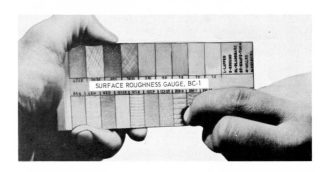

Fig. 2-3. A surface roughness comparison standard. This measuring device contains sections of metal that have been machined by various methods (turned, shaped, milled, etc.) to predetermined degrees of roughness. (H. B. Tools)

block. A drawing made one-half size would be shown by figures 1:2 while 2:1 would mean that the drawing is twice the actual size. See Fig. 2-4.

ASSEMBLY OR SUB-ASSEMBLY

This information is necessary to correctly fit the various pieces together.

NAME OF THE OBJECT AND ON WHAT IT IS TO BE USED

A portion of the title block is designed especially for this information. It tells the mechanic the correct name of the piece, and the name of the major unit on which it is to be used.

Very seldom are the original drawings used in the shop because they might be lost, damaged or destroyed. On many jobs several sets of plans are needed.

Several methods of duplicating original drawings have been developed including:

1. BLUEPRINTS. The lines are white on a blue background. Seldom used in the modern shop.
2. OZALID (Trade-mark). White background with black, blue, green or maroon lines depending on the chemicals used to sensitize the paper. The print is developed by ammonia vapor.
3. VAN DYKE (Trade-mark). Similar to the blueprint except that the background is dark brown with white lines. Van Dyke

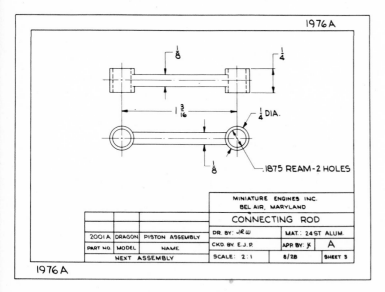

Fig. 2-4. Detail drawing. Note indication of scale in panel block.

Most products made by industry require numerous drawings to give a complete description of the object. Each piece, even the smallest rivet, requires a drawing. Such drawings are called WORKING DRAWINGS, because they give the craftsman the necessary information to make and assemble the many pieces that make up the product. There are two kinds of working drawings. The DETAIL DRAWING, Fig. 2-4, includes a drawing of the part, usually multiview drawing, with dimensions and other information needed to make the part. The other type of working drawing is called an ASSEMBLY DRAWING, Fig. 2-5, because it shows where and how the parts described on the detail drawings fit into the complete assembly of the unit. On large or complicated objects SUB-ASSEMBLY DRAWINGS, Fig. 2-6, are frequently used. Each drawing shows the assembly of a small portion of the complete object.

The detail drawing, in most instances, gives information on only one item. However, if the mechanism is small in size or if it is composed

prints are made on thin paper and are often used as masters to make additional prints.

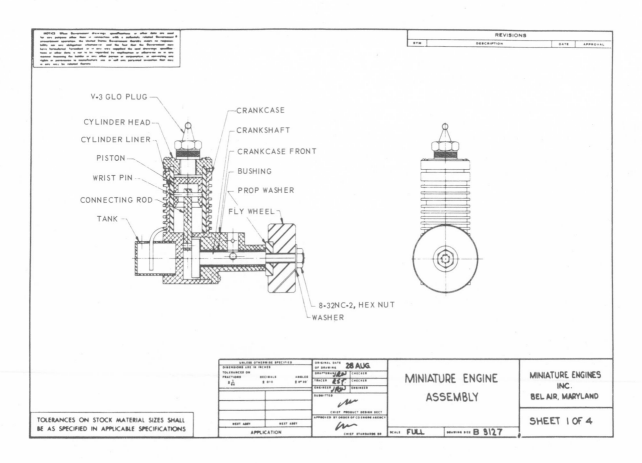

Fig. 2-5. Assembly drawing.

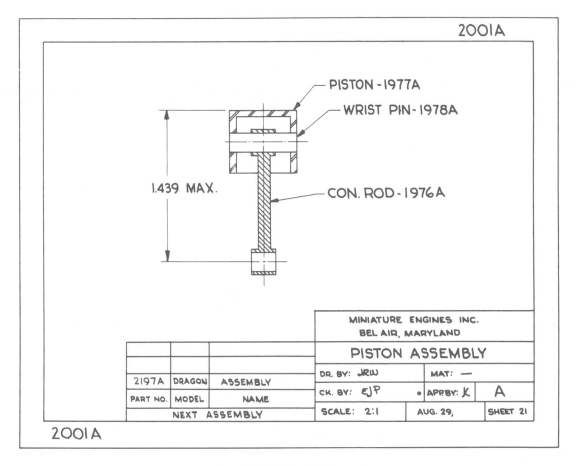

Fig. 2-6. Sub-assembly drawing.

of only a few parts, the details and assembly may appear on the same sheet.

The parts are identified by numbers which may be circled and/or shown on a title note.

The number of pieces required in the assembly will also be included. Some drawings will have a PARTS LIST or BILL OF MATERIALS, Fig. 2-7.

PARTS LIST		
Nº	NAME	QUAN.
1	CRANKCASE	1
2	CRANKSHAFT	1
3	CRANK CASE COV.	1
4	CYLINDER	2
5	PISTON	2

PARTS LIST

1776 A	WASHER	STEEL	6
1985A	NUT	STEEL	6
1761 A	BOLT	STEEL	6
17652B	PLATE	ALUM.	1
17671C	CYLINDER	C. I.	2
PART Nº	NAME	MATERIAL	QUAN
BILL OF MATERIALS			

BILL OF MATERIALS

Fig. 2-7. Parts list and bill of materials.

Most firms use standard size sheets for their drawings. This simplifies the storage of completed drawings.

For convenience in filing and locating drawings, industry gives each plate or drawing an identifying number.

TEST YOUR KNOWLEDGE, Unit 2

1. Drawings are used to:
   a. Standardize parts.
   b. Protect the original sketches.
   c. Show what to make and how to make it.
   d. Show in multiview what an object looks like before it is made.
2. The symbols and lines used to make drawings are frequently called the language of industry. True or false?
3. Drawings often indicate which machinist is to do the job. True or false?
4. A pictorial drawing shows separate views of the object that is to be machined. True or false?
5. A drawing seldom shows all of the dimensions needed to machine the object. True or false?
6. Drawings are often numbered to make them easier to file and locate. True or false?
7. A sub-assembly differs from an assembly drawing by:
   a. Showing only a small portion of the complete object.
   b. Making it easier to use smaller drawings.
   c. Showing the object without all needed dimensions.
   d. None of the above.
8. Prints are used instead of the actual drawing because:
   a. The actual drawing does not show all of the details.
   b. They might be lost, damaged or destroyed.
   c. They are easier to read.
   d. None of the above.
9. _____ drawings give the craftsman all of the information needed to make the part.
10. _____ show the object in two or more views.
11. _____ drawings show where and how the parts described on other drawings fit into the complete assembly of the unit.
12. Standard size drawings have been developed to:
   a. Make them easier to store.
   b. Causes less confusion.
   c. Make them easier to handle.
   d. None of the above.

RESEARCH AND DEVELOPMENT

1. Secure sample drawings from a local industry. Develop a bulletin board display around them.
2. Make a tracing and reproduce it in print form.
3. Secure samples of reproductions made by the blueprint, Ozalid and Van Dyke processes.
4. Prepare a display panel showing a simple project from drawing to completed object.
5. Prepare transparencies for the overhead projector that show the title block, parts list, and material list of an actual industrial drawing. Use these to explain or describe an industrial drawing to the class. If possible, secure a sample of the product shown on the drawing.
6. Make a display panel showing how six metals are identified by section lines. Fasten a sample of the actual metal under each drawing.
7. Contact a local industry and secure the drawings of a simple assembly. If possible, also secure samples of the piece that was manufactured from each print. Develop a display panel around the drawings and pieces made from them.

Unit 3

SHOP SAFETY

The development of safe work habits is one aspect of metalworking that cannot be over-emphasized. YOUR safety and well-being are of paramount importance to your instructor. Please remember this when he insists on safe work

Fig. 3-1. Instructor and students in school metal shop wearing industrial quality safety glasses. These industrial workers of to-morrow are learning good safety habits.
(National Society for Prevention of Blindness)

practices. If you are diligent and follow his instructions with care, safe work practices will be observed by force of habit.

You are not a "sissy" if you wear goggles, use machine guards, and observe the one-thousand and one safe work practices of metal-working. Eyesight that is destroyed cannot be replaced. Most accidents are caused because simple safety rules were not observed.

The safety practices presented in this unit are general in nature. Safety precautions for specific tools and machines are described in the text along with the descriptions of the tools. Study them carefully and apply as necessary. Do not take chances - IT HURTS TO GET HURT.

FOR THE SHOP

The shop is a place to work. It is not for "horseplay" or trick playing which frequently ends up tragically. Daydreaming increases your chance of injury.

Keep the shop clean. Metal scraps should be thrown in a scrap box rather than just letting them drop on the floor. There they may cause you or a fellow student to trip and fall.

Never use compressed air to clean machines of chips and cutting oil. The flying chips can cause painful eye injuries, and the vaporized oil may be ignited and cause serious burns.

Oily rags must be placed in a closed container. Rags used to clean machines become imbedded with metal slivers. Place them where they will not be used again and dispose of them.

Keep hand tools in good condition and store them in such a way that a person will not be injured when he secures a tool from the tool panel or storage rack.

Get help when moving heavy machine accessories or large pieces of metal stock.

Have adequate ventilation for jobs where dust and fumes are a hazard. Replace oils and solvents to proper storage. Wipe up any that has been spilled.

Dress properly. Never wear loose fitting sweaters or clothing. Rings and other jewelry that might be caught in moving parts should be removed. Keep your sleeves rolled up. If you wear a tie, make it a bow tie.

ALWAYS protect your eyes. Wear safety glasses, goggles, or a face shield. See Figs. 3-1 and 3-2. It is good practice to have personal

Fig. 3-2. Note safety equipment being worn by this workman in Garwood, N. J. works of Aluminum Co. of America.

safety glasses or goggles. The cost is reasonable. Your instructor can help you determine what kind and style is best suited for your needs. Take no chances. Protect your eyes at all times when you are in the shop.

Know your job. It is foolish to operate machines without first receiving instructions. Get additional instructions if you are not sure what must be done or how it is to be done.

When operating machines:

1. Never operate a machine unless all of the guards are in place.
2. Stop the machine to make measurements or adjustments. Resist the urge to touch the machined surface while the machine is running.
3. Keep the floor around the machine clear of chips and scraps.
4. Do not talk to classmates while operating

machines. You might become distracted and injure yourself.

5. Never attempt to remove chips or cuttings with your hands, or while the machine is running. Use a brush, Fig. 3-3. Use pliers to remove long, stringy chips from the lathe. Better still, grind the cutting tool to break the chips off shorter.
6. Get prompt medical attention for any cut, bruise, or scratch, no matter how minor it might appear.

Do not carry sharp pointed tools, or for that matter any tools, in your pockets. Neither

Fig. 3-3. Use a brush to remove metal chips. NEVER use your hand.

should you try to carry a hand full of tools to or from the tool crib. Many injuries have been received this way.

Be sure all tools are sharp, are in good condition, and are fitted with suitable handles.

THINK BEFORE ACTING, it does not cost a thing and may save you from a painful injury as well as complete disability.

TEST YOUR KNOWLEDGE, Unit 3

1. Safety goggles or spectacles must be worn in the shop to:
   a. Prevent eye injury.
   b. Prevent sweat from running into the eyes.
   c. Keep fumes from entering the eyes.
   d. Help you to see better.
   e. None of the above.

2. Always stop machines before making _____ and_____.
3. Most accidents are caused because_____
   _____ _____ _____.
4. Compressed air should not be used to clean chips from machines because:
   a. It does the job too quickly.

b. It may damage the machine.

c. Flying chips may cause serious eye injuries.

d. None of the above.

5. Make every possible effort to catch a heavy falling machine accessory. True or False?

6. Adequate ventilation is not necessary if you plan to work for only a short time in an area contaminated with dust and fumes. True or false?

7. Loose clothing may be worn when operating machines if you are careful. True or false?

8. Chips should be removed with a brush not your hands. True or false?

RESEARCH AND DEVELOPMENT

1. Invite a safety expert from a local industry or a supplier of safety equipment to evaluate your present shop safety program and make recommendations, if necessary, to improve it.

2. Work with school officials to see that necessary protective eyewear is available for each student.

3. Develop and produce a series of safety posters for the shop.

4. Contact the NATIONAL SOCIETY FOR THE PREVENTION OF BLINDNESS, 1790 Broadway, New York 19, N. Y., for information on the WISE OWL CLUB OF AMERICA, sponsored by that organization.

5. Produce a series of 35mm slides on safe work habits to be observed when using hand tools.

6. Design a bulletin board display on eye safety.

Note the safety equipment worn by this machine operator while he performs work on a band machine.
(DoAll Co.)

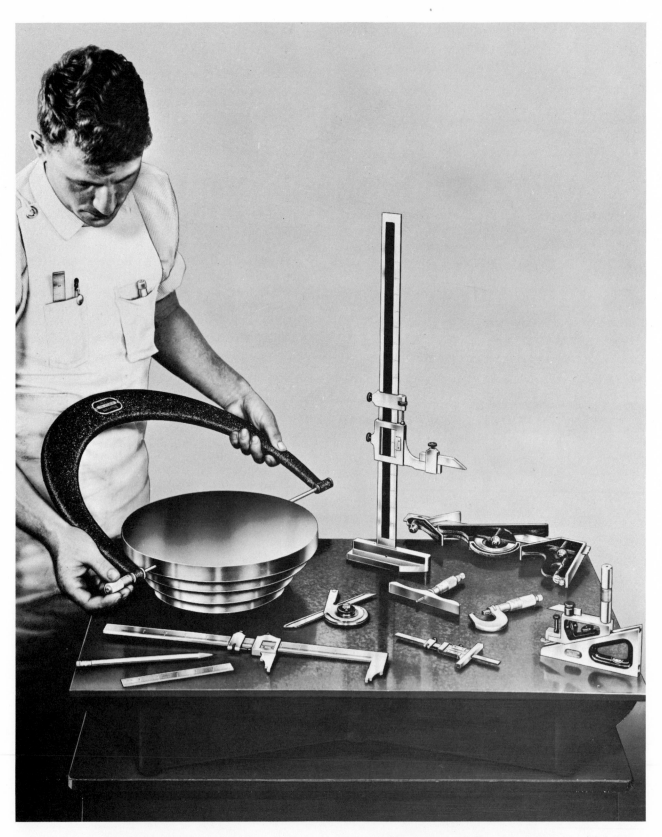

Many of the common measuring tools used by the machinist. Many of them measure to 1/1000 in. This is about one-third the thickness of a human hair or a newspaper page.

Unit 4

MEASUREMENT

Today, industry makes measurements accurately to a millionth (0.000001) part of an inch. This is known as a MICRO-INCH. If the micro-inch were the thickness of a dime, an inch would be as high as four Empire State buildings. An engineer, with tongue in cheek, once estimated that a millionth of an inch was the distance a railroad rail sagged when a fat horsefly landed on it.

Regardless of how fine industry can measure, the task at hand is to learn to read the rule to 1/64 in.: progress through 1/1000 (0.001) in. by micrometer caliper and Vernier caliper; and finally to 1/10000 (0.0001) in. by the Vernier scale on the hub of a micrometer caliper.

THE RULE

TYPES OF RULES

The steel rule, incorrectly referred to as a scale, is the simplest measuring tool in the shop. A few of the many types and how they are used are shown in Figs. 4-1a to 1p incl.

READING THE RULE

A careful study of the enlarged section of the rule, Fig. 4-2, will show the different fractional divisions of the inch from 1/8 to 1/64 in. The lines representing the divisions are called

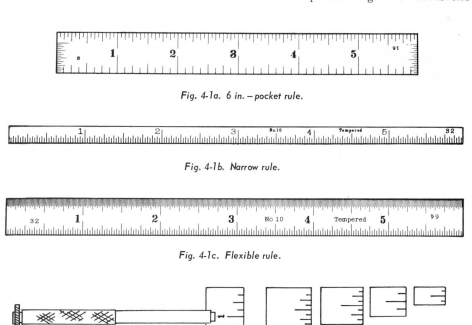

Fig. 4-1a. 6 in. – pocket rule.

Fig. 4-1b. Narrow rule.

Fig. 4-1c. Flexible rule.

Fig. 4-1d. Narrow rules with holder. The five small rule sections are interchangeable in the holder, and can be set at various angles. Rules are graduated in 1/32 and 1/64.

Fig. 4-1e. Rule with a beveled edge that puts the graduations closer to the work thus reducing the possibility for error.

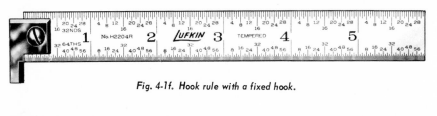

Fig. 4-1f. Hook rule with a fixed hook.

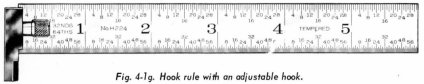

Fig. 4-1g. Hook rule with an adjustable hook.

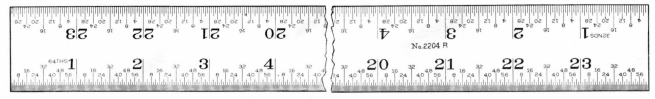

Fig. 4-1h. 12-in. rule. Note how the graduations are numbered. This rule has No. 4 graduations (see table).

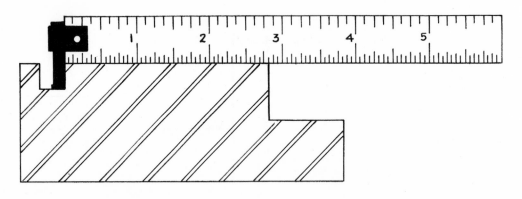

Fig. 4-1j. How the hooked rule is used.

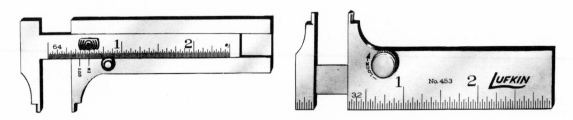

Fig. 4-1k. A slide caliper rule is fitted to the work and locked. Outside dimensions are read at the point marked "out." Inside dimensions at the point marked "in."

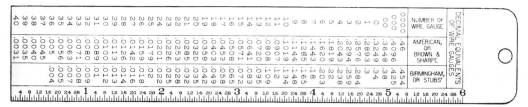

Fig. 4-1l. Mechanics steel reference table (back side).

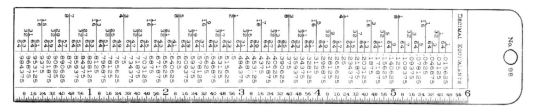

Fig. 4-1m. Mechanics steel reference table (front side).

Fig. 4-1n. Semi-flexible steel rule (front side).

Fig. 4-1p. Semi-flexible steel rule (back side).

GRADUATIONS. On many rules, every fourth graduation is numbered on the 1/32 edge, and every eighth graduation on the 1/64 edge.

The best way to learn to read the rule is to:
1. Become thoroughly familiar with the 1/8 and 1/16 measurements.
2. Do the same with the 1/32 and 1/64 measurements.
3. Practice until you become proficient enough to read measurements accurately and quickly.

As noted in the table, Fig. 4-3, some steel rules are graduated in 10ths, 20ths, 50ths and 100ths. Additional practice will be necessary to read these rules accurately and quickly.

Fractional measurements are always reduced to the lowest terms. A measurement of 14/16 is 7/8; 2/8 is 1/4; etc.

CARE OF THE RULE

The steel rule is precision made and, like all tools, the quality of service depends upon the care it receives. Here are a few suggestions:
1. Use a screwdriver and not a rule to loosen and tighten screws.
2. Keep the rule clear of moving machinery. Using it to clean metal chips as they form on the machine will not only ruin the rule, but will prove extremely dangerous to the person attempting it.
3. Do not lay other tools on the rule.
4. Frequent wiping with an oily cloth will prevent the formation of rust.
5. An occasional cleaning with fine steel wool will keep the graduations legible.
6. Make it a practice to take measurements and tool settings from the 1-in. line or other major graduation rather than from the end.
7. Store the rule separately. Do not throw it in a drawer with other tools.
8. Use the rule carefully so that the ends and edges do not become nicked or worn.
9. Use the correct rule for the job at hand.
10. Coat the tool with wax or a rust pre-

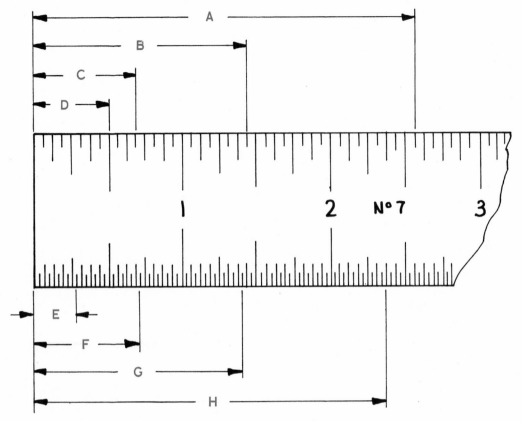

Fig. 4-2. A section of a steel rule. How many measurements can you read?

ventative if it is to be stored for a prolonged period.

THE MICROMETER CALIPER

A Frenchman, Jean Palmer, devised and patented a measuring tool that made use of a screw thread to make it possible to read measurements quickly and accurately without calculations. It incorporated a series of engraved lines on the hub and around the thimble. The device, called "Systeme Palmer," is shown in Fig. 4-4, and is the basis for the modern MICROMETER CALIPER.

The modern micrometer caliper, known as a "mike," is a precision measuring tool capable of

GRADUATIONS FOR STEEL RULES

Graduations	No. 1	No. 3	No. 4	No. 5	No. 6	No. 7	No. 9	No. 10	No. 11	No. 12	No. 16
First edge (Front Side)	10ths 20ths 50ths 100ths	32nds	64ths	10ths	50ths	100ths	--	64ths	64ths	100ths	100ths
Second Edge	12ths 24ths 48ths	64ths	32nds	100ths	50ths	64ths	64ths	32nds	100ths	50ths	50ths
Third Edge (Reverse Side)	16ths 32nds 64ths	50ths	16ths	64ths	10ths	16ths	32nds	---	---	---	32nds
Fourth Edge	14ths 28ths	10ths	8ths	32nds	10ths	32nds	16ths	---	---	---	64ths

Fig. 4-3. Table of rule graduations.

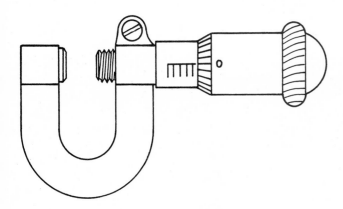

Fig. 4-4. A drawing of "Systeme Palmer." The modern micrometer caliper works on the same principle as this 1848 measuring tool.

measuring to 1/1000 (0.001) in. and when fitted with a Vernier scale to 1/10000 (0.0001) in. While manufactured in sizes up to 60 in., the movement of the spindle is limited to 1 in. Only the frame is enlarged.

TYPES OF MICROMETERS

Micrometers are made in a large variety of models. A few of the more commonly used are: OUTSIDE MICROMETER CALIPER, Fig. 4-5. Used to measure outside diameters and

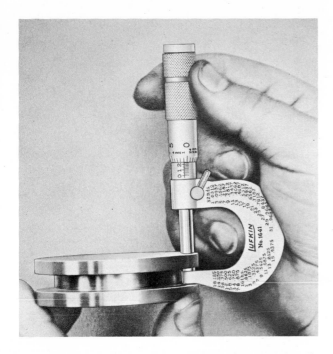

Fig. 4-5. The 0 to 1-in. outside micrometer caliper. Note how the machinist is holding it.

thicknesses of material, parts, etc.
INSIDE MICROMETER, Fig. 4-6. Excellent for measuring inside diameters of cylinders and rings, measuring parallel slots, and for setting calipers, gauges, etc. There are two generally used styles: the CONVENTIONAL INSIDE CALIPER, Fig. 4-6a, whose range can be extended by fitting longer rods to the micrometer head, and the JAW-TYPE IN-SIDE CALIPER, Fig. 4-6b. It is used in much the same manner, however, its range is limited to 1 in. Note that the scale on the hub of the jaw-type is graduated from RIGHT TO LEFT.

Fig. 4-6a. Conventional inside micrometer.

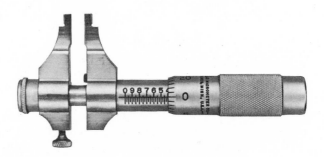

*Fig. 4-6b. Jaw-type inside micrometer.
(Scherr-Tumico)*

DIRECT READING MICROMETER, Fig. 4-7. Measurements are read directly from the numbers appearing in the three openings in the frame.
MICROMETER DEPTH GAUGE, Fig. 4-8. Depths of holes, slots, projections, etc., can be measured with this tool. The measuring range can be increased by changing to measuring rods of longer lengths.
SCREW THREAD MICROMETER CALIPER, Fig. 4-9. This micrometer has a pointed spindle and a double "V" anvil, both correctly shaped to contact the screw thread. It gives the reading for the true pitch diameter, in thousandths of an inch, which equals the outside diameter less the depth of one thread.
SPECIAL MICROMETERS, Fig. 4-10. Many cutting tools have cutting edges that are uneven in number. This makes it impossible to measure their diameter with the conventional "mike." Special micrometers have

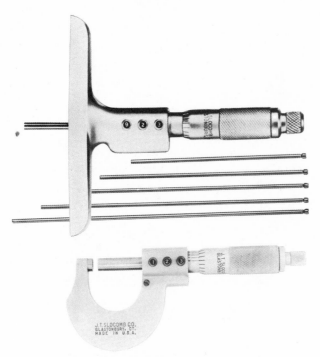

Fig. 4-7. Direct reading micrometers. The reading is made in the three openings.

Fig. 4-8. The micrometer depth gauge.

section has 40 threads per inch; therefore, each revolution of the thimble moves the spindle 1/40 in. (0.025).

The line engraved lengthwise on the HUB is divided into 40 equal parts per inch that correspond to the number of threads on the spindle. Each vertical line represents 1/40 or 0.025 in. Every fourth division is numbered 1, 2, 3, etc., representing 0.100 in., 0.200 in., etc.

The beveled edge of the THIMBLE (J) is divided into 25 equal parts, each representing 1/1000 (0.001) in. Each division is numbered on some micrometers, while every fifth di-

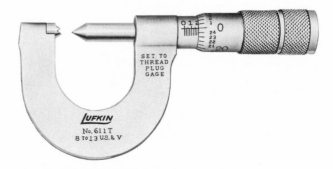

Fig. 4-9. The screw thread micrometer caliper.

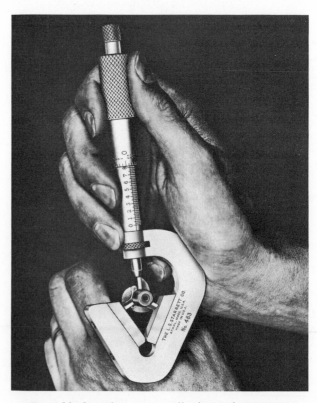

Fig. 4-10. One of many specially designed micrometer-type measuring tools.

been devised to handle this and other situations.

HOW TO READ A MICROMETER

The principle of the micrometer, a sectional view of which is shown in Fig. 4-11, consists of a very accurately made screw thread that rotates in a fixed nut. The screw thread is ground on the SPINDLE (C) and is attached to the THIMBLE (J). The spindle advances or recedes from the ANVIL (B) by rotating the thimble. The threaded

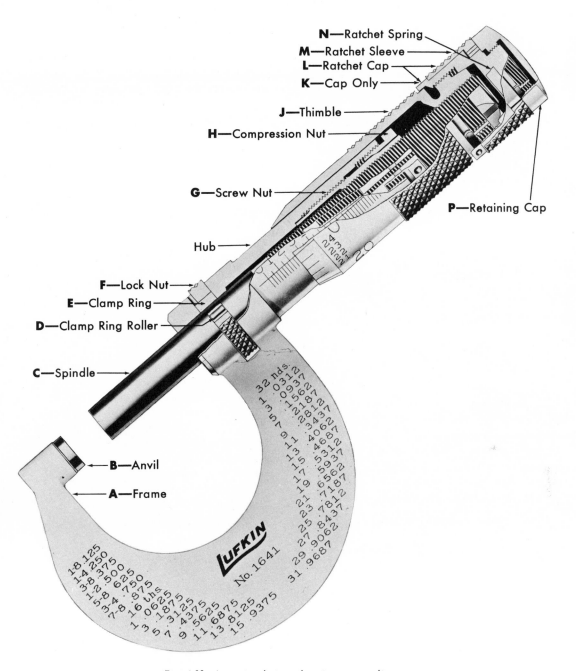

N—Ratchet Spring
M—Ratchet Sleeve
L—Ratchet Cap
K—Cap Only
J—Thimble
H—Compression Nut
G—Screw Nut
P—Retaining Cap
Hub
F—Lock Nut
E—Clamp Ring
D—Clamp Ring Roller
C—Spindle
B—Anvil
A—Frame

Fig. 4-11. A sectional view of a micrometer caliper.

vision is numbered on others.

The micrometer caliper is read by recording the highest figure visible on the HUB, 1 = 0.100, 2 = 0.200, etc. To this number is added the number of vertical lines visible between the number and the thimble edge, 1 = 0.025, 2 = 0.050, etc. To this total is added the number of thousandths indicated by the line on the thimble that coincides with the horizontal line on the hub.

See Fig. 4-12.

EXAMPLE 1:

The reading is composed of:

4 large graduations or 4 x 0.100 = 0.400
2 small graduations or 2 x 0.025 = 0.050
and 8 graduations on the
       thimble or 8 x 0.001 = <u>0.008</u>

       Total reading = 0.458 in.

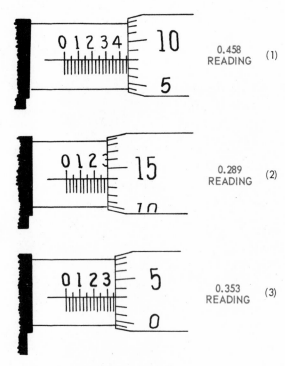

0.458
READING (1)

0.289
READING (2)

0.353
READING (3)

Fig. 4-12. Micrometer caliper readings,
examples 1, 2, and 3.

EXAMPLE 2:

The reading is composed of:
2 large graduations or 2 x 0.100 = 0.200
3 small graduations or 3 x 0.025 = 0.075
and 14 graduations on the
        thimble or 14 x 0.001 = 0.014

                Total reading = 0.289 in.

EXAMPLE 3:

The reading is composed of:
3 large graduations or 3 x 0.100 = 0.300
2 small graduations or 2 x 0.025 = 0.050
and 3 graduations on the
        thimble or 3 x 0.001 = 0.003

                Total reading = 0.353 in.

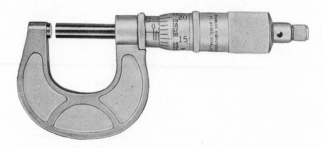

Fig. 4-13. Vernier micrometer caliper.

HOW TO READ A VERNIER MICROMETER CALIPER

On occasions, it becomes necessary to measure finer than 1/1000 in. When this situation is encountered, the Vernier micrometer caliper is used. This micrometer has a third scale AROUND THE HUB, Fig. 4-13, that furnishes the 1/10000 in. reading without estimating. The Vernier has 11 parallel lines occupying the same space as 10 lines on the thimble. The lines around the hub are numbered 0 to 10. The difference between the spaces on the hub and those on the thimble is one-tenth of a space on the thimble or 1/10 of a thousandth (0.001). To read, first obtain the thousandths reading, then observe which of the lines on the Vernier scale coincide with a line on the thimble. If it is line 1, add 0.0001 to the reading; if line 2, add 0.0002 to the reading; etc.

EXAMPLE:
Fig. 4-14.
    The reading is composed of:
    2 large graduations or 2 x 0.100 = 0.200
    3 small graduations or 3 x 0.025 = 0.075
    11 graduations on the
            thimble or 11 x 0.001 = 0.011
and the additional distance the
thimble has advanced beyond
the 0.011 inch mark.
        In this case it has advanced   0.0002

                Total reading 0.2862 in.

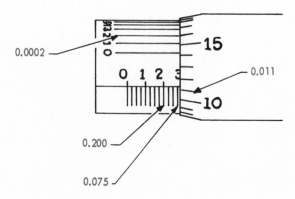

Fig. 4-14. Vernier micrometer caliper reading.

HOW TO USE THE MICROMETER

Fig. 4-15, shows the proper way to hold the micrometer when making measurements. The work is placed into position, and the thimble rotated until it is clamped lightly between the anvil and spindle. Guard against excessive pressure

and insures consistent, accurate measurement by limiting the spindle pressure on the work to a definite amount, even when different ma-

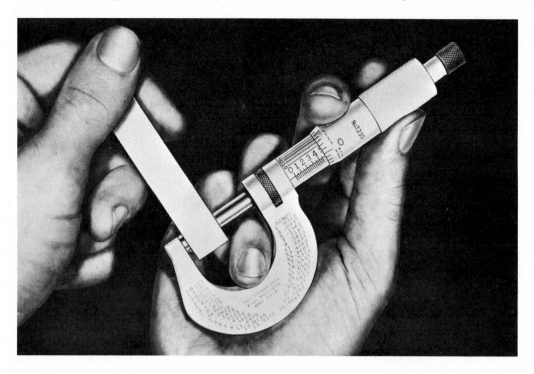

Fig. 4-15a. The correct way to hold 0-1 in. micrometer caliper for making measurements.   (L. S. Starrett Co.)

Fig. 4-15b. The proper way to hold a micrometer when making measurements on work held in a machine. (Lufkin Rule Co.)

Fig. 4-15c. Making measurements over a large piece. The frame is hollow to reduce weight.

sure as it will cause an erroneous reading. The correct contact pressure will be applied if a mike with a RATCHET STOP is employed, Fig. 4-16. This device is used to rotate the spindle

chinists use the same micrometer. When pressure reaches a predetermined amount, the ratchet stop slips and prevents further tightening.

Some micrometers are fitted with a FRIC-

TION CLUTCH, Fig. 4-5. The attachment will slip the instant the correct pressure is applied for an accurate measurement.

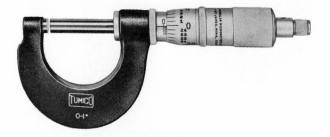

Fig. 4-16. Micrometer with a ratchet stop.

Where several pieces are to be gauged, lock the spindle in place with the LOCK NUT, Fig. 4-11 (F). When a piece is gauged with the micrometer locked at the proper setting, it is quite easy to identify the piece as being oversize, correct size or undersize.

HOW TO READ AN INSIDE MICROMETER

To get a correct reading with an INSIDE MICROMETER, it is important that the instrument be held square across the diameter and positioned so it will measure the diameter on

Fig. 4-17. Inside micrometer. Extension rods have been fitted for measuring large opening. (Lufkin Rule Co.)

exact center. When measuring large diameters, Fig. 4-17, hold one end of the instrument in place and "feel" for the maximum possible setting by moving the other end from left to right, and in and out of the hole with the other hand. The measurement is taken when no left to right movement is felt, and a slight drag is noticeable on the in-and-out swing. It may be necessary to make several readings and average them.

HOW TO READ THE MICROMETER DEPTH GAUGE

Be sure to read the micrometer depth gauge, Fig. 4-8, correctly. Unlike the outside micrometer, the graduations on this tool are in REVERSE order. That is, they read 0, 9, 8, 7, 6, etc. The graduations UNDER the thimble must be read rather than those that are exposed.

CARE OF THE MICROMETER

Micrometers must be handled with care or their accuracy will be destroyed. The following techniques are recommended:

1. Apply the micrometer to the work carefully so as not to damage the measuring faces. The same applies when removing it from the work after the measurement has been made.
2. Keep it clean. Wipe it down with an oily cloth to prevent rust and tarnish. A drop of light oil on the screw thread will keep it operating smoothly.
3. Do not spring micrometers not fitted with ratchets by applying too much pressure, when making a measurement.
4. Clean the face of the spindle and anvil before use, with a soft cloth or by lightly closing on a piece of paper and drawing the paper out.
5. Check for accuracy by closing the spindle gently and note whether the zero line on the thimble coincides with the zero on the spindle. If they are not aligned, make adjustments by FOLLOWING THE MANUFACTURER'S RECOMMENDATIONS FOR THIS OPERATION.
6. Do not place micrometers where they may fall on the floor, or where other tools will be placed on them.
7. If the micrometer must be opened or closed a considerable distance, do not

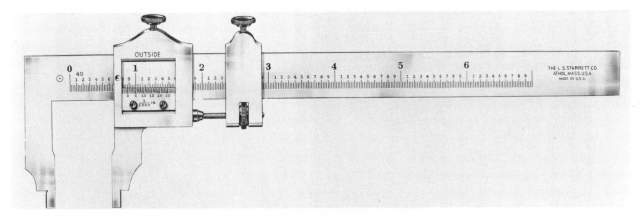

Fig. 4-18. Vernier caliper.

"twirl" the frame but rather roll the thimble on the palm of the hand.

8. Clean and oil if the tool is to be stored for some time. If possible, place the micrometer in a small box for protection.

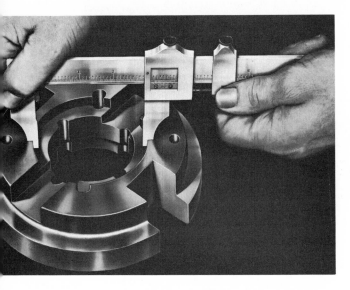

Fig. 4-19a. Making an inside measurement with Vernier caliper. (L. S. Starrett Co.)

VERNIER MEASURING TOOLS

The Vernier principle of measuring was named for its inventor, Pierre Vernier (1580-1637), a French mathematician.

The VERNIER CALIPER, Fig. 4-18, unlike the micrometer caliper, can make both inside and outside measurements, Fig. 4-19, over a large range of sizes. It is manufactured as a standard item in 6-in., 12-in., 24-in., 36-in. and 48-in. lengths. The 6-in. and 12-in. sizes are most commonly used.

The Vernier caliper can make accurate measurements to 1/1000 (0.001) in.

The Vernier principle is found on the following other measuring tools:

VERNIER HEIGHT GAUGE, Fig. 4-20, is designed for use in toolrooms and inspection departments on layout, jig and fixture work to measure or mark off vertical distance and locate center distances in thousandths of an inch.

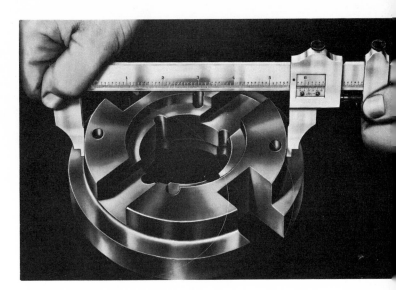

Fig. 4-19b. Making an outside measurement with Vernier caliper. Note how the machinist is making the final adjustment with the adjusting nut.

VERNIER DEPTH GAUGE, Fig. 4-21, is ideal for measuring depth of holes, slots and recesses. It is ordinarily fitted with a 6-in. or 12-in. blade.

GEAR TOOTH VERNIER CALIPER, Fig. 4-22b, is used to measure gear teeth, form and threading tools.

Fig. 4-20. Using Vernier height gauge.

UNIVERSAL VERNIER BEVEL PROTRAC-TOR, Fig. 4-23, is designed for the precision layout and measurement of angles.

The Vernier caliper is composed of a graduated beam with a fixed measuring jaw and the Vernier slide assembly. The movable jaw, Vernier plate, clamping screws and adjusting nut makes up the slide assembly. The slide moves as a unit along the beam.

Unlike other Vernier measuring tools, the caliper beam is graduated on both sides. The OUTSIDE measurements are taken on the scale reading from left to right. When the jaws are together, the "0" on the outside measuring scale will be aligned with the "0" on the Vernier plate.

HOW TO USE THE VERNIER CALIPER

As with any precision measuring tool, the Vernier caliper must not be forced on the work. Slide the assembly until the jaws almost contact the work. Lock the clamping screw and make the final adjustment with the fine adjusting nut. The jaws must engage the work firmly but not tightly. Lock the unit to the beam, remove it from the work carefully, and make your reading.

Points permitting accurate divider and trammel point settings, for precise layout work, are located on the outside measuring scale and on the slide assembly.

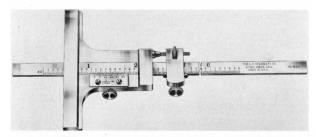

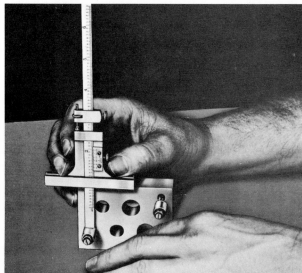

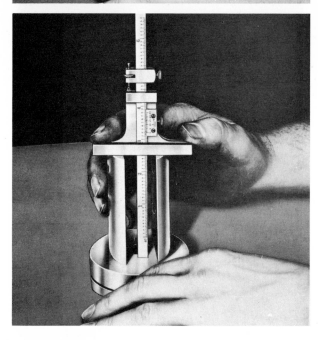

Fig. 4-21. The Vernier depth gauge.

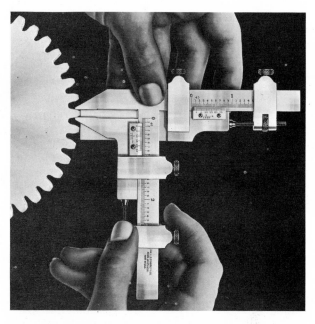

Fig. 4-22a. Measuring gear tooth with a gear tooth Vernier caliper. The instrument is read in the same manner as a Vernier caliper and a Vernier height gauge.

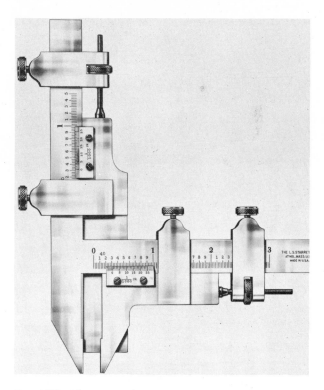

Fig. 4-22b. The gear tooth Vernier caliper. (L. S. Starrett Co.)

HOW TO READ A VERNIER SCALE

Like the hub on the micrometer caliper, each 1-in. section of the beam is graduated into forty

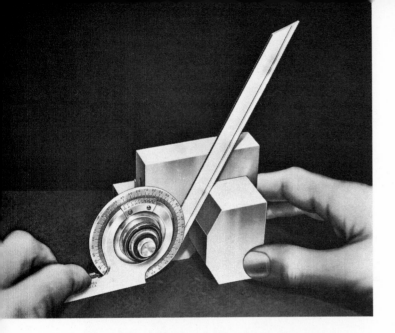

Fig. 4-23. *Universal Vernier bevel protractor.*

equal parts. Each graduation equals 1/40 or 0.025 in. Every fourth division, representing 1/10 in., is numbered. The Vernier plate is divided into twenty-five equal divisions and are numbered 0, 5, 10, 15, 20, and 25. The twenty-five divisions on the plate occupy the same space as twenty-four divisions on the beam. This slight difference, equal to 1/1000 in. per division, is the basis of the Vernier principle of measuring.

To read the Vernier, note how many inches (1, 2, 3, etc.), tenths (0.100, 0.200, etc.), and

Fig. 4-24. *Photo of Vernier scale. To be used as example for reading.*

fortieths (0.025, 0.050 or 0.075) the "0" on the Vernier slide is from the "0" on the beam. Add to this total the number of thousandths indicated by the line on the Vernier scale that coincides with a line on the beam scale.

EXAMPLE:
Fig. 4-24.

The reading is composed of:	
The "0" is between 1 and 2 on the beam or	1.000
Four 1/10 graduations or	0.400
One 1/40 graduation or	0.025
and eleven 1/000 graduations or (as indicated by the stars)	0.011
Total reading	1.436

HOW TO READ THE UNIVERSAL VERNIER BEVEL PROTRACTOR

There are many times when angles must be measured very accurately. The Universal Vernier Bevel Protractor can measure angles

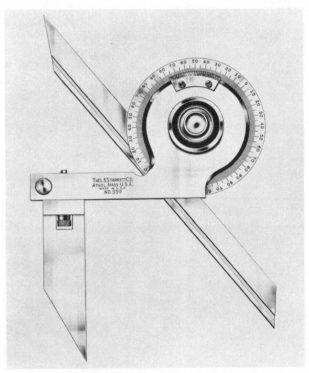

Fig. 4-25. *The Vernier protractor.*

accurately to 1/12 degree or 5 minutes. A quick review of the circle, angles and the units of measurement associated with them will aid in understanding how to read this instrument.

DEGREE - A circle, no matter what size, contains 360 degrees. This is normally written 360°. Angles are also measured by degrees.

MINUTE - If a degree were divided into 60 equal parts, each part would represent 1-minute. The minute is used to represent a fractional part of a degree. It is written 0° 0'.

SECOND - Very accurate work requires that the minute be divided into smaller units known

resenting minutes. Each space equals 5 minutes.

To read the protractor, note the number of degrees that can be read up to the "0" line on the Vernier plate. To this, add the number of minutes

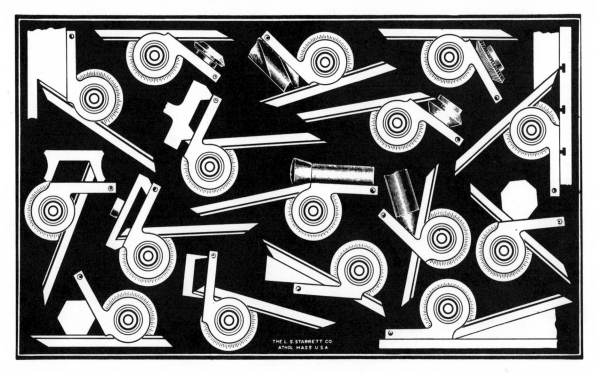

Fig. 4-26. Applications of the bevel protractor.

as seconds. There are 60 seconds in one minute. An angular measurement written in degrees, minutes and seconds would be 36° 18' 22". This would read 36 degrees, 18 minutes and 22 seconds.

The Universal Bevel Protractor, Fig. 4-25, is a finely made tool with a dial graduated into degrees, a base or stock, a sliding blade that can be extended in either direction or set at any angle to the stock. The blade can be locked against the dial by tightening the blade clamp nut. The blade and dial can be rotated as a unit to any desired position, and locked by tightening the dial clamp nut. Fig. 4-26 shows a few applications of this tool.

The protractor dial, graduated into 360 degrees, reads 0 - 90 degrees, 90 - 0 degrees, 0 - 90 degrees and 90 - 0 degrees. Every 10 degrees is numbered, and each 5 degrees is indicated by a line longer than those on either side. The Vernier scale is divided into twelve equal parts on each part of the "0." Every third graduation is numbered 0, 15, 30, 45 and 60, rep-

indicated by the line beyond the "0" on the Vernier plate that aligns exactly with a line on the dial.

EXAMPLE:
Fig. 4-27.

The reading is composed of:
The "0" is slightly beyond 50 = 50° 00'
The line indicating 20 minutes
is aligned with a line on dial = 20'

Total reading 50° 20'

Fig. 4-27. Photo of the protractor Vernier scale used as the example.

CARE OF VERNIER TOOLS

Reasonable care in handling these tools will insure their accuracy.

1. Wipe with a soft lint free cloth before using. This will prevent rust and grit from being "ground" in and eventually destroying the accuracy of the tool.
2. Store Vernier in case.
3. Never force tool when making measurement.
4. Use a magnifying or jeweler's lope to take Vernier readings. Hold the tool so that the light is reflected on the scale.
5. Hold the tool as little as possible. Sweat and body acids cause rapid rusting.
6. Periodically check for accuracy. Use a measuring standard or ground parallel.
7. Wipe tool with a lightly oiled soft cloth after use and before storage. Return tool to manufacturer for adjustment or repair.

*Fig. 4-28. Double end cylindrical plug gauge.
(Standard Tool Co.)*

GAUGES

It is obviously impractical, considering the large number of individual parts manufactured each year, to check every dimension on every piece with conventional measuring tools. To

Fig. 4-29. Progressive or step plug gauge.

facilitate rapid checking, PLUG, RING AND SNAP GAUGES, PRECISION GAUGE BLOCKS, DIAL INDICATORS and other ELECTRONIC, OPTICAL and AIR-TYPE GAUGES are used to determine whether the dimensions of the item are within specified limits.

Gauging, which is the term used when checking parts with various gauges, differs somewhat from measuring. Measuring requires the skill-

ful use of precision measuring tools to determine the exact size of the piece; whereas, gauging simply shows whether the piece is made within the specified tolerances.

When great numbers of an item, with several critical dimensions, are manufactured, it may not be possible to check each piece. It therefore becomes necessary to decide how many pieces, picked at random, must be checked to assure satisfactory quality and adherence to specifications. This technique is called STATISTICAL QUALITY CONTROL.

TYPES OF GAUGES

Several types of gauges have been developed over the years, each designed to do a specific job.

PLUG GAUGE

The plug gauge is used to check whether hole diameters are within specified tolerances. The DOUBLE END CYLINDRICAL PLUG GAUGE, Fig. 4-28, has two gauging members known as GO and NO GO plugs. The GO plug measures the lower limit of the hole, and the NO GO checks the upper limit. The GO plug is made longer to distinguish it from the NO GO plug. The PROGRESSIVE or STEP PLUG GAUGE, Fig. 4-29, is able to check the GO and NO GO dimensions in one motion.

RING GAUGE

The ring gauge is used to check the external diameter. The GO and NO GO RING GAUGE, Fig. 4-30, are separate units, and can be distinguished from each other by a groove cut on the knurled outer surface of the NO GO gauge. On ring gauges the gauge tolerance is opposite to that applied to the plug gauge. The opening of the GO gauge is larger than that of the NO GO gauge.

Fig. 4-30. Ring gauges. The larger sizes are cut away to reduce weight. (Standard Tool Co.)

Fig. 4-31. Adjustable type snap gauge. (Taft-Pierce Mfg. Co.)

SNAP GAUGE

The snap gauge functions much the same as the ring gauge. It is made in two general types, the ADJUSTABLE, Fig. 4-31, which can be

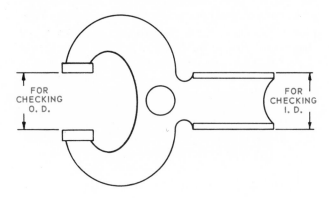

Fig. 4-32a. A combination internal and external non-adjustable gauge.

Fig. 4-32b. Non-adjustable type snap gauge.

adjusted through a range of sizes, and the NON-ADJUSTABLE, Fig. 4-32, which is made for one specific size.

Gauges similar to those just described are used to check screw thread fits and tolerances,

Fig. 4-33a. Using a thread plug gauge to check a job. (Greenfield Tap and Die Co.)

and are known as THREAD PLUG GAUGES, Fig. 4-33, THREAD RING GAUGES, Fig. 4-34, and THREAD ROLL SNAP GAUGES, Fig. 4-35.

Fig. 4-33b. Thread plug gauge. (Standard Tool Co.)

Fig. 4-34. Thread ring gauges. (Standard Tool Co.)

GAUGE BLOCKS

Gauge blocks, Fig. 4-36, are super accurate steel measuring standards commonly known as JO-BLOCKS. They are accepted by major world powers as standards of accuracy for all types of manufacturing.

Gauge blocks are used widely to check and verify the accuracy of master gauges; as working gauges for toolroom work; and for laying out and

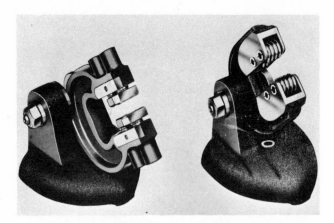

Fig. 4-35. A Go-No Go thread snap gauge. (Taft-Pierce Mfg. Co.)

Fig. 4-36a. Measuring a taper with Johannson sine bar and precision gauge blocks.

setting up work for machining where extreme accuracy is required.

Gauge blocks can be purchased in various combinations or sets ranging from a few carefully selected blocks that meet conditions found in most shops, to a complete set of 121 blocks, Fig. 4-37.

DIAL INDICATORS

Industry is constantly searching for ways to reduce costs, yet maintain quality. Inspection has always been a costly part of manufacturing. To speed up this phase of production, without sacri-

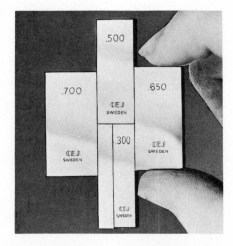

Fig. 4-36b. Gauge blocks are so accurately made that clean blocks will adhere to one another with considerable pressure when they are "wrung" together. Two or more smaller blocks can be assembled into a larger unit and still maintain the accuracy of the single unit. (C. E. Johannson & Co.)

ficing accuracy, the dial indicator is receiving increased use. Much use is made of dial indicators for centering work on machines, Fig. 4-38; checking for eccentricity, Fig. 4-39; and visual inspection of work, Fig. 4-40.

Dial indicators are made like fine watches with shockproof movements and jeweled bearings. They are either of the BALANCED TYPE, Fig. 4-41, where the figures read in both directions from "0," and the CONTINUOUS TYPE,

Fig. 4-37. A typical set of Jo-Blocks (gauge blocks.)

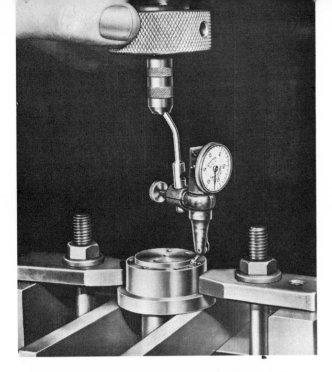

Fig. 4-38. Centering work on a vertical milling machine. (L. S. Starrett Co.)

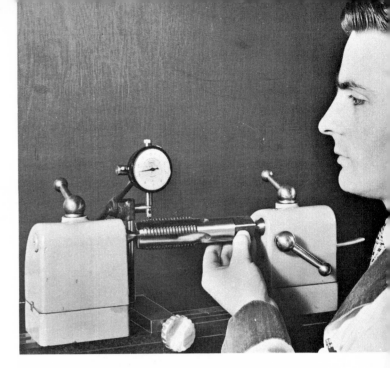

Fig. 4-39. Checking run-out of tap using a dial indicator. Bench centers aid the inspector with this job. (DoAll Co.)

Fig. 4-42, that reads from "0" in a clockwise direction. Dial faces are available in a wide range of graduations, and usually read in 1/1000 (0.001) or 1/10000 (0.0001) inch increments. Dial indicators must be mounted to rigid holding devices.

HOW TO USE THE DIAL INDICATOR

The hand on the dial is actuated by a plunger that is in contact with the work. Place the plunger lightly against the work until the hand moves. The dial face is turned until the "0" line coincides with the hand. As the work is slowly moved, the indicator will show the difference between the high and low points or the total run-out of the piece. Adjustments are made until there is little or no indicator movement.

OTHER GAUGING TOOLS

Industry makes wide use of other types of gauging tools. Most of them are for special purposes and are not found in a school shop. It is well to learn something about such tools.

AIR GAUGE

The air gauge, Fig. 4-43, is especially useful for measuring deep internal bores. There is no actual contact between the measuring plug and the walls of the bore being measured, but the measurement depends on the air leakage between the plug and the hole walls. Pressure is built up and the measurement of the back pres-

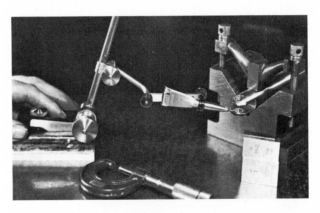

Fig. 4-40. Inspecting a job using a dial indicator. The indicator is a balanced type and has been set to "0" on Jo-Blocks. (Lufkin Rule Co.)

Fig. 4-41. Balanced type dial indicator face. (Scherr-Tumico)

Fig. 4-42. Continuous type
dial indicator face.

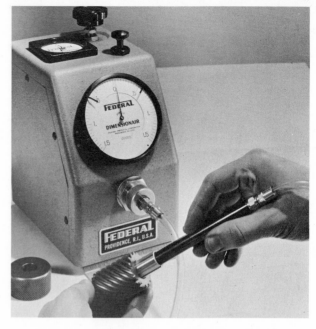

Fig. 4-43a. An air gauge in use. Note the graduations
on the dial. The knurled device is the ring used to
set and check the gauge accuracy.
(Federal Products Corp.)

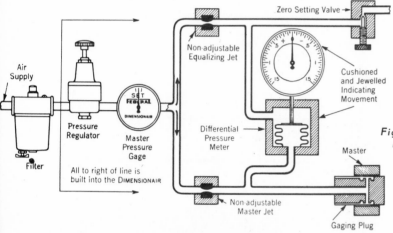

Air
Supply

Pressure
Regulator

Filter

Master
Pressure
Gage

All to right of line is
built into the DIMENSIONAIR

Non-adjustable
Equalizing Jet

Zero Setting Valve

Cushioned
and Jewelled
Indicating
Movement

Differential
Pressure
Meter

Non-adjustable
Master Jet

Master

Gaging Plug

Fig. 4-43b. A diagram illustrating
how the air gauge operates.

Fig. 4-44. An electronic comparator checking the
pitch diameter of a tap by means of the thread wire
method. (DoAll Co.)

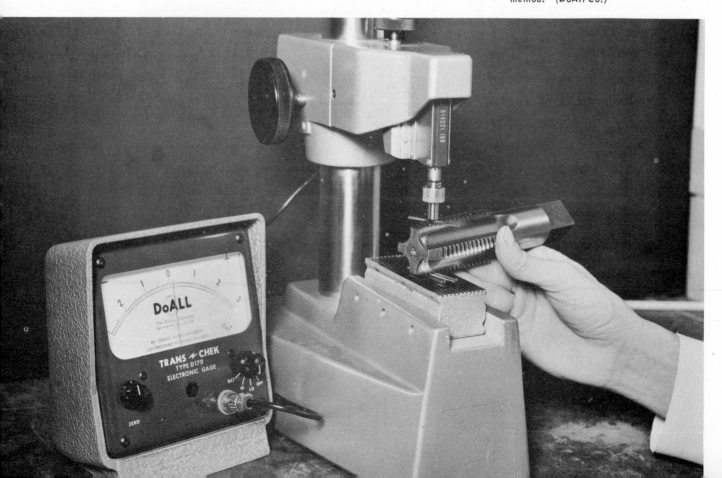

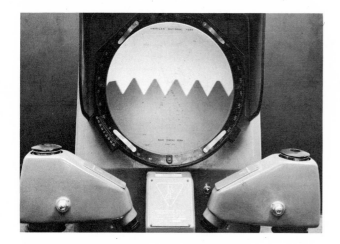

Fig. 4-45. A 50-power optical comparator permits a fast check on the tooth formation of tap.

sure gives an accurate measurement of the hole size. Change in pressure is measured by a dial type indicator, a cork floating on the air stream or by a manometer type U-tube in which the height of the fluid in the tube indicates the pressure.

ELECTRONIC GAUGE

Another gauge that is used to make extremely close measurements is the electronic

gauge, Fig. 4-44. It is a comparison type gauge and must be set by means of master gauge blocks.

OPTICAL COMPARATOR

The optical comparator, Fig. 4-45, is used for production inspection. An enlarged image of the part is projected on a screen where it is superimposed upon an accurate drawing of the correct size and shape. The comparison is made visually. Variations as small as 0.0005 in. can be noted by a skilled operator.

OPTICAL FLATS

Optical flats, Fig. 4-46, are precise measuring instruments. They make use of light waves as a measuring standard. The flats are made

Fig. 4-46. Optical flats.

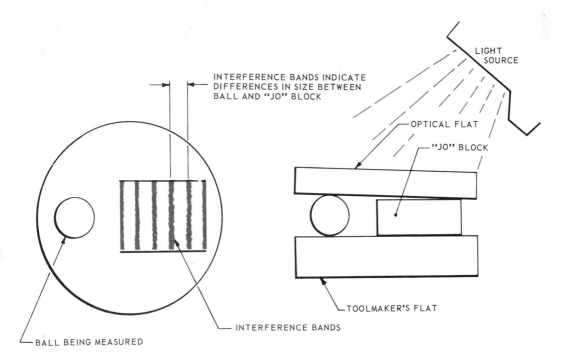

Fig. 4-47. The principle of the optical flat.

of Quartz with one face ground and polished to optical flatness. When this face is placed on a machined surface and a special light passed through the flat, bands set up by the light appear on the surface, Fig. 4-47. The shape of these bands indicate to the inspector the accuracy of the measurement in millionths, ten-millionths and hundred millionths inches.

MISCELLANEOUS MEASURING TOOLS

There are some measuring tools that do not fall under a specific category, yet are frequently used.

THICKNESS (FEELER) GAUGE

Thickness gauges, Fig. 4-48, are usually arranged in leaf form, although individual thicknesses (0.0015 to 0.015 in.) are available in 12-

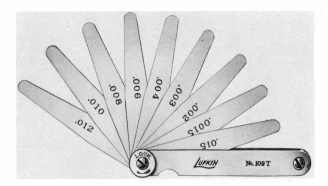

Fig. 4-48. The thickness or feeler gauge.

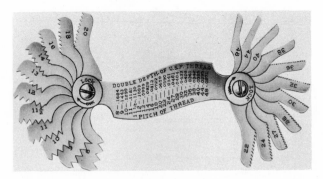

Fig. 4-49. The screw pitch gauge.

in. lengths and 25-ft. rolls. For convenience the thickness is marked at regular intervals. Thickness gauges are made of tempered steel and are 1/2-in. in width.

Thickness gauges are ideal for measuring narrow slots, setting small gaps and clearances,

Fig. 4-50. A set of radius and fillet gauges.

determining fit between large mating surfaces and for checking flatness of parts in straightening operations.

SCREW PITCH GAUGE

Screw pitch gauges, Fig. 4-49, are used to determine the pitch or number of threads per inch of threads. Each blade is stamped with the number of threads per inch it measures.

FILLET AND RADIUS GAUGE

The thin steel blades of the fillet and radius gauge, Fig. 4-50, are used to check concave and convex radii on corners or against shoulders, for layout work and inspection, as a template when grinding form cutting tools, etc. A holder, Fig. 4-51, is especially useful for checking radii in hard to reach locations. The gauges increase in radius by 1/64-in. increments.

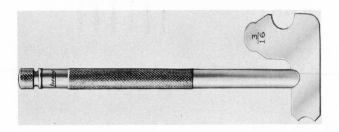

Fig. 4-51. A radius gauge and holder. The holder is made in such a manner that it permits the gauge to be set at different angles.

DRILL ROD

Drill rods are steel rods manufactured to close tolerances to twist drill diameters. They are useful for inspecting hole alignment and location, checking hole diameters in the same manner as a plug gauge, etc.

TELESCOPING GAUGE

The telescoping gauge, Fig. 4-52, is intended for use with the micrometer to determine in-

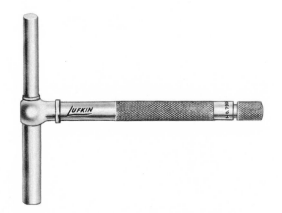

Fig. 4-52. A telescoping gauge.

Fig. 4-53. Fitting the telescoping gauge in the hole.

ternal dimensions. To use such a gauge, compress the contact points - they telescope within one another under spring tension, insert it into the hole and permit the contacts to expand,

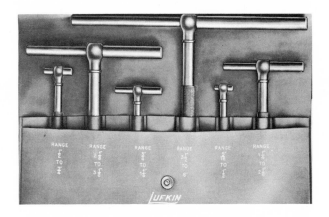

Fig. 4-54. A set of telescoping gauges.

Fig. 4-53. After the proper fitting is obtained, lock the contacts into position, remove gauge from hole and make your reading with a micrometer.

Six telescoping gauges, with a measuring capacity of 5/16 to 6 in., comprise a set, Fig. 4-54.

SMALL HOLE GAUGE

The small hole gauge, Fig. 4-55, permits measuring smaller openings than is possible with a telescoping gauge. The contacts are designed to permit accurate measurement of shallow grooves, and are adjusted to size by the knurled knob at the end of the handle. Measurement is made over the contacts with a micrometer, Fig. 4-56.

A set consists of four gauges with a range of 1/8 to 1/2 in. Fig. 4-57.

Fig. 4-55. Measuring a shallow groove with a small hole gauge.

Fig. 4-56. Correct way to measure small hole gauge with a micrometer. (L. S. Starrett Co.)

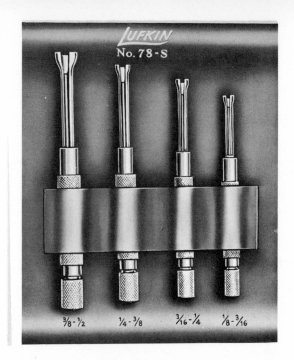

Fig. 4-57. Small hole gauge. A set has a range of 1/8 to 1/2 in. gauges.

TEST YOUR KNOWLEDGE, Unit 4

1. Make readings from the rule at right and place them in the proper blank.

a._____
b._____
c._____
d._____
e._____
f._____
g._____

2. Make readings from the micrometer drawings and place them in the proper blank.

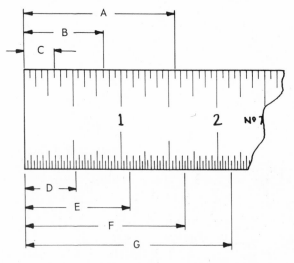

(A)____ (B)____ (C)____ (D)____ (E)____ (F)____

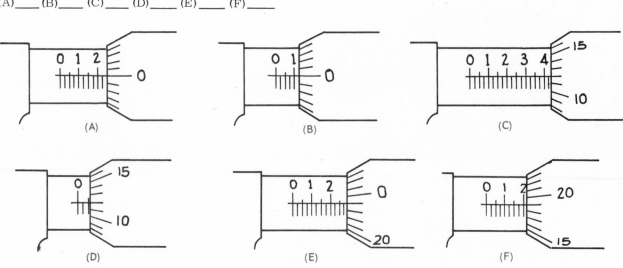

3. Make readings from the Vernier drawings and place them in the proper blank.

(A) ____ (B) ____ (C) ____ (D) ____ (E) ____ (F) ____

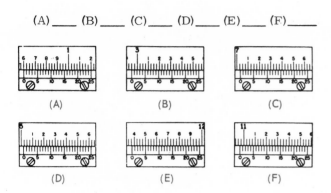

(A)   (B)   (C)

(D)   (E)   (F)

4. The Vernier caliper has an advantage over the micrometer in that it:
   a. Is more accurate.
   b. Is easier and quicker to use.
   c. Can be used to make both inside and outside measurements over a range of sizes.
   d. Does not cost as much.
5. The micrometer has been nicknamed _____.
6. A _____ is a tool that can be used to make accurate measurements but must be used with a micrometer of Vernier caliper.
   a. Rule
   b. Dial indicator
   c. Telescoping gauge.
   d. Inside micrometer
   e. Ring gauge.
7. The one-millionth part of a standard inch is known as a _____.
8. The micrometer can measure to the _____ and _____ part of an inch.
9. The Vernier caliper can measure to the _____ part of an inch.
10. The #4 rule measures to the 1/64, 1/32, 1/16 and 1/8 parts of the inch. True or false?
11. The plug gauge is used to check hole diameters that are within specified tolerances. True or false?
12. Ring gauges can be used for the same operation. True or false?
13. Gauge blocks are usually referred to as "Jo" blocks. True or false?
14. Dial indicators are direct reading measuring tools. True or false?
15. The air gauge type measuring tool uses air wave frequencies to measure the OD of a cylinder. True or false?

RESEARCH AND DEVELOPMENT

1. Early man used parts of the body of measuring. Prepare drawings of the parts of the body that represented the:
   a. Cubit b. Inch c. Yard (2 methods) d. Foot
   If your school has the facilities, use the above drawings to prepare transparencies for use with the overhead projector.
2. Make a large working model of the hub and thimble of the micrometer. Use different size cardboard mailing tubes.
3. Develop a working model of the Vernier scale and a section of the Vernier caliper. Make the model at least six times actual size.
4. Arrange for an inspector employed by one of the local industries to describe his job and the specialized measuring tools he uses. Use a tape recorder to transcribe your conversation. Do not go to the meeting "cold." Have several questions ready to ask in case the interview starts to "drag."
5. If it can be arranged, have someone demonstrate how optical flats are used. Use a film or film strip if the actual tools cannot be borrowed.
6. Prepare a research paper on how temperature changes affect measuring accuracy. Prepare one-inch long pieces of aluminum, brass, steel, plastic, and cast iron. Record their exact length at room temperature with a micrometer. Place the pieces in a freezer for 24 hours and quickly measure them again. Record your findings. Place the pieces in boiling water for 15 minutes. Measure and record your findings.

   Prepare a table to show how much the lengths varied from one extreme to the other, and how they differed at each extreme, from room temperature.
7. Make an enlarged section of a #4 rule 10 times actual size. Use plywood or hardboard.
8. Prepare a transparency (use several overlays if necessary) that can be used with an overhead projector to teach beginners how to read a rule or a micrometer.

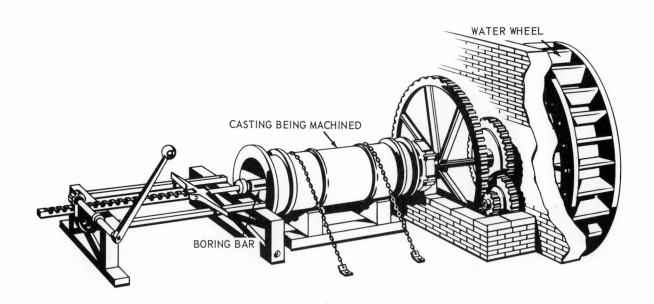

*First machine tool, a boring mill invented by John Wilkinson in 1774, which enabled Watt to com-
plete his first successful steam engine. The boring bar was rigidly supported at both ends, and
was rotated by water power.   (DoAll Co.)*

Unit 5

CALIPERS

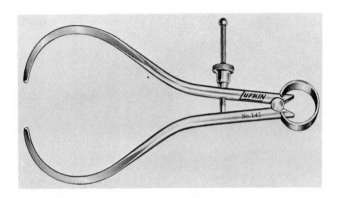

Fig. 5-1. The spring-joint outside caliper.

The OUTSIDE CALIPER, Fig. 5-1, is used to make external measurements where a 1/64-in. tolerance is permitted. A caliper does not have a dial or gauge which shows a measurement, and must be used with a steel rule.

Round stock is measured by setting the cali-

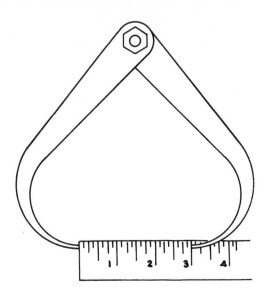

Fig. 5-2. Setting outside calipers.

per to the approximate diameter of the material. Then, hold the caliper square with the work and move the caliper legs down on the stock. Adjust the tool until the caliper points bear lightly on the centerline of the stock. The weight of the caliper should cause the tool to pass over the diameter. Hold the caliper to the rule, Fig. 5-2, to read the size.

The INSIDE CALIPER, Fig. 5-3, is used for making internal measurements where 1/64-in. accuracy is acceptable.

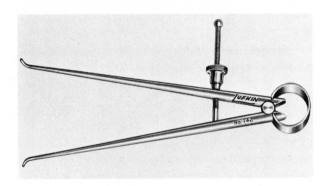

Fig. 5-3. The spring-joint inside caliper.

A hole diameter can be measured, Fig. 5-4, by setting the caliper to the approximate size of the hole, and inserting the legs into the opening. Hold one leg firmly against the hole wall, and adjust the thumbscrew until the other leg lightly touches the wall exactly opposite the first leg. The legs should "drag" slightly when moved in and out, or from side to side. Read the hole size by holding the caliper to a steel rule, Fig. 5-5.

There are times when a shaft must be turned to fit a hole, and it becomes necessary to transfer the measurement from one caliper to another. This can be accomplished quickly by setting the inside caliper to fit the hole diameter. Place one leg of the inside caliper against one leg of the

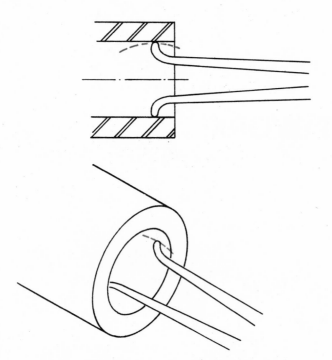

Fig. 5-4. Measuring with the inside caliper.

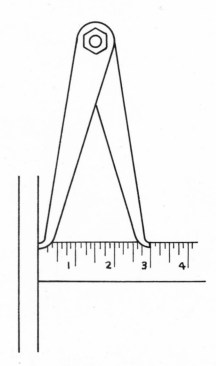

Fig. 5-5. Reading the inside caliper.

outside caliper, and adjust the outside caliper until the second leg lightly touches the other leg of the inside caliper.

Considerable skill is required to make accurate measurements with calipers. Much de-pends upon the machinist's sense of touch. With practice, measurements to within 0.003 to 0.005 in. can be made. A micrometer or Vernier cali-per should be used if greater accuracy is required.

TEST YOUR KNOWLEDGE, Unit 5

1. The _____caliper is used to make ex-ternal measurements.
2. The _____ caliper is used to make internal measurements.
3. Calipers are used where _____in. accuracy is acceptable.
4. A _____ or _____caliper should be used when accuracy closer than .003 to .005 is required.

Unit 6

LAYOUT WORK

LAYING OUT is the term used to describe the locating and marking out of lines, circles, arcs and points for drilling holes. These lines and reference points on the metal show the machinist where to machine.

The tools used for this work are known as LAYOUT TOOLS. Many common hand tools fall into this category. The accuracy of the job will depend upon the proper and careful use of these tools.

MAKING LINES ON METAL

The shiny finish of metal makes it difficult to distinguish the layout lines from the metal. LAYOUT DYE, Fig. 6-1, is probably the easiest to use of the many coatings devised to make the lines stand out better. This blue colored fluid, when applied to the metal, offers an excellent contrast between the metal and the layout lines. All grease and oil must be removed before

Fig. 6-1. Applying layout fluid preparatory to making the layout.

applying the dye, otherwise it will not adhere properly. In a pinch, layout fluid can be made by dissolving the coating on spirit duplicator carbons in alcohol. Chalk can be used on hot rolled metal as a layout background.

A layout, to be accurate, requires fine lines that must be scribed or scratched in the metal. A SCRIBER, Fig. 6-2, is used to produce these

Fig. 6-2a. Scriber.

Fig. 6-2b. Pocket scriber. The point is reversed and stored in the handle when the tool is not being used.

lines. The point is made of hardened steel, and is kept needle sharp by frequent honing on a fine oilstone. Many styles of scribers are available. CAUTION: NEVER CARRY AN OPEN SCRIBER IN YOUR POCKET.

Where the scriber is used to draw straight and gradually curved lines, circles and arcs are made with the DIVIDER, Fig. 6-3a. It is essential

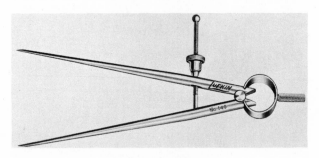

Fig. 6-3a. The divider.

that both legs of the tool be equal in length and kept pointed. The divider can be used to lay off and measure distances, Fig. 6-3b. To set the tool to the correct dimension, place one point on an inch mark of a steel rule, and open the divider until the other leg is set to the proper distance, Fig. 6-3c.

Circles and arcs that are too large to be made with the divider are drawn with a TRAMMEL, Fig. 6-4. This consists of a long thin rod, called a BEAM, on which two SLIDING HEADS with

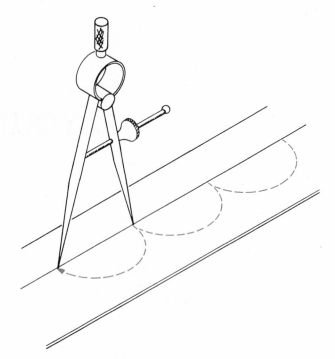

Fig. 6-3b. Laying out equal spaces with a divider.

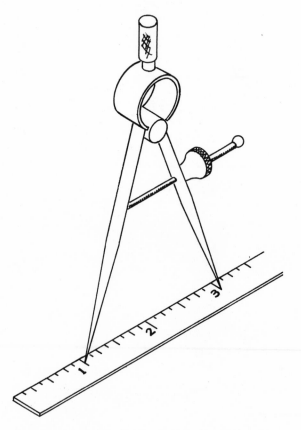

Fig. 6-3c. Setting a divider to the correct dimension.

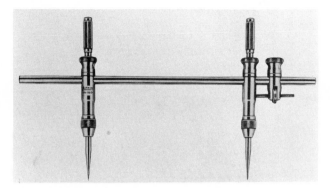

Fig. 6-4. The trammel.

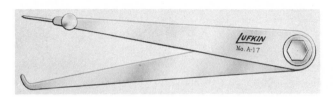

Fig. 6-5a. Hermaphrodite caliper.

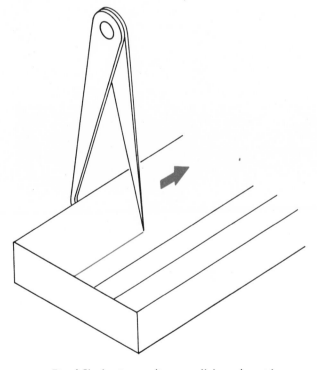

Fig. 6-5b. Laying out lines parallel to edge with hermaphrodite caliper.

scriber points are mounted. One head is fitted with an ADJUSTING SCREW. EXTENSION RODS can be added to the beam to increase the capacity of the tool.

The HERMAPHRODITE CALIPER, Fig. 6-5a,

is a layout tool which has one leg shaped like a caliper, and the other pointed like a divider. The tool is used to lay out lines parallel to the edge of the material, Fig. 6-5b, and to locate the center of irregularly shaped stock.

A SURFACE GAUGE, Fig. 6-6a, is used for many purposes, but is most frequently used for layout work. It consists of a BASE, SPINDLE and

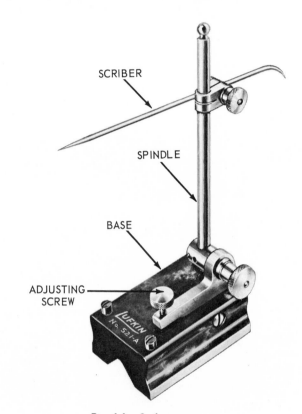

Fig. 6-6a. Surface gauge.

SCRIBER. An ADJUSTING SCREW is fitted for making fine adjustments. The scriber is mounted in such a manner that it can be pivoted into any position. The surface gauge can be used for scribing lines, at a given height and parallel to the surface, Fig. 6-6b. A V-slot in the base permits the tool to be used on a curved surface.

Parallelism of a part can be checked when the tool is fitted with a dial indicator. The indicator is set to the required dimension by using gauge blocks, and it is then moved back and forth along the work, Fig. 6-6c. PRECISION LAYOUT TOOLS, Fig. 6-7, are used when the drawings call for positions to be located to within 0.001 in.

An extremely precise surface is needed if accurate layout work is to be done. A SURFACE PLATE, Fig. 6-8a, is most frequently used.

The surface plate can be purchased in sizes

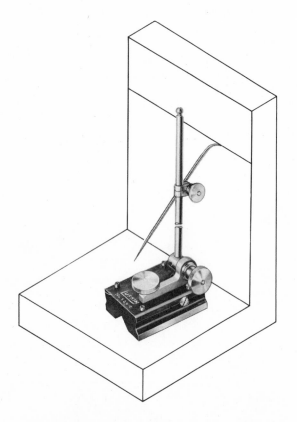

Fig. 6-6b. Using surface gauge to scribe lines parallel to base.

up to 72 by 144 in. and in semi-steel or granite. A TOOLMAKER'S BENCH, Fig. 6-8b, is ideal for many operations that require a smooth, accurate work surface.

Surface plates are used primarily for lay-out and inspection work, and should never be used for any job that would mar or nick the surface.

When square reference surfaces are needed, the RIGHT ANGLE PLATE, Fig. 6-9, is used. The blocks can be placed in about any position with the work clamped to the face for layout and measurement.

Accurate working surfaces parallel to the surface plate can be obtained by using BOX PARALLELS, Fig. 6-10. All surfaces are precision ground to close tolerances.

V-BLOCKS, Fig. 6-11, are used to support round work for layout and inspection. They are furnished in matched pairs with surfaces that are ground square to close tolerances. Ribs are cast into the body of the block for strength, weight reduction, and to provide clamping surfaces.

Long flat surfaces are checked for accuracy with a steel STRAIGHTEDGE, Fig. 6-12. This tool is also used for laying out long straight lines.

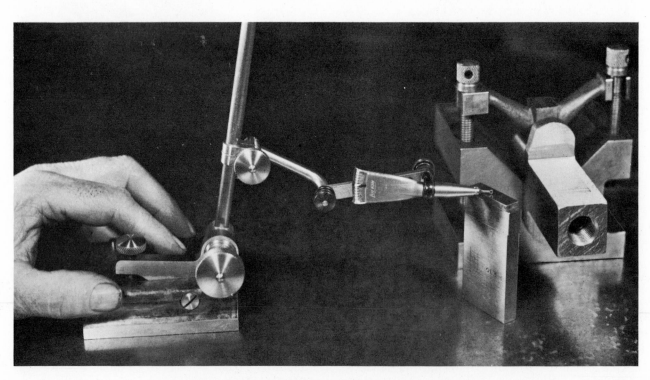

Fig. 6-6c. Setting indicator mounted on surface gauge, using gauge blocks.
(Lufkin Rule Co.)

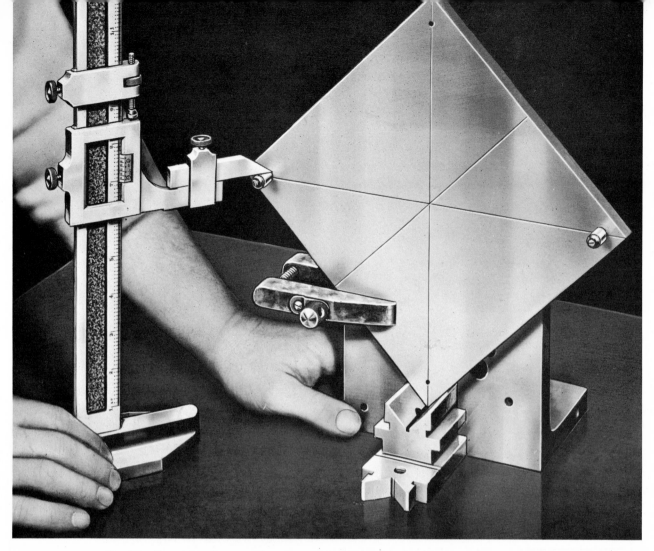

Fig. 6-7a. Vernier height gauge. Note that a V-block and angle plate are used to support the job.
(L. S. Starrett Co.)

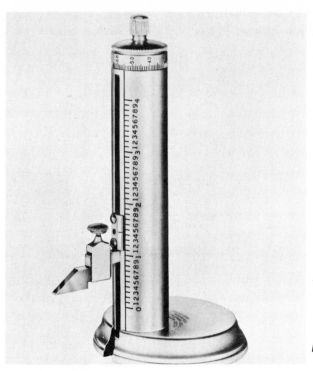

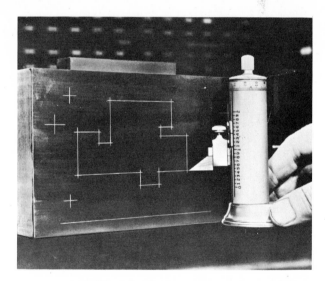

Fig. 6-7c. Height gauge in use.

Fig. 6-7b. Another type of Vernier height gauge.
(H. B. Tools)

Fig. 6-8a. A semi-steel surface plate.

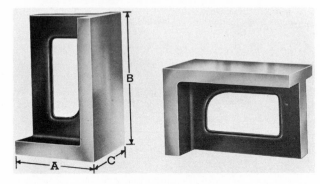

Fig. 6-8b. Toolmaker's and machinist's workbench.
(Challenge Machinery Co.)

Fig. 6-9. The right angle plate.
(Challenge Machinery Co.)

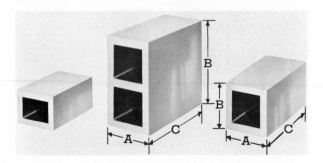

Fig. 6-10. Box parallels. (Challenge Machinery Co.)

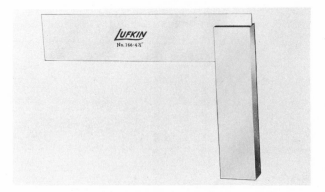

Fig. 6-11. V-blocks.

Fig. 6-12. Steel straightedge. (Challenge Machinery Co.)

SQUARES

The square is used to check the accuracy of 90 deg. (square) angles. The tool is also used for laying out lines that must be at right angles to a given edge or parallel with one another. Some simple machine setups can be made quickly and easily with the square.

Many different types of squares are available. A few of the most commonly used are:

The HARDENED STEEL SQUARE, Fig. 6-13, is recommended for use where extreme accuracy is required. It has true right angles, both inside

Fig. 6-13. Hardened steel square.

and outside, and is accurately ground and lapped for straightness and parallelism. The tool is manufactured in sizes up to 36 in. Extreme care must be exercised in handling these tools. The blade is mounted solidly to the beam and if the tool is dropped the blade can be "sprung."

The DOUBLE SQUARE, Fig. 6-14, is more practical for many jobs than the solid square because the sliding blade is adjustable and interchangeable with other blades. The tool should not be used where great precision is required. The bevel blade has one angle for measuring octagons, and one for checking hexagons. A drill grinding blade is also available for this square. One end is beveled to 59 deg. for drill grinding and the other at 41 deg. for checking the cutting angle of machine screw countersinks. Both ends are graduated for measuring the length of the cutting lips, to assure that the cutting tool is sharpened on center.

COMBINATION SETS, Fig. 6-15a, are adaptable to a large variety of operations, making them especially valuable in the shop. The com-

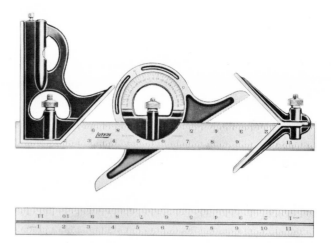

Fig. 6-15a. The combination set.

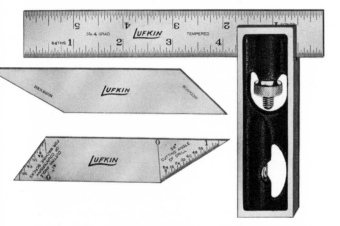

Fig. 6-14. Double square.

Fig. 6-15b. The square head being used as a depth gauge.

plete combination set consists of a hardened BLADE (#4 graduated rule), SQUARE HEAD, CENTER HEAD and a BEVEL PROTRACTOR. The blade fits all three heads.

The square head, having one 45 deg. edge, makes it possible for the tool to serve as both a try and miter square. By projecting the blade the desired distance below the edge, it serves as a depth gauge, Fig. 6-15b. The spirit level built into one edge makes it possible to use it as a simple level.

With the rule properly inserted the center head can be used to quickly locate the center of round stock, Fig. 6-15c.

The protractor head can be rotated through 180 deg. and is graduated accordingly. The head can be locked with a locking nut making it possible to accurately determine or lay out angles. The head also has a level built in making it possible to use it as a level.

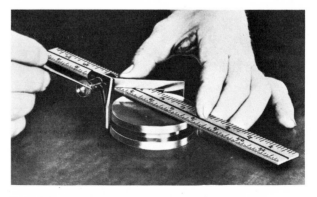

Fig. 6-15c. Using center head to locate the center of a piece of round stock. (Lufkin Rule Co.)

MEASURING ANGLES

Other angle measuring tools are used in layout work in addition to the protractor head of the combination set. The accuracy required by the job will determine which tool must be used.

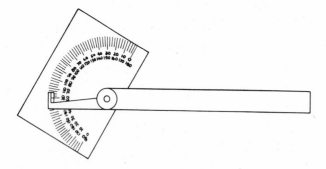

Fig. 6-16a. Plain steel protractor.

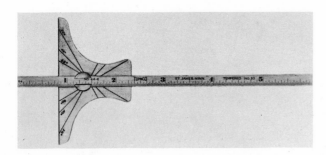

Fig. 6-16b. A protractor depth gauge.
(Scherr-Tumico)

When angles do not have to be checked or laid out to extreme accuracy a PLAIN PROTRACTOR, Fig. 6-16a, will prove satisfactory.

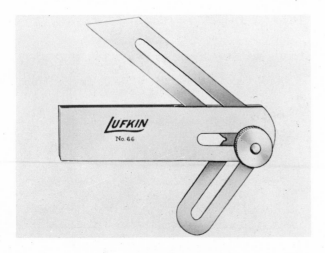

Fig. 6-17. A Universal bevel.

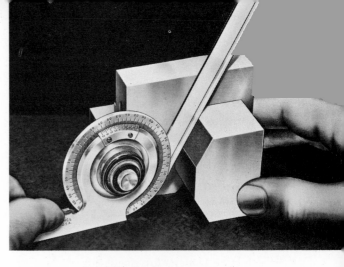

Fig. 6-18. The Vernier protractor.
(L. S. Starrett Co.)

The head is graduated from 0 to 180 deg. in both directions for easy reading. The PROTRACTOR DEPTH GAUGE, Fig. 6-16b, can be used to check angles and measure slot depths.

The UNIVERSAL BEVEL, Fig. 6-17, is useful for checking, laying out and transferring angles. Both the blade and stock are slotted, making it possible to adjust the blade into any desired position. A thumbscrew locks it tightly.

When the job requires extreme accuracy, the machinist uses the VERNIER PROTRACTOR, Fig. 6-18. With this tool it is possible to accurately measure angles of 1/12 of a degree (5 minutes).

STEPS IN MAKING A LAYOUT

Each layout job has its peculiarities and requires some planning before the operation can be started. Fig. 6-19 shows a typical job.

1. Study the drawings carefully.
2. Cut the stock to size and remove all burrs and sharp edges.
3. Clean the work surface of all oil and grease and apply layout dye.
4. Locate and scribe a REFERENCE or BASE LINE. Make all of your measurements from this line. If the material has one true edge, it can be used in place of the reference line.
5. Locate the center points of all circles and arcs.
6. Use the PRICK PUNCH, Fig. 6-20a, to mark the point where the center lines intersect. The sharp point (30 to 60 deg.) of this punch makes it easy to locate this position. After the prick punch mark has been checked and found on center, it is enlarged with the CENTER PUNCH, Fig. 6-20b.
7. Using the divider or trammel, scribe in all circles and arcs.

8. If angular lines are necesary, use the proper protractor type tool, or locate the correct points by measuring, and connect them by using a rule or straightedge.

9. Scribe in all other internal openings.

10. Use only clean sharp lines. Any double or

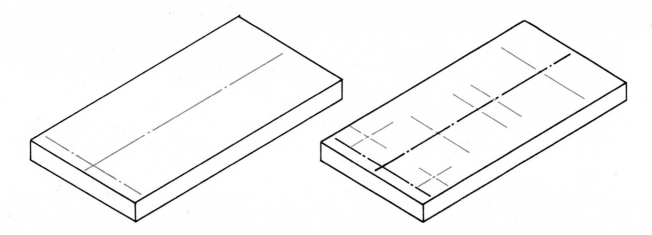

1. LOCATE AND SCRIBE THE BASE LINES

2. LOCATE ALL CIRCLE AND ARC CENTERLINES

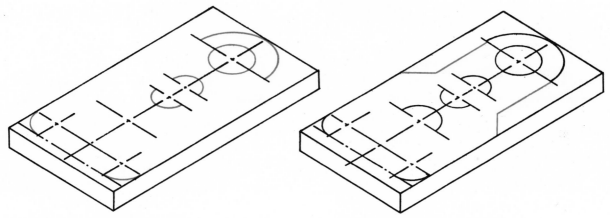

3. SCRIBE IN ALL CIRCLES AND ARCS

4. LOCATE AND SCRIBE IN ANGULAR LINES

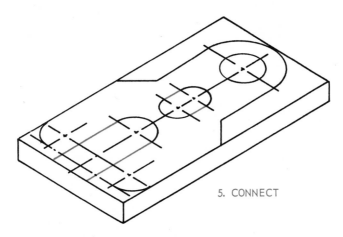

5. CONNECT

Fig. 6-19. Steps in laying out a job.

sloppy line work should be removed by cleaning, or applying another coat of dye and the line rescribed.

SAFETY

1. Never carry an open scriber, divider, trammel or hermaphrodite caliper in your pocket.
2. Always cover all sharp points with a cork when the tool is not being used.
3. Wear goggles when grinding the points of scriber type tools.
4. Get help when you must move heavy angle

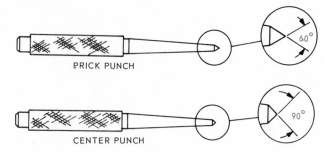

Fig. 6-20. *Differences between a prick punch and a center punch.*

plates, large V-blocks, etc.
5. Remove all burrs and sharp edges from stock before starting to work on it.

TEST YOUR KNOWLEDGE, Unit 6

1. Layout lines are used to:
   a. Take the place of blueprints.
   b. Tell the machinist where to machine.
   c. Give the machinist practice in measuring.
   d. None of the above.
2. _____is used to make the layout lines easier to see.
3. A_____is used to draw circles and arcs on metal.
4. The_____is used to draw circles and arcs that are too large for the above tool to draw.
5. A_____is used to draw lines on metal.
6. A surface plate is the flat surface used for layout work and inspection. True or false?
7. The combination set cannot be used to:
   a. Draw angular lines.
   b. Measure shoulders.
   c. Draw circles and arcs.
   d. Level angular surfaces.
8. A good layout job is determined by:
   a. Its neatness.
   b. Its accuracy.
   c. The time it took to make it.
   d. None of the above.
9. _____are frequently used to support round stock layout and inspection.
10. Long flat surfaces are checked with a straightedge. True or false?
11. The_____of the combination set is used to quickly locate the center of a round piece.
12. Angular lines may be laid out with a:
   a. Straightedge.
   b. Rule.
   c. Square.
   d. Bevel protractor.
13. The center punch has a sharper point than a prick punch. True or false?

RESEARCH AND DEVELOPMENT

1. Write a term paper on how surface plates are made. Why are they made of cast iron and granite and not of other materials?
2. Prepare a transparency for the overhead projector (use several overlays if needed) that will show the proper layout sequence. Record your narration for presentation to the class.
3. Make a display panel that shows the different layout fluids used. Protect your samples with clear plastic spray to prevent the scribed lines from rusting.

Unit 7

STRIKING TOOLS

The MACHINIST'S BALL-PEEN HAMMER, Fig. 7-1, is the most commonly used shop hammer. It has a hardened striking face and is used for all general purpose work. Ball-peen ham-

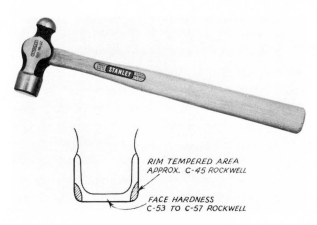

Fig. 7-1. Ball-peen hammer.

mers are classified according to the weight of the head without the handle. They weigh 2, 4, 8, or 12 ounces, or 1, 1-1/4, 1-1/2, 2, or 3 pounds.

SOFT-FACE HAMMERS or MALLETS, Fig. 7-2, are used for striking heavy blows where steel-face hammers would damage or mar the work surface. They are especially useful for setting work tightly on parallels when mounting work in a vise for machining.

Soft-face hammers are made of many different materials: copper, lead, rawhide, and plastic, and range in weight from a few ounces to several pounds.

SAFETY

1. NEVER strike two hammers together. The faces are very hard and the blow might cause a chip to break off and fly out at high speed.

2. Do not use a hammer unless the head is on tightly and the handle is solid.
3. Knuckles can be injured if you "choke up" too far on the handle when striking a blow.
4. Unless the blow is struck squarely the hammer may glance off of the work and cause injuries.
5. Place the hammer on the bench carefully. A falling hammer can cause serious foot injuries.

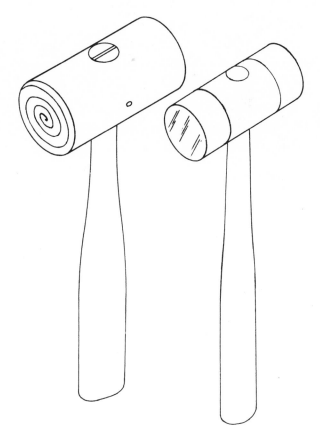

Fig. 7-2a. Rawhide mallet.

Fig. 7-2b. Plastic or soft-face hammer.

TEST YOUR KNOWLEDGE, Unit 7

1. The_____ _____hammer is the most commonly used hammer in the machine shop.
2. The hammer described above is classed according to its:
   a. Length.
   b. Size.
   c. Weight.
   d. Length of the handle.
3. The mallet or soft-face hammer is used as a striking tool when the regular hammer would _____the work.
4. Striking two hammer faces together may:
   a. Loosen the hammer handles.
   b. Cause a chip to fly out at high speed.
   c. Damage the hammer faces.
5. The hand can be injured if you_____ _____ too far on the hammer handle when striking a blow.

Unit 8

CHISELS

Chisels are tools used to cut cold metal and for this reason are called "cold" chisels. The four chisels illustrated in Fig. 8-1, are the most widely used types. The general term COLD CHISEL is used when referring to these chisels. Other chisels in this category are variations or combinations of these four chisels.

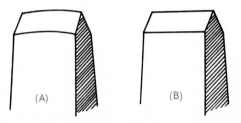

Fig. 8-2. The work to be done determines how the chisel should be sharpened. Slightly rounded (A) for cutting on flat plates. Flat (B) for shearing.

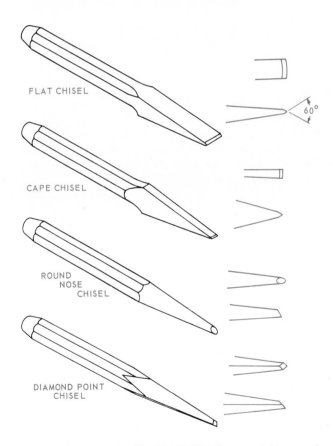

Fig. 8-1. Cold chisels. The FLAT CHISEL is used for general cutting and chipping work. The CAPE CHISEL has a narrower cutting edge than the flat chisel and is used to cut grooves. The ROUND NOSE CHISEL is used for cutting radii and round grooves. The DIAMOND POINT CHISEL is principally used for squaring corners.

The work to be cut will determine how the chisel should be sharpened. A chisel with a slightly curved cutting edge, Fig. 8-2(A), will work better when cutting on a flat plate. If it is to be used to shear metal held in a vise, it will work best if the cutting edge is straight, Fig. 8-2(B). The curved edge will help prevent the chisel from cutting unwanted grooves in the surrounding metal when shearing rivet heads.

The chisel is frequently used to chip castings. Chipping is started by holding the chisel at an angle as shown in Fig. 8-3(A). The angle must be great enough to cause the cutting edge to enter the metal. After the cut has been started and the proper depth reached, the chisel angle can be decreased enough to hold the cutting action at the proper depth, Fig. 8-3(B). The cut depth can be reduced by decreasing the chisel angle. Decrease the angle too much and the chisel will ride on the cutting edge heel, Fig. 8-3(C), and lift out of the cut.

Grip the metal so the layout line is just below the vise jaws when shearing it to a line. This will leave sufficient metal to finish by filing or grinding. When cutting, it is best to hold the metal in the vise without using vise jaw caps. This provides a better shearing action between the vise jaw and the chisel. Advance the chisel after each blow so that the cutting is done by the center of the cutting edge.

8-1

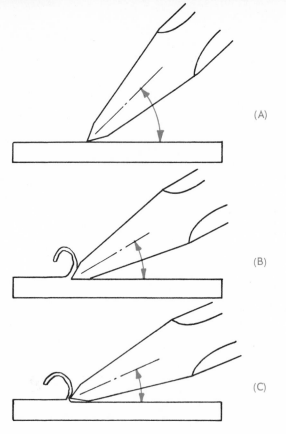

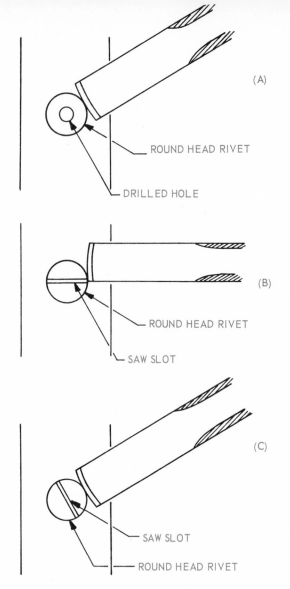

(A)

ROUND HEAD RIVET

DRILLED HOLE

(B)

ROUND HEAD RIVET

SAW SLOT

(C)

SAW SLOT

ROUND HEAD RIVET

Fig. 8-3. The proper angles for various cutting situations. (A) Starting the cut. (B) Maintaining the cut at the desired depth. (C) Reducing the cutting angle too much will cause the chisel to lift out of the cut.

Fig. 8-4. This chisel (variation of flat chisel) is often referred to as a "rivet buster." Note drawing in color which shows how it is sharpened.

Fig. 8-5. Recommended practices for removing rivet heads, when: (A) There is not enough room to swing the hammer with sufficient force. (B) and (C) When the rivet heads are too large to be removed at one time.

Fig. 8-5a. The cape chisel is also frequently used to remove rivets.
(Crescent Tool Co.)

Chisels

The chisel is an ideal tool for removing rivets. The head is sheared off and the rivet punched out. A variation of the conventional cold chisel used to remove rivet heads is called a "rivet buster," Fig. 8-4.

When there is not enough room to swing a hammer with sufficient force to cut the rivet,

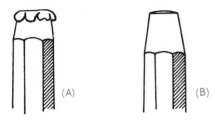

Fig. 8-6. The dangerous mushroom head (A), should be ground to a safe condition (B), before a chip flying from it injures someone.

drill a hole about the size of the rivet body and almost through the head, Fig. 8-5(A). The head can then be removed with the chisel.

If the rivet head is so large that the entire head cannot be removed in one piece, saw the head almost through and cut away half of the

head at a time. Figs. 8-5(B), and 8-5(C), show how this may be done. A cape chisel can also be used to remove rivets, Fig. 8-5a.

There are few things that are more dangerous than metal knocked off a chisel head that has been allowed to become mushroomed, Fig. 8-6(A). Remove this dangerous condition by grinding, Fig. 8-6(B), before a painful injury results.

SAFETY

1. Flying chips are dangerous. Wear safety goggles and erect a shield when using a chisel to protect yourself and the people working near you.
2. Hold the chisel in such a manner that should you miss a stroke with the hammer it will not strike and injure your hand.
3. Remove any chisel head mushrooming by grinding, before it becomes dangerous.
4. Edges cut with the chisel are sharp and can cause bad cuts. Remove them by grinding or filing.

TEST YOUR KNOWLEDGE, Unit 8

1. List the four basic types of chisels:
   a._____
   b._____
   c._____
   d._____
2. The cutting edge of the chisel should be ground _____ if it is to be used to shear metal held in a vise.
3. The chisel designed to remove rivets is called a _____ _____.
4. A_____ chisel head should be ground away before the chisel is used because of the possibility of pieces of the head flying off and injuring someone.
5. The ____ ____ ____ ____ will determine how the cutting edge should be sharpened.

RESEARCH AND DEVELOPMENT

1. The pneumatic chisel is often used in industry. Secure information on this tool for a bulletin board display and, if possible, borrow a sample of the actual tool for examination, from one of the local industries.
2. Make a small panel with two chisels - one that shows a mushroomed head chisel, and the other a head that is safe to use.
3. Design a safety poster showing the correct

way to use a chisel.
4. Demonstrate the proper way to sharpen a chisel.
5. Secure samples of work cut by chisels as used by industries in your locality and compare these with a piece of work you have cut with a chisel. Mount both, your samples and the industry samples, on a small panel for the class to see.

In constructing the modern helicopter metals that are light in weight yet have great strength are required. (Cessna Aircraft Co.)

Unit 9

SAWING METALS
BY HAND

The typical HACK SAW, Fig. 9-1, is composed of a frame with a handle and a replaceable blade. Almost all hack saws made today are adjustable to accommodate several different blade lengths,

Fig. 9-1. A typical hack saw. (Stanley Tool Co.)

and are made so that the blade can be installed in either a vertical or horizontal position, Fig. 9-2.

When placing a blade in the saw frame, make sure the frame is adjusted for the blade length to be used with sufficient adjustment remaining to permit tightening the blade until it "pings" when snapped with the finger. The blade is positioned with the teeth pointing AWAY from the handle, Fig. 9-3. Frequently, a new blade must be retightened after a few strokes because it stretched slightly from the heat produced while cutting.

HOLDING THE WORK

The work must be held securely with the point to be cut as close to the vise as practical. This eliminates "chatter" and vibration that dulls the saw teeth. Fig. 9-4, offers suggestions for holding irregular shaped work. Note that the work is clamped so the cut is started on the flat side rather than on a corner or edge. This lessens the possibility of breaking the blade.

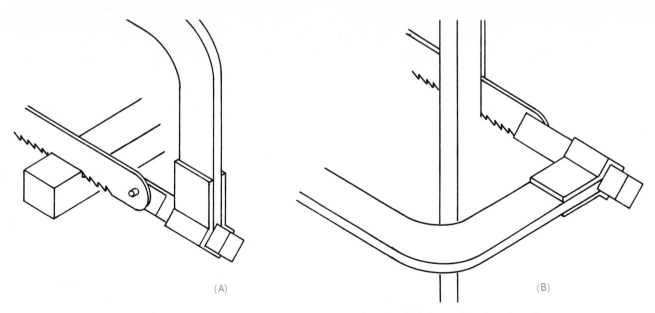

(A)

(B)

Fig. 9-2. The modern hack saw accommodates several different lengths of blades, and can be adjusted to position the blade in either (A) vertical position; or, (B) a horizontal position.

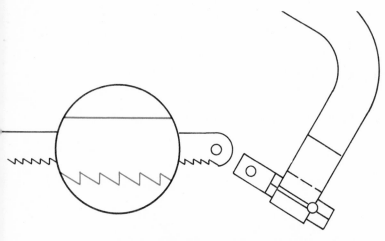

Fig. 9-3. Inserting the blade. The blade is inserted with the teeth positioned to cut on the forward stroke.

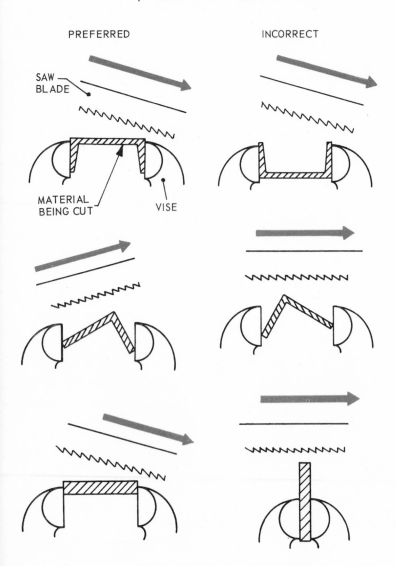

Fig. 9-4. Holding irregular shaped work for sawing.

HOW TO START THE CUT

When starting to cut to a marked line, it is best to notch the work with a file, Fig. 9-5, or to use the thumb of the left hand to guide the blade until it starts to cut. Some blades are manufactured with very fine teeth at the front to make starting the cut easier. Use enough pressure so the blade will begin to cut immediately.

CUTTING METAL

Grasp the saw firmly by the handle and the front of the frame. Apply enough pressure on the forward stroke to make the teeth cut. Insufficient pressure will permit the teeth to slide over the material and become dull. Also, lift the saw slightly on the return stroke, as the blade cuts only on the forward stroke.

Use the complete length of the blade and make about 40 to 50 strokes per minute. More strokes per minute may generate enough heat to draw the blade temper and dull the teeth. Keep the blade moving in a straight line. Avoid any twisting or binding which can break the blade.

DULLING OR BREAKING A BLADE BEFORE COMPLETING THE CUT

If the cut is started with an old blade and it becomes necessary to replace it with a new blade because of breakage or dullness, do not continue in the same cut with the new blade. As the blade becomes dull, the KERF, the term given to the slot made by the blade, becomes narrower and to continue the cut in the slot will cause the new blade to bind and stick and be ruined in the first few strokes. Start a new cut by rotating the work, if possible, or by starting a new cut.

FINISHING THE CUT

Saw carefully when the blade has cut almost through the material, and support the stock being cut off with your left hand, so it will not drop when the cut is completed.

SAW BLADES

All hack saw blades are heat treated to provide hardness and toughness needed to cut. The FLEXIBLE BACK BLADE has only the teeth hardened. The ALL-HARD BLADE is hardened throughout except that the hardness is reduced

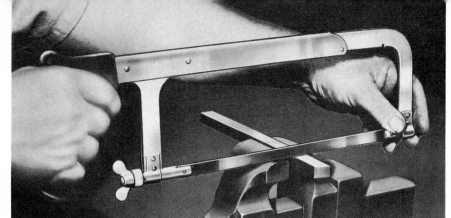

Fig. 9-5. Starting the cut. A file was used to notch the work to permit easier starting. (L. S. Starrett Co.)

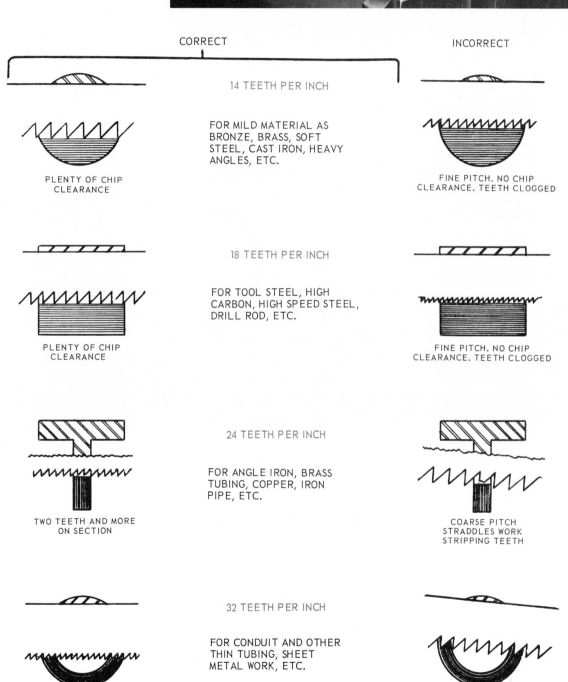

CORRECT   INCORRECT

14 TEETH PER INCH

FOR MILD MATERIAL AS
BRONZE, BRASS, SOFT
STEEL, CAST IRON, HEAVY
ANGLES, ETC.

PLENTY OF CHIP
CLEARANCE

FINE PITCH. NO CHIP
CLEARANCE. TEETH CLOGGED

18 TEETH PER INCH

FOR TOOL STEEL, HIGH
CARBON, HIGH SPEED STEEL,
DRILL ROD, ETC.

PLENTY OF CHIP
CLEARANCE

FINE PITCH. NO CHIP
CLEARANCE. TEETH CLOGGED

24 TEETH PER INCH

FOR ANGLE IRON, BRASS
TUBING, COPPER, IRON
PIPE, ETC.

TWO TEETH AND MORE
ON SECTION

COARSE PITCH
STRADDLES WORK
STRIPPING TEETH

32 TEETH PER INCH

FOR CONDUIT AND OTHER
THIN TUBING, SHEET
METAL WORK, ETC.

TWO OR MORE TEETH
ON SECTION

COARSE PITCH
STRADDLES WORK

Fig. 9-6. The proper blade should be used for each job to assure long blade life and rapid cutting action.

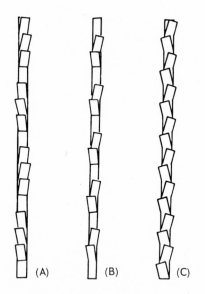

Fig. 9-7. Types of set in hack saw teeth. (A) Undulated, (B) Raker, and (C) Alternate.

The SET of the blade provides the necessary clearance, and prevents the blade from binding in the cut. The blade may have one of three sets: RAKER, ALTERNATE, or UNDULATING, Fig. 9-7.

UNUSUAL CUTTING SITUATIONS

Cutting soft metal tubing can be a problem. The blade may bind and tear the tubing or the tubing may flatten. This can be eliminated by inserting a wooden dowel of the proper size into the tubing, and cutting through the tubing and dowel, Fig. 9-8.

Cutting a narrow strip of considerable length can be accomplished by setting the blade at right angles to the frame and making the cut in the usual way, Fig. 9-9. Strips of any width up to the capacity of the saw frame can be made in this manner.

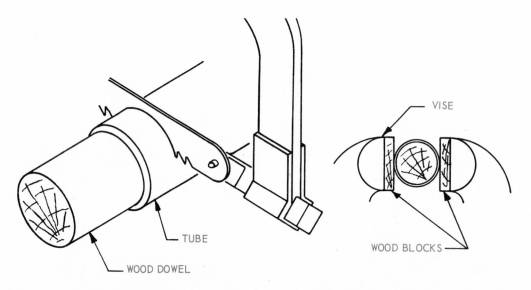

VISE

TUBE

WOOD DOWEL

WOOD BLOCKS

Fig. 9-8. The proper procedure for sawing thin wall metal tubing.

near the holes to reduce the possibility of breakage at this point. Flexible back blades are used for sawing soft materials or materials with thin cross-sections. The all-hard blade does not buckle when heavy pressure is applied. It is best for cutting hard metals.

The number of teeth per inch of blade has an important bearing on the shape and kind of material to be cut and upon the blade life. Two or three teeth should be cutting at all times, otherwise, the teeth will straddle the section being cut and snap off when cutting pressure is applied, Fig. 9-6.

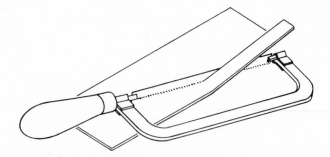

Fig. 9-9. The blade is pivoted to the horizontal position for cutting long narrow strips. Best results can be obtained if the strip is bent up as shown during the sawing operation.

Thin metal can be cut by putting it between two pieces of wood, and cutting through both of them, Fig. 9-10.

HACK SAW SAFETY

1. Do not test the sharpness of the blade by running your fingers across the teeth.
2. Store the saw so you will not accidentally reach into the teeth when you pick it up.
3. The burr formed on the cut surface is sharp and can cause a serious cut. Do not brush away the chips with your hand.
4. All-hard blades can shatter and produce flying chips. Wear your goggles!
5. Be sure the blade is properly tensioned. If the blade should break while you are on the cutting stroke, your hand may strike the work and cause a painful injury.

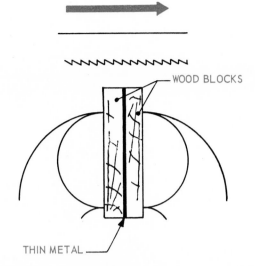

Fig. 9-10. Thin metal can be cut easily by sandwiching it between two pieces of wood.

TEST YOUR KNOWLEDGE, Unit 9

1. A typical hack saw is composed of a:
   a._____
   b._____ c._____
2. The hack saw blade is fitted in the frame correctly when it cuts on the _____ stroke.
3. If the work is not mounted solidly and close to the vise:
   a. The blade will break.
   b. The work will vibrate or "chatter" causing the teeth to snap off.
   c. The blade will slide over the work.
   d. None of the above.
   e. All of the above.
4. The _____ of the teeth keeps the blade from binding in the cut.
5. A new blade started in a cut made by a dull blade will _____
   a. Cut faster and cleaner.
   b. Stick and bind and ruin the blade.
   c. Require care in restarting the cut.
   d. None of the above.
   e. All of the above.
6. The _____ _____ blade has only the teeth hardened.
7. The _____ _____ blade is hardened throughout and is used to cut hard metals.

*Equipment used by modern industry--vertical
gear shaper cutting a 120-in. external gear.
(Fellows Gear Shaper Co.)*

Unit 10

HAND REAMING

A drill does not produce a smooth or accurate enough hole for a precision fit. Reaming is the operation that is used to produce smoothness and accuracy. Ordinarily, only final sizing is done by hand reaming.

a hole with a keyway or other interruption, it is better to use a reamer with spiral flutes. When preparing a piece to be reamed by hand, 0.005 to 0.010 in. of stock should be left in the hole for removal by the tool.

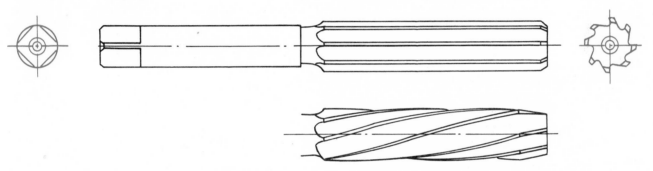

Fig. 10-1. The hand reamer. Above, straight flutes. Below, spiral flutes.

HAND REAMER

The hand reamer, Fig. 10-1, has a square on the shank end that is suitable for holding it in a tap wrench. The reamer may be made of high speed steel or carbon steel, and is available in sizes from 1/8 to 1-1/2 in. The cutting end is ground with a slight taper to provide easy starting in the hole. Straight fluted reamers are suitable for most work, however, when reaming

The EXPANSION HAND REAMER, Fig. 10-2, is used when the hole must be cut a few thousandths over nominal size for fitting purposes. Slots are cut into the hollow center of the tool, and the center opening is machined on a slight

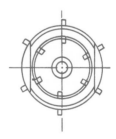

Fig. 10-2. The expansion hand reamer.

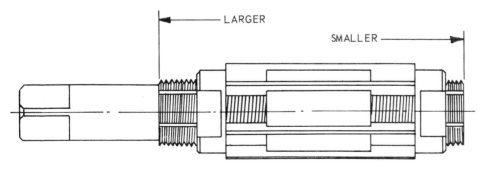

Fig. 10-3. The adjustable hand reamer.

taper. The reamer is expanded by tightening a taper screw into this opening. The amount of expansion is limited and the reamer may be broken if expanded too much. It is not recommended that the expansion reamer be used in place of a solid reamer because of the danger of producing oversize holes.

The ADJUSTABLE HAND REAMER, Fig. 10-3, is threaded its entire length and fitted with tapered slots to receive the adjustable blades. The blades are tapered along one edge to correspond with the taper slots in the reamer

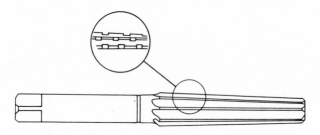

Fig. 10-4. The taper hand reamer. Inset shows how the cutting edges are notched on the roughing taper reamer.

body so that when they are in position, the cutting edges of the blade are parallel. The diameter of the reamer is set by loosening one adjusting nut and tightening the other. The blade can be moved in either direction. This type reamer is manufactured in sizes ranging from 3/8 to 3-1/2 in. and each reamer has sufficient adjustment to increase the diameter to the size of the next larger reamer.

The TAPER REAMER, Fig. 10-4, is used to finish a taper hole accurately and with a smooth

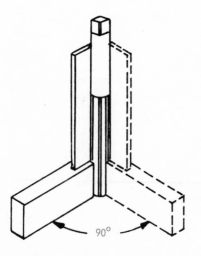

Fig. 10-5. Checking reamer for squareness with the work.

finish. Because of the long cutting edges, taper reamers are somewhat difficult to operate. To provide for easier removal of the surplus metal, a roughing reamer is run into the hole first. This reamer is slightly smaller (0.010 in.) than the finish reamer and has a left hand spiral groove cut along the cutting edges to break up the chips.

USING THE HAND REAMER

A two-handle tap wrench is used as a handle because it permits an even application of pressure. It is virtually impossible to secure a satisfactory hole using a single end wrench. To start, rotate the reamer slowly to allow it to align with the hole. It is desirable to check whether the reamer has started square at several points around its circumference, Fig. 10-5. Feed should be steady and rapid. Keep the reamer cutting, or it will start to "chatter" and produce a series of tool marks in the surface of the hole, and may cause it to be out-of-round. Turning pres-

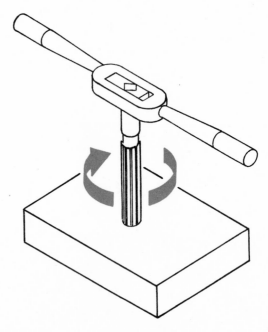

Fig. 10-6. The reamer is ALWAYS turned in a clockwise direction.

sure is applied evenly with both hands, and ALWAYS in a clockwise direction, Fig. 10-6. NEVER TURN A REAMER IN A COUNTERCLOCKWISE DIRECTION, as the cutting edges will be dulled. Feed the reamer deeply enough into the hole to take care of the starting taper. Cutting fluid to be applied will depend upon the metal being reamed.

Hand Reaming

SAFETY

1. Remove all burrs from reamed holes.
2. Never use your hands to remove chips and cutting fluid from the reamer. Use a piece of cotton waste.

3. Store reamers carefully so they do not touch one another. Reamers should never be thrown in a drawer.
4. Clamp the work solidly before starting to ream.
5. Never clean a reamed hole with an air hose.

TEST YOUR KNOWLEDGE, Unit 10

1. Reaming will produce a hole which is smooth and accurate. True or false?
2. This can also be done with a properly sharpened drill. True or false?
3. Usually____ to ____inch of stock is left in a hole to be hand reamed.
4. The expansion hand reamer is used when the hole must be made a few thousandths over nominal size. True or false?
5. Turning a hand reamer_____will ruin the cutting edges.
6. The roughing taper reamer has grooves cut along the cutting edges to make a smoother cut. True or false?
7. It is virtually impossible to produce an accurate and smooth reamed hole using an ad-justable wrench to apply power because:
   a. It applies pressure unevenly causing "chatter."
   b. It applies too much pressure.
   c. Prevents the reamer from starting square.
   d. None of the above applies.
   e. All of the above applies.

RESEARCH AND DEVELOPMENT

1. Prepare a sample block of metal that can be used to illustrate the difference between a drilled and a reamed hole.
2. Make a large drawing of a reamer and letter in the names of the various parts.

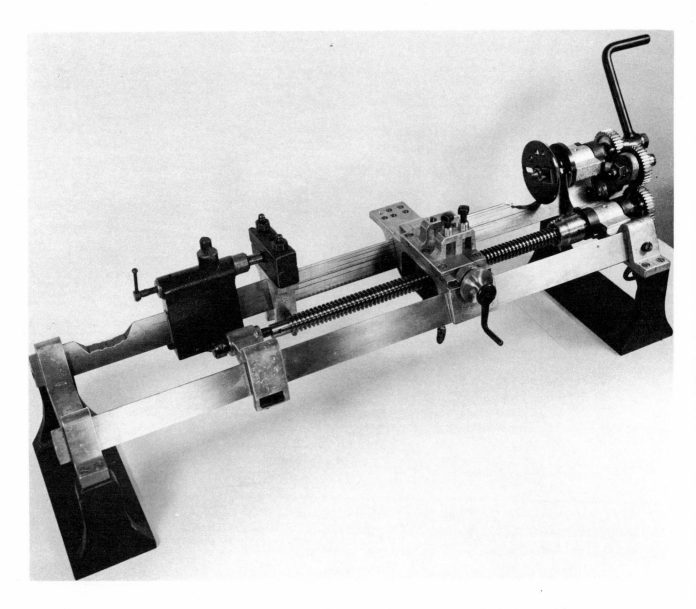

Screw-cutting lathe invented by Maudslay. This machine combined a master lead screw, a slide rest and gears to change the speed, on a sturdy metal frame.
(DoAll Co.)

Unit 11

HAND THREADING

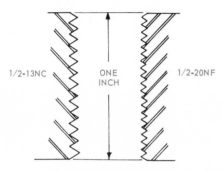

Fig. 11-1. A comparison of the National Coarse (NC), and the National Fine (NF) threads. Both have the same geometric shape.

The AMERICAN NATIONAL THREAD SYSTEM was adopted in 1911. It is the common thread form used in the United States and is characterized by the 60 deg. angle formed by the sides of the thread and the small flat at the thread crest and root, Fig. 11-2.

The NATIONAL COARSE (NC), used for general purpose work, and the NATIONAL FINE (NF), used for precision assemblies, are the most widely used thread series in the American National Thread Series. The NF series has more threads per inch for a given diameter than the NC series, Fig. 11-1.

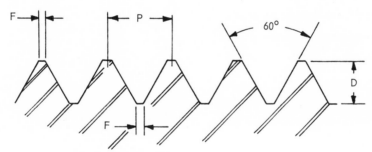

AMERICAN NATIONAL THREAD FORM

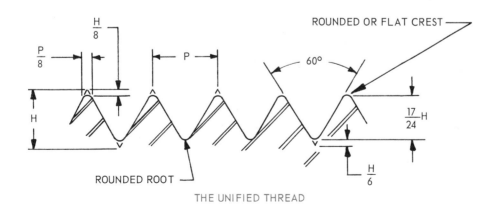

THE UNIFIED THREAD

Fig. 11-2. The drawings illustrate the difference between the American National Thread form, and the Unified Thread form.

11-1

Because of the confusion that resulted during World War II from the many different forms and kinds of threads used by the Allies, the powers that make up NATO (North Atlantic Treaty Organization) adopted a standard thread form. It is referred to as the UNIFIED SYSTEM, Fig. 11-2, and is very similar to the American National Thread System. It differs only in the shape of the root, which is rounded, and the crest, which may be flat or rounded. The threads are identified by UNF and UNC. Fasteners using this thread series are interchangeable with fasteners using the American National thread.

THREAD SIZE

Threads smaller than 1/4 in. diameter are not measured as fractional sizes but by NUMBER SIZES that range, for most purposes, from #0 (approximately 1/16 in. (0.060) in diameter) to #12 (just under 1/4 in. (0.216) in diameter). NC and NF series are available. Care must be taken so that the numbers denoting the thread diameter and number of threads per inch are not mistaken for a fraction.

Fig. 11-4. Standard hand taps are manufactured in sets of three. Top, Taper-for starting the thread; Center, Plug-for continuing the thread after the taper tap has cut as far into the hole as it can; Below, Bottoming-for continuing the threads to the bottom of the hole. (Threadwell Manufacturing Co.)

CUTTING THREADS

Because thread dimensions have been standardized, the use of TAPS to cut internal threads, and DIES to cut external threads have become universal practice whenever threads are to be cut by hand, Fig. 11-3.

INTERNAL THREADS

Internal threads are made by using a TAP, Fig. 11-3. Taps are made of CARBON STEEL or HIGH SPEED STEEL (HSS) and are carefully hardened and tempered for long life. Taps are quite brittle and are easily damaged if not handled properly.

To meet demands for varying degrees of threaded accuracy, it became necessary for industry to adopt standard working tolerances for threads. Working tolerances have been divided into CLASSES OF FITS which is indicated by the last number on the thread description (1/2-13NC-2). The fits are:

Class 1 . . . . Loose Fit
Class 2 . . . . Free Fit
Class 3 . . . . Medium Fit
Class 4 . . . . Close Fit

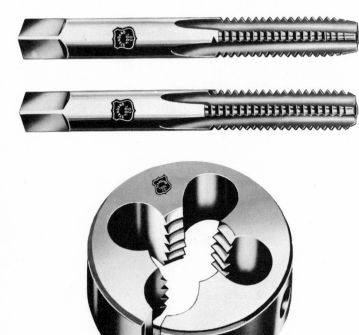

Fig. 11-3. Above. Tap (for cutting internal threads). Below. Die (for cutting external threads). (Standard Tool Co.)

TAPS

Standard hand taps over 1/4 in. diameter are made in sets of three known as TAPER, PLUG, and BOTTOMING TAPS, Fig. 11-4. The TAPER TAP is used to start the thread and is tapered back from the end 6 to 10 threads before the full thread diameter is reached. The PLUG TAP is used after the taper tap has cut threads as far into the hole as possible. It tapers back 3 or 4 threads before the full thread diameter is reached. The BOTTOMING TAP is used to cut threads to the bottom of the hole. It is necessary to use the full set of taps to cut threads in the different types of holes shown in Fig. 11-5.

Fig. 11-5. Openings in this metal block illustrate the three types of threaded holes: Left, Open or through hole; Center, Blind hole that has been drilled deeper than the desired threads; Right, Blind hole with threads tapped to the bottom.

The PIPE TAP, Fig. 11-6, is another tap that is used in the shop. It cuts a tapered thread so that a "wedging" action is·set up to make a leak-tight joint. The fraction that indicates the tap size may be confusing at first because it indicates the pipe size AND NOT the thread diameter. A pipe thread is indicated by NPT and the threads taper 3/4 in. per foot of length.

CUTTING INTERNAL THREADS

The TAPER TAP should be used for tapping a through hole in the stock, Fig. 11-5(Left). The long taper permits easier and straighter starting. However, it cannot be used to thread a blind hole as the end of the tap will strike the bottom of the hole before a full thread has been cut to the proper depth.

The PLUG TAP can be used in much the same manner as the taper tap if soft material is being

Fig. 11-6. Photo which shows 1/8 standard thread, and 1/8 pipe thread.

threaded. It can be used to thread a blind hole, if the hole has been drilled deeper than necessary, Fig. 11-5(Center).

The BOTTOMING TAP is used when the thread must be cut to the very bottom of a blind hole, Fig. 11-5(Right). Normally, the thread is started with the taper tap, cut further with the plug tap, and finished with the bottoming tap.

TAP DRILL SIZES

The drill used to make the hole prior to tapping is called the TAP DRILL. Theoretically, it

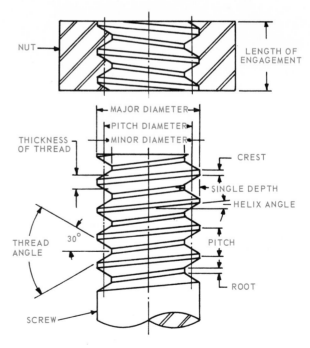

Fig. 11-7. Nomenclature of a thread.

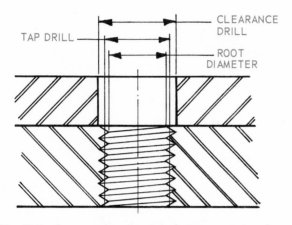

Fig. 11-7a. Cross section of a typical piece at a point where a bolt will be used to clamp the two pieces together. The clearance drill permits the bolt or threaded section to enter without binding.

should be equal in diameter to the minor diameter of the screw that is to be fitted in the completed thread, Fig. 11-7. To accomplish this, the tap must cut a full depth thread which would require too much pressure to drive the tap, and cause excess tap breakage to occur. However, full depth threads are not necessary. With three-quarter depth threads usually the fastener will break before the threads strip.

Drill size can be secured from a TAP DRILL CHART, Fig. 11-8.

TAP HOLDERS

Two types of tap holders are available. The type to be used will depend upon the tap size. A

NATIONAL COARSE, AND NATIONAL FINE THREADS AND TAP DRILLS

Size	Threads Per Inch	Major Dia.	Minor Dia.	Pitch Dia.	Tap Drill 75% Thread	Decimal Equivalent	Clearance Drill	Decimal Equivalent
2	56	.0860	.0628	.0744	50	.0700	42	.0935
	64	.0860	.0657	.0759	50	.0700	42	.0935
3	48	.099	.0719	.0855	47	.0785	36	.1065
	56	.099	.0758	.0874	45	.0820	36	.1065
4	40	.112	.0795	.0958	43	.0890	31	.1200
	48	.112	.0849	.0985	42	.0935	31	.1200
6	32	.138	.0974	.1177	36	.1065	26	.1470
	40	.138	.1055	.1218	33	.1130	26	.1470
8	32	.164	.1234	.1437	29	.1360	17	.1730
	36	.164	.1279	.1460	29	.1360	17	.1730
10	24	.190	.1359	.1629	25	.1495	8	.1990
	32	.190	.1494	.1697	21	.1590	8	.1990
12	24	.216	.1619	.1889	16	.1770	1	.2280
	28	.216	.1696	.1928	14	.1820	2	.2210
1/4	20	.250	.1850	.2175	7	.2010	G	.2610
	28	.250	.2036	.2268	3	.2130	G	.2610
5/16	18	.3125	.2403	.2764	F	.2570	21/64	.3281
	24	.3125	.2584	.2854	I	.2720	21/64	.3281
3/8	16	.3750	.2938	.3344	5/16	.3125	25/64	.3906
	24	.3750	.3209	.3479	Q	.3320	25/64	.3906
7/16	14	.4375	.3447	.3911	U	.3680	15/32	.4687
	20	.4375	.3725	.4050	25/64	.3906	29/64	.4531
1/2	13	.5000	.4001	.4500	27/64	.4219	17/32	.5312
	20	.5000	.4350	.4675	29/64	.4531	33/64	.5156
9/16	12	.5625	.4542	.5084	31/64	.4844	19/32	.5937
	18	.5625	.4903	.5264	33/64	.5156	37/64	.5781
5/8	11	.6250	.5069	.5660	17/32	.5312	21/32	.6562
	18	.6250	.5528	.5889	37/64	.5781	41/64	.6406
3/4	10	.7500	.6201	.6850	21/32	.6562	25/32	.7812
	16	.7500	.6688	.7094	11/16	.6875	49/64	.7656
7/8	9	.8750	.7307	.8028	49/64	.7656	29/32	.9062
	14	.8750	.7822	.8286	13/16	.8125	57/64	.8906
1	8	1.0000	.8376	.9188	7/8	.8750	1- 1/32	1.0312
	14	1.0000	.9072	.9536	15/16	.9375	1- 1/64	1.0156
1-1/8	7	1.1250	.9394	1.0322	63/64	.9844	1- 5/32	1.1562
	12	1.1250	1.0167	1.0709	1- 3/64	1.0469	1- 5/32	1.1562
1-1/4	7	1.2500	1.0644	1.1572	1- 7/64	1.1094	1- 9/32	1.2812
	12	1.2500	1.1417	1.1959	1-11/64	1.1719	1- 9/32	1.2812
1-1/2	6	1.5000	1.2835	1.3917	1-11/32	1.3437	1-17/32	1.5312
	12	1.5000	1.3917	1.4459	1-27/64	1.4219	1-17/32	1.5312

Fig. 11-8. Thread and tap drill sizes.

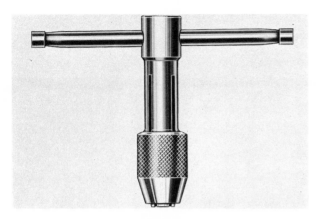

Fig. 11-9. T-Handle tap wrench. (Threadwell Mfg. Co.)

T-HANDLE TAP WRENCH, Fig. 11-9, should be used with all small taps as it allows a more sensitive "feel" when tapping. The HAND TAP WRENCH, Fig. 11-10, is used with larger taps

Fig. 11-10. The hand tap wrench. (Threadwell Mfg. Co.)

when more leverage is required.

When tapping by hand, the chief requirement is to see that the tap is started straight and remains square during the entire threading operation, Fig. 11-11. The tap should be backed off a half turn every one or two cutting turns to break the chips free and allow them to drop down through the flutes. This prevents them from jamming and damaging the threads. Some machinists, when tapping a blind hole, insert a piece of grease pencil, crayon, or dab of grease in the hole. As the tap cuts, the grease is forced up and out of the hole carrying the chips with it.

CARE IN TAPPING

Considerable care must be excerised when tapping:
1. Use the correct tap drill.
2. Use a sharp tap and use sufficient quantities of cutting oil.
3. Start the tap square.
4. Do not force a tap to cut. Remove the chips as necessary.
5. Do not run the tap to the bottom of a blind hole and continue to apply pressure. Also be sure that the hole does not fill with chips and jam the tap.

BROKEN TAPS

Taps sometimes break off in the hole. Several tools and techniques have been developed for their removal. THEY DO NOT ALWAYS WORK and the work may have to be discarded.

Fig. 11-11. The tap must be started square with the hole if accurate threads are to be cut. A quick way to do this is to use a square as illustrated.

A pointed tool like a scribe can be used to pick out the pieces of a tap that has shattered. Broken carbon steel taps can be annealed and drilled out. This CANNOT be done with high speed steel taps. They may have to be ground out.

A TAP EXTRACTOR, Fig. 11-12, can be used at times to remove a broken tap. Penetrating oil should be applied and permitted to work for a short time before the fingers of the extractor are fitted into the flutes of the broken tap. The collar of the extractor is slipped down flush with the work surface, and a tap wrench is fitted to its head. The tool is twisted back and forth very lightly to loosen the broken parts of the tap. After the broken parts have been loosened, it is a simple matter to remove them.

CUTTING EXTERNAL THREADS

DIES, Fig. 11-13, are used to cut external threads by hand. SOLID DIES, Fig. 11-13(Left and Center), are not adjustable and for that reason are seldom used. The ADJUSTABLE ROUND DIE, Fig. 11-13(Right), and the TWO PART

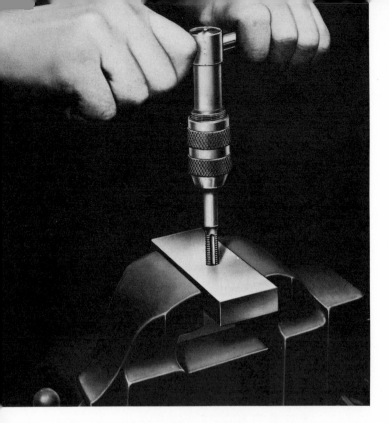

Fig. 11-11a. In tapping by hand, see to it the tap is started straight and remains square with the hole.

ADJUSTABLE DIE, Fig. 11-13a, are the most widely used dies for hand use.

The latter has a wide range of adjustment and is fitted with guides to keep it true. Dies are available for cutting most standard threads.

DIE STOCKS

DIE STOCKS, Fig. 11-14, are used to hold the die and to serve as a wrench for operating the die.

When cutting external threads, it is necessary to remember:

1. Stock diameter is the same size as the desired threads. That is, 1/2-13NC threads are cut on a 1/2 in. diameter shaft.
2. Hold the work securely.
3. Set the die to the proper size. If it is not set to the desired size, make trial cuts

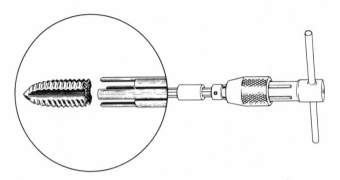

Fig. 11-12. Tap extractor. The close-up shows the fingers of the extractor, and how they fit into the flutes of the broken tap.

on a piece of scrap until the proper adjustment is made.
4. Grind a small chamfer on the end of the rod to be threaded, Fig. 11-15.
5. Start the cut with the tapered end of the die.
6. Back off the die every two or three turns to break the chips.
7. Apply liberal quantities of cutting oil.

Fig. 11-13. Dies which are used to cut external threads by hand. Left. Hex. rethreading die. Center. Square bolt die. Right. Adjustable found die.

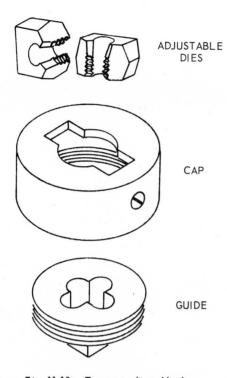

ADJUSTABLE DIES

CAP

GUIDE

Fig. 11-13a. Two-part adjustable die.

Fig. 11-14. The die stock holds the die and serves as the means for applying pressure to make the die cut. (Threadwell Mfg. Co.)

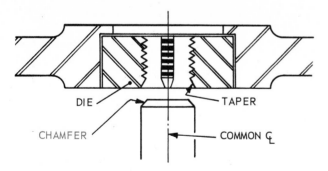

DIE

CHAMFER

TAPER

COMMON $\mathcal{C}_L$

Fig. 11-15. The die will start easier if a small chamfer is cut or ground on the end of the shaft to be threaded. Section through die in the die stock showing the proper way to start the threads.

THREADING TO A SHOULDER

When it is necessary to cut threads up to a shoulder, the threads are started and run down as far as posssible in the usual manner, Fig. 11-16(A). Remove the die and turn it over, with the guide up. Reverse the cutters and run the threads down to the shoulder, Fig. 11-16(B). Never attempt this operation without first starting the threads in the usual manner.

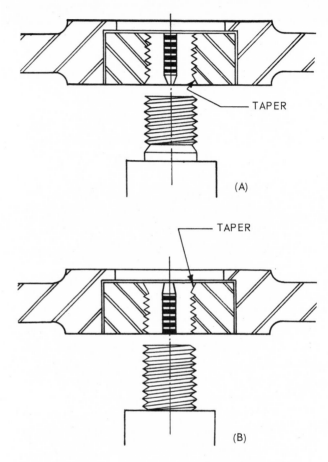

TAPER

(A)

TAPER

(B)

Fig. 11-16. Cutting a thread up to a shoulder. After die has been run down as far as possible the die is reversed, the cutters are reversed if it is a two-part die, and run down the shaft until threads are cut up to the shoulder.

HAND THREADING SAFETY

1. If the tap, die or piece threaded is to be cleaned of chips with compressed air protect your eyes from flying chips by wearing goggles. Take care that other persons working in the area are also wearing them.
2. Chips produced by threading are sharp. Use a brush or a piece of cloth to remove them-- not your hand.
3. Newly cut external threads are also sharp and should not be cleaned with the bare hand.

4. Wash your hands after using cutting fluids. Some cutting fluids may cause skin rash, and develop into a serious skin disorder if they are left on your hand for a long period of time.
5. Have any cuts taken care of by a qualified person. Infections occur when injuries are

not properly treated.
6. Be sure that the die is clamped firmly in the die stock. If it is not it may fall from the holder and cause a painful foot injury.
7. Broken taps have sharp edges and are very dangerous. Handle them like you would a piece of broken glass.

TEST YOUR KNOWLEDGE, Unit 11

1. The_____is used to cut internal threads.
2. The_____is used to cut external threads.
3. The NF thread series differs from the NC series in that it has:
   a. Fewer threads per inch for a given diameter.
   b. More threads per inch for a given thread size.
   c. It is an internal thread while the NC is an external thread.
   d. None of the above.
   e. All of the above.
4. The hole to be tapped must be the same size as the tap. True or false?
5. An external thread must be cut on a diameter equal to the thread size. True or false?
6. List the taps in the sequence they would be used to thread a blind hole:

a._____.
b._____.
c._____.
7. Explain what 1/2-13NC-2 means.
   a. 1/2_____.
   b. 13 _____.
   c. NC _____.
   d. -2 _____.
8. The drill used to make the hole prior to tapping is called a_____ _____.
9. The_____tap wrench is used with small taps because it allows the machinist a more sensitive "feel" when tapping.
10. It has been established that the hole to be threaded must be smaller than the thread - for example: a 5/16 in. diameter hole must be drilled for a 3/8-16NC thread. How much larger must a shaft be machined to receive a 3/8-16NC thread?

Unit 12

PLIERS

The COMBINATION or SLIP-JOINT PLIERS, Fig. 12-1, are widely used. The slip-joint permits the pliers to be opened wider at the hinge

Fig. 12-1. Combination or slip-joint pliers.

pin to grip larger diameter work. It is made in 5, 6, 8, and 10-in. sizes. The size indicates the over-all length. Some combination pliers are made with cutting edges for clipping wire and small metal pieces. The better grades are forged.

DIAGONAL PLIERS, Fig. 12-2, are another widely used tool. The cutting edges are at an

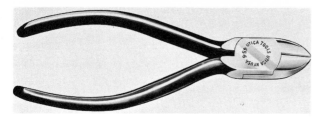

Fig. 12-2. Diagonal pliers.

angle to permit the pliers to cut flush with the work surface. Diagonals are made in 4, 5, 6, and 7 in. lengths.

SIDE-CUTTING PLIERS, Fig. 12-3, are useful for cutting heavier wire and pins. Some side-cutting pliers have a wire stripping groove and insulated handles. They are made in 6, 7, and 8 in. lengths.

ROUND-NOSE PLIERS, Fig. 12-4, are used to form wire and light metal, without marring the

Fig. 12-3. Side-cutting pliers.

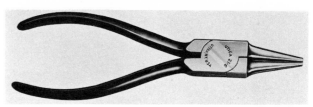

Fig. 12-4. Round-nose pliers.

surface. Round-nose pliers are available in 4, 4-1/2, 5, and 6-in. sizes.

NEEDLE-NOSE PLIERS, both straight, Fig. 12-5a, and curved-nose, Fig. 12-5b, are made. They are handy when work space is limited, and for holding small work.

Like other tools, pliers will give long, useful

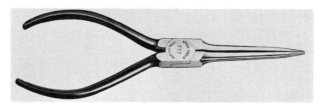

Fig. 12-5a. Straight needle-nose pliers.

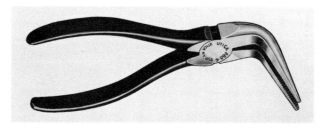

Fig. 12-5b. Curved needle-nose pliers.

service if a few simple precautions are taken:
1. Do not use pliers as a substitute for a wrench.
2. The jaws will deform or break if the tool is used to cut diameters that are too large

or heat treated work. Breakage will also occur if additional leverage is applied to the handles.
3. Clean and oil them occasionally.
4. Store them in a clean, dry place.

TEST YOUR KNOWLEDGE, Unit 12

1. Combination pliers are also known as_____ pliers.
2. Combination plier size indicates their_____.
3. The cutting edge of the diagonal pliers is at an angle to:
   a. Permit work to be cut close to the surface.
   b. Permit work to be cut flush with the surface.
   c. Permit work to be cut on a diagonal.
   d. All of the above.
   e. None of the above.
4. _____pliers are used to form wire and small metal pieces.
5. _____pliers are very useful for cutting heavier wire and pins.
6. _____pliers are used when the work is confined to small or restricted places and for holding small work.
7. Pliers should never be used as a substitute for a _____.

Unit 13

CLAMPING DEVICES

Fig. 13-1a. A solid base machinist's or bench vise.
(Wilton Tool Mfg. Co., Inc.)

VISES

The MACHINIST'S or BENCH VISE is used to hold metal while it is being worked. It is mounted far enough out on the bench edge to permit clamping long work in a vertical position. It may be a SOLID BASE VISE, Fig. 13-1a, or of the SWIVEL BASE type, Fig. 13-1b, which

allows the vise to be rotated. A SMALL BENCH VISE, Fig. 13-1c, is used to hold small precision parts.

Fig. 13-1c. A small vise used by the toolmaker. It can be rotated and pivoted to secure the desired working position.

Fig. 13-1b. A swivel base vise. Note that the base is split. After it has been rotated to the desired position it is locked by tightening the locking screw at the right on the base.

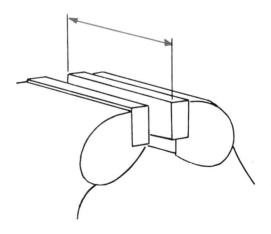

Fig. 13-2. The size of the vise is determined by the width of the vise jaws.

13-1

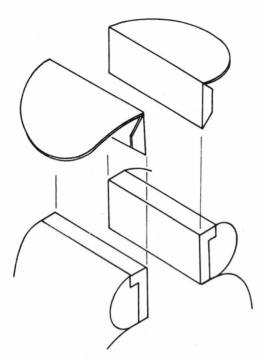

Fig. 13-3. Caps made of copper, lead, or some other soft metal are slipped over the hardened vise jaws to protect the work from becoming damaged or marred.

Vise size is determined by the width of the jaws, Fig. 13-2.

Clamping action of the vise is obtained from a heavy screw turned by the handle which is long enough to apply ample pressure for all work that will fit the vise. Under no circumstance should the handle be hammered tight, nor should additional pressure be applied by using a piece of pipe for leverage.

Vise jaws are hardened and, unless they are covered with CAPS, Fig. 13-3, should not be used to clamp work that may be damaged or marred by the jaw serrations.

CLAMPS

The C-CLAMP, Fig. 13-4, and the PARALLEL CLAMP, Fig. 13-5, are tools used to clamp parts together while they are being worked upon. The C-clamp is made in many sizes. The jaw opening determines the size.

The parallel clamp is ideal for holding small work. For maximum clamping action, the jaw faces must be parallel.

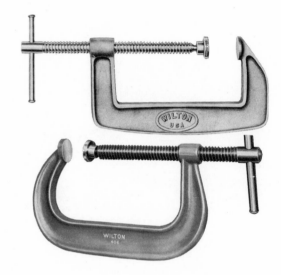

Fig. 13-4. The C-Clamp. Widely used in the metal working industry.

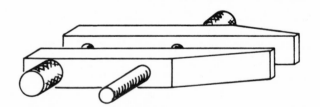

Fig. 13-5. The parallel clamp.

TEST YOUR KNOWLEDGE, Unit 13

1. The bench vise is mounted on the edge of the bench to:
   a. Make it easier to use.
   b. Permit clamping long pieces of work.
   c. Hold small parts.
   d. All of the above.
   e. None of the above.

2. _____ are used to protect work that will be damaged by the serrations on the vise jaws.
3. The vise _____ is determined by the width of the jaws.
4. The _____ is used to hold pieces together while they are being worked on. The _____ determines their size.

Unit 14

HAND POLISHING WITH ABRASIVES

What is an abrasive? It is commonly thought of as any hard, sharp material that can be used to wear away another material. The material, grain size, backing material and the manner the abrasive is bonded to the backing material determines the performance of the abrasive.

ABRASIVE MATERIALS

EMERY is a natural abrasive material that has a long history, dating back to Biblical times. It is black in color and cuts slowly with a tendency to polish.

ALUMINUM OXIDE has replaced emery as an abrasive when large quantities of metal must be removed. Its grain structure is such that it is an excellent abrasive for sanding operations on high-tensile materials such as high carbon and alloy steels. When used as an abrasive for metals, the technique for crushing the crude aluminum oxide is slightly varied to produce a grain shape that is not as sharp as that used in woodworking.

Aluminum oxide is a man-made abrasive that is produced by purifying bauxite to crystalline form in an electric furnace, and adding small quantities of titanium to impart extra toughness.

SILICON CARBIDE is the hardest and sharpest of the synthetic abrasives. These characteristics make it an ideal material for sanding low-tensile metals like cast iron, bronze, and aluminum.

Silicon carbide which is also produced in an electric furnace, is greenish black in color. It is superior to aluminum oxide in its ability to cut fast under light pressure.

CROCUS may be synthetic or natural iron oxide. It is bright red in color, very soft and is used for cleaning and polishing when a very minimum of stock should be removed.

GRAIN SIZE

Emery, aluminum oxide and silicon carbide are crushed and graded in much the same manner. All of them come in large chunk form that is crushed in large crushers to about 3/4-in. size. Roll crushers reduce these lumps to useable sizes. The grain size is determined by passing the crushed particles over a series of silk cloth screens. These screens are carefully controlled in size and the resulting grains are checked frequently against standards established by the abrasive industries to insure conformance to rigid specifications. Grades too small for separating by screens, known as flours, are graded hydraulically.

Technical Grades		Simplified Grades	Other Grades
Mesh	Aluminum Oxide Silicon Carbide	Emery	Emery Polishing
600			4/0
			3/0
500			2/0
400	10/0		0
360			
320	9/0		1/2
280	8/0		
240	7/0		1 G
220	6/0		2
180	5/0		3
150	4/0	Fine	
120	3/0		
100	2/0	Medium	
80	0	Coarse	
60	1/2		
50	1	Extra Coarse	
40	1-1/2		
36	2		
30	2-1/2		
24	3		
20	3-1/2		
16	4		
12	4-1/2		

Fig. 14-1. Abrasive Comparative Grading Chart. (Coated Abrasives Manufacturers' Institute)

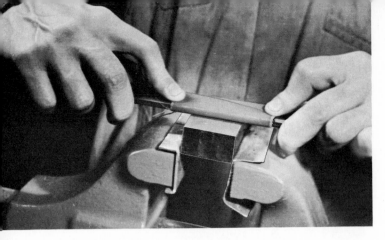

Fig. 14-2. Abrasive cloth should be supported with a block of wood or a file.

ALUMINUM OXIDE and SILICON CARBIDE are given additional treatment during processing to remove impurities and increase hardness. Standard grain sizes range from 12 - extremely coarse, to 600 - superfine. As these abrasives are man-made the grain size, grain shape and grain hardness can be graded very accurately. The table in Fig. 14-1 will give a comparison of grain size and how the various abrasives are graded.

COATED ABRASIVES

A coated abrasive is cloth or paper with abrasive grains cemented to the surface. Because of its flexibility, cloth is used as the backing material for coated abrasives used in metalworking. It is available in 9 by 11-in. sheets, or in rolls starting at 1/2-in. in width and is called ABRASIVE CLOTH.

ABRASIVE GRAINS

There are some polishing jobs that cannot be done satisfactorily with abrasive cloth. Abrasive grains are frequently used for these situations. Most grain sizes, including flours, can be purchased in small quantities at automotive supply houses.

USING ABRASIVE CLOTH

1. Abrasive cloth is quite expensive, use only what you need. Tear the correct amount from the roll or sheet.

2. Do not throw used abrasive cloth away unless it is completely worthless. Used cloth is excellent for polishing.

3. If the piece has been filed properly, only a fine-grain cloth will be necessary to polish the surface. However, if scratches are deep start the polishing operation by using a coarse-grain cloth first. Change to a medium-grain cloth next and finally a fine-grain abrasive. A few drops of oil will speed the operation. For a high polish, leave the oil on the surface after the scratches have been removed. Reverse the cloth and rub the cloth, or smooth backing over the work.

4. The abrasive cloth must be supported to work efficiently. To get this support, wrap it around a block of wood or a file, Fig. 14-2. Apply pressure and rub the cloth back and forth in a straight line, if possible, parallel to the long edge of the work piece. It is a waste of time, and dangerous, to try to polish the piece by rubbing the cloth over the surface while it is supported with your thumb.

5. DO NOT POLISH MACHINED SURFACES.

SAFETY

1. Do not rub your fingers or hand over polished or surfaces to be polished. Burrs on the edges of the metal can cause painful cuts.

2. Wash your hands thoroughly after the polishing operations.

3. Treat all cuts, no matter how small, immediately.

4. Place all oily rags in a closed container. They should never be put in the pocket of your shop coat or apron.

5. Wipe any oil that may have dropped on the floor during the polishing operation.

6. Cover the lathe ways with paper if any polishing is done on the lathe. The abrasive grains that fall from the abrasive cloth can cause rapid wear to the lathe.

TEST YOUR KNOWLEDGE, Unit 14

1. An abrasive is:
   a. A hard substance.
   b. Any hard, sharp substance than can be used to wear away another material.
   c. Used to polish metal.
   d. None of the above.
   e. All of the above.
2. Emery is a_____abrasive.
3. List three man-made abrasives:
   a._____ .
   b._____ .
   c._____ .
4. _____ _____ is the hardest and sharpest of the synthetic abrasives. This makes it an ideal material for sanding metals like cast iron, bronze and aluminum.
5. _____ may be _____ or _____ iron oxide. It is _____ _____ in color, very soft and used for cleaning and polishing when a very minimum of material is to be removed.

RESEARCH AND DEVELOPMENT

1. Develop and construct displays that show:
   a. Samples of the various abrasive materials.
   b. A flow chart showing how synthetic abrasives are manufactured. If possible, secure samples of the raw materials.
   c. Metal samples in various stages of polishing. (Spray them with lacquer or acrylic plastic to prevent rust.)
2. Set up an experiment to determine what abrasive materials are best for aluminum, brass, steel, cast iron and tool steel. The investigation should include the quantity of material removed within a specified period of time; surface finish of the finished piece; clogging of the abrasive cloth; and, the effect lubricating oil has on the surface finish. (Abrasives of similar grade value must be used if the tests are to be valid.)

Safety Precaution--DO NOT carry tools in your pockets.

Unit 15

WRENCHES

Wrenches comprise a family of tools that are used for assembling and disassembling threaded fasteners.

Torque wrenches are used when fasteners must be tightened to within certain limits to prevent undue stresses and strains from developing, that might cause the work to warp or spring out of shape. See Fig. 15-1. Torque is the amount of turning or twisting force applied to the fastener.

Fig. 15-1. The torque wrench.

There are many different types of torque wrenches, Fig. 15-2. It is possible to obtain torque wrenches that are direct reading or those that feature a sensory signalling mechanism that warns the operator the moment the predetermined torque is reached.

Fig. 15-3, illustrates the right and wrong methods of gripping the wrench handle. Under NO condition should the handle be lengthened for additional leverage. These tools are designed to take a specific maximum load. Any force over this unit will destroy the accuracy of the wrench.

The wrench will give accurate measurement whether it is pushed or pulled. The preferred method is to pull on the torque wrench.

The term adjustable wrench is a misnomer in as much as other wrenches, monkey wrench and pipe wrench, are also adjustable. However, the wrench which is somewhat like an open-end wrench, but with an adjustable jaw, is commonly referred to as an ADJUSTABLE WRENCH, Fig. 15-4.

As the term implies, the wrench can be ad-

justed to fit a range of bolt head and nut sizes. Although convenient to use at times, the adjustable wrench is not intended to take the place

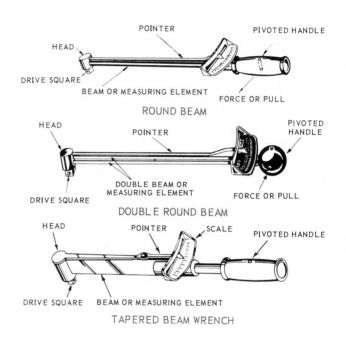

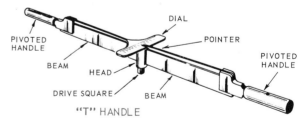

Fig. 15-2. Several kinds of torque wrenches.
(P. A. Sturtevant Co.)

of standard open-end, box or socket wrenches.

Three important points must be remembered when using the adjustable wrench:

1. The wrench should be placed on the bolt head or nut so that the movable jaw faces

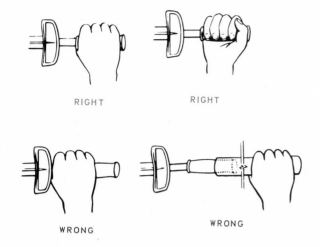

Fig. 15-3. Right and wrong ways to use the torque wrench.

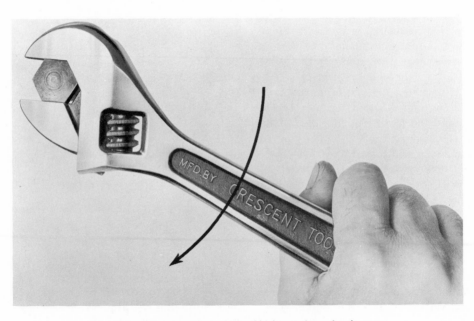

Fig. 15-4. Adjustable wrench. (Snap-on Tool Corp.)

the direction the fastener is to be rotated, Fig. 15-5a.

2. Adjust the thumbscrew so the jaws fit the bolt head or nut snugly, Fig. 15-5b.

3. Never place an extension on the wrench

handle for additional leverage, nor hammer on it to loosen a stubborn nut or bolt. In some applications, it may be possible to use two adjustable wrenches, Fig. 15-5c.

The MONKEY WRENCH, Fig. 15-6, has been replaced almost completely by the lighter and more compact adjustable wrench.

PULL - DO NOT PUSH

Pushing on any wrench is normally considered dangerous. When the fastener fails, or loosens unexpectedly, you will almost invariably strike and injure your knuckles on the work. This operation is commonly known as "Knuckle dusting." ALWAYS PULL ON A WRENCH.

The PIPE WRENCH, Fig. 15-7, is a wrench that will grip round stock. The jaws always leave marks on the work. A pipe wrench should never be used on bolt heads or nuts unless the corners have been rounded so they cannot be turned with another type of wrench.

The OPEN-END WRENCH, Fig. 15-8, is usually double ended with two different size openings. The openings are made about 0.005 in. larger than the size stamped on the handle to permit them to easily slip on bolt heads or nuts of that size. The openings are angled with the wrench body so they can be used in close quarters.

The BOX WRENCH, Fig. 15-9, is so called because the wrench body completely surrounds

Fig. 15-5a. The movable jaw should always face the direction of rotation. (Crescent Tool Co.)

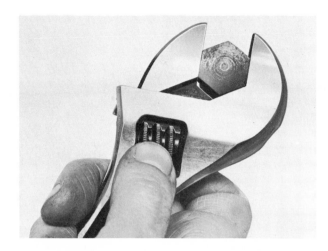

Fig. 15-5b. The wrench must fit the nut or bolt snugly.

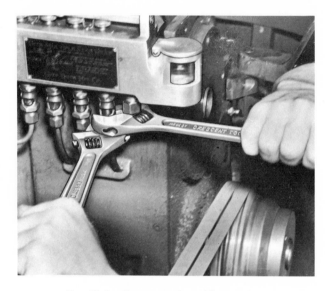

Fig. 15-5c. Using two adjustable wrenches.

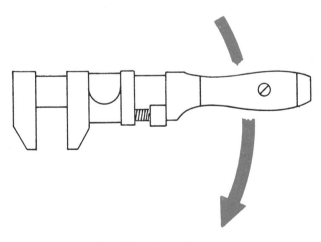

Fig. 15-6. The monkey wrench.

the bolt head or nut. It is usually preferred over other wrenches because it will not slip. Box wrenches are available in the same sizes as open-end wrenches and with straight or offset handles.

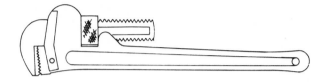

Fig. 15-7. The pipe wrench.

Fig. 15-8. Open-end wrench.

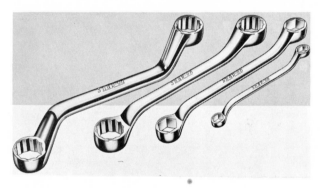

Fig. 15-9. Box wrenches. (Snap-on Tool Corp.)

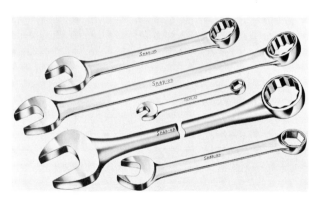

Fig. 15-10. Combination wrenches.

The COMBINATION OPEN AND BOX WRENCH, Fig. 15-10, has one open end and a box wrench at the other end of the handle.

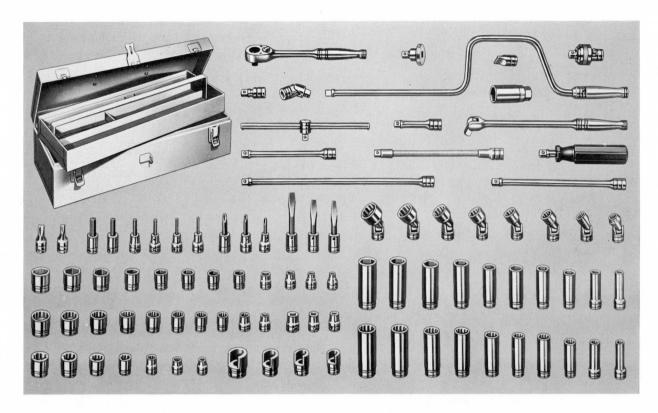

Fig. 15-11. Socket wrench set. (Snap-on Tool Corp.)

SOCKET WRENCHES, Fig. 15-11, are box-like and are made as a detachable tool that fits many different types of handles. A typical socket wrench set contains various handles and a wide range of socket sizes and styles.

SPANNER WRENCHES are special wrenches usually furnished as standard equipment with machine tools and attachments. They are used to turn flush and recessed type threaded fittings. The fittings have slots to receive the wrench lug.

The HOOK SPANNER, Fig. 15-12a, is equipped with a single lug that is placed in the notch. The handle points towards the direction the fitting is to be rotated.

The END SPANNER, Fig. 15-12b, has lugs on the face of the wrench to fit in notches machined in the face of the fitting.

On PIN SPANNER WRENCHES the lugs are replaced with pins. The pins fit into holes rather than notches.

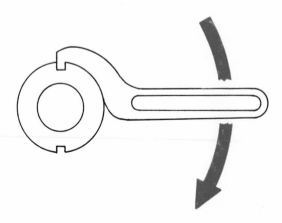

Fig. 15-12a. The hook spanner wrench.

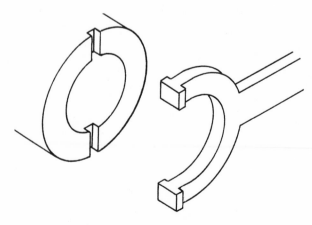

Fig. 15-12b. End spanner wrench.

SAFETY

1. Always pull on a wrench. You have more control over the tool and there is less chance of injury.
2. Select a wrench that fits properly. A loose-fitting wrench may slip and round off the corners of the bolt head or nut.
3. Never hammer on a wrench to loosen a stubborn fastener, unless the tool has been designed for this job.
4. It is dangerous practice to lengthen the wrench handle for additional leverage. Use a larger wrench.
5. When using wrenches clean grease and oil from the floor in the work area. This will reduce the possibility of slipping and losing your balance.
6. Do not use a wrench on moving machinery.

TEST YOUR KNOWLEDGE, Unit 15

1. _____ wrenches are used when fasteners must be tightened to a predetermined pressure to prevent undue stresses and strains in the mating pieces.
2. The _____ wrench has a jaw that can be moved to fit a wide range of bolt head and nut sizes.
3. The _____ wrench and _____ wrench also fit this description.
4. List three important steps to be remembered when using the above wrenches:
   a. _____ .
   b. _____ .
   c. _____ .
5. To prevent skinned knuckles, always _____ on a wrench.
6. The box wrench is preferred over the open-end wrench because:
   a. It is cheaper.
   b. It can be used on several sizes of fasteners.
   c. It completely surrounds the fastener and cannot slip.
   d. None of the above applies.
   e. All of the above applies.

RESEARCH AND DEVELOPMENT

1. Prepare an article featuring wrenches not described in this unit. Include drawings. Reproduce it by the spirit duplicator process for distribution to the class.
2. Give a demonstration on the proper way to use a torque wrench.
3. Repair all adjustable wrenches in the shop. Secure parts lists from manufacturers.
4. Contact the various tool manufacturers for information on how wrenches are manufactured. If a motion picture is available, review it and if your instructor permits, show it to the class.
5. Make a safety poster on the proper way to use a wrench.

Jet engine turbine blades being finished by semi-skilled workers.
(Westinghouse Electric Corp.)

Unit 16

SCREWDRIVERS

The STANDARD and PHILLIPS type screwdrivers, Fig. 16-1, are familiar to all shop workers. The STANDARD SCREWDRIVER has a flattened wedge shaped end that fits into the slot in the screw head. This tool is manufacutred

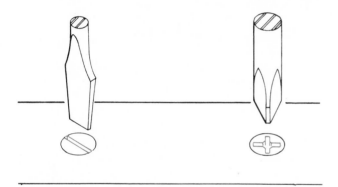

Fig. 16-1. Standard and Phillips type screwdriver tips.

in 3 to 12-in. lengths with the diameter of the shank and the width and thickness of the tip being proportional with the length. The length is measured from the blade tip to the handle. The blade is heat treated to give it the necessary hardness and toughness to withstand the pressures put upon it.

Well-known and used for most work is the conventional straight shank screwdriver, Fig. 16-2(A). The ELECTRICIAN'S screwdriver, Fig. 16-2(B), has a long thin shank and an insulated handle. It is very useful when handling small screws. The HEAVY DUTY type, Fig. 16-2(C), has a heavy square shank so that a wrench can be applied for driving or removing large or stubborn screws. The double-end OFFSET screwdriver, Fig. 16-2(D), is used when there is insufficient space to use the conventional straight shank tool. STUBBY or CLOSE QUARTER screwdrivers, Fig. 16-2(E), are designed to be used where there is limited work room.

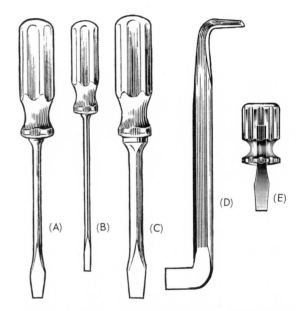

Fig. 16-2. Styles and types of standard screwdrivers: (A) Conventional straight shank. (B) Electrician's. (C) Heavy duty. (D) Double-end offset. (E) Stubby or close quarter.

Both the standard and Phillips type screwdrivers are made with ratchet devices. This moves the screw on the power stroke but not on the return stroke. It can be adjusted for right or left-hand operation. See Fig. 16-3a and 16-3b.

The PHILLIPS TYPE SCREWDRIVER has an X-shaped point for use with Phillips recessed

Fig. 16-3a. Ratchet type offset screwdriver.

Fig. 16-3b. Spiral ratchet type screwdriver.

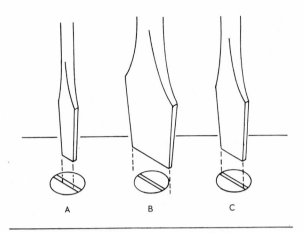

Fig. 16-4. Use the correct tip for the job being done. Tip A is too narrow and will damage the screw head. Tip B is too wide and will damage the work. Tip C is the correct width.

head screws. Four sizes (#1, #2, #3 and #4) handle the full range of this type screw. This is manufactured in the same styles as the standard screwdriver.

USING THE SCREWDRIVER

Always select the correct size screwdriver for the screw being handled, Fig. 16-4. A poor fit damages the screw slot and frequently the tip. Damaged screw heads are dangerous and difficult to drive and remove.

When driving or removing a screw hold the screwdriver square with the screw. Guide the tip with the left hand.

A worn screwdriver tip, shown at the left, Fig. 16-5, must be reground. Use a fine grinding wheel and little pressure. The tip should be checked during the grinding operation by fitting it to a screw slot. A properly ground tip is shown at the right, Fig. 16-5. CAUTION: Do not overheat the tip during the grinding operation as the temper will be destroyed.

The screwdriver is not a substitute for a chisel; nor, is it made to be hammered on, or used as a pry.

SAFETY

1. Wear goggles when resharpening screwdriver tips.
2. Screws with burred heads are dangerous and should be replaced or the burrs removed with a file or abrasive cloth.
3. Use only screwdrivers with insulated handles when working on electrical equipment.

TEST YOUR KNOWLEDGE, Unit 16

1. The_____screwdriver has an X-shaped tip.
2. The_____or_____screwdriver is used when there is insufficient space to use a conventional straight shank screwdriver.
3. Identify the following screwdrivers. Place the letter that indicates the correct answer in the blank space at the left of the question:
   _____Has a flattened wedge shaped tip.
   _____Is short and is used where there is limited work room.
   _____Has a square shank to permit additional force to be applied with a wrench.
   _____Useful for handling small screws.
   a. Stubby   b. Offset   c. Electrician
   d. Ratchet   e. Standard   f. Heavy duty
   g. Automatic.
4. The screwdriver is not a substitute for a _____ , nor should it be used as a_____.

RESEARCH AND DEVELOPMENT

1. Do a study on other types of screwdriver tips that are used by industry but are not covered in this unit. Secure the actual tools or make large scale drawings showing how they differ from the standard and Phillips type tips.
2. Regrind a worn screwdriver tip.
3. Make a large model of a properly sharpened screwdriver tip and how it fits into a screw head.

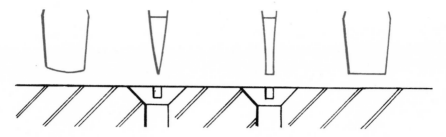

Fig. 16-5. The tip on the left is badly worn and will damage the screw head. The tip to the right is ground correctly. Note that the sides are concave, this holds the tip more firm-ly in the slot when pressure is applied.

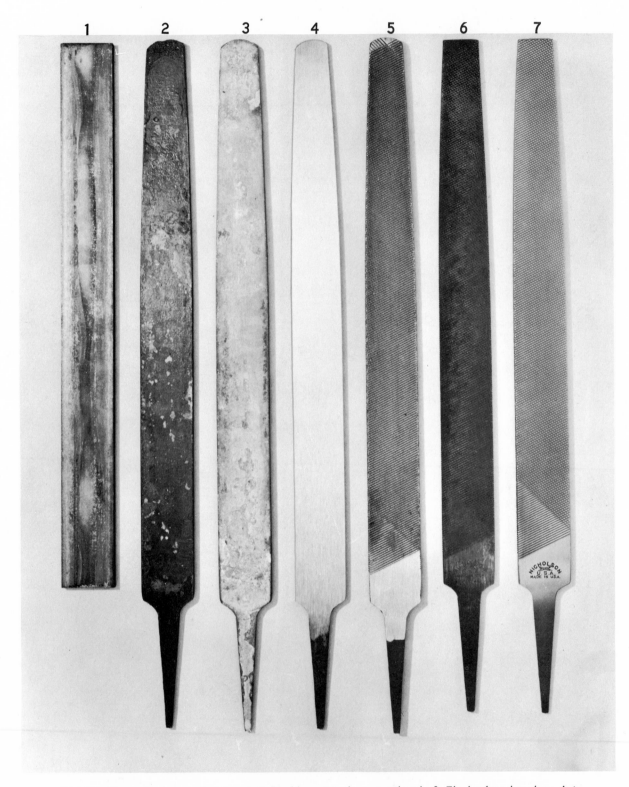

Fig. 17-1. How a file is manufactured: 1. Steel bar cut to the correct length. 2. The bar forged to shape. It is called a BLANK. 3. The blank after it has been annealed. 4. The annealed blank straightened and ground smooth to remove the scale. 5. The teeth cut on the blank. 6. The blank trimmed, and coated for heat treatment. 7. The completed file, cleaned and inspected. (Nicholson File Co.)

Unit 17

FILES

Until about 1860, all files were laboriously made by hand. Steel blanks were forged to shape and the teeth were cut by hammer and chisel, one row at a time.

Today files are made from high grade carbon steel and heat treated for hardness and

Fig. 17-2. Blunt and tapered files.

toughness. In the first production step, the blank is cut to approximate shape and size. The tang and point are formed next after which the blank is annealed and straightened. The point and tang are trimmed after the sides and faces have been ground and the teeth cut. After another straight-

ening, they are heat treated, cleaned and oiled. Tests are made continually to assure a quality tool. Fig. 17-1 shows the steps in the manufacture of a modern file.

HOW FILES ARE CLASSIFIED

Files are classified by their shape. The shape of the file is its general outline and cross section. The outline, Fig. 17-2, is either tapered or blunt.

Files are also classified according to the cut of the teeth, SINGLE-CUT, DOUBLE-CUT, RASP, and CURVED-TOOTH, Fig. 17-3; and to the coarseness of the teeth, ROUGH, COARSE, BASTARD, SECOND-CUT, SMOOTH, and DEAD SMOOTH.

FILE SAFETY

A file should never be used without a handle. It is too easy to drive the unprotected tang into

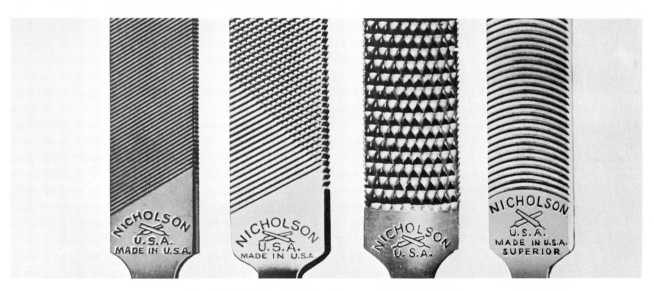

Fig. 17-3. Single-cut, double-cut, rasp and curved-tooth files.

your hand. Fit the handle to the file by drilling a hole in the handle equal in diameter to the tang at its mid-point, Fig. 17-4. Mate the file and

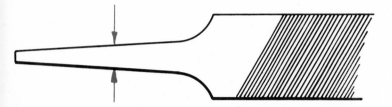

Fig. 17-4. The hole in the file handle should be equal in diameter to the width of the file tang at the point indicated.

handle by placing the tang into the hole and sharply strike the handle on a solid surface, Fig. 17-5.

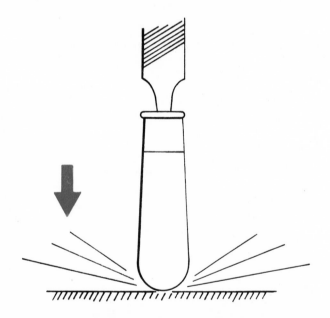

Fig. 17-5. Insert the tang into the hole drilled in the handle — strike against the bench top as shown, to seat the file tang in the handle. NEVER USE A FILE THAT DOES NOT HAVE A HANDLE.

FILE CARE

Files should be stored in such a manner that they are always separated. NEVER THROW FILES IN A DRAWER OR STORE THEM IN A DAMP PLACE.

Clean files frequently with a FILE CARD or BRUSH, Fig. 17-6. Some soft metals cause PINNING, that is, the teeth become loaded with some of the material the file has removed. Pinning causes gouging and scratching on the work surface. The particles can be removed from the

file by using a PICK or SCORER (the point of a scriber will do nicely). A file card combines the card, brush, and pick.

FILE SELECTION

There is almost no limit to the number of different kinds, shapes, and cuts of files (Fig. 17-7) that are manufactured. We will confine this material to the general classification of files.

Fig. 17-6. Using a combination file card and brush to clean a file.

Files have three distinct characteristics: LENGTH, KIND, and CUT. The length is always measured from the heel to the point, Fig. 17-8. The tang is not included in this measurement.

The kind of a file refers to its shape or style, as FLAT, MILL, HALF-ROUND, SQUARE, etc.

The cut of a file indicates the relative coarseness of the teeth. SINGLE-CUT files are usually used to produce a smooth surface finish. Their use requires light pressure. DOUBLE-CUT files remove metal much faster than single-cut files. They require heavier pressure and they produce a rougher surface finish. RASPS are used for working wood and soft materials. The CURVED-TOOTH file is used to file flat surfaces of aluminum and steel sheet.

Some files have SAFE EDGES, Fig. 17-9. The term safe edge denotes that the file has one or

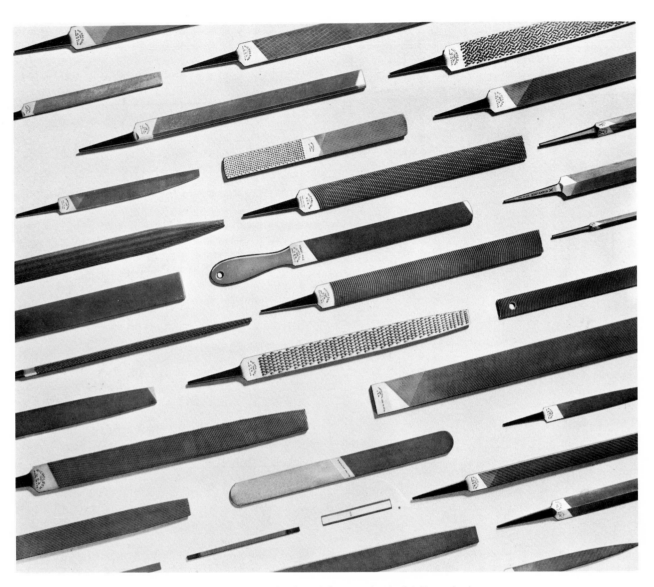

Fig. 17-7. A photo of a few of the many hundred different kinds
of files that are manufactured. (Nicholson File Co.)

both edges without teeth. This permits filing
corners without danger to the portion of the
work that is not to be filed.

Many factors must be considered in selecting

Fig. 17-8. How the file is measured. (Nicholson File Co.)

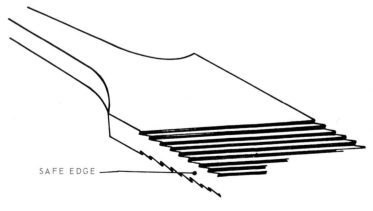

SAFE EDGE

Fig. 17-9. The safe edge of a file does not have teeth.

the file if maximum cutting efficiency is desired:
1. The nature of the work - flat, concave, convex, notched, grooved, etc.
2. The kind of material.
3. The amount of material to be removed.
4. The surface finish and accuracy demanded.

Of the many file shapes available, the most commonly used shapes are: FLAT, PILLAR, SQUARE, 3-SQUARE, KNIFE, HALF-ROUND, ROUND, and CROSSING, Fig. 17-10.

when a smooth finish is required. A mill file is used for draw filing, lathe work, and working on brass and bronze.
3. SWISS PATTERN and JEWELERS FILES are manufactured in over a hundred different shapes. They are used primarily by tool and diemakers, jewelers, and others who do precision filing.
4. The RASP has teeth that are individually formed and disconnected from each other.

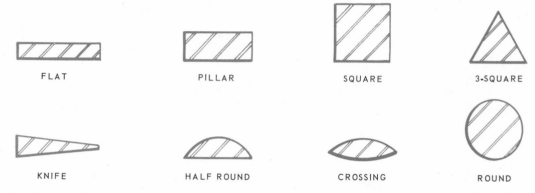

FLAT   PILLAR   SQUARE   3-SQUARE

KNIFE   HALF ROUND   CROSSING   ROUND

Fig. 17-10. Cross sectional views of the most widely used file shapes.

Each shape is available in many sizes and degrees of coarseness: ROUGH, COARSE, BASTARD, SECOND-CUT, SMOOTH, and DEAD SMOOTH, Fig. 17-11. A rough cut small file (4 in.) may be as fine as a large (16 in.) second-cut file.

It is used for woodworking and for working relatively soft metals when quantities of material must be removed rapidly.
5. The group of SPECIAL PURPOSE FILES include those specifically designed to cut one type of metal. The long-angle lathe

Fig. 17-11. The range in coarseness of a typical machinists' flat bastard file. File size ranges from 4 to 16 in.

KINDS OF FILES

The vast variety of files fall into five general groups:
1. The MACHINIST FILE is used whenever metal must be removed rapidly, and the finish is of secondary importance. It is made in a large range of shapes and sizes, and is double-cut.
2. The MILL FILE is a single-cut file and tapers the last third of the length toward the point. It is used for general filing

file, Fig. 17-12, that does a more efficient filing job on the lathe, and the curved-tooth file used by the auto body repair industry fall into this category.

HOW TO USE THE FILE

Much consideration has been given to the proper technique of using the file, the correct way to grasp it, how to hold the work, and the proper height to hold the work.

The vise is most frequently used to hold work

Fig. 17-12. Long angle file.

for filing. Cover the vise jaws with CAPS made of soft copper sheet if there is any danger of the vise jaw serrations damaging the work.

Hold the work at about elbow height for general filing, Fig. 17-13, and slightly lower if a large quantity of material must be removed by

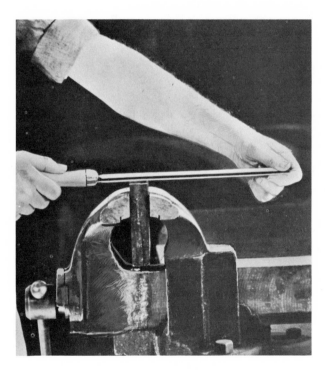

Fig. 17-13. The correct way to hold a file for general filing. (Nicholson File Co.)

heavy filing. Hold the work solidly or "chattering" may occur making it difficult to get a smooth finish.

STRAIGHT or CROSS FILING consists of pushing the file lengthwise, straight ahead or at a slight angle, across the work. Grasp the file as shown in Fig. 17-14. Heavy-duty filing requires heavy pressure and can best be done if the file is held as shown in Fig. 17-15.

Files can be ruined by using too much pressure or too little pressure on the cutting stroke.

Apply just enough pressure to permit the file to cut on the entire forward stroke. Too little pressure allows the file to slide over the work and it becomes dull. Too much pressure "overloads" the file and causes the teeth to clog and chip. Lift the file from the work on the reverse

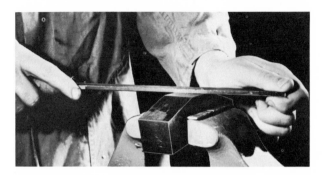

Fig. 17-14. The correct way to hold the file for straight or cross filing.

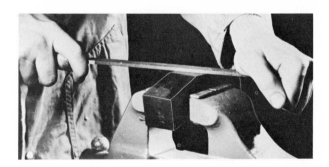

Fig. 17-15. Additional pressure is required when a considerable quantity of metal must be removed.

stroke except when filing soft metal. Then the pressure on the return stroke should be no more than the weight of the file.

DRAW FILING, when properly done, produces a finer finish than straight filing. Hold the file as shown in Fig. 17-16. Do not use a short angle file for draw filing, as there is the likelihood of scoring or scratching instead of shaving and

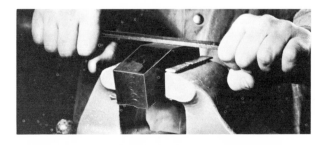

Fig. 17-16. Draw filing produces a finer finish than straight filing.

shearing, as the file should, as it is pushed and pulled across the metal. Use a double-cut file to "rough down" the surface and a single-cut file to produce the final finish.

FILE SAFETY

1. Never use a file without a handle. Painful injuries may result.

2. Use a file card to clean the file. Not your hand. The chips can penetrate your hand and cause a painful infection.
3. Files are very brittle and should never be used as a pry.
4. Use a piece of cloth to wipe the surface being filed. Short burrs are formed in filing and can cause serious cuts.
5. Never hammer on or with a file. It may shatter and chips fly in all directions.

TEST YOUR KNOWLEDGE, Unit 17

1. Modern files are made from_____ _____
   _____.
2. Files are classified by their shape. The shape of a file is its:
   a. General outline and cross section.
   b. Length and width.
   c. Taper and thickness.
   d. None of the above.
3. Files are also classified according to the cut of their teeth. List the four cuts:
   a._____.
   b._____.
   c._____.
   d._____.
4. Files are manufactured in six degrees of coarseness. Name them:
   a._____.
   b._____.
   c._____.
   d._____.
   e._____.
   f._____.
5. Sketch the cross sections of the following files:
   a. Three-square.
   b. Half-round.
   c. Knife

   d. Rat-tail
   e. Mill.
6. The_____ _____is used to clean the file.
7. The_____removes material much faster than the single-cut file.
8. The edge that does not have teeth cut on it is called a _____ _____.
9. The_____file is used when metal must be removed rapidly with little regard for the quality of the finish.
10. The_____and_____are made in over a hundred different shapes.
11. Work should be held at _____height for general filing.
12. When the file is pushed and pulled across the work it is called:
    a. Push-pull filing.
    b. Straight filing.
    c. Draw filing.
    d. None of the above.
13. When the file is pushed lengthwise, straight ahead or at a slight angle, across the work, it is called:
    a. Push-pull filing.
    b. Straight filing.
    c. Draw filing.
    d. None of the above.

RESEARCH AND DEVELOPMENT

1. Make a display panel of drawings which show the cross sections of the most widely used file shapes. This should be large enough to be used for class discussion.

2. Design and produce safety posters around the following unsafe practices:
   a. Using the file as a pry.
   b. The file without a handle.

c. The file used as a hammer.
3. Design a panel that shows the file in various stages of manufacture. Try to secure actual samples.
4. Contact local industries to discover whether they use any special-purpose files. Secure worn samples of the files and the material on which they were used.
5. Inspect the files in your school shop. Clean them, repair or replace missing handles, and make a new file rack if the present rack is not suitable.

A few of the many fasteners used in modern industry.
(Industrial Fasteners Institute)

Unit 18

FASTENERS

Industry uses many methods to assemble parts: screws, nuts and bolts, rivets, pins, staples, and adhesives. One or several methods may be used on the same job. Proper fastener selection often shows up as a tremendous saving in assembly labor costs while securing a superior assembly.

THREADED FASTENERS

Threaded fasteners utilize the wedging action of the screw thread to clamp the assembly together. They comprise the group of fasteners most often used in the school shop.

MACHINE SCREWS

Machine screws, Fig. 18-1, are available with slotted or recessed heads and in a number of

Fig. 18-1. Machine screws.

head styles, Fig. 18-2. They are made in the coarse and fine thread series and are used for general assembly work. Machine screws vary

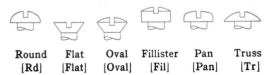

| Round [Rd] | Flat [Flat] | Oval [Oval] | Fillister [Fil] | Pan [Pan] | Truss [Tr] |

Fig. 18-2. Machine screw head styles.

in diameter from #0 (0.060) to 1/2 (0.500) in. and in lengths from 1/8 to 3 in. Nuts (square or hexagonal) are purchased separately.

MACHINE BOLTS

Machine bolts, Fig. 18-3, are used to assemble items that do not require close tolerance fasteners. They are manufactured with square

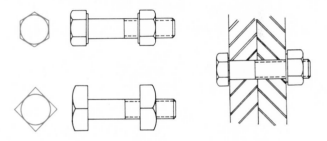

Fig. 18-3. Machine bolts.

and hexagonal heads and in a range of diameters from 1/4 to 3 in. and in lengths from 1/2 to 30 in. Nuts are usually furnished with machine bolts.

CAP SCREWS

Cap screws, Fig. 18-4, are used in assemblies requiring higher quality and a more finished appearance. Their function is much the same as the machine bolt. However, the cap screw passes through a clearance hole in one of the pieces and screws into a threaded hole in the other. Clamping action is accomplished by tightening the bolt whereas, tightening the nut on the machine bolt develops its clamping action.

Cap screws are held to much closer tolerances in their manufacture and are given a semi-finished (machined) bearing surface. They are stocked in coarse and fine threads and in diameters from 1/4 to 2 in. Lengths from 3/8 to 10 in. are available. Nuts are not included with cap screws.

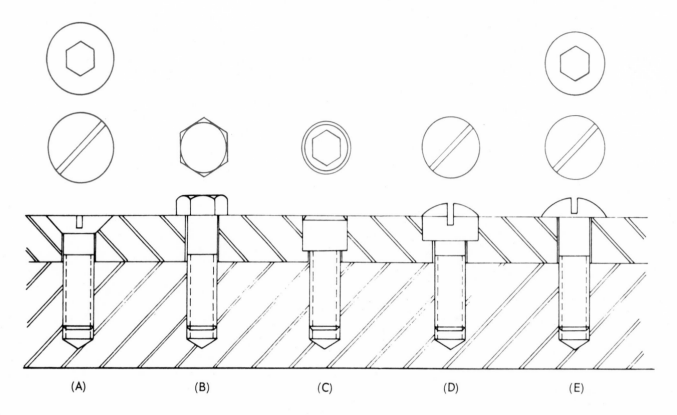

(A)   (B)   (C)   (D)   (E)

Fig. 18-4. Cap screws are available in a wide variety of head styles. (A) Flat head. (B) Hex. head. (C) Socket head. (D) Fillister head. (E) Button head.

SETSCREWS

Setscrews, Fig. 18-5, are usually made of heat-treated steel. Major uses for setscrews are to prevent pulleys from slipping on shafts,

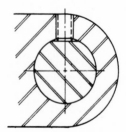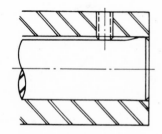

Fig. 18-5. A typical application using a setscrew.

holding collars in place on shafts, and to hold shafts in place in assemblies. They are made in a large selection of head and point styles, Fig. 18-6. Headless setscrews have either a slotted or socket head. The head type has a square head.

STUD BOLT

Stud bolts, Fig. 18-7, are usually made of low carbon steel and are threaded the entire length, or on both ends. One end is screwed into a tapped hole, the piece to be clamped is fitted over the stud, and a nut is screwed on, to clamp the two pieces together. Automobile engine heads are held to the block with studs.

(A)   (B)   (C)   (D)   (E)

Fig. 18-6. Setscrew points. (A) The FLAT POINT setscrew is used on parts requiring frequent adjustment. (B) The OVAL POINT setscrew is against a shaft that has been spotted to receive it. (C) The CONE POINT setscrew is used for setting machine parts permanently on the shaft. It is also used as a pivot or hanger and for adjustment. (D) The HALF DOG POINT setscrew is probably one of the most useful. It can be used as a dowel. A hole is drilled to receive the point. (E) The FULL DOG POINT setscrew is suitable for use as a key that slides in a keyway. For permanent installation a hole is drilled to receive the point.

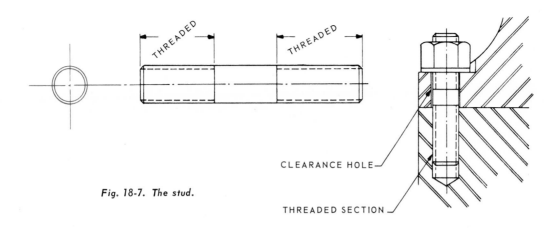

Fig. 18-7. The stud.

CLEARANCE HOLE

THREADED SECTION

SELF-TAPPING SCREWS

Thread forming screws, Fig. 18-8, form a thread as they are driven. Their use eliminates a costly tapping operation.

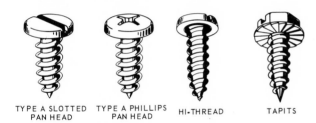

TYPE A SLOTTED
PAN HEAD   TYPE A PHILLIPS
PAN HEAD   HI-THREAD   TAPITS

Fig. 18-8. Thread forming screws.

THREAD CUTTING SCREWS

Thread cutting screws, Fig. 18-9, differ from the thread forming screw in that they actually cut threads in the metal. They are hardened and are used to make fastenings to non-ferrous metals and to join heavy-gauge sheet metals.

TYPE B HEX HEAD   TYPE F PHILLIPS
ROUND HEAD   TYPE BF PHILLIPS
ROUND HEAD   TYPE L PHILLIPS
ROUND HEAD

Fig. 18-9.
Thread cutting screws.
(Parker Kalon)

TYPE B SLOTTED
ROUND HEAD   TYPE B PHILLIPS
ROUND HEAD

DRIVE SCREWS

Drive screws, Fig. 18-10, are simply hammered into a drilled or punched hole of the proper size to make a permanent fastening.

TYPE U DRIVE
SCREW   TYPE 21 DRIVE
SCREW

Fig. 18-10. Drive screws.

NUTS

Nuts have an external hexagonal or square head and are utilized with bolts with the same shaped head. The standard hex nut, Fig. 18-11(A), is available in various degrees of finish: REGULAR is not machined on any surface except the threads; REGULAR SEMI-FINISHED is machined on the bearing face to provide a truer surface for the washer; and FINISHED which is the same as the regular semi-finished nut but with closer body tolerances. The standard machine screw nut is regular.

JAM NUT

Thinner than the standard nut, the jam nut, Fig. 18-11(B), is frequently used to lock a full nut in place.

CASTELLATED AND SLOTTED NUT

Slotted and castellated nuts, Figs. 18-11(C) and 18-11(D), are slotted across the flats to re-

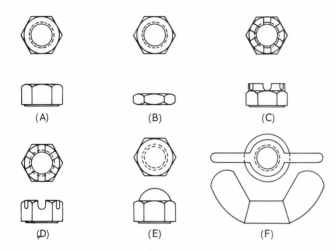

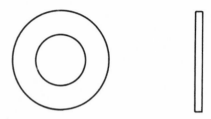

over a larger area, and prevent marring. The STANDARD WASHER, Fig. 18-12, is produced in light, medium, heavy-duty, and extra heavy-duty series.

LOCK WASHER

The application of a lock washer will prevent a bolt or nut from loosening under vibration.

Fig. 18-12. Standard washer.

Fig. 18-11. Nut designs: (A) Hex. nut. (B) Jam nut. (C) Castellated nut. (D) Slotted nut. (E) Acorn or cap nut. (F) Wing nut.

ceive a cotter pin after the nut has been tightened. The cotter pin prevents the nut from turning loose.

CAP OR ACORN NUT

Cap or acorn nuts, Fig. 18-11(E), are applied when appearance is of primary importance.

WING NUT

The wing nut, Fig. 18-11(F), is used when frequent adjustment or removal is necessary. Its shape permits rapid loosening and tightening without the need of a wrench.

WASHERS

Washers provide an increased bearing surface for bolt heads and nuts, distribute load

The SPLIT-RING LOCK WASHER, Fig. 18-13(A), is being rapidly replaced by the TOOTH-TYPE LOCK WASHER, Fig. 18-13(B) to 13(E), which have greater holding power. PRE-ASSEMBLED LOCK WASHER AND SCREW UNITS and LOCK WASHER AND NUT UNITS, Fig. 18-14, are receiving wide acceptance in the mass-assembly market. Costs are lowered because assembly time is reduced.

NON-THREADED FASTENING DEVICES

Permanent assemblies are made with RIVETS, Fig. 18-15. BLIND RIVETS, Fig. 18-16, have been developed for applications where it is not possible to back up a rivet for driving. Blind rivets require special tools to put them in place.

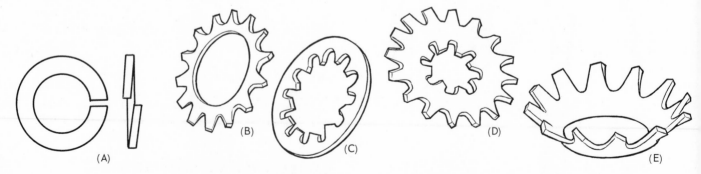

Fig. 18-13. Lock washer variations: (A) Split-ring type. (B) External type. Should be used when possible as it provides the greatest resistance. (C) Internal type. Used with small head screws and where it is desirable to hide the teeth either for appearance or to prevent snagging. (D) Internal-external type. Used when the mounting holes are oversize. (E) Countersunk type. For use with flat or oval-head screws.

Fig. 18-14. Lock washer and screw units, and lock washer and nut units. (Shakeproof Division, Illinois Tool Works, Inc.)

support a major portion of the load placed upon the component.

Taper pins are made with a uniform taper of 1/4 in. per foot in lengths up to 6 in. with diameters as small as 5/32 in. at the large diameter.

COTTER PIN

The cotter pin, Fig. 18-18, is fitted into a hole drilled crosswise in a shaft and prevents parts from slipping or turning off.

RETAINING RING

The retaining ring, Fig. 18-19a, is a relatively new fastening device. It has been developed

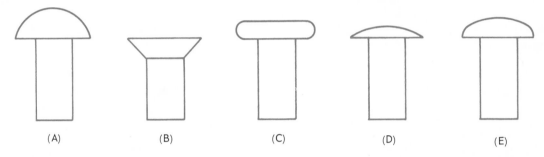

Fig. 18-15. Rivet head styles: (A) Button head. (B) Countersunk head. (C) Flat head. (D) Truss head. (E) Pan head.

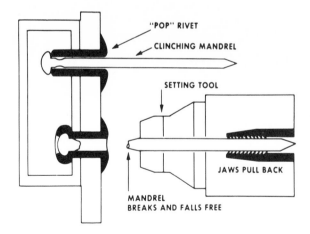

Fig. 18-16. Above. A blind rivet in place ready to be "set." Below. The rivet expanded into place. The tool at the right is the head of the special tool needed to expand the rivet and remove the mandrel. (United Pop Rivets)

DOWEL PINS

Dowel pins, Fig. 18-17, are fitted into reamed holes to position two mating parts. They often

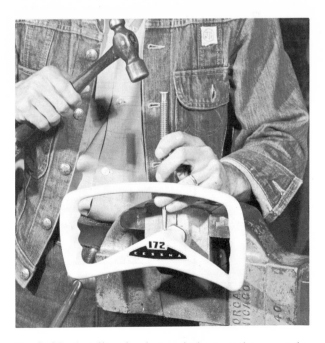

Fig. 18-17a. Installing dowel pins which are used to mount the control wheel of airplane to the control shaft. (Cessna Aircraft)

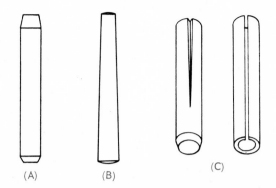

Fig. 18-17b. Dowel pins. (A) Straight dowel pin. (B) Tapered dowel pin. (C) Special dowel pins.

for both internal and external applications. While most retaining rings are seated in grooves, a self-locking type does not require a recess. Special pliers, Fig. 18-19b, are needed to facilitate assembly and disassembly of the rings.

Retaining rings are finding wide use as a means of reducing costs and weight.

METAL STITCHING AND STAPLING

Metal stitching and stapling joins two pieces of material with wire staples. In stitching, the wire is fed from a coil, cut to length, formed,

driven through the material, and clinched in one operation. Stapling differs from stitching in that the fastener is preformed. These techniques are limited to joining fairly thin materials.

ADHESIVES

One of the newest ways to join metals is by use of adhesives that are load bearing and contribute to the strength of the structure. In many applications, the joints are stronger than the metals joined. This new joining technique is often called CHEMICAL WELDING.

Fastening with adhesives does not require elaborate equipment or preparation. Hole making, countersinking, riveting, drive screws,

Fig. 18-18. Cotter pin.

etc., is eliminated.

There are five steps involved in using adhesives:
1. SURFACE PREPARATION - cleaning, degreasing, etc.

function	for axial assembly				for taking up end-play					
					axial assembly				radial assembly	
nomenclature	basic		inverted		bowed		beveled		locking prong	bowed e-ring
series no.	5000	5100	5008	5108	5001	5101	5002	5102	5139	5131
application	Internal for Housing Bores	External for Shafts	Internal for Housing Bores	External for Shafts	Internal for Housing Bores	External for Shafts	Internal for Housing Bores	External for Shafts	External for Shafts	External for Shafts
range in.	.250-10.0	.125-10.0	.750-4.0	.500-4.0	.250-1.456	.188-1.438	1.0-10.0	1.0-10.0	.094-.438	.110-1.375
range mm.	6.4-253.8	3.2-253.8	19.0-101.5	12.7-101.5	6.4-37.0	4.8-36.5	25.4-253.8	25.4-253.8	2.4-11.1	2.8-35.0

function	for radial assembly				self-locking types					
nomenclature	crescent	e-ring	reinforced e-ring	interlocking	circular self-locking			triangular self-locking	triangular nut	grip-ring
series no.	5103	5133	5144	5107	5005	5115	5105	5305	5300	5555
application	External for Shafts	External for Shafts	External for Shafts	External for Shafts	Internal for Housing Bores	External for Shafts	External for Shafts	External for Shafts	With Threaded Screw	External for Shafts
range in.	.125-2.0	.040-1.375	.094-.438	.469-3.375	.312-2.0	.094-1.0	.094-1.0	.062-.437	●	.077-.755
range mm.	3.2-51.0	1.0-35.0	2.4-11.1	11.9-85.7	7.9-50.8	2.4-25.4	2.4-25.4	1.55-11.1	●	

Fig. 18-19a. Truarc (trademark) retaining rings.
(Waldes Kohinoor Inc.)

2. ADHESIVE PREPARATION - mixing, delivery to work area, etc.
3. ADHESIVE APPLICATION - brush, roller, spray, etc.
4. ASSEMBLY.
5. BOND DEVELOPMENT - curing, evaporation of solvents, etc.

The joints must be specially designed for adhesives.

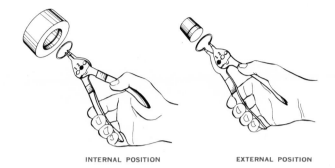

INTERNAL POSITION   EXTERNAL POSITION

Fig. 18-19b. Special pliers are used to install Truarc (trademark) rings. (Waldes Kohinoor Inc.)

SAFETY

1. Wear goggles when making openings (drilling, punching, etc.) to receive fasteners.
2. Do not clean away chips with your hand. Use a brush. Burrs may be raised that can cause nasty cuts.
3. If air is used to blow clean tapped or drilled holes, wear goggles. Protect the piece in such a manner that there is no danger of flying chips hitting anyone.

4. Remove all burrs.
5. Read all instructions carefully when preparing adhesives. Wear goggles to protect your eyes from any fumes and any adhesive that may splash during the mixing process. Do not inhale any of the fumes generated and remove any adhesive from your skin by prompt washing.

TEST YOUR KNOWLEDGE, Unit 18

1. List four methods used to join materials:
   a._____.
   b._____.
   c._____.
   d._____.
2. Name four threaded fasteners:
   a._____- used for general assembly work.
   b._____- prevents pulleys from slipping on shafts.
   c._____- threaded on both ends.
   d._____- hammered into drilled or punched hole.
3. Rivets are used when the pieces are not fastened together permanently. True or false?
4. Lock washers are used to prevent bolts or nuts from loosening under vibration. True or false?
5. The shape of the wing nut permits it to be loosened and tightened without a wrench. True or false?
6. Cotter pins are substitutes for dowel pins. True or false?

7. A jam nut is used when:
   a. Two pieces must be held together.
   b. A regular nut cannot be used.
   c. A regular nut must be locked on a shaft.
   d. None of the above.
8. What are the five steps involved in applying adhesives?
   a._____.
   b._____.
   c._____.
   d._____.
   e._____.
9. Fill in the names of the following non-threaded fasteners:
   a._____Used when parts are assembled permanently.
   b._____Position mating parts.
   c._____Prevents parts from slipping or turning off.
   d._____Can be used only on thin sheet metal.
10. Joining metals together with adhesives is often called_____.

RESEARCH AND DEVELOPMENT

1. Prepare a panel that displays samples of the fasteners described in this unit.
2. Secure or make samples of threaded and non-threaded fasteners applied to an actual job. Mount them on a display panel.
3. Research to determine how early screw threads were made. Develop your findings into a bulletin board display.
4. Epoxy resin adhesive is a modern material capable of bonding metals solidly. Develop an apparatus that can be used to test the holding power of this adhesive. Use test pieces of aluminum one-inch wide. Prepare

them exactly as described in the instructions supplied with the adhesive. Make tests to determine:
   a. How improperly prepared surfaces affect the holding power of the adhesive.
   b. How varying the proportions of resin and catalyst affects the holding power.
   c. How heat affects the bond and its strength.
5. Develop a panel that will show in flow chart form, the various steps several types of fasteners go through as they are formed. Try to secure actual samples. If this is not possible make drawings that show the same thing.

Unit 19

SHEET METAL

Fig. 19-1. Making tin plate.   (Blaw-Knox)

Many methods have been devised to work and shape sheet metal. Production applications are are covered in UNIT 47 - COLD FORMING METAL SHEET. This unit will be concerned with the techniques applicable to the tools and equipment normally found in a school shop.

PATTERNS

Sheet metal is given three-dimensional shape and rigidity by bending and forming it to a pre-determined pattern. The pattern is a full-size drawing of the surface of the object stretched out on a single plane, Fig. 19-2. For this reason, a pattern is often referred to as a STRETCHOUT. Sheet metal pattern development falls into two

basic classifications: PARALLEL-LINE DEVELOPMENTS, and RADIAL-LINE DEVELOPMENTS. Combinations and variations of the basic developments are used to develop the patterns for more complex geometric shapes.

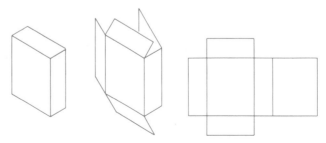

Fig. 19-2. A simple pattern or stretchout.

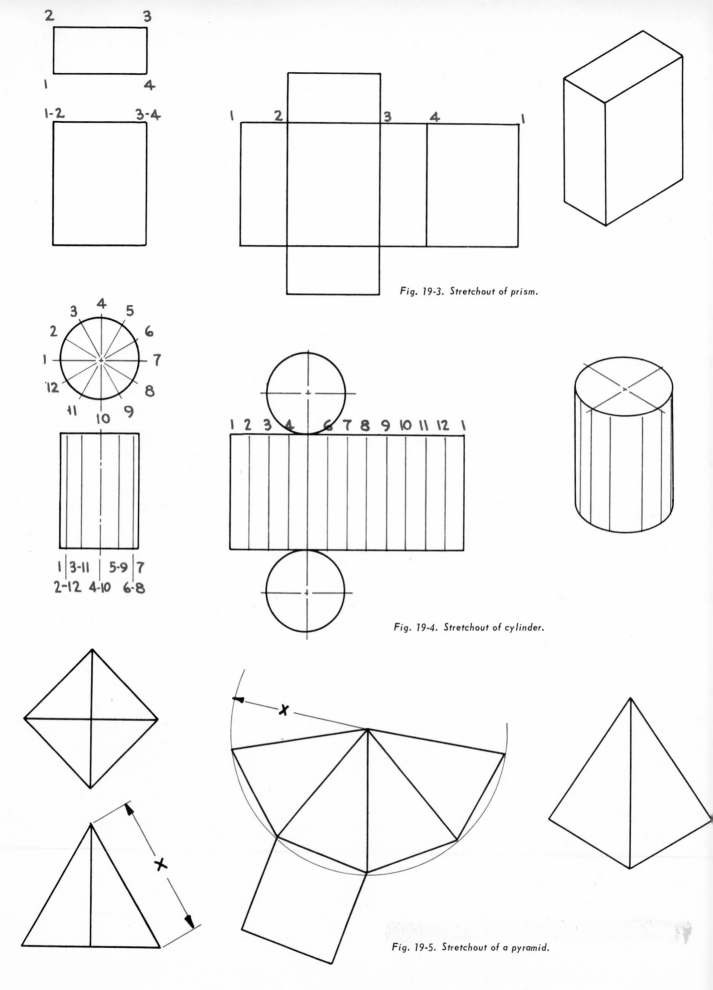

Fig. 19-3. Stretchout of prism.

Fig. 19-4. Stretchout of cylinder.

Fig. 19-5. Stretchout of a pyramid.

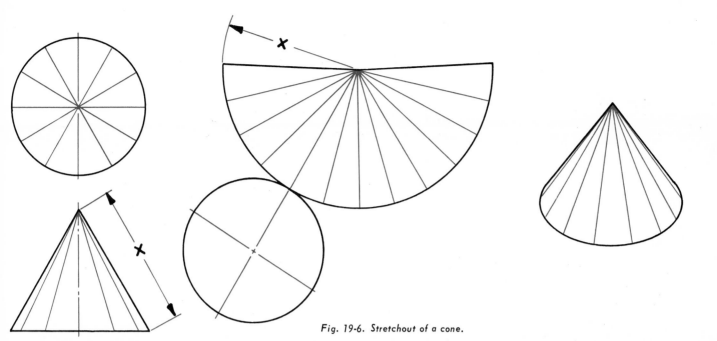

Fig. 19-6. Stretchout of a cone.

Parallel-line developments are those like the PRISM, Fig. 19-3, and the CYLINDER, Fig. 19-4, that unfold into rectangular patterns. Radial-line developments, like the PYRAMID, Fig. 19-5, and CONE, Fig. 19-6, unfold into a triangular pattern.

TRUNCATED geometrical shapes, those cut off at an angle, are developed as shown in Fig. 19-7. The TRANSITION PIECE is used to connect two different shaped openings like a circular opening to a square opening, Fig. 19-8.

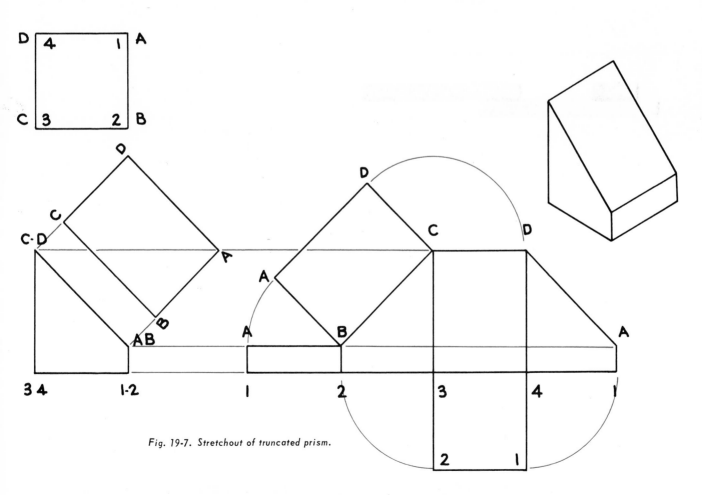

Fig. 19-7. Stretchout of truncated prism.

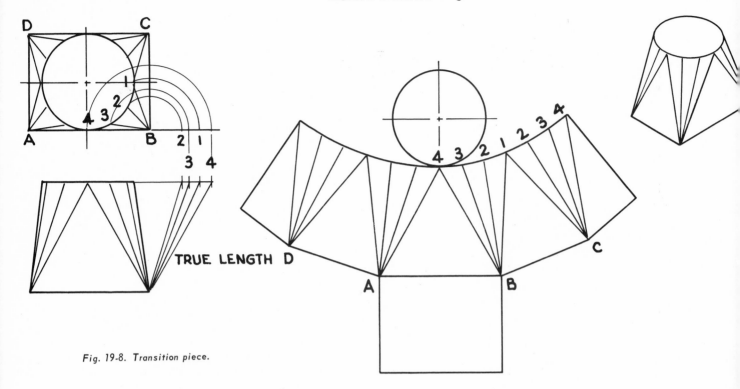

TRUE LENGTH D

Fig. 19-8. Transition piece.

HEMS, EDGES AND SEAMS

When developing a pattern or stretchout, allow additional metal for hems, edges and seams.

HEMS, Fig. 19-9, are used to strengthen the lips of sheet metal objects. They are made in

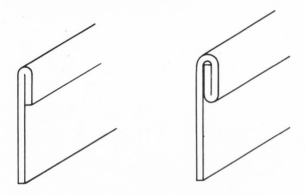

Fig. 19-9. Single and double hems.

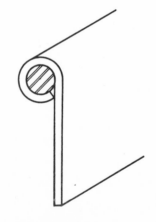

Fig. 19-10. Wired edge.

Fig. 19-11. Grooved seam.

standard fractional sizes, 3/16 in., 1/4 in., 3/8 in., etc.

The WIRED EDGE, Fig. 19-10, gives additional strength and rigidity to sheet metal edges.

SEAMS, Fig. 19-11, make it possible to join sheet metal sections. They are usually finished by soldering and/or riveting.

The pattern may be developed directly on the sheet metal, Fig. 19-12, or on paper and transferred to the metal. A metal TEMPLATE should be made if a number of identical pieces must be fabricated.

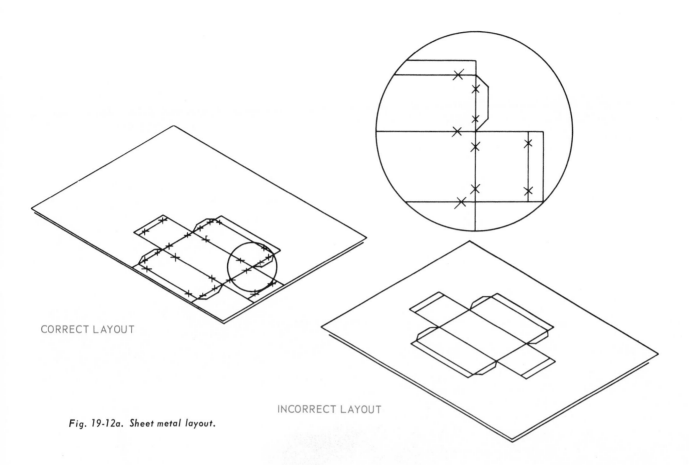

CORRECT LAYOUT

INCORRECT LAYOUT

Fig. 19-12a. Sheet metal layout.

CUTTING SHEET METAL

SNIPS or HAND SHEARS for cutting the layout from the metal sheet are made in a number of sizes and styles. Large sheet metal sections are cut on SQUARING SHEARS.

Fig. 19-12b. Developing a pattern directly on sheet metal.

CUTTING STRAIGHT AND CURVED SECTIONS

Circular work is cut with CIRCULAR SNIPS, Fig. 19-13. Straight and circular work can be cut

Fig. 19-13. Circular snips.

Fig. 19-14. Combination snips.

with COMBINATION SNIPS, Fig. 19-14. AVI-ATION SNIPS, Fig. 19-15, find wide use for cutting compound curves and intricate designs in sheet metal. They are usually color coded in keeping with industry standards--green cuts

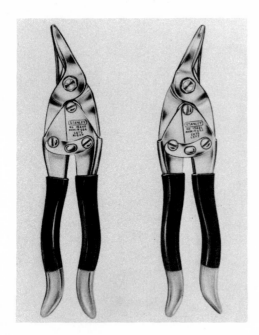

Fig. 19-15. Aviation snips. (Stanley Tools)

right, red cuts left, yellow cuts straight. Internal openings are cut with HAWK-BILLED SNIPS, Fig. 19-16.

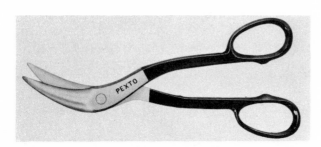

Fig. 19-16. Hawk-billed snips.

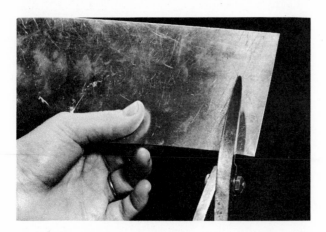

Fig. 19-17. Proper method for cutting a straight edge.

Modern snips are designed to cut freely with a minimum curling of the metal. The snips are generally held in the right hand, at right angles to the work, Fig. 19-17. Open the blades widely to obtain maximum leverage. Do not permit them to close completely at the end of a cut or a rough edge will result. Cut circular sections from the right side, Fig. 19-18.

Fig. 19-18. Making a circular cut.

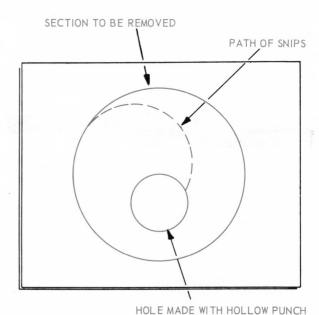

Fig. 19-19. Cutting a circular opening in a sheet metal section.

When making internal circular cuts, make a small opening near the center of the opening, insert the snips and cut from the upper side, gradually increasing the radius of the cut until the opening is completed, Fig. 19-19.

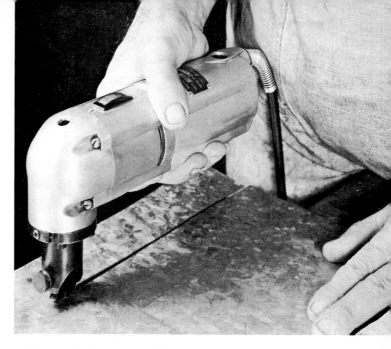

Fig. 19-22a. Cutting a straight section with power shears.
(Skil Corp.)

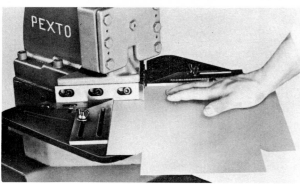

Fig. 19-20. Combination notcher, coper and shear.

The COMBINATION NOTCHER, COPER & SHEAR, Fig. 19-20, is ideal for notching corners or the edge of sheet metal. The blades are adjustable for conventional notching or for piercing, starting inside the blank.

PORTABLE POWER SHEARS, Fig. 19-21, make it possible to do production work. They are designed to do straight or circular cutting, Fig. 19-22.

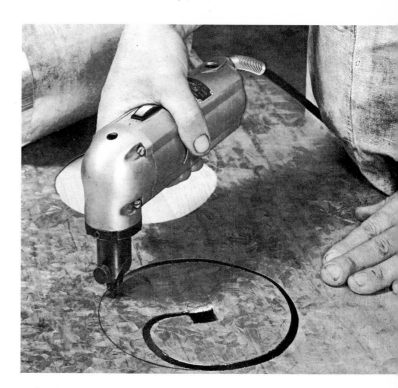

Fig. 19-22b. Cutting a circular section with power shears.

Fig. 19-21. Portable power shears.

Fig. 19-23. Solid punch.

Small diameter openings can be made with a SOLID PUNCH, Fig. 19-23, or a HOLLOW PUNCH, Fig. 19-24. Locate the position of the hole; select the correct size punch and hammer, then place the metal section on a lead cake or on the end grain of a block of hard wood, Fig. 19-25. Strike the punch sharply with the hammer. Turn

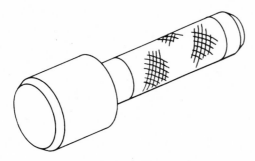

Fig. 19-24. Hollow punch.

the punched section over so the burred section is up, then smooth it with a mallet.

FOOT OPERATED SQUARING SHEARS, Fig. 19-26, make it possible to square and trim large sheets. Do not attempt to cut metal thicker than the designed capacity of the shears. The maximum capacity of the machine is stamped on the manufacturer's specification plate on the front of the shears. Check the thickness of the metal against this size, with a SHEET METAL GAUGE, Fig. 19-27.

DO NOT cut wire, band iron or steel rods on the squaring shears.

The length of the cut is determined by the position of the BACK GAUGE when the metal is inserted from the front of the shears. The

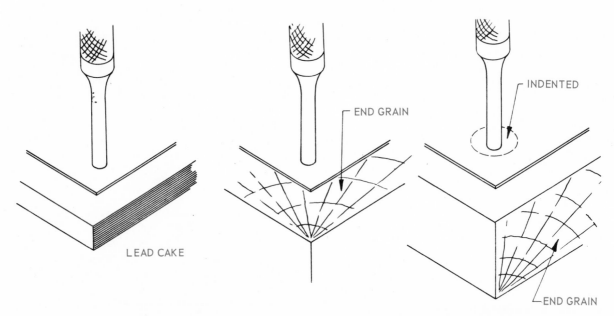

Fig. 19-25. Correct and incorrect method of backing sheet metal for making hole with punch.

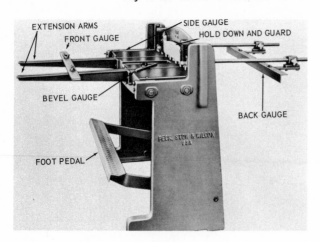

Fig. 19-26. Squaring shears.

Fig. 19-27. Using a sheet metal gauge to check sheet thickness.

Fig. 19-28. Ring and circular shears.

FRONT GAUGE controls the length of the cut when the metal sheet is inserted from the rear. The front gauge is seldom used and is usually removed from the shears. A BEVEL GAUGE permits angular cuts to be made.

To make a cut, set the back gauge to the required dimension by using the graduated scale on the top of the extension arms or on the graduated section on the bed top. Hold the piece firmly against the SIDE GAUGE with both hands until the HOLD DOWN comes into position and apply pressure to the FOOT PEDAL.

SAFETY

1. Sheet metal can cause serious cuts. Handle it with care. Wear steel reinforced gloves whenever possible.
2. Treat every cut immediately, no matter how minor.
3. Remove all burrs from the metal sheet before attempting further work on it.
4. Use a brush to clean the work area. NEVER brush metal with your hands.
5. Use tools that are sharp.
6. Keep your hands clear of the blade on the squaring shears.
7. A serious and painful foot injury will result if your foot is under the foot pedal of the squaring shears when a cut is made.
8. Do not run your hands over the surface of sheet metal that has just been cut or drilled. Painful cuts can be received from the burrs.
9. Get help when cutting large pieces of sheet metal. Keep your helper well clear of the shears when you are making the cut.
10. Keep your hands and fingers clear of the rotating parts on forming machines.
11. Place scrap pieces of sheet metal in the scrap box.
12. Do not use tools that are not in first-class condition--hammer heads loose on the handle, chisels with mushroomed heads, power tools with guards removed, etc.
13. Wear goggles when in the shop.

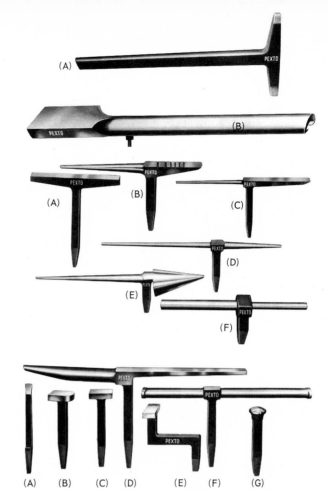

Fig. 19-29. TOP. Cast iron stakes. (A) Solid mandrel stake, (B) Hollow mandrel.
CENTER. Forged steel stakes. (A) Hatchet stake, (B) Creasing stake with horn, (C) Needle case stake, (D) Candle mould stake, (E) Blowhorn stake, (F) Conductor stake.
BOTTOM. Stakes. (A) Bottom stake, (B) Coppersmith's square stake, (C) Common square stake, (D) Beakhorn stake, (E) Bevel edge square stake, (F) Double seaming stake, (G) Round head stake.

KEEP THE HANDS CLEAR OF THE BLADE AND THE FOOT FROM BENEATH THE FOOT PEDAL.

RING AND CIRCULAR SHEARS, Fig. 19-28, are intended for cutting inside and outside circles in sheet metal. The CLAMPING HEAD is positioned for the desired diameter and the blank inserted. Lower the CUTTING DISC and make the cut.

BENDING SHEET METAL

Metal sheet is given three-dimensional shape and rigidity by bending. Both hand and machine bending techniques have been developed. Several of the methods are described in the following section.

BENDING SHEET METAL BY HAND

METAL STAKES, Fig. 19-29, enable the sheet metal craftsman to make a variety of bends by hand. Stakes, available in a number of shapes and sizes, are designed to fit in a BENCH PLATE, Fig. 19-30, or a UNIVERSAL STAKE HOLDER, Fig. 19-31, that clamps to the bench.

Fig. 19-30. Bench plate.

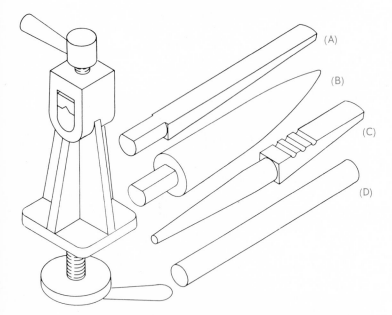

Fig. 19-31. Universal stake holder and stakes. (A) Rectangular end of beakhorn stake, (B) Beakhorn stake, (C) Creasing stake with horn, (D) Conductor stake.

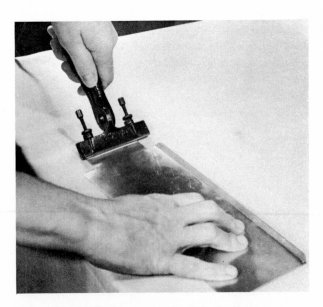

Fig. 19-32. Forming an edge with a hand seamer.

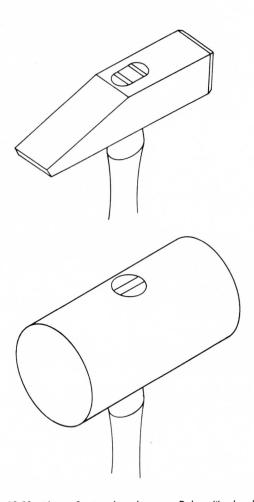

Fig. 19-33. Above. Setting-down hammer. Below. Wood mallet.

Narrow sections can be formed with the HAND SEAMER, Fig. 19-32. Its main use is for bending an edge or folding a seam.

The SETTING-DOWN HAMMER and MALLET, Fig. 19-33, provide the necessary force when using wooden or angle iron forming blocks to make angular bends in sheet metal, Fig. 19-34.

Curved sections are formed over a stake or metal rod of a suitable shape and size, Fig. 19-35.

BENDING SHEET METAL BY MACHINE

Many machines have been devised to perform specific sheet metal bending operations.

THE BAR FOLDER AND BRAKE

The BAR FOLDER, Fig. 19-36, is designed to bend sheet metal to form edges and prepare the metal for a wire edge. Seams can also be formed on this machine.

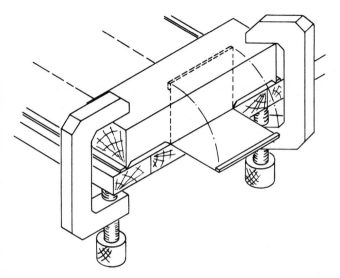

Fig. 19-34. Using a wood block to make an angular bend.

The width of the folder edge is determined by the setting of the DEPTH GAUGE, Fig. 19-37. The sharpness of the folded edge, whether it is to be sharp for a hem or seam or rounded to

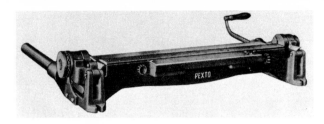

Fig. 19-36. Bar folder.

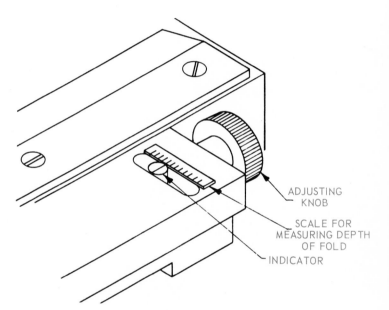

Fig. 19-37. Fold size is determined by setting of depth gauge.

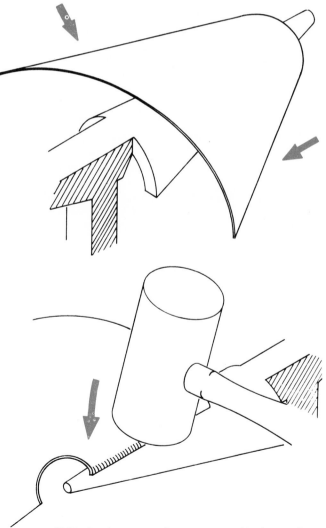

Fig. 19-35. Bending a conical section over a blowhorn stake.

make a wire edge, is determined by the position of the WING, Fig. 19-38. Right angle (90 deg.) and 45 deg. bends can be made by using the 90 deg. and 45 deg. ANGLE STOP.

Hemmed edges are made in the following manner, Fig. 19-39:

1. Adjust the depth gauge for the required size and position the wing for the desired fold sharpness.
2. Set the metal in place resting it lightly against the gauge fingers.
3. With the left hand holding the metal, pull the handle as far forward as it will go. Return the handle to its original position.
4. Place the folded section on the beveled section of the blade, as close to the wing as possible. Flatten the fold by pulling the handle forward rapidly.

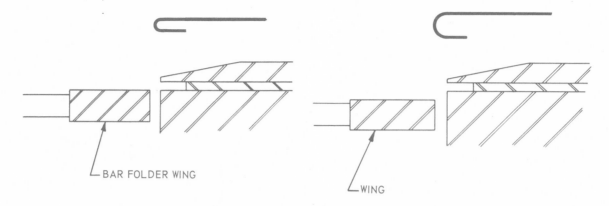

BAR FOLDER WING

WING

Fig. 19-38. Wing setting determines tightness of fold.

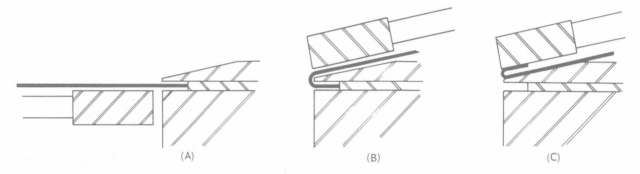

(A)　　　　　　　　(B)　　　　　　　　(C)

Fig. 19-39. Making a hemmed edge. (A) Adjust depth gauge to size. (B) Make the Fold. (C) Flatten the fold.

Fig. 19-40. Cornice Brake.　(Dreis and Krump)

BRAKES

Large sheet metal sections are formed on BENDING BRAKES. The CORNICE BRAKE, Fig. 19-40, is capable of bending metal sections that are many feet in length. Fig. 19-41 illustrates several shapes that can be formed by using various shaped forming blocks on the BENDING LEAF BAR, Fig. 19-42.

It is often impossible to bend all four sides of a box on a conventional brake. The BOX AND

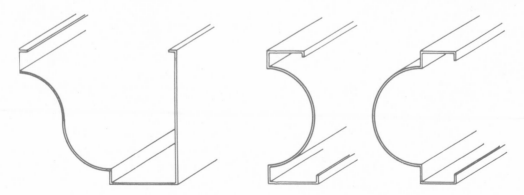

Fig. 19-41. Typical sections that can be formed on a cornice brake.

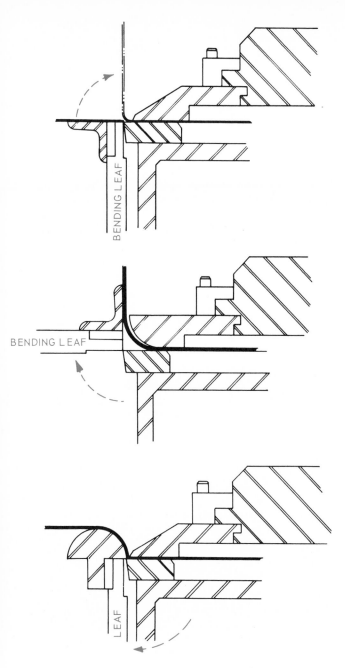

BENDING LEAF

BENDING LEAF

LEAF

Fig. 19-42. Forming blocks in place on cornice brake.

Fig. 19-43. Box and pan brake.

thicknesses of metal. The rear roll, also adjustable, gives the section the desired curvature. The top roll pivots up to permit the cylinder to be removed without danger of distortion. Grooves are machined in the two bottom rolls for the purpose of accommodating a wired edge when forming a section with this type edge, or for rolling wire into a ring.

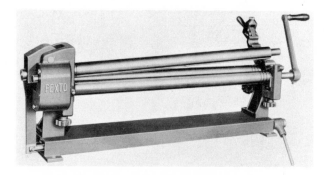

Fig. 19-44. Slip roll forming machine.

PAN BRAKE, Fig. 19-43, has been designed to handle this situation. The upper jaw is made up of a number of blocks of varied widths that can be positioned or removed easily to permit all four sides of a box to be formed.

FORMING ROLLS

When forming cylinders and conical shapes, no sharp bends are necessary; rather, a gradual curve must be put into the metal until the ends meet. The easiest method of forming these shapes is on the SLIP ROLL FORMING MACHINE, Fig. 19-44. Three rolls do the forming, Fig. 19-45. The two front rolls are the feed rolls and can be adjusted to accommodate various

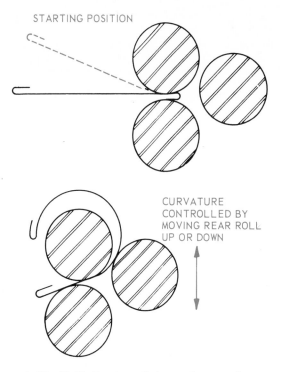

STARTING POSITION

CURVATURE CONTROLLED BY MOVING REAR ROLL UP OR DOWN

Fig. 19-45. Forming cylinders on forming rolls.

TURNING FOR A WIRED EDGE, BURRING, BEADING AND CRIMPING

Preparing sheet metal for a wired edge, turning a burr, beading and crimping are probably the most difficult of the sheet metal forming operations to perform. When production warrants, large shops have a machine for each operation. However, a COMBINATION ROTARY MACHINE, Fig. 19-46, with a selection of rolls will prove satisfactory for school shop applications.

Fig. 19-46. Combination rotary machine with extra forming rolls.

WIRING AN EDGE

There are many methods of preparing an edge for wiring. Cylindrical shapes should be wired before forming to shape. In this case, the wire edge is constructed by using the bar folder to make the initial bend, Fig. 19-47, and, after the wire is inserted, by turning the edge down on the rotary machine. An allowance of two and one half times the wire diameter must be added to the basic size of the pattern for a wired edge, Fig. 19-48.

The wire edge must be applied to tapered shapes after they are formed. This is accomplished by turning the edge on the rotary machine, Fig. 19-49. Gradually lower the upper roll until the groove is large enough for the wire. The edge is pressed around the wire with the rotary machine in the same manner as illustrated in Fig. 19-47.

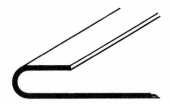

Fig. 19-47. Initial bend for a wire edge.

2-1/2 x WIRE DIA.

Fig. 19-48. Allowance for making wire edge.

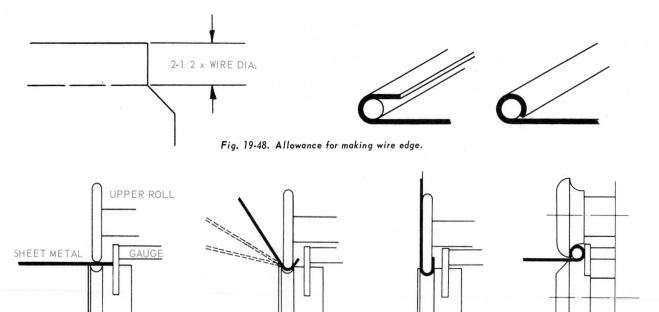

Fig. 19-49. Turning a wire edge with a rotary machine.

Sheet Metal

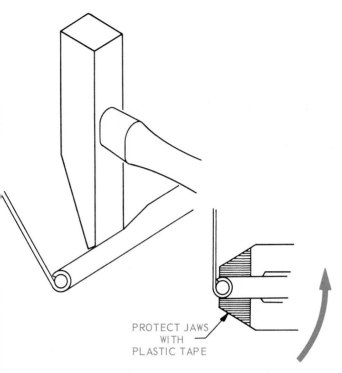

Fig. 19-50. Setting wire edge with setting-down hammer or pliers.

The wire edge can be finished by hand if a rotary machine is not available. The edge is formed on the bar folder and forced in place around the wire with a setting-down hammer or pliers, Fig. 19-50.

TURNING A BURR

A BURR, in sheet metal terminology, is a narrow flange turned on the circular section to be attached to the end of a cylinder, Fig. 19-51.

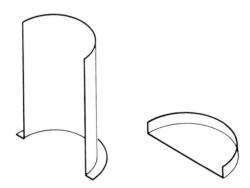

Fig. 19-51. Burrs turned on cylindrical section.

Before cutting the section, remember that additional material must be added to the basic dimensions of the object for the burr. Fig. 19-52 shows how to calculate this additional material.

After the rotary machine has been adjusted to turn the proper size burr, the work is placed in position and the upper roll lowered. Make one complete revolution of the piece, scoring the edge slightly. Lower the upper roll a bit further and

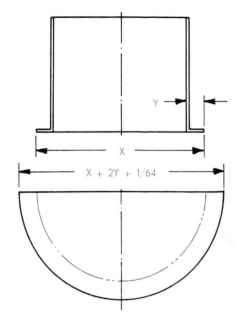

Fig. 19-52. Calculating the material needed for a double seam. X = Diameter of cylindrical section with burred edge. Y = Width of burred edge.

make another revolution. Continue this operation, raising the disc slightly after each turn until the burr is turned to the desired angle, Fig. 19-53.

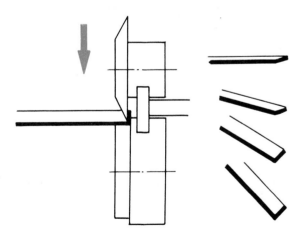

Fig. 19-53. Turning a burred edge with a rotary machine.

This technique is also used to turn the burr on the bottom of the cylinder for a double seam, Fig. 19-54. The two pieces are snapped together,

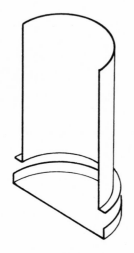

Fig. 19-54. Fitting the burred sections together.

the burr set down, and the seam completed, Fig. 19-55.

Turning a burr is a difficult operation, it is suggested that several practice pieces be turned to develop skill before turning the burr on the actual piece to be used.

BEADING

BEADING, Fig. 19-56, is used to give additional rigidity to cylindrical sheet metal objects, for decorative purposes, or for both reasons. It can be a simple bead or an ogee (S-shape) bead. They are made on the rotary machine using beading rolls.

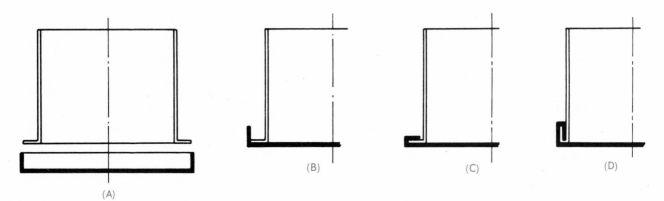

Fig. 19-55. Making a double seam on a cylindrical section. (A) Check the sections for size. (B) Snap the two sections together. (C) Set the burr down. (D) Complete the seam.

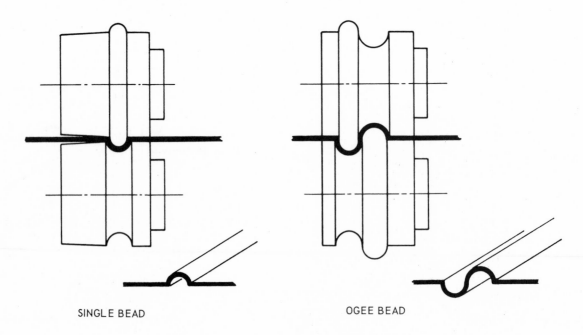

SINGLE BEAD   OGEE BEAD

Fig. 19-56. Turning a bead with a rotary machine.

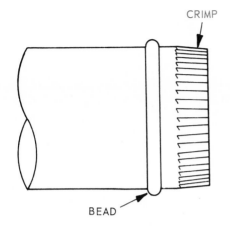

Fig. 19-57. A crimped section.

CRIMPING

CRIMPING, Fig. 19-57, reduces the diameter of a cylindrical shape permitting it to be slipped into the next section eliminating the costly process of making each cylinder on a slight taper.

MAKING COMMON SHEET METAL JOINTS

Many kinds of seams are used to join sheet metal sections. Several of the more widely used seams are shown in Fig. 19-58. When developing the pattern, be sure to add sufficient material to the basic dimensions to make the seams. The folds can be made by hand; however, they are

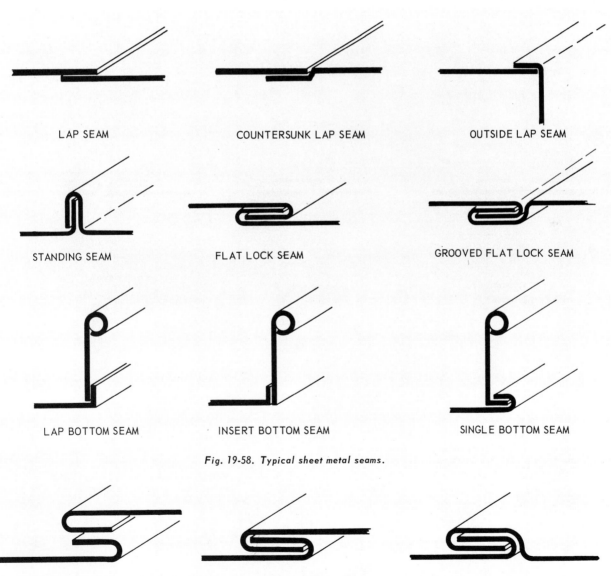

Fig. 19-58. Typical sheet metal seams.

Fig. 19-59. Making a grooved seam.

made much more easily on a bar folder or brake. The joints can be finished by soldering and/or riveting.

GROOVED SEAM JOINT

The GROOVED SEAM JOINT, Fig. 19-59, is one of the most widely used methods for joining light and medium gauge sheet metal. It consists of two folded edges that are locked together with a HAND GROOVER, Fig. 19-60.

Fig. 19-60. Hand groover.

FASTENING SHEET METAL

Sheet metal joints are usually soldered or riveted. However, sheet metal screws are being used more and more. Soldering and using sheet metal screws are described in other units in this text.

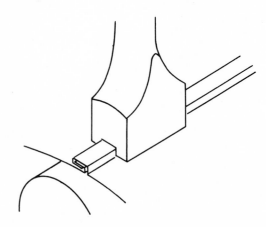

Fig. 19-61. Locking a grooved seam with a hand groover.

Fig. 19-62. Cap strip seam.

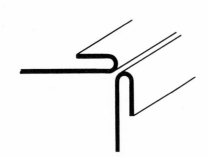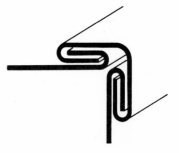

Fig. 19-63. Locked corner seam.

When making a grooved seam on a cylinder, the piece is fitted over a stake and locked with the hand groover, Fig. 19-61.

CAP STRIP JOINT

The CAP STRIP JOINT, Fig. 19-62, is often used to assemble air conditioning and heating ducts. A variation of the joint, the LOCKED CORNER SEAM, Fig. 19-63, is widely accepted for the assembly of rectangular shapes.

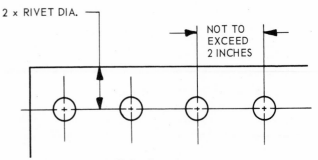

Fig. 19-64. Spacing rivets.

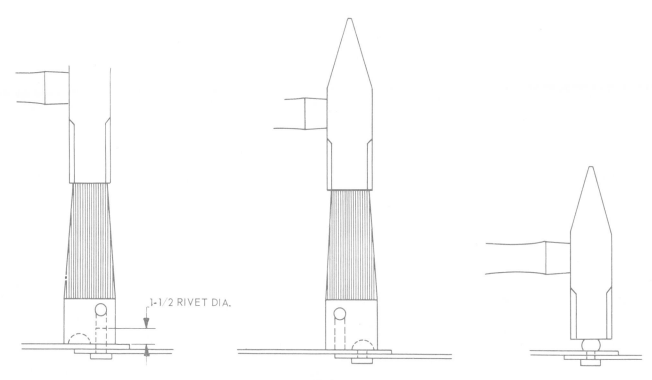

Fig. 19-65. Setting a rivet.

1-1/2 RIVET DIA.

RIVETING

Drill or punch a hole of the proper size for the rivet being used. The correct spacing of rivets is also important. The space from the edge of the metal should be at least twice the diameter of the rivet, Fig. 19-64.

With practice, a good job of riveting can be done with a minimum of hammer blows, Fig. 19-65:

1. Seat the rivet and draw the sheets together.
2. Flatten the rivet.
3. Form the rivet head with a RIVET SET.

TEST YOUR KNOWLEDGE, Unit 19

1. A sheet metal pattern is:
   a. A three-dimensional drawing of the object.
   b. A full-size drawing of the object.
   c. An isometric drawing of the object.
   d. None of the above.
2. Sheet metal patterns are also known as _____.
3. Pattern developments fall into two basic classifications:
   a. _____ developments unfold into rectangular patterns.
   b. _____ developments unfold into triangular patterns.
4. _____ and _____ are examples of the patterns described in "a" above.
5. _____ and _____ are examples of the patterns described in "b" above.
6. A transition piece is used to connect _____ _____.
7. Sheet metal can be cut by hand with _____.
8. _____ _____ are foot operated and used to cut and trim large sheet metal sections.
9. Cylindrical shapes are formed on a:
   a. Cornice brake.
   b. Forming rolls.
   c. Cylinder maker.
   d. None of the above.
10. Small diameter holes can be made in sheet metal with a _____ punch or a _____ punch.

11. The bar folder and brake permit_____ and_____to be folded quickly and accurately.
12. The wired edge is added to the lip of a sheet metal object for_____.
13. A burr is:
    a. A narrow flange turned on the edge of a circular sheet metal section to form part of a joint.
    b. A rounded edge on the lip of a sheet metal object.
    c. An edge formed on the bar folder.
    d. None of the above.
14. Beading is added to the sheet metal object for added rigidity and for_____ purposes.
15. Most sheet metal joints are finished by _____ and/or_____.
16. Seams are used to_____ _____ _____.

RESEARCH AND DEVELOPMENT

1. Make large scale models of the most common sheet metal joints. If suitable sheet metal equipment is not available, make sectional views of the joints using heavy cardboard. Mount the samples on a suitable display panel.
2. Secure samples of sheet metal work made by local sheet metal shops. Prepare a display around them. Explain how they were made.
3. Demonstrate how sheet metal is worked at a PTA Meeting, during American Education Week, or during your school's open house program.
4. Prepare a list of the objects in your home that were made of sheet metal. How many different joining methods can be identified? How many different metals are used?
5. Prepare a report on the job opportunities for sheet metal work in your community. Use classified advertisements, employment service reports and actual interviews for your report to the class.

Unit 20

ART METAL

Fig. 20-1. Small copper bowl, silver plated interior.
(Robert Rednack)

Fig. 20-3. Viking boat of metal strip.
(Robert Tule)

There is no clear dividing point where sheet metal ceases and art metal begins, as many of the shaping and forming operations are common to both areas.

Art metal falls into many categories - hollow ware, Fig. 20-1, flat ware, Fig. 20-2, strip

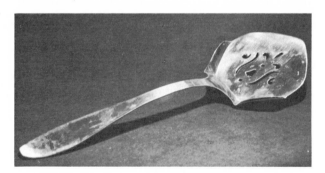

Fig. 20-2. Nickel silver server.
(Robert Tule)

Fig. 20-4. Contemporary pitcher in pewter.
(Paul Rueger)

work, Fig. 20-3, and jewelry making. Regardless of the area of interest, art metal offers the individual an opportunity to develop true craftsmanship since most of the work is hand crafted, with machines playing but a minor role.

INDUSTRIAL TECHNIQUES

While hand crafted pieces as in Fig. 20-4, are highly cherished, demand has reached such proportions that production techniques have been incorporated to produce pieces in sufficient quantities. Many well-designed quality pieces are available that have been produced, in large part by mechanical processes, Fig. 20-5. A portion of the sequence followed in manufacturing quality tableware is shown in Figs. 20-6a to 20-6i incl.

Fig. 20-5. Sterling bowl, enamel lined.
(Towle Silversmiths)

AN INTRODUCTION TO ART METAL

ANNEALING AND PICKLING

Annealing is a process of softening metal by carefully heating and controlling the cooling sequence.

Metal becomes hard and brittle as it is worked and must be annealed from time to time before further shaping can be done. Reworking without annealing may cause the metal to fracture.

Closely related to annealing is the PICKLING operation. During annealing an oxide forms on the metal. If not removed before reworking, the oxide scale will be forced into the surface, marring its appearance. It can be removed with abrasives; however, this is a time consuming process. The scale can be removed rapidly by submerging the piece in a dilute solution of sulphuric acid.

Copper and sterling silver are annealed by heating to a dull red, and quenching in water or pickling solution.

Alloyed metals, such as brass, bronze and

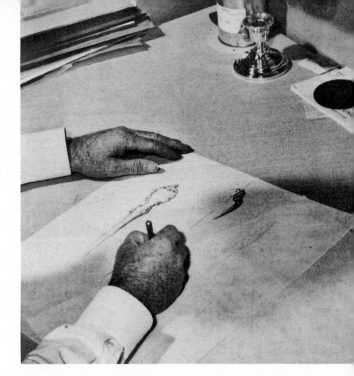

Fig. 20-6a. A flatware pattern begins with the artist who sketches the design. (International Silver Co.)

Fig. 20-6b. A model of the design is fashioned in red wax about twice the size of a tablespoon to permit every detail of the design to be brought out and perfected.

Fig. 20-6c. SHEET METAL -- The proper proportions of copper, zinc and nickel are melted together in an electric furnace. The molten metal is then poured into molds where it hardens gradually, forming bars of nickel silver.

Fig. 20-6d. ROLLING -- Bars of nickel silver are rolled down in a series of passes between steel rollers, annealed (heated), and rolled again until required gauge of metal is attained.

Fig. 20-6e. CROSS ROLLING--Blanks are passed between heavy rollers to distribute the metal in correct proportions for length, width and thickness.

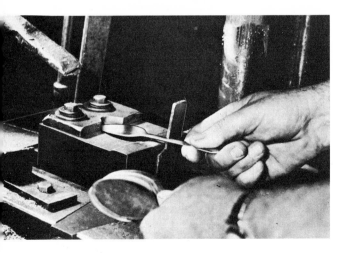

Fig. 20-6f. BOWL FORMING -- Bowl forming is accomplished by stamping the bowl or tine portion of article in contour die designed especially for each piece.

Fig. 20-6g. STAMPING -- Striking the design on front and back of handle.

Fig. 20-6h. SPOT PLATING -- Backs of forks are placed on rack so the most used sections to be overlaid with pure silver are in a silver cyanide solution giving the wear points overlaid reinforcing.

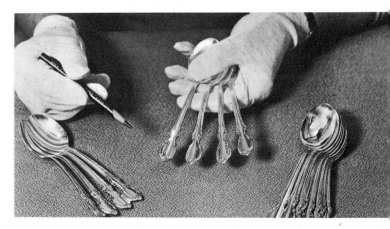

Fig. 20-6i. FINAL INSPECTION -- Each item is individually checked by experienced inspectors to rigid standards of quality.

nickel silver (German silver), are heated to a dull red and allowed to cool slightly before plunging into water or pickling solution.

Aluminum may be difficult to anneal because it is not easy to determine when the metal has reached the required temperature. Two methods for determining when the correct annealing temperature of aluminum has been reached are:

1. Heat carefully and occasionally touch the surface of the metal with a piece of white pine. When the surface is hot enough to cause the pine to char and leave a mark, withdraw the heat and permit the aluminum to cool at room temperature.

2. Rub cutting oil on the piece and heat until the oil burns. This indicates that annealing temperature has been reached. Allow to cool at room temperature.

As no oxide forms on aluminum during annealing, it is not necessary to clean the surface in a pickling solution.

The pickling solution for copper, brass and silver is made by slowly adding 8 oz. of sulphuric acid to a gallon of cold water contained in a glass or earthenware jar. NEVER ADD THE WATER TO THE ACID. Stir the mixture with a stick of wood. Use only in a well-ventilated area and cover the container with a wooden top when not in use. Avoid breathing the fumes.

The annealing and pickling operations are usually part of the same work sequence. The heated metal is held by tongs at arm's length and dropped into the pickling solution. WEAR GOGGLES. When the oxide has dissolved, remove the piece from the solution with wooden tongs, rinse thoroughly in running water, and dry it in clean sawdust or with paper towels.

When shaping is complete and it is not necessary to anneal the piece again, place it in the solution without heating. Permit it to remain in the bath until it is clean. Remove, rinse and dry as previously described.

DECORATING METAL

SAWING AND PIERCING

Internal designs are cut into metal with a JEWELER'S SAW, Fig. 20-7. This operation, called PIERCING, is performed by drilling a small hole to permit the blade to be inserted. Use a solid support when sawing, Fig. 20-8.

Blades for the jeweler's saw are designated by numbers, Fig. 20-9. Note that the smaller

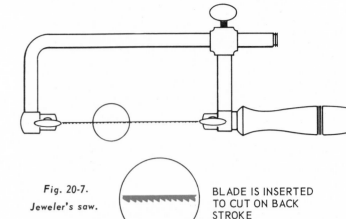

Fig. 20-7.
Jeweler's saw.

BLADE IS INSERTED TO CUT ON BACK STROKE

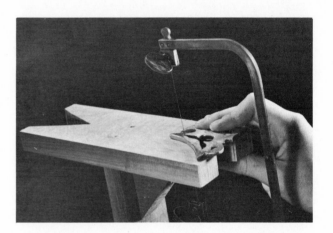

Fig. 20-8. A solid work support is needed when using a jeweler's saw.

Size No.	Thickness	Width	Blades
8/0	.006	.013	Saws Finer Than 4/0
7/0	.007	.014	Not Illustrated
6/0	.007	.014	
5/0	.008	.015	
4/0	.008	.017	
3/0	.010	.019	
2/0	.010	.020	
0	.011	.023	
1	.012	.025	
1½	.012	.025	

Size No.	Thickness	Width	Blades
2	.014	.027	
3	.014	.029	
4	.015	.031	
5	.016	.034	
6	.019	.041	
8	.020	.048	
10	.020	.058	
12	.023	.064	
14	.024	.068	

Fig. 20-9. Jeweler's saw blade schedule

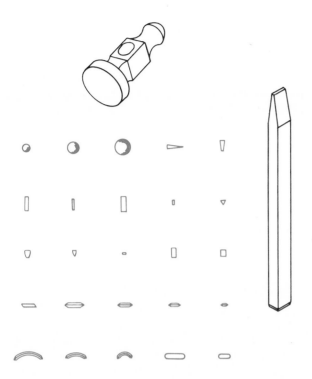

Fig. 20-10. *Chasing hammer and assortment of punch shapes.*

the number the finer the blade. The #2 blade is well suited for general work.

Piercing weakens the metal, so it is advisable to allow sufficient metal in the surrounding area for rigidity and strength.

Fig. 20-11. *A handmade fork in sterling silver is hand chased by a craftsman who is a talented artist. The height and depth of the design bring out the shadows and highlights.*
(International Silver Co.)

REPOUSSE' (CHASING)

Repousse' is a French word meaning "to thrust back." It might better be called "sculpturing in metal." The actual tooling, done with punches and light hammer, Fig. 20-10, is called CHASING, Fig. 20-11.

Often hollow ware, Fig. 20-12, is decorated with raised designs. Obviously, it is impossible to get the punches and hammer inside the object.

Fig. 20-12. *Copper mug, silver plated interior.*
(Bernard B. Gavula)

A device known as a SNARLING IRON, Fig. 20-13, is used to raise or push up the necessary metal. It works by vibration. One end is fastened in a vise, the work is positioned, and the snarling iron is struck with a hammer, Fig. 20-14.

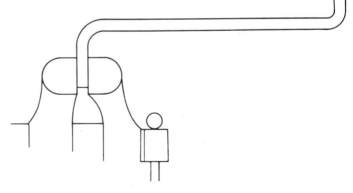

Fig. 20-13. *A snarling iron mounted in a vise.*

RAISING METAL

Raising is the process of giving three-dimensional shape to flat sheet metal by using hammers, mallets, stakes and sandbag.

Modern Metalworking

Fig. 20-14. A snarling iron in use.

SAFETY

1. Remove all burrs and sharp edges from metal before attempting to work it.
2. Use caution when handling hot metal. Do not place it where it could start a fire.
3. Pour acid into water, NEVER water into acid.
4. Wear goggles when working with pickling solutions.
5. Use pickling solution in well-ventilated areas. Do not breathe fumes.
6. Do not stand over the pickling solution when plunging hot metal into it.
7. Secure medical attention for any cut, bruise or burn.
8. Clear the soldering area of solvents and other flammable material before soldering.

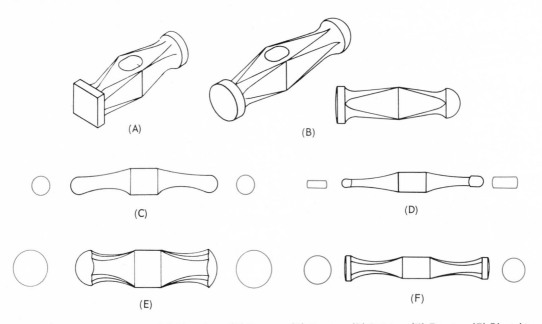

Fig. 20-15. Art metal hammers. (A) Planishing. (B) Forming. (C) Forming. (D) Raising. (E) Forming. (F) Planishing.

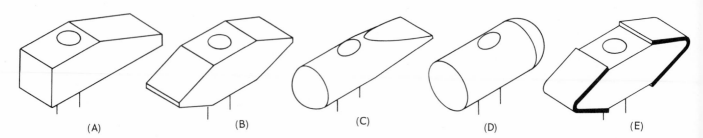

Fig. 20-16. Mallets. (A) Hardwood forming mallet. (B) Double wedge forming mallet. (C) Round end forming mallet. (D) Round end forming mallet. (E) Leather-faced forming mallet.

20-6

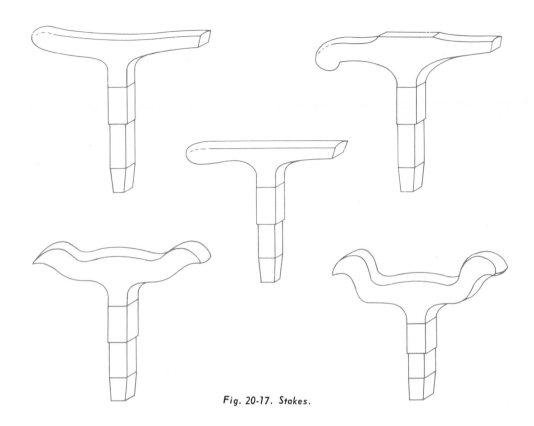

Fig. 20-17. Stakes.

HAMMERS

Several different types of hammers are used in art metalwork, Fig. 20-15. These are made of steel with faces that should be clear of nicks and rough spots. The faces of planishing hammers should be polished to a mirror finish.

MALLETS

Like hammers, many styles of mallets, Fig. 20-16, are used. They are made of wood, rawhide, plastic or live rubber, and are used for forming the softer metals. After forming with a mallet, the piece is finished with a hammer.

STAKES AND ANVIL HEADS

Stakes and anvil heads are used to support the metal while it is being worked. They have a smooth, hard surface which should be free from nicks and scratches. Avoid striking the surface of the stake with a hammer and never cut metal on it with a cold chisel. The more commonly used stakes and anvil heads are shown in Figs. 20-17 and 20-17a.

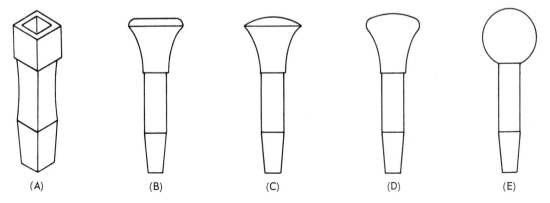

(A)   (B)   (C)   (D)   (E)

Fig. 20-17a. Anvils. (A) Extension arm. (B) Mushroom. (C) Mushroom. (D) Mushroom. (E) Mushroom.

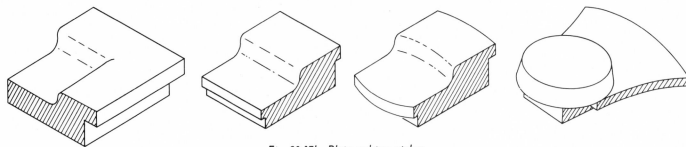

Fig. 20-17b. Plate and tray stakes.

SANDBAG

A sandbag, Fig. 20-18, is made of several layers of heavy canvas and is partially filled with fine, clean sand. It is only partially filled with sand, so it can be adjusted easily to fit many different shapes.

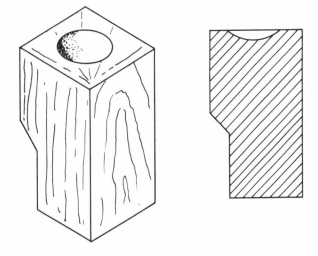

Fig. 20-19. Hardwood block with depression.

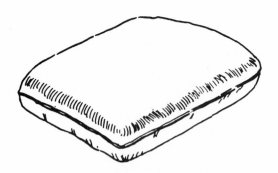

Fig. 20-18. Sandbag.

RAISING AN OBJECT

Several methods may be employed to raise a bowl. The design of the object and the equipment available will determine the method to use.

The simplest method for raising a shallow piece is to use a block of hardwood having a hollow depression in the end-grain side, Fig. 20-19.

Hammer the metal along the outer edge with a forming hammer and slowly work toward the center. As this is a stretching operation, the depth of the piece is limited. Place the piece on a mushroom stake and smooth with a mallet. Clean and anneal, and planish on a stake.

Place the piece on a flat surface and use a surface gauge to mark off the height of the finished piece, Fig. 20-20. Trim, smooth the edge and polish.

The diameter of the metal blank can be determined for this and other raising methods as

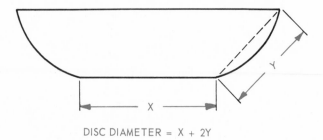

Fig. 20-20. Surface gauge being used to mark desired height.

DISC DIAMETER = X + 2Y

Fig. 20-21. Determining the diameter of a blank for bowl.

shown in Fig. 20-21. Use care when making the layout, to eliminate waste, Fig. 20-22.

The sandbag and mallet can also be used to

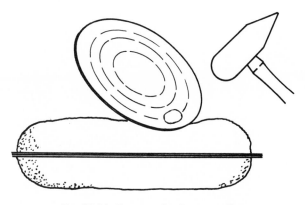

Fig. 20-24. Raising a bowl on a sandbag.

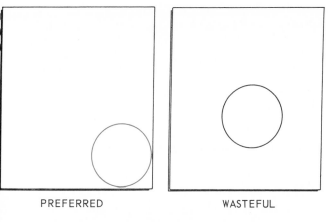

PREFERRED   WASTEFUL

Fig. 20-22. Use care when making layout.

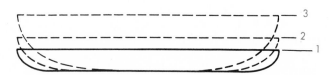

Fig. 20-25. Sequence in raising a bowl.

raise a bowl. Cut a disc of the required size and scribe a series of concentric circles, Fig. 20-23. Place the disc on the sandbag and elevate the

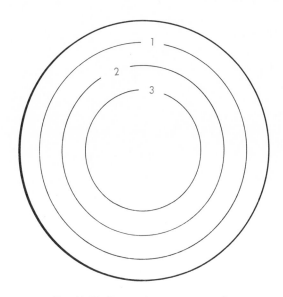

Fig. 20-23. Disc with concentric circles.

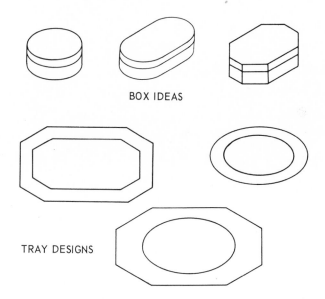

BOX IDEAS

TRAY DESIGNS

Fig. 20-26. Box and tray ideas.

edge opposite the one to be struck with the mallet, Fig. 20-24. Strike the disc a series of blows around circle #1 until it has been completely rotated, Fig. 20-25. Continue working on circle #2 and #3 until the desired depth is obtained. Planish on a stake, trim to height and polish.

Trays and boxes, Fig. 20-26, can be raised by a unique method. Two blocks of hardwood are

cut to size and shape. A metal blank of suitable size and shape is placed between the blocks and the unit is mounted in a vise, Fig. 20-27. Then strike the metal near the block with a forming hammer (a leather-faced mallet is used with pewter), Fig. 20-28. Make a complete rotation around the blocks. Anneal if necessary, and continue working until the desired depth has been obtained. Remove the piece from between the blocks, trim and finish.

Fig. 20-27. Forming blocks and metal disc.

Fig. 20-28. Strike near the block.

Fig. 20-29. Raising a form on a stake. (Henry J. Kauffman)

Avoid sharp corners when designing pieces to be made by this technique as wrinkles may form at these points. Should folds and wrinkles start to develop in spite of careful planning, they can be hammered out on a stake.

The final method involves raising a form over a stake, Fig. 20-29. Objects of considerable height can be obtained by using this technique if one is careful, and does not try to do too much hammering between annealing operations.

Cut a disc of the required size and draw the series of concentric circles. Start the raising operation on the sandbag. After annealing, place the work on the raising stake and begin hammering by going round and round. It is important to hold the work on the stake in such a manner that the blows land just above the point where the metal touches the stake, Fig. 20-30.

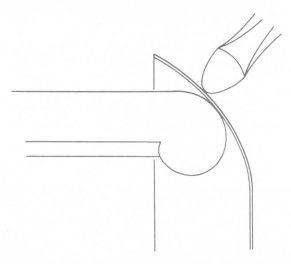

Fig. 20-30. Strike the bowl at a point just above where it touches the stake.

From this point, the above operations are repeated until the desired height is reached. After annealing and pickling, the piece is trimmed, planished and polished.

BEATING DOWN

A rather simple way of sinking shallow trays and plates is by beating down portions of the metal over a hardwood stake, Fig. 20-31.

Develop the pattern. Use guide lines to indicate the portion to be beat down. Allow an additional one-quarter inch of material outside the rim guide lines to offset the drawing-in effect of this method of forming.

Hold the metal blank over the wood block with the inner guide line about one-eighth inch

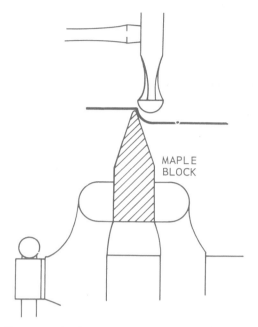

Fig. 20-31. Beating down a tray on a maple block.

back from the edge of the block. Hammering is done with a forming hammer. Rotate the blank slightly after each series of blows until the desired depth is reached. Use a cardboard or metal template to check the progress.

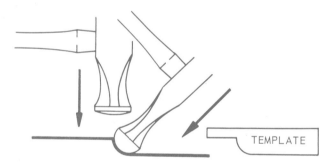

Fig. 20-32. Working edge to clean sharp corner.

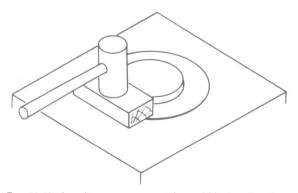

Fig. 20-33. Leveling unevenness with wood block and mallet.

A clean sharp edge at the point where the depression meets the rim, is made by the alternate use of a planishing hammer and forming hammer, Fig. 20-32, on a plate and tray stake or a hardwood block.

Trim, planish and polish.

As work done by this method has a tendency to warp slightly, it must be flattened by placing on a flat, clean surface, and using a wooden block and mallet to hammer the surface true, Fig. 20-33.

PLANISHING

Planishing is the process of making the surface of the metal smooth by hammering with a planishing hammer, Fig. 20-34. Only a hammer

Fig. 20-34. Planishing on a stake.

with a mirror smooth face should be used. Planishing does not change the shape of the piece appreciably; but rather, should true it and remove any irregularities from the surface.

The hammer blows should be laid on evenly, with the work being rotated slowly so that no two blows fall in the same place. Select a stake with a curvature as near to the desired shape as possible.

SOLDERING

Soldering, both soft and hard types, are explained in detail in Unit 29. This section will be concerned with how to solder pewter and how to bind and support work for soldering.

SOLDERING PEWTER

Pewter, being almost pure tin, can be soldered so readily that it is difficult to detect a properly made joint. A 60-40 solder (60 per cent tin - 40 per cent lead) is well suited for joining pewter. For some work, snippets of pewter itself are recommended. However, they should not be used until considerable soldering experience has been gained. In soldering pewter, it

Fig. 20-35. Soldering pewter with a blowpipe and alcohol lamp.

is important that the flame be kept moving constantly. A blowpipe and alcohol lamp are commonly used, Fig. 20-35. A soldering copper is NEVER used.

Flux is also necessary when soldering pewter. A suitable flux may be made by adding 10

drops of hydrochloric acid to one ounce of glycerine. Commercial fluxes are available. Wash excess flux from joint after soldering.

BINDING WORK FOR SOLDERING

In order to secure satisfactory joints and to prevent the pieces from slipping while being soldered, it is frequently necessary to bind the pieces together with wire. Soft iron wire in sizes 18 and 24 are commonly used.

Considerable ingenuity must sometimes be employed to bind the various pieces together for soldering. Three ideas are shown in Fig. 20-36.

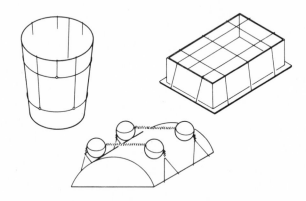

Fig. 20-36. Typical binding setups, as used to prevent movement of the pieces during soldering.

POLISHING

Polishing actually starts when the joints and edges are first filed. The care taken from this point on will determine the final polish. Full details on metal are included in UNIT 32.

TEST YOUR KNOWLEDGE, Unit 20

1. Annealing is the process of _____ metal by heating and allowing it to cool under controlled conditions.
2. _____ is the operation that is used to remove the oxide scale that forms on most metals during annealing.
3. _____ does not need to be pickled because no oxide scale forms during annealing.
4. When making the pickling solution, the acid should be poured into the water. True or false?
5. Goggles need not be worn if the hot metal is held at arms length and dropped into the pickling solution. True or false?
6. Annealing and pickling operations are seldom part of the same work sequence. True or false?
7. Internal designs are cut into metal by a technique called _____.
8. Repousse' is a French word meaning:
   a. To thrust back.
   b. Sculpturing in metal.
   c. Chasing.
   d. None of the above.
9. Raising is the process of _____
   _____.
10. _____ are used to support metal while it is being worked.

RESEARCH AND DEVELOPMENT

1. Visit a nearby museum and study samples of art metalwork made by well-known craftsmen.
2. Secure catalogs from sources that sell pieces which are recognized as being of good design and quality. Use the photos and drawings as design suggestions for your work.
3. Invite a local craftsman to demonstrate how he produces art metalwork.
4. Design and craft a pewter or sterling silver chalice of traditional colonial style for your church.
5. Many early pieces that fall into the art metal category were stamped with a touch mark. What was its purpose?
6. Design and craft an award to be presented to the outstanding student craftsman.

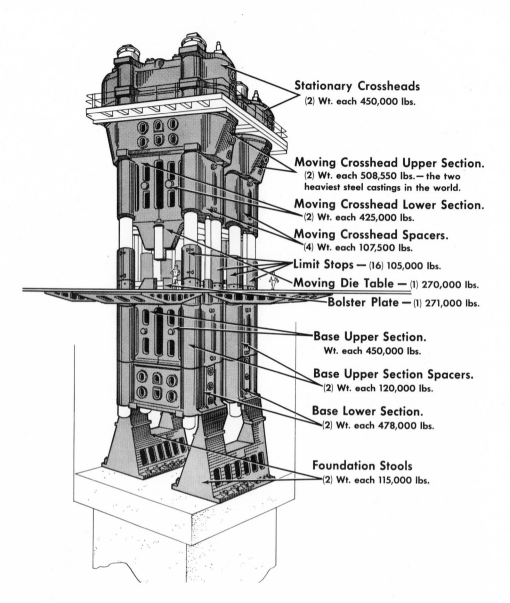

Stationary Crossheads
(2) Wt. each 450,000 lbs.

Moving Crosshead Upper Section.
(2) Wt. each 508,550 lbs.— the two
heaviest steel castings in the world.

Moving Crosshead Lower Section.
(2) Wt. each 425,000 lbs.

Moving Crosshead Spacers.
(4) Wt. each 107,500 lbs.

Limit Stops — (16) 105,000 lbs.

Moving Die Table — (1) 270,000 lbs.

Bolster Plate — (1) 271,000 lbs.

Base Upper Section.
Wt. each 450,000 lbs.

Base Upper Section Spacers.
(2) Wt. each 120,000 lbs.

Base Lower Section.
(2) Wt. each 478,000 lbs.

Foundation Stools
(2) Wt. each 115,000 lbs.

*Equipment used in modern industry--a giant hydrau-
lic die forging press with 50,000 ton capacity.
(Mesta Machine Co.)*

Unit 21

SAND CASTING

The technique of making a sand mold casting in the school shop is similar to that used by industry. The major differences concern casting size, and quantity of castings produced.

The manufacture of castings is a two-step operation. The first step is to convert the raw exact size of the article to be cast, in a medium suitable for holding the molten metal.

Sand was perhaps the earliest material used for mold making and is still the most widely used material although other materials, described in later Units, are being used to pro-

Fig. 21-1. Converting raw materials into molten metal.
(Reading Gray Iron Castings)

materials into molten metal of the proper temperature and chemical composition, Fig. 21-1.

The second step is to prepare the MOLD, Fig. 21-2. A mold is a cavity or opening the duce an increasingly larger percentage of castings.

The sand may be used in the moist state. A mold made with moist sand is called a GREEN

Fig. 21-2. The floor or pit mold illustrated is to be used to cast the stationary crosshead for a huge Forging Press. The finished casting will weigh 450,000 lbs.
(Steel Founders' Society of America)

Fig. 21-4. Hand molding of loose work which is gradually disappearing due to modern equipment. The setting of cores is also shown.

SAND MOLD. Or, it may be held together with plastic binders and baked dry, to form a DRY SAND MOLD. A dry sand mold is more costly to produce, but it turns out a more accurate casting. Green sand molding is the most widely used method in the production of castings. Sand molds can be used only once as they must be destroyed to remove the finished casting. The green molding sand is a mixture of sand grains, clay, water and other materials that serve as binders. In industry the ingredients are blended together in MULLING MACHINES, Fig. 21-3.

Fig. 21-5. Modern motive sand slinger for floor work. The machine moves from mold to mold packing sand around the patterns.
(Reading Gray Iron Castings, Inc.)

Fig. 21-3. Modern mulling equipment for producing molding sands.
(Reading Gray Iron Castings, Inc.)

Fig. 21-6. An overhead sand unit and molding station for light squeezer work. The squeezer packs small molds that were at one time rammed up by hand.

The sand mold is made by packing the sand in a box called a FLASK, around a PATTERN of the shape to be cast. Hand ramming of sand around the pattern is rarely used today except under special circumstances, Fig. 21-4. Today, a SAND SLINGER, Fig. 21-5, or a JOLT SQUEEZE

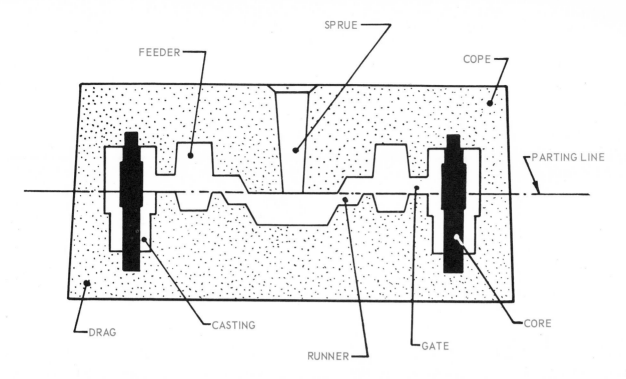

FEEDER — SPRUE — COPE

PARTING LINE

DRAG — CASTING — RUNNER — GATE — CORE

Fig. 21-7. Sectional view of a typical two-part mold, showing cope and drag, cores in place, casting cavity, sprue, runners and gates.

MACHINE, Fig. 21-6, is generally used to pack the sand in the mold. To allow for easy removal of the pattern, the flask is made to separate horizontally at a point called the PARTING LINE. When the pattern has been DRAWN (removed) from the mold and the two mold halves, called the COPE and the DRAG, are reassembled,

SAFETY

1. Never pour a casting unless you are wearing protective clothing and goggles.
2. Moisture and molten metal react violently. Under no condition should moist or wet metal be added to molten metal.
3. Place hot castings where they will not cause accidental burns or fires.
4. Keep the foundry area clean.
5. Be sure your safety clothing is in first-class condition.
6. Do not talk with anyone while pouring a casting.
7. Stand to one side of the mold as you pour, never directly in front of it. Steam is generated during the pouring operation and may scald you. Molten metal may spurt from the mold if it is too moist.
8. Clamp or weight down molds of large castings to prevent the mold from floating and permitting molten metal to escape from the mold at the parting line.

a cavity remains. The molten metal reaches the cavity through the GATING SYSTEM, which consists of vertical openings called SPRUES, through horizontal distribution channels, RUNNERS, and finally through the GATES to the cavity proper, Fig. 21-7.

Because metals shrink as they cool, provisions must be made to supply additional metal to those parts of the casting that freeze last, or voids and hollows will occur in the finished casting. These reservoirs of molten metal are called FEEDERS or RISERS.

Holes and cavities are often required in castings. They are made by inserts of sand called CORES, Fig. 21-8. The cores are fitted into po-

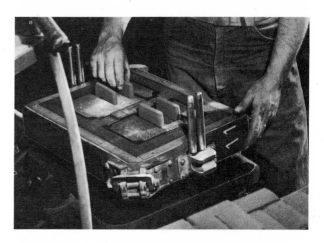

Fig. 21-8. Setting cores in a squeezer mold before closing it.

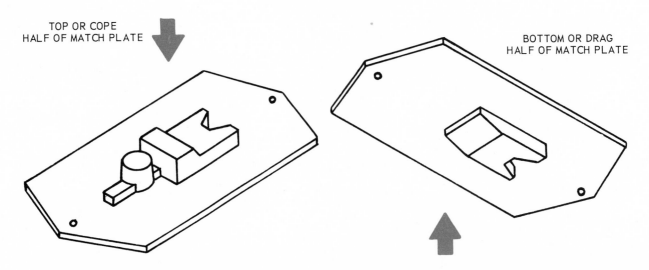

TOP OR COPE
HALF OF MATCH PLATE

BOTTOM OR DRAG
HALF OF MATCH PLATE

Fig. 21-9. Drawing of a match plate showing both the top and the bottom. The plates are usually made from metal and are used when the production run is large enough to justify the expense.

sition in the mold cavity before the mold is closed. They are knocked out of the finished casting.

The PATTERNS that shape the mold cavities are usually made from wood, if production is of a limited nature. For longer production runs, MATCH PLATES, Fig. 21-9, are used. A match plate is a plate of metal on which the pattern and gating system is split along the parting line and mounted back to back to form a single piece.

Fig. 21-11. Pouring a floor mold. The casting will weigh about 800 lbs.

Fig. 21-10. A view of a foundry. The photo shows squeezer machines in the background, completed molds awaiting pouring, and in the foreground molds being poured.
(Steel Founders Society of America)

After the mold has been prepared, the necessary cores inserted, and the mold halves closed, the mold is moved to the pouring area, Fig. 21-10, and is poured by the foundryman, Fig. 21-11.

Fig. 21-12. Castings being cleaned. Small castings are cleaned in the roto-blast barrel at the left. Larger castings are cleaned on the table to the right.

When the mold has solidified, it is taken to the "shake-out" area where the sand is broken from around the casting and cleaned, Fig. 21-12. From here it is inspected, passes through chipping and grinding, and is then ready for shipment to the customer.

METAL CASTING IN THE SCHOOL SHOP

In order to produce a sound casting in the school shop, a similar sequence of operations must be followed.

PATTERNMAKING

A pattern is used to make a cavity in the sand mold into which the molten metal is poured. A SIMPLE PATTERN, Fig. 21-13, is made in

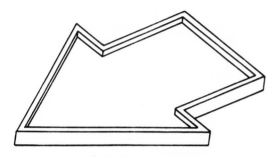

Fig. 21-13. A simple pattern.

one piece. More complex patterns, for round or irregular shaped work, are made in two or more parts and are called SPLIT PATTERNS, Fig. 21-14.

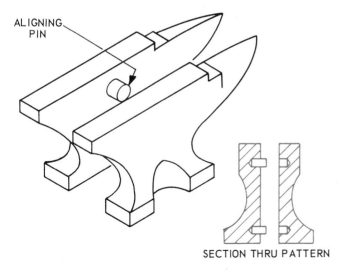

ALIGNING PIN

SECTION THRU PATTERN

Fig. 21-14. A split pattern. The point of separation is the parting line of the mold.

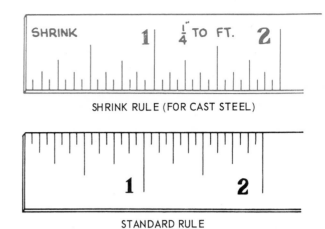

SHRINK   1   ¼" TO FT.   2

SHRINK RULE (FOR CAST STEEL)

1   2

STANDARD RULE

Fig. 21-15. The shrink rule takes into consideration the amount the metal will shrink as it cools after casting. A different shrink rule must be used to make the pattern for each type of metal used.

As metal contracts when it cools, patterns must be made oversize to allow for shrinkage. A SHRINK RULE, Fig. 21-15, on which the inch measurements are slightly larger than the standard inch, is used by the PATTERNMAKER when constructing a pattern. This rule allows for dimensional changes as the casting cools.

A pattern must have DRAFT, Fig. 21-16, if it is to be pulled from the sand without damaging

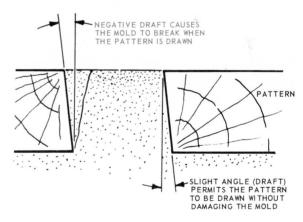

NEGATIVE DRAFT CAUSES THE MOLD TO BREAK WHEN THE PATTERN IS DRAWN

PATTERN

SLIGHT ANGLE (DRAFT) PERMITS THE PATTERN TO BE DRAWN WITHOUT DAMAGING THE MOLD

Fig. 21-16. Draft permits the pattern to be lifted from the sand without damaging the mold.

the mold. Sharp inside corners are to be avoided whenever possible. When they do occur on a pattern, they may be rounded off with FILLETS, Fig. 21-17, made of wax, leather or wood.

SAND CORES

Sand cores are used to make openings in the casting. Special sands are mixed with binders and rammed into a CORE BOX, Fig. 21-18, that has been made to produce cores of the proper dimensions. Cores must be baked in a carefully controlled temperature to make them hard

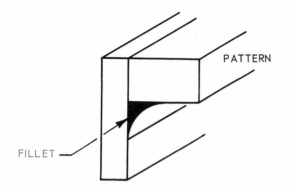

FILLET

PATTERN

Fig. 21-17. A typical fillet.

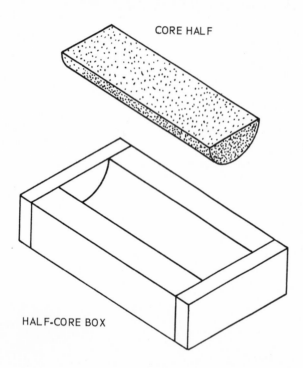

CORE HALF

HALF-CORE BOX

Fig. 21-18. The two core halves will be cemented together to form an opening in a casting.

enough to withstand the pressures of casting. Cores of complex shapes may be made in several sections and cemented together.

Industry makes wide use of cores made from a mixture of sand and waterglass into which carbon dioxide gas has been released, Fig. 21-19. The technique can be adapted to school shop foundry work.

Fig. 21-19. Cores being solidified with CO_2. The carbon dioxide is injected into the specially prepared sand core with a long slender tube.

MOLDING SAND

Sand must possess three qualities before it can be used to make molds. It must:

1. Withstand the heat of the molten metal without breaking down.
2. Hold the shape of the mold cavity while the metal is being poured.
3. Be porous enough to permit gases generated when the molten metal comes in contact with the moist sand, to escape.

Sand must be TEMPERED or dampened enough to be workable. After mixing water and

Fig. 21-20. Properly tempered sand.

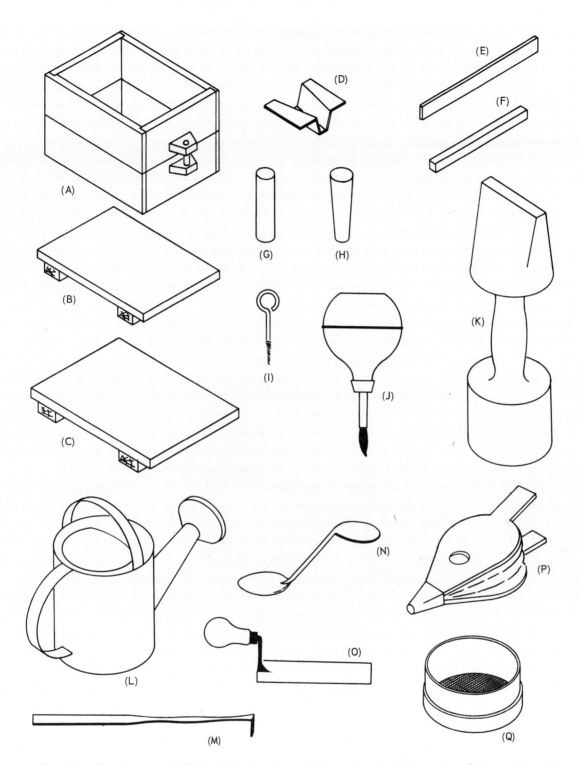

Fig. 21-21. Foundry tools. (A) Flask; (B) Molding board; (C) Bottom board; (D) Gate cutter; (E) Strike-off bar; (F) Rapping bar; (G) Riser pin; (H) Sprue pin; (I) Draw screw; (J) Bulb sponge; (K) Bench rammer; (L) Sprinkling can; (M) Lifter; (N) Slick and oval; (O) Trowel; (P) Molder's bellows; (Q) Riddle

sand thoroughly, test by squeezing a hand full of sand and breaking it in two. When properly tempered, the sand will bear the imprint of your fingers and break cleanly, Fig. 21-20. It will crumble when too dry and sand will adhere to your hands if it is too moist.

TOOLS AND EQUIPMENT

Tools and equipment needed for foundry work in the school shop are shown in Fig. 21-21. How these items are used will be explained and illustrated as they are needed to make a mold.

MAKING A SIMPLE MOLD

1. Temper the molding sand.
2. Select or make the required pattern. Clean the pattern and remove any rough spots.
3. Position the DRAG on the MOLDING BOARD with the aligning pins pointing downward, Fig. 21-22.
4. Place the pattern on the molding board near the center of the flask. The flat back of the pattern should be placed on the board, Fig. 21-22.
5. Dust the pattern lightly with PARTING COMPOUND. This is a waterproof material that prevents the moist sand from adhering to the pattern and allows the sand on the parting surfaces of the cope and drag to separate without clinging.
6. Sift a 1-in. layer of molding sand over the pattern with the RIDDLE. The sand is riddled to reduce it to fine loose particles, Fig. 21-23.
7. Pack the riddled sand around the pattern with your fingers. Roughen the surface of the packed sand and fill the flask with unriddled, tempered sand, Fig. 21-24.
8. Use the PEEN end of the BENCH RAMMER and pack the loose sand firmly around the pattern and the inside edges of the flask, Fig. 21-25.
9. Add sufficient additional sand to permit the drag to be fully packed with sand. Use the BUTT end of the rammer, Fig. 21-26.
10. Strike off the excess sand with the STRIKE-OFF BAR, Fig. 21-27.
11. Place the BOTTOM BOARD on the top of the

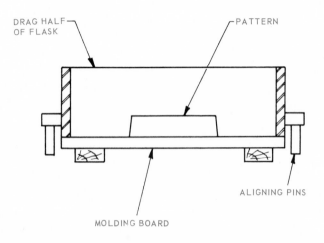

Fig. 21-22. Drag and pattern are in position on the molding board ready to receive the sand.

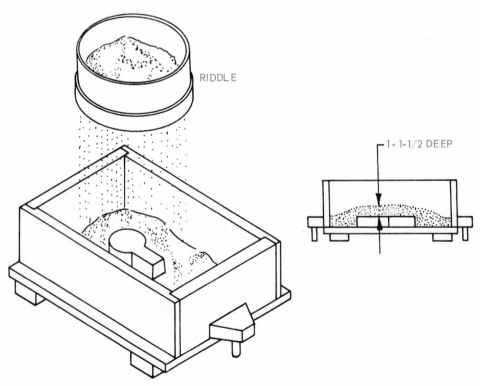

Fig. 21-23. Sand is riddled over the pattern until it is about 1-1/2 in. deep. Riddling removes debris from the sand that is packed around the pattern.

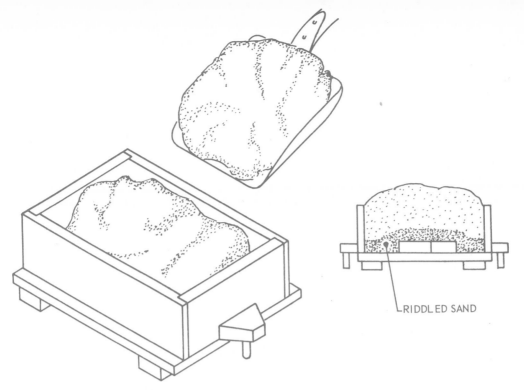

Fig. 21-24. Filling of drag is completed with unriddled sand.

RIDDLED SAND

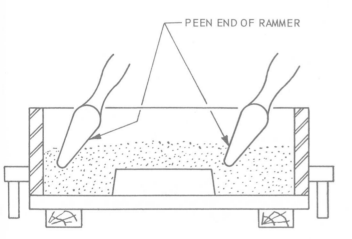

PEEN END OF RAMMER

Fig. 21-25. Ramming sand around pattern with the peen end of the bench rammer.

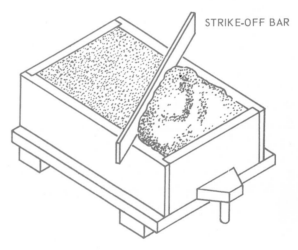

STRIKE-OFF BAR

Fig. 21-27. Packed sand is leveled with the strike-off bar.

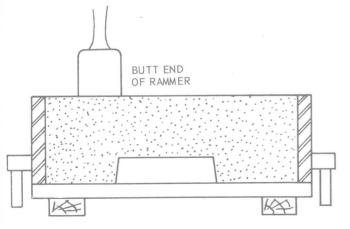

BUTT END OF RAMMER

Fig. 21-26. Packing sand in the drag is completed with the butt end of the bench rammer.

drag and ROLL (turn) it over. The aligning pins will point upwards, Fig. 21-28.

12. Expose the pattern by removing the molding board. Examine the sand surface and, if necessary, smooth and level the sand with a TROWEL or SLICK.

13. Place the COPE on the drag and press the SPRUE and RISER PINS in the sand in the drag about 1 in. away from each end of the pattern, Fig. 21-29. The riser pin should be located near the heaviest section of the pattern.

14. Dust the entire unit with parting compound. This will prevent the surfaces from sticking together when the cope is separated from the drag.

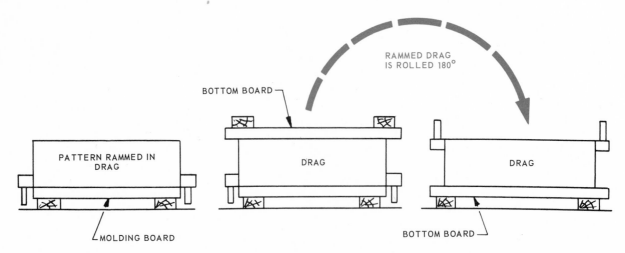

Fig. 21-28. Rolling the drag over.

15. Riddle, ram and strike off the sand in the cope as was done before. Take care not to pack the sand too tightly.
16. Most molds require venting to permit the gases to escape. Pierce the mold with a

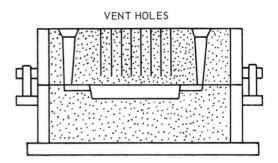

VENT HOLES

Fig. 21-30. Vent holes.

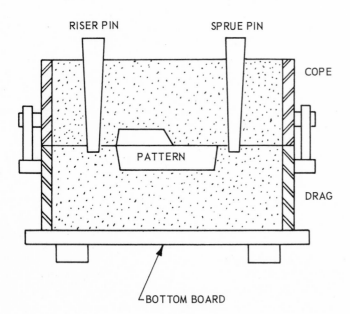

RISER PIN   SPRUE PIN

COPE

PATTERN

DRAG

BOTTOM BOARD

Fig. 21-29. The sprue and riser pins are placed about 1-in. away from the pattern.

VENT WIRE. The vent holes should almost, but not quite, touch the pattern, Fig. 21-30.
17. Remove the sprue and riser pins and smooth the resulting holes into a funnel shape, Fig. 21-31, with your fingers.
18. Carefully lift the cope from the drag and place it on edge to one side where it will not be damaged.

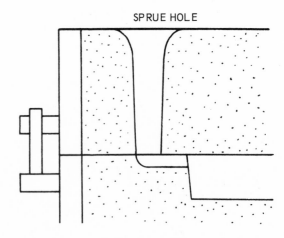

SPRUE HOLE

Fig. 21-31. Properly shaped sprue hole.

19. Moisten the sand around the edge of the pattern with the BULB SPONGE. This prevents the sand from breaking up when the pattern is drawn, Fig. 21-32.
20. Insert a DRAW SCREW into the pattern near its center. Tap the screw lightly with the

RAPPING BAR to loosen the pattern in the mold.

21. Carefully draw the pattern from the mold. Steady your hand on the flask to prevent the edge of the cavity from being damaged by the pattern.

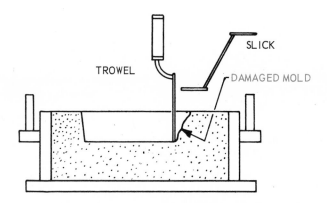

Fig. 21-33. Repairing a damaged mold.

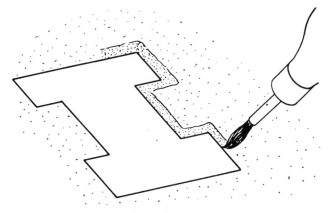

Fig. 21-32. Sand is dampened around the pattern to prevent the sand from breaking up when the pattern is removed from the mold.

22. Repair any defects in the mold with the SLICK and SPOON, Fig. 21-33.
23. Cut a GATE from the mold cavity to the

sprue hole and to the riser hole with the GATE CUTTER, Fig. 21-34. This should be about 1/2 in. wide and 1/2 in. deep. Smooth the resulting surfaces with your finger or a slick.

24. Remove any loose sand particles that are in the mold cavity using a MOLDER'S BELLOWS.
25. Replace the cope on the drag.
26. Remove the entire unit to the pouring area and let it dry for a short time.

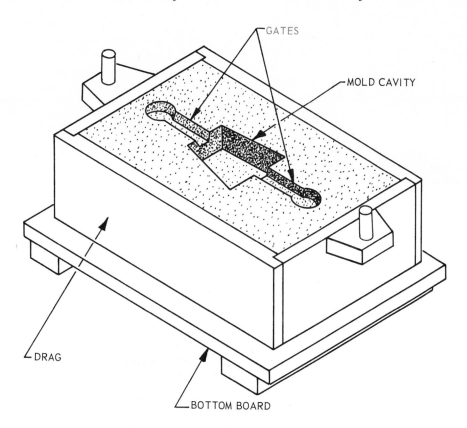

Fig. 21-34. Metal enters the mold cavity through the gates.

27. Pour molten metal into the sprue hole carefully and rapidly. Hold the ladle or crucible close to the surface of the mold. Large molds may have to be weighted or clamped

of heating these metals to the correct pouring temperature. Other metals, like type metal, lead, pewter and the zinc alloys (garalloy), are used when smaller quantities are needed. These can

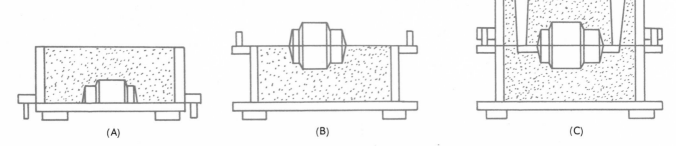

Fig. 21-35. Ramming up a split pattern. (A) Pattern half with aligning holes is rammed first. (B) After drag is rolled over, the pattern half with aligning pins is put in place. (C) Mold is rammed up in conventional manner.

to prevent the cope from FLOATING and permitting the molten metal from flowing out of the mold at the parting line.

28. Allow the casting to cool, then break the mold from around it.

Molds that require the use of a split pattern are made in much the same manner. The major deviation involves the use of the pattern. It is made in two parts, one of which is fitted with aligning pins (dowels), the other has the holes into which the pins fit. The pattern half with the holes is rammed up in the drag. The second half, the one with the pins, is put on after the drag has been rolled over, Fig. 21-35.

MELTING METAL

While almost any metal can be melted and cast, aluminum and brass are most frequently cast in the school shop. A gas fired CRUCIBLE FURNACE, as shown in Fig. 21-36, is capable

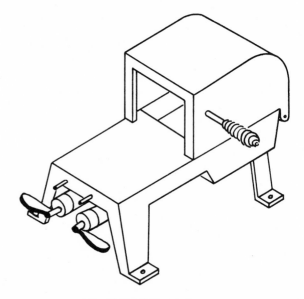

Fig. 21-37. Soldering furnace.

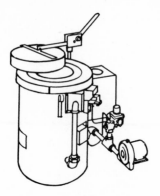

Fig. 21-36. Crucible Furnace. (Johnson Gas Appliance)

be melted in a SOLDERING FURNACE, Fig. 21-37, because of their lower melting temperature.

Aluminum and brass are melted in a graphite CRUCIBLE, Fig. 21-38. This type container is capable of withstanding the higher temperature. The crucible is removed from the furnace with CRUCIBLE TONGS, Fig. 21-39, and placed in a CRUCIBLE SHANK, Fig. 21-40, for pouring.

As metals are melted, they absorb impurities from many sources. A FLUX must be added to remove them. In most cases it is added while the metal is melting. However, with aluminum and its alloys, flux should be added just prior to pouring.

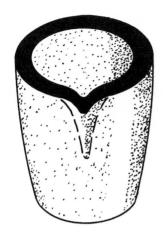

Fig. 21-38. Clay graphite crucible.

POURING THE METAL

Get a sufficient quantity of metal together before lighting the furnace. Take care that different metals are not mixed in accidentally. Secure a crucible of the correct size, add the metal and insert the crucible into the furnace.

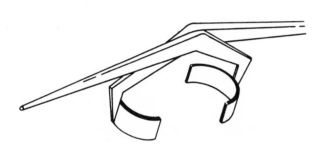

Fig. 21-39. Crucible tongs.

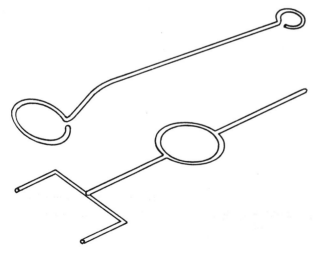

Fig. 21-40. Crucible shank. Above. One-man type. Below. Two-man type.

Light the furnace and allow the metal to come to pouring temperature. If additional metal must be added to the crucible, take every precaution to prevent metal with moisture from being added to the molten metal. WATER AND MOLTEN METAL REACT VIOLENTLY WHEN THEY COME IN CONTACT WITH ONE ANOTHER. KEEP THEM SEPARATE.

Check frequently as the metal approaches pouring temperature. This can be done visually or with a PYROMETER, Fig. 21-41. A pyrometer measures the temperature with extreme accuracy. Do not permit the metal to become overheated as this will produce defective castings. Upon reaching the proper temperature, add the flux and stir it in. The impurities will rise to the surface as SLAG. Skim off the slag.

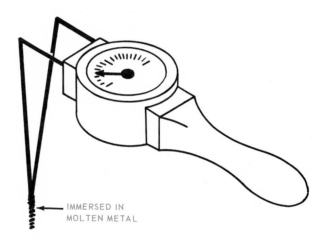

IMMERSED IN MOLTEN METAL

Fig. 21-41. Immersion-type pyrometer.

The high temperatures needed to melt aluminum and brass for casting makes protective clothing mandatory. Goggles, asbestos gloves (gauntlet type), leggings and apron must be worn.

Turn off the furnace and remove the crucible of molten metal from the furnace with crucible tongs and insert it in the crucible shank for pouring. STAND TO ONE SIDE OF THE MOLD AS YOU POUR, NEVER DIRECTLY OVER IT. Steam is generated when the metal is poured into the mold and may burn you. Also, molten metal may spurt out if the mold is too moist.

Pour the metal as rapidly as possible. Stop when the riser and sprue holes remain full. Return the crucible to the furnace and allow it to cool slowly. Surplus metal should be poured into an ingot mold.

Allow the casting to cool, then SHAKE OUT

(break up) the mold. When the casting is cool enough to handle with bare hands, cut off the metal that forms the sprues and risers. The casting is then ready for machining and finishing.

TEST YOUR KNOWLEDGE, Unit 21

Matching questions. Each word in the left column matches one of the sentences. Place the letter of the word in the appropriate blank space.

a. Flask
b. Cope
c. Drag
d. Green sand mold
e. Mold
f. Gating system
g. Mulling machine
h. Parting line
i. Core
j. Split pattern
k. Simple pattern
l. Draft
m. Riddle
n. Bench rammer
o. Crucible

1. ___The container in which metal is melted.
2. ___The sieve that breaks the sand down into fine loose particles.
3. ___The box into which the sand is packed to make the mold.
4. ___Mold made with moist sand.
5. ___The opening or cavity in the sand into which the molten metal is poured to produce the required casting.
6. ___The bottom half of the flask.
7. ___The machine that mixes the sand.
8. ___The device used to pack sand in the flask.
9. ___How the molten metal reaches the mold.
10. ___The top half of the flask.
11. ___A single piece pattern.
12. ___Necessary if the pattern is to be removed from the sand without damaging the mold.
13. ___A pattern made in two or more parts.
14. ___Point at which the flask comes apart.
15. ___Inserts to make holes and cavities in castings.

16. Sand molds can be used more than once. True or false?
17. Casting metal is a relatively new process. True or false?
18. The match plate is used for production casting. True or false?
19. The foundryman makes the mold. True or false?
20. The shrink rule is used by the pattern maker in place of the standard rule. True or false?
21. Molding sand must be tempered before it can be used to make a mold. True or false?
22. Excess sand is removed from a rammed drag with the strike-off bar. True or false?
23. List the three qualities needed in a molding sand.
    a._____.
    b._____.
    c._____.
24. Flux is used to _____ _____ _____ _____ _____.

RESEARCH AND DEVELOPMENT

1. Visit a local foundry. Use a portable tape recorder to record a description of what you see and hear as you follow the mold making sequence from start to finish. Play back the recording to the class.
2. If you do not have access to a tape recorder, secure samples of the various ingredients a foundry uses in the production of a casting. Secure plastic pill bottles from a drug store to display them.
3. Prepare a chart that will show the procedure followed in making a casting. Mount samples of ingredients used on the panel chart.
4. Secure a sample of a commercially made casting as it comes from the mold, and a similar casting after it has been cleaned and the sprues and gates have been removed.
5. Present a motion picture on the casting process.
6. Prepare a sand mold with a core, and use it as the center of a display in the school exhibition case. Use colored twine to lead from the mold to the tools used to make the mold.
7. Prepare and cast a mold with a core.

Unit 22

PLASTER
MOLD CASTING

In this foundry process the mold is made of plaster or primarily of plaster in combination with sand. The use of plaster molds makes it possible to produce castings of very intricate design. As a matter of fact, some of the castings are so complex, Fig. 22-1, that they must be

remove all traces of moisture. The mold segments are again inspected and then assembled into a single mold with a plastic resin cement, Fig. 22-3. After assembly, the entire mold is fired again to set the cement after which it is sent to the foundry for casting. Plaster molds

Fig. 22-1. Checking dimensional accuracy of a tire mold tread ring made by the plaster cast process. Note the intricate tread design and the smooth surface finish. These are characteristic of the process.
(Aluminum Co. of America)

made in sections. These sections are cast in plaster in plastic molds, Fig. 22-2, and when the plaster has "set" sufficiently they are removed, inspected and fired in low temperature ovens to

of this type can be used only once as they must be broken up to remove the casting.

Recent improvements have made it possible to adapt this method of shaping metal to modern

Fig. 22-2. Pouring plaster segments for the tire mold tread ring. Supports have been inserted in the tread mold to provide additional strength to the mold.

Fig. 22-3. Assembling plaster segments into mold for the tire mold tread ring. The pieces are cemented together.
(Aluminum Co. of America)

production techniques. The plaster mold process combines the intricacies of sand casting with the close dimensional accuracies and smooth surface finishes usually associated with die castings. Another advantage of this process is that the dried plaster mold has less chilling action on the metal being cast than a sand or metal mold. This makes it possible to cast thinner sections than with the normal sand or permanent mold.

Plaster molds have been successfully to produce turbines in the automatic transmission of an automobile, Fig. 22-4. These parts, cast in aluminum, weigh about 10 lbs. and are about 14 in. in diameter. However, parts up to 40 in. in diameter and up to 300 lbs. have been cast experimentally.

Fig. 22-4. Cast aluminum automatic transmission parts. The turbines contain from nineteen to thirty-three intricately formed blades.
(Aluminum Co. of America)

SAFETY

1. If you attempt to prepare a plaster mold one point of safety cannot be overemphasized. DO NOT POUR MOLTEN METAL INTO A PLASTER MOLD UNTIL THE MOLD IS THOROUGHLY DRY.
2. Wear protective clothing and goggles.
3. Do not place hot castings where they might cause a serious burn.
4. Moisture and molten metal are very dangerous when they are combined. DO NOT ATTEMPT TO REMELT A PIECE OF METAL THAT HAS BEEN COOLED IN WATER UNTIL ALL TRACES OF MOISTURE HAS EVAPORATED.

TEST YOUR KNOWLEDGE, Unit 22

1. Plaster molds are fired at low temperature in an oven to remove all traces of moisture because:
   a. The moisture will cause the molds to break down.
   b. The moisture will create steam when it comes into contact with molten metal and literally cause the mold to explode.
   c. The mold cannot be handled when it is moist.
   d. None of the above.
2. Plaster molds used to make complex castings

are made in several sections or pieces. These
pieces must be aligned and fastened together
with:

a. Pins.

b. Screws.

c. Nails.

d. None of the above.

3. Many plaster molds are made in _____
because of the complex shape of the object
that is to be cast.

RESEARCH AND DEVELOPMENT

1. Simple plaster molds can be made in the
school shop. Develop several small molds to
cast such objects as buttons, soldiers, and
model boat fittings. Experiment with several
gating arrangements until the most satisfactory casting is made.

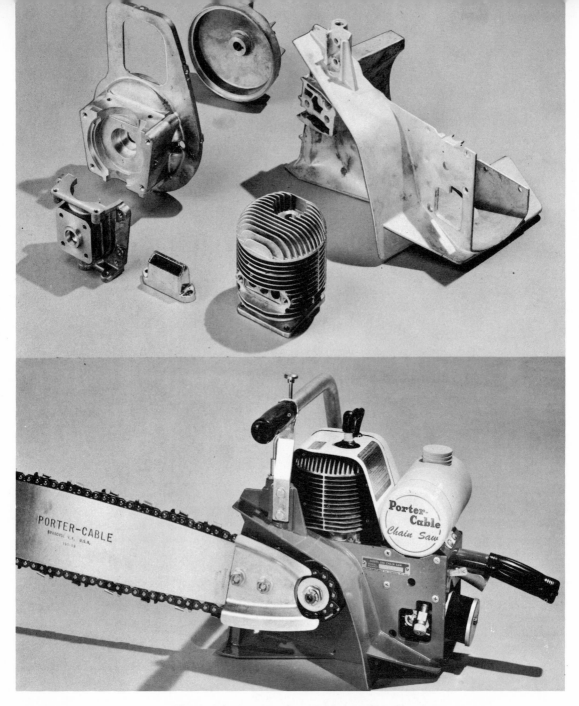

Aluminum die castings shown in the top photo form the
principal parts of the chain saw shown in the lower photo.
(American Die Casting Institute)

Unit 23

DIE CASTING

DIE CASTING is one of the most important and versatile quantity production processes used by the American metalworking industry. In this process molten metal is forced into a DIE or MOLD under pressure. The pressure is maintained until the metal has solidified at which time the die is opened and the cast piece is ejected, Fig. 23-1. After the casting has been removed, the die is closed and the cycle is ready to be repeated. To run this cycle at a high rate of speed a die casting machine is used. The cycle speed, or the number of castings that can

Fig. 23-1. View of an automobile engine block casting operation. The photo shows a 2,000-ton casting machine, with the ejector half of the die in the machine. The mechanism mounted on the upper bars of the machine automatically removes the casting from the die, and loads the cylinder liners into the machine. (Doehler-Jarvis Div., National Lead Co.)

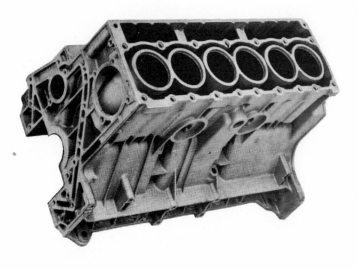

Fig. 23-2. Die cast aluminum engine block. The block weighs 68 lbs., including 14 lbs. of cast iron cylinder liners.

be produced per hours, is governed by the casting size, its complexity, and the alloy used to cast it.

A DIE CASTING, the term also used to de-

scribe the casting made by the above process, is characterized by dimensional accuracy and its sharply defined smooth surfaces, Fig. 23-2. When properly designed a die casting requires little finish machining.

As in other casting processes, after the die casting is formed and removed from the die (or mold), the sprue and runners must be cut or broken off and the flash that forms at the die parting line must be trimmed off. Simple machines are used to perform this operation.

TYPES OF DIE CASTING MACHINES

In die casting machines it is very important that the dies are securely locked in the machines. The greater the locking pressure the higher the metal injection pressure which in turn means better castings. All modern die casting machines have safety devices that prevent the injection of the metal into the die until the machine is securely locked closed, and does not allow the die to be opened until the metal has solidified.

Die casting machines vary fundamentally

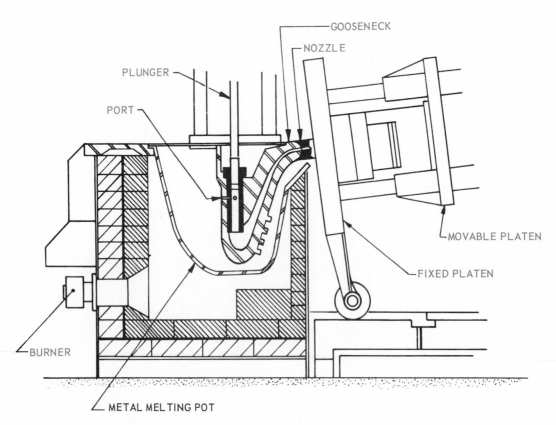

Fig. 23-3. Cross section of a portion of a Plunger Die Casting machine for zinc alloy, showing a vertical plunger actuated by compressed air or hydraulic pressure. (American Die Casting Institute)

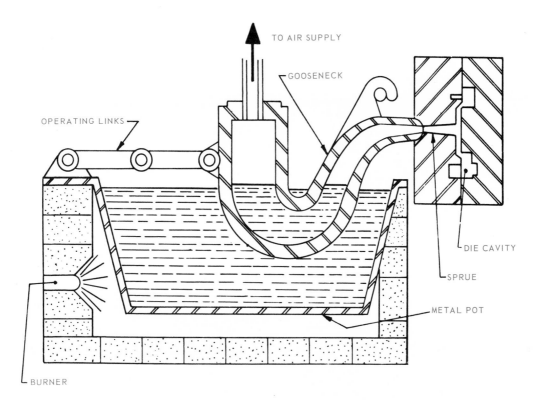

OPERATING LINKS

TO AIR SUPPLY

GOOSENECK

DIE CAVITY

SPRUE

METAL POT

BURNER

Fig. 23-4. Diagram showing the arrangement of an air injection machine having a horizontal nozzle in position for filling a die by air pressure without a plunger.

only in the method of injecting metal into the die, and are classified as follows:

1. PLUNGER (Hot Chamber)
2. AIR INJECTION
3. COLD CHAMBER

PLUNGER type die casting machines, Fig. 23-3, are primarily designed for casting zinc alloys and metals of low melting temperatures. In this machine there is a main metal pot in which is immersed a fixed cylinder having a spout that is firmly connected against or connected with the die. A plunger operates in the cylinder. When the plunger is raised, it uncovers a port or opening that is below the metal level, and molten metal fills the cylinder. When the plunger is forced downward, the metal in the cylinder is forced out through the spout into the die, which has been locked in place securely. As soon as the metal has solidified in the die, the plunger is withdrawn, the die is opened and the casting is ejected. Then the die is closed and locked into position, and the cycle is repeated.

The AIR INJECTION die casting machine, Fig. 23-4, has a chamber (called a "gooseneck") that contains the desired amount of molten metal. This gooseneck usually is supported above a larger metal pot and is filled by dipping the spout

into the metal. The spout of the gooseneck is locked against the die. Air under pressure forces the molten metal through the spout into the die.

The air pressure is released after the metal in the die hardens and the gooseneck is lowered, breaking it away from the die, to be refilled. The die is opened and the die casting is ejected. Relocking the die and bringing the spout into position readies the machine for another cycle. This type machine is used chiefly to cast aluminum alloys, but it can be used for alloys of lower melting points.

The COLD CHAMBER machine, Fig. 23-5, differs from the plunger type machine only in that the injecting plunger and cylinder are not submerged in the molten metal. The metal is still forced into the die by a hydraulically operated plunger, but the metal is poured into the "cold chamber" through a port or pouring slot by a ladle which holds only enough metal for one die filling. Immediately after the ladle is emptied the plunger advances, seals the port, and forces the charge into the die.

As the molten metal does not remain very long in the "cold chamber" the higher melting point metals, like the copper alloys, can be cast in this type machine. It operates at a much

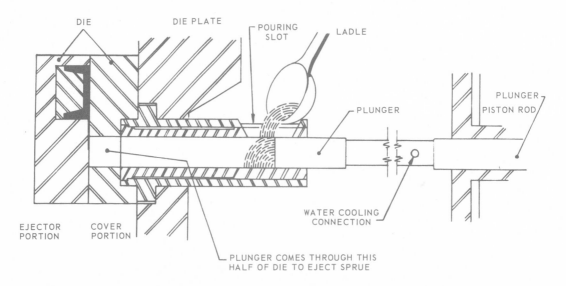

DIE   DIE PLATE   POURING SLOT   LADLE

PLUNGER

PLUNGER PISTON ROD

WATER COOLING CONNECTION

EJECTOR PORTION   COVER PORTION

PLUNGER COMES THROUGH THIS HALF OF DIE TO EJECT SPRUE

Fig. 23-5. Sectional diagram showing the die, cold chamber, and horizontal ram or plunger (in charging position) of a modern cold chamber type of die casting machine.

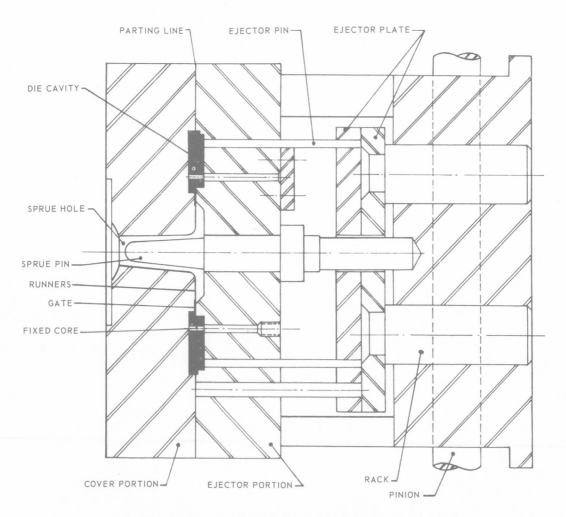

PARTING LINE   EJECTOR PIN   EJECTOR PLATE

DIE CAVITY

SPRUE HOLE

SPRUE PIN

RUNNERS

GATE

FIXED CORE

COVER PORTION   EJECTOR PORTION   RACK

PINION

*Fig. 23-6. Cross section of a typical die in which the parts are identified.
(American Die Casting Institute)*

slower cycle rate than the other two types. In all cases, enough metal is charged to more than fill the die. A slug which is left at the end of the cylinder is either sheared off, or is left to be ejected with the casting.

DIES USED IN DIE CASTING

Steel is nearly always used to make the dies used in the die casting process. The dies used for the higher melting point alloys must be hardened. Dies must be highly polished if they are to produce castings of exceptional smoothness.

The die is constructed of two or more parts, Fig. 23-6. Two-part dies are composed of the cover half (on the side toward the metal pot or cold chamber) which is usually fixed to the front of the machine; and the ejector half (to which it is intended to have the casting adhere) which is movable, and permits the ejector pins that pass through this half of the die to push the casting from the die.

Molten metal enters the die CAVITY (the opening in the mold in which the piece is cast) through a series of passages called SPRUES,

GATES and RUNNERS. These openings distribute the metal so that the die cavity is properly filled. When molten metal enters the mold, the air within the cavity must be expelled through vents on the PARTING LINE of the die. These are often shallow passages, frequently only 0.005 in. deep, and are partially filled by metal which forms FLASH. The metal solidifies almost instantly which prevents molten metal from squirting through the die where the two parts join.

Some dies have only a single cavity. Others have several cavities for simultaneous filling. If all of the cavities are identical, the dies are called "multiple-cavity" dies. If different shapes of cavities are provided, the dies are called "combination" dies. The latter are often used to produce several parts for the same assembly.

DIE CASTING ALLOYS

Only nonferrous alloys are suitable for die casting and the range of these, though more limited than for sand castings, is adequate for most needs. Alloys based on zinc account for most of the die castings. Next in approximate order come the alloys based on aluminum, copper, magnesium, lead and tin.

TEST YOUR KNOWLEDGE, Unit 23

1. In die casting, the molten metal is forced into the mold under_____.
2. The cycle of the die casting machine refers to:
   a. The sequence followed to make a casting.
   b. The speed at which the machine operates.
   c. The number of castings produced per hour.
   d. None of the above.
3. A die casting requires a great deal of finishing before it can be used. True or false?
4. The die in die casting is the same as a mold. True or false?
5. Which of the following metals cannot be

die cast:
   a. Cast iron.
   b. Aluminum.
   c. Copper based alloys.
6. One very important safety device is built into every die casting machine:
   a. The machine will not operate if the metal supply is low.
   b. An inexperienced operator cannot operate the machine.
   c. Molten metal cannot be injected into the mold until it has been locked in place.
   d. None of the above.

Modern Metalworking

RESEARCH AND DEVELOPMENT

1. Prepare a display board showing the die casting cycle. Illustrate the various steps with drawings and photos taken from booklets and advertisements prepared by die casting producers.
2. Produce transparencies of the three die casting machines and a die for use on the overhead projector.
3. Secure several castings made by the die casting process. Locate the parting lines of the mold parts. Can you detect the number of parts of the mold?
4. Make a small panel that will illustrate the differences between a die casting and a sand casting. Use actual castings.
5. Try to locate and arrange to visit a plant that makes castings by this technique. If this is not possible, try to secure die castings before the sprues and flashings are removed.

Scene in a small foundry--Pouring molten metal into sand floor molds.

23-6

Unit 24
PERMANENT MOLD CASTING

Fig. 24-1. The permanent mold used to produce the crankcase front of a miniature gasoline engine.

Fig. 24-2. Pouring molten aluminum into a permanent mold. (Aluminum Co. of America)

Some molds used for metal casting are made of metal. These molds are called PERMANENT MOLDS because they do not have to be destroyed to remove the castings, Figs. 24-1, 2, 3. The process produces castings with a fine surface finish and a high degree of accuracy. Permanent molds are generally used with lower melting temperature metals, although the process has been used to cast iron and steel products. The higher melting temperature alloys require special surface finishes for the molds to protect them from the heat.

The fishing sinker and toy soldier molds are familiar samples of the permanent mold process. The process is also used to cast such items as automobile and truck pistons, home appliance parts and many other familiar items.

A variation of the permanent mold casting process is known as SLUSH MOLDING. Molten metal, usually alloys of zinc, lead or tin, is

Fig. 24-4. Master pattern used in Dip Molding. (Cerro Sales Corp.)

Fig. 24-3. Removing initial core from large permanent mold casting prior to taking iron mold away from the casting. Molds and cores are re-usable thousands of times.

master pattern, Fig. 24-4, is dipped into a container of molten metal, Fig. 24-5, and is immediately removed. During this brief period of contact a shell of metal freezes to the pattern. This shell is easily removed, Fig. 24-6, and forms a mold. Electronic components are positioned inside the mold and the resin is poured

poured into the mold and left long enough to form a thin shell of metal in the mold. The remaining metal is poured out leaving a hollow casting. This process is primarily used to cast inexpensive toys and the souvenirs found at most places of historical interest.

DIP MOLDING is a form of slush casting. It is used in the electronics industry in making electronic components. A highly polished metal

Fig. 24-5. Dipping master into container of molten metal.

in. After a sufficient curing period the mold is peeled from the unit, Fig. 24-7. The process has much to recommend it. Close tolerances specified for military components present no problems. It is economical because the male

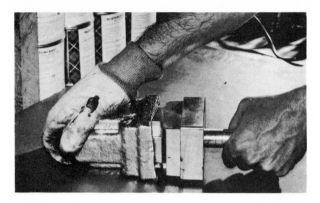

Fig. 24-6. Removing thin metal shell from master pattern.

master is easier to machine than its female counterpart. The mold metal can also be used over and over again.

Fig. 24-7. Stripping thin metal shell from around electronic component after the encapsulating plastic has cured. The metal will be remelted and used again. (Cerro Sales Corp.)

The permanent mold is also used in the CENTRIFUGAL CASTING process. The mold is rotated rapidly while the molten metal is poured into it. Centrifugal force presses the molten metal against the wall of the mold producing a very fine smooth finish, and a casting with a fine grain metal structure. The process is widely used to cast pipe, gun tubes and items of cylindrical form.

TEST YOUR KNOWLEDGE, Unit 24

1. Permanent mold is the term applied to molds that:
   a. Do not wear out.
   b. Do not have to be destroyed to remove the casting.
   c. Protect the casting.
   d. None of the above.

2. The_____and_____are familiar examples of this casting process.
3. In_____, molten metal is poured into the mold and left long enough to form a thin shell of metal in the mold.
4. The mold is rotated while the molten metal is poured into it in the_____process.

RESEARCH AND DEVELOPMENT

1. Try to secure samples of items made by the various permanent mold processes. Prepare a display panel that shows, with a series of colored drawings, how they were made.
2. Prepare a series of projectuals for the overhead projector that illustrate how the four permanent mold processes work. Write a script on the processes and record it. Pre-

sent the slides and recording the class, or as a display in the school library.
3. Secure or make samples of permanent molds and demonstrate them to the class. For safety reasons, you may want to record the demonstrations on 35mm slides for presentation. A recording can be made as described in No. 2.

The advent of the jet engine and the need for components made from corrosion and heat resistant metals has stimulated the development of Investment Castings as a modern industrial technique.
(U. S. Air Force)

Unit 25

INVESTMENT CASTING

INVESTMENT or LOST WAX CASTING is primarily a precision method of molding castable metals and alloys that are difficult to work, and parts which, because of their complex shape or intricate design, are expensive to machine.

In the Investment Casting process, patterns made of wax or plastic are placed in a refractory plaster mold (mold that will withstand heat). After the mold has hardened, it is placed in an oven and heated until the wax or plastic material

Fig. 25-1. Multiple cavity mold prepared from oversize metal master patterns, ready for injection.

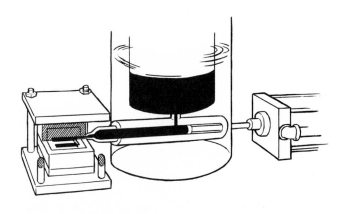

Fig. 25-2. Wax injected into mold under pressure, to insure maximum uniformity and dimensional accuracy.

Fig. 25-3. Wax patterns removed from mold and inspected for accuracy and surface smoothness.

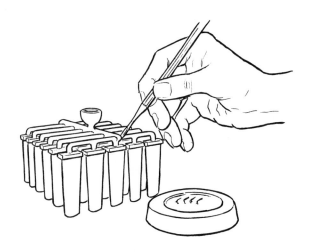

Fig. 25-4. Sections of wax patterns grouped into a cluster of patterns, for mass production of castings.

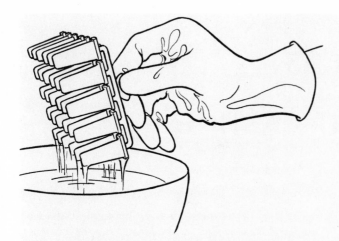

Fig. 25-5. Cluster of patterns coated with primary investment, to promote smooth castings and intricate detail.

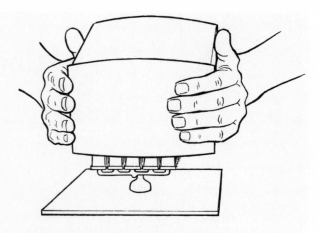

Fig. 25-6. Encased with high temperature metal rings, the cluster is made ready for secondary investment.

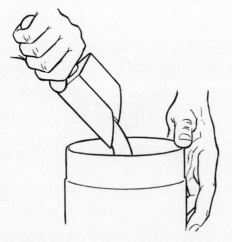

Fig. 25-7. The refractory mold is filled with secondary investment, vibrated, hardened, steamed, and made ready for the furnace.

Fig. 25-8. Mold removed from furnace after proper drying and heating, is directly clamped to casting furnace.

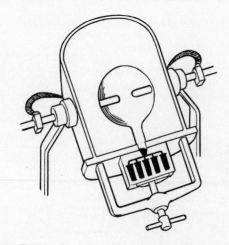

Fig. 25-9. The casting furnace is inverted and the molten metal under pressure is cast into its final form.

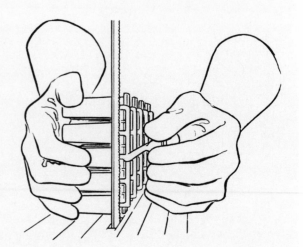

Fig. 25-10. Removing sprues and gates from the completed casting.

(Figs. 25-1 to 25-12 - Austenal Co. Div. of Howe Sound Co.)

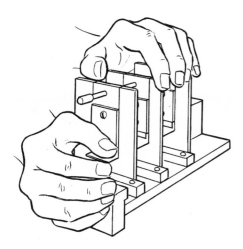

Fig. 25-11. Parts are inspected for dimensional accuracy; then X-ray and Zyglo inspected for sound structure, if required.

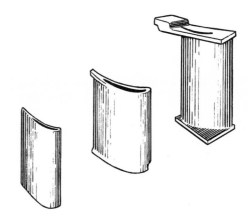

Fig. 25-12. Typical examples of Microcast parts--turbine blades for Allison, General Electric and Pratt and Whitney turbines.

is burned out. This leaves a cavity in the mold the shape of the pattern. Molten metal is forced into the mold cavity. After solidifying, the metal is broken from the mold and the casting goes through finishing operations, as required.

The drawings, Figs. 25-1 to 25-12 incl. illustrate the fundamentals of the Investment Casting process.

The Dental profession makes wide use of this process, in casting stainless steel and silver to exact specifications. The Medical profession makes considerable use of the process too in

making such items as pins for repairing of fractures, and to replace bone sections and joints.

Investment Casting has been developed to the point, economically, where it can compete with other machining and casting processes, and is being widely used to produce parts that were originally made by other methods. Casting sizes vary from a fraction of an ounce to several pounds.

The complex contoured metal turbine blades that are corrosion and heat resistant, used by jet engines, are a good example of modern use of the Investment Casting process.

TEST YOUR KNOWLEDGE, Unit 25

1. Investment casting is also known as _____ _____ _____.
2. Investment casting patterns are made of _____ or _____.
3. Investment casting is a technique which makes it possible to:
   a. Lower the cost of making simple castings.
   b. Use one pattern over and over again.
   c. Cast metals that are difficult to machine.
   d. None of the above.
4. The _____ and _____ profession also makes wide use of the technique.
5. All castings made by this process weigh less than a pound. True or false?

RESEARCH AND DEVELOPMENT

1. Visit your dentist or local dental supply house to see how the dental profession makes use of investment casting. Give a short report on what you were able to learn.
2. Prepare a short paper on the professional life of Benvenuto Cellini. Try to secure photographs, pictures or drawings of his more famous work. Visit the museum and inquire if any of his work is on display.
3. Give a demonstration on how investment casting is done. It can be done inexpensively and with limited equipment by using plaster of

Paris for the mold, wax for the pattern and lead or type metal for the metal.

CAUTION: Allow the plaster to dry thoroughly before pouring in the molten metal. The heat that was applied to melt the wax pattern often is not hot enough to dry the plaster completely. WEAR GOGGLES WHEN POURING MOLTEN METAL.

4. Show a motion picture on investment casting.
5. Make arrangements for visiting a foundry making castings by this method.
6. Secure samples of objects made by this technique. Mount them on a panel and prepare a series of drawings that show the steps followed to turn out a casting by investment casting.

Unit 26

SHELL MOLDING

SHELL MOLDING is a foundry process in which the molds are made in the form of thin shells. Castings produced by this process have a superior finish and improved dimensional accuracy over castings produced in green sand molds. Shell molds can be used to produce castings with thin sections or of intricate designs because they contain very little moisture to chill the molten metal as in other kinds of molds. This results in savings in machining costs. Machining operations can often be eliminated completely.

The process is well adapted to mass-production techniques. Two men operating four-station shell molding and closing machines, as in Fig. 26-1, can produce up to 240 molds per hour. The finished molds can be easily stored.

Shell molds are made in the following sequence of operations:

1. The metal pattern, Fig. 26-2, is inserted in the molding machine, Fig. 26-3. Castings produced from the mold made with this pattern will be the crankshaft for an outboard motor.

2. After the pattern has been set in the molding machine, a water jacketed flask over the pattern, Fig. 26-4, holds a measured volume of mix consisting of thermosetting resin and sand. This material adheres to the heated pattern and the sand and resin fuse to form a thin plastic shell. Water cooling of the flask prevents a buildup of

Fig. 26-1. A typical shell molding operation. The four-station shell molding machine and controls are on the right. The four-station shell closing machine is at the left. Sand and resin storage is behind the shell molding machine.

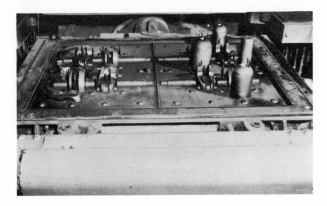

Fig. 26-2. Note metal patterns used to make molds for crankshafts. The four cylindrical objects on the cope half (right) are risers which are connected to the casting and provides liquid metal to the casting during the period the casting is solidifying to compensate for the internal shrinkage of the casting as it cools and solidifies. Patterns are inserted in the Molding Machine shown in Fig. 26-3.

Fig. 26-3. Four-station shell molding machine. Each station performs a different operation automatically: 1. Loading with resin and sand then the roll over motion to remove the excess sand; 2. and 3. Curing stations where desired mold hardness is obtained; 4. The ejection of the finished shell.

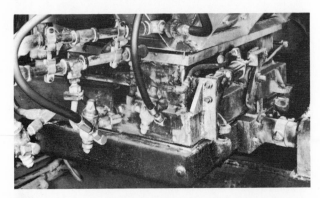

Fig. 26-4. The water jacketed flask is fitted over the heated metal pattern and holds the resin and sand mixture. The water cools the flask and prevents the buildup of sand on the inside of the flask.

Fig. 26-5. The roll over operation dumps the excess sand and resin leaving a thin, soft shell on the face of the pattern. The surplus sand and resin mix are recycled back into the sand handling system.

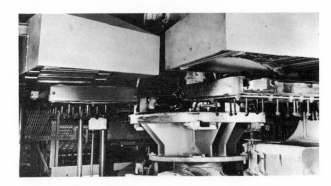

Fig. 26-6. Mold curing stations where the desired mold hardness is obtained. These stations (2) are fitted with infrared heaters.

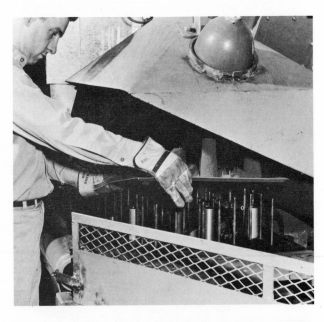

Fig. 26-7. After the shell has been cured properly it is automatically ejected by the machine.

the mix on the inside of the flask.

3. Excess sand is removed by a roll-over operation, Fig. 26-5. The flask is removed and the thin soft shell on the face of the pattern moves on through curing stations where the desired hardness is obtained, Fig. 26-6.

4. The finished mold is automatically ejected by the machine, Fig. 26-7. This particular shell consists of a cope half and a drag half which are easily separated by the machine operator.

5. The drag half (left), and the cope half, Fig. 26-8, move on to the closing machine.

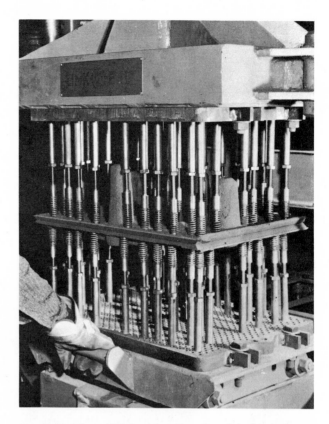

Fig. 26-10. The mold halves are clamped until the bonding agent has cured. Close tolerances obtained by the shell molding process minimize objectional fins on finished castings.

Fig. 26-8. Completed mold halves ready to have the cores, if needed, inserted. This shows patterns for two crankshaft castings.

Fig. 26-9. At the closing machine the cope and drag are united for bonding. The mold halves are held together with adhesives, however, in some instances the shells are joined together with clamps.

Fig. 26-11. The lightweight shell molds can be stored easily, without loss of their dimensional accuracy.

(Photos 26-1 to 26-11 incl., courtesy of Link-Belt Co.)

6. At the closing machine, Fig. 26-9, the cope is placed on the drag on which cores have been set in place and adhesive has been applied to the two mold pieces.

7. The halves are bonded together, Fig. 26-10. The molds can be used immediately or stored for an indefinite period, Fig. 26-11.

8. After the molten metal has been poured, Fig. 26-12, and solidified, the molds are "shaken out." That is, the mold is broken from around the casting. The casting is cleaned by shot blasting and after it is heat treated, it is machined.

The nature of the shell molding process permits it to be fitted into limited spaces. The use of shells permits an almost dustless operation from the preparation of the mold to final shake out of the castings. Waste sand and cores are quickly disposed of, in contrast to the large volume of hot sand which must be handled and disposed of in the conventional sand mold process.

Fig. 26-12. A foundry man pouring molten metal into a shell mold. (Union Carbide Corp., Bakelite Div.)

Shell Molding

TEST YOUR KNOWLEDGE, Unit 26

1. Castings made by shell molding have the following advantages over sand castings:
   a. Are more accurate and have a better surface finish.
   b. Castings with thin sections and intricate designs can be produced.
   c. Well suited to mass-production techniques.
   d. All of the above.
2. In shell molding wooden patterns are used. True or false?
3. The sand is held together with a resin mixture. True or false?
4. Excess sand is brushed off by the operator. True or false?
5. Shell molding requires a large space in the foundry. True or false?
6. The sand mixture used in shell molding is used several times before it is scrapped. True or false?
7. Castings are cleaned by _____ _____.

RESEARCH AND DEVELOPMENT

1. Contact a local foundry that uses the shell molding technique and request a mold sample. If this is not possible, try to secure a casting made by the process. Compare it with a sand casting and evaluate it with respect to:
   a. Surface finish.
   b. Dimensional accuracy.
   c. Fins on the parting line.
   Prepare a short report on what you found.
2. Shell molds have been produced in the school shop. Investigate the possibilities of preparing shell molds in your school shop, and, if possible, prepare a few experimental molds.
3. Prepare diagrams showing the manufacturing sequence of shell molding, for reproduction by the spirit duplicator process. Present copies to members of the class. Such information may be secured from companies that make shell molds, and companies that manufacture machines to make them.

Industry photo--Removing spurs and gates from
completed castings in Westinghouse plant.

Unit 27

WROUGHT METAL

Wrought ironwork was originally metal hardware shaped by the colonial blacksmith. His work was not only decorative; it was highly functional, Fig. 27-1. Today the iron hand railing, porch supports, and some forms of metal

Fig. 27-1. Colonial wrought ironwork was functional as well as attractive.

Fig. 27-2. Contemporary ironwork.

furniture are synonymous with wrought ironwork, Fig. 27-2. Wrought ironwork is presently also known as ornamental ironwork and bench metal.

Wrought iron is almost pure iron with most of the carbon removed. It is easily bent, hot or cold, and may be readily welded. However, many hot rolled steel shapes can be, and are frequently used for contemporary wrought ironwork because they are less costly.

BENDING AND FORMING WITH HAND TOOLS

Metal bars, flats and rods often need to be bent to usable shapes. Metal up to 1/4 in. thick can be bent cold. Heavier sections should be heated.

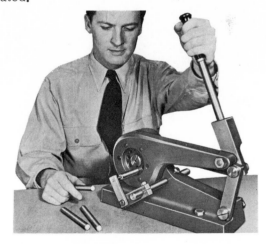

Fig. 27-2a. Metal rod being cut with a rod parter.

While the metal rods may be cut with a hacksaw, considerable time can be saved if a ROD PARTER, Fig. 27-2a, is used. The cutting head is designed to accommodate several different rod sizes. The rod is inserted into the appropriate opening and with the application of pressure the rod is sheared or cut.

BENDING ANGLES

Several factors must be considered when making a bend in metal:

1. Allowance must be made in the layout for the thickness of the metal. One-half of its thickness must be added to the length for each bend.

2. If several bends must be made in the same piece, the bending sequence must be planned beforehand or difficulties may be encountered, Fig. 27-3.

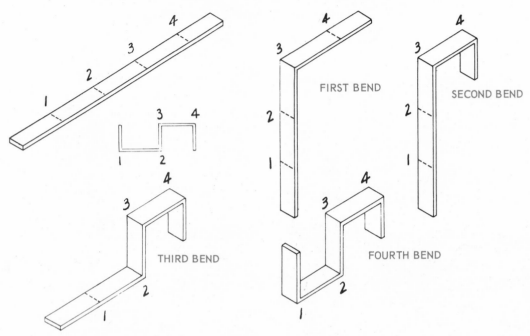

Fig. 27-3. Plan the bending sequence with care.

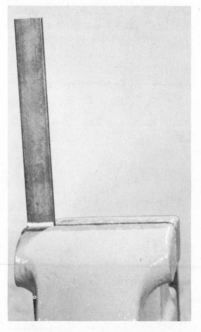

Fig. 27-4. An allowance of one-half the metal's thickness must be added to the total length of the piece for each bend. The section with this additional length is placed above the vise.

Most metal bends can be made in a heavy vise. After making the layout, place the metal in the vise with the extra material allowed for the bend projecting above the vise jaws, Fig. 27-4. Start the bend by striking the metal with the flat of the hammer near the vise, Fig. 27-5. Square the bend, if it is a right angle bend, by placing the metal in the vise parallel with the vise jaw, Fig. 27-6.

Acute angles, angles less than 90 deg., are made by squeezing the metal in a vise after the initial bend has been made, Fig. 27-7. Obtuse angles, those more than 90 deg., can be made by using a monkey wrench as the bending tool, Fig. 27-8.

Angular bends can be made in sheet metal by placing the metal between two pieces of angle iron or wooden blocks held in a vise, and using a mallet to make the bend, Fig. 27-9.

TWISTING METAL

Metal is, at times, twisted to permit it to be fastened, for additional stiffness or to break the

SAFETY

1. Remove burrs from the stock before attempting to make bends.
2. Have any cuts, bruises and burns treated promptly.
3. Keep fingers clear of moving bender parts.
4. Do not use a bending machine without studying or receiving instructions, or checking over the machine.
5. Wear approved safety glasses when cutting metal with a chisel or when operating the grinder.
6. Use extreme care when handling long sections of small diameter rods. Carelessness can cause serious injury to nearby persons.
7. Finishing materials are never used near an open flame nor in an area that is not properly ventilated. Store oily and solvent soaked rags in a closed container.

Fig. 27-7. Acute angles, those less than 90 deg. are made in the vise after the initial bend has been made.

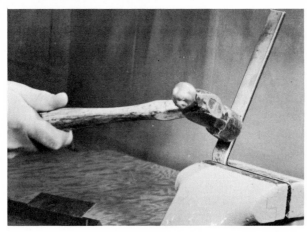

Fig. 27-5. Start the bend by striking the metal close to the vise.

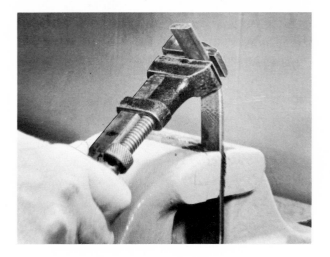

Fig. 27-8. Obtuse angles, those more than 90 deg., may be made with the aid of a monkey wrench.

Fig. 27-6. Square the bend by placing the piece in the vise parallel to the jaws.

Fig. 27-9. When bending thin metal, mount it between two pieces of angle iron or blocks of hardwood.

monotony of a long flat surface, Fig. 27-10.

Lay out the section to be twisted. As the length of the metal decreases when it is twisted, cut the piece slightly longer than the finished

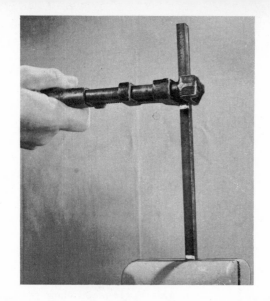

Fig. 27-12. The monkey wrench is placed even with the upper limit mark.

Fig. 27-10. Twisted sections.

Fig. 27-11. The lower limit mark is placed flush with the vise jaws.

piece. Place short pieces vertically in the vise with the lower limit mark even with the top of the vise jaw, Fig. 27-11. Long strips should be clamped in a horizontal position. Place a monkey wrench at the other limit mark and rotate it to twist the metal, Fig. 27-12. A piece of pipe slipped over long sections will help keep them

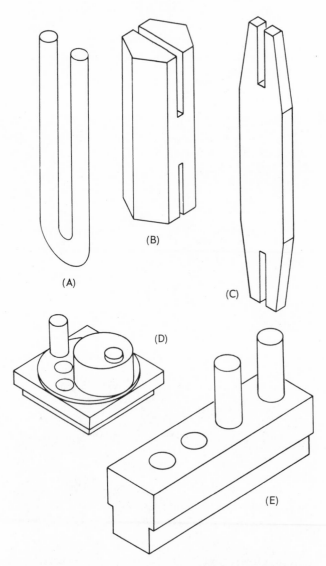

Fig. 27-13. Bending jigs. (A) Bending fork. (B) Hexagonal bar with slots for bending. (C) Bending fork machined from flat metal stock. (D) Adjustable bending device. (E) Bending block with movable pins.

from bending out of line during the twisting operation. Rotate the wrench clockwise for a right hand twist; counterclockwise for a left hand twist.

Minor straightening of a twisted section can be done with a mallet.

BENDING CIRCULAR SHAPES

Curved sections can be made over the edge or horn of the anvil or with a bending jig or bending fork, Fig. 27-13. Whatever method is used, it is advisable to make a full-size pattern of the required curved section, Fig. 27-14. This is used to check the curves during the bending operation.

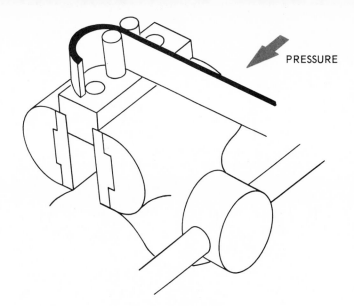

Fig. 27-16. Bending a scroll.

The SCROLL is a curved section widely used for decorative purposes. It is not a true circle but a curve with a constantly expanding radius - something like a loose clock spring, Fig. 27-15. The scroll is made by placing the metal in a bending jig and applying pressure to start the curve, Fig. 27-16. After starting the bend, the operation is repeated to form a portion of the scroll at a time until it is completed, Fig. 27-17.

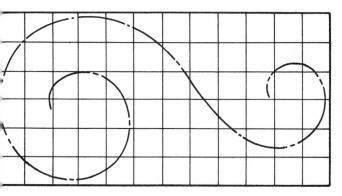

Fig. 27-14. Make a full-size pattern or layout of the desired curved section.

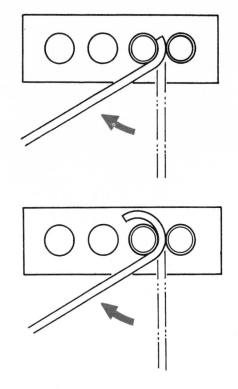

Fig. 27-17. A section of the scroll is bent at a time.

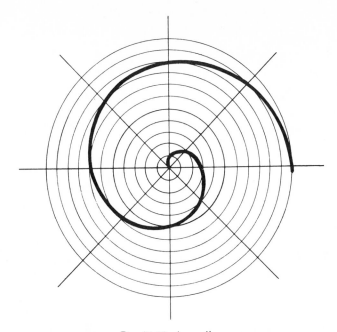

Fig. 27-15. A scroll.

Check the curve against the pattern from time to time to assure accuracy.

Some scroll applications require the starting

end of the section to be flared or decorated, Fig. 27-18. This must be done before starting the bending operation.

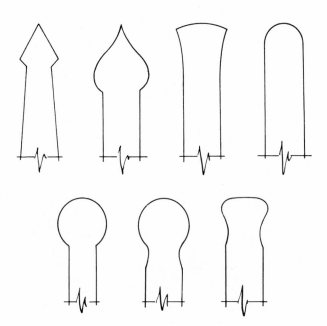

Fig. 27-18. Typical scroll ends.

Often a scroll is required on both ends of the piece. Care must be taken in bending them so that they blend together smoothly, Fig. 27-19.

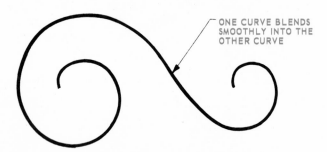

ONE CURVE BLENDS SMOOTHLY INTO THE OTHER CURVE

Fig. 27-19. Double end scroll.

Curves of a given radius can be formed by several techniques:

1. Place the work in the vise with a piece of rod or pipe with a diameter equal to the inside diameter of the required curve. Pull the metal forward and as the curve takes shape, loosen the vise and move the work further in and around the pipe; reclamp it as before, and repeat the operation until the curved section is completed, Fig. 27-20. The same technique can be used to

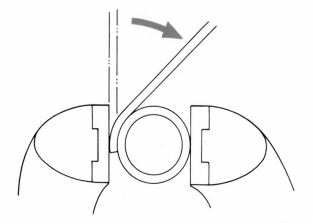

Fig. 27-20. Forming a radius in a vise.

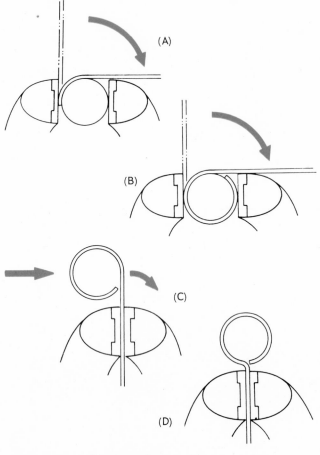

(A)

(B)

(C)

(D)

Fig. 27-21. Forming an eye.

shape an eye on the end of a rod, Fig. 27-21.

2. Shape the curve by bending it over a piece of pipe or rod of the correct diameter held in a vise, Fig. 27-22.

3. Bend it over a stake, Fig. 27-23.

Fig. 27-22. Bending over a metal rod.

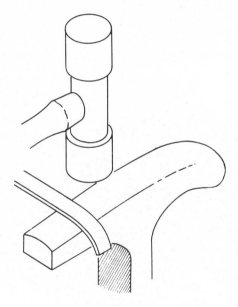

Fig. 27-23. Bending over a stake.

Wire rings are made by bending wire around a rod with a diameter equal to the inside diameter of the ring to form a coil, Fig. 27-24. The coil is cut along its length and the resulting rings can be closed or fitted together to make a section of wire chain. Weld or solder the joints if desired.

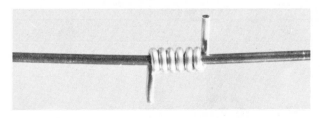

Fig. 27-24. Forming a wire coil.

BENDING AND FORMING WITH SPECIAL TOOLS

Several bending machines have been developed that have light production and school shop applications. All of them, basically, are means of applying power either manually or mechanically to perform the bending operation.

When using bending machines, certain elementary principles must be observed:

1. Plan the bending sequence BEFORE cutting the metal. Do not fail to make allowances for the bends.
2. Select material sizes that will provide sufficient strength and rigidity and yet permit satisfactory bending.
3. Use the largest bend radius that is practical for the job. This will often produce a better bend in both strength and appearance.
4. The smallest recommended radius for bending tubing is one and one-half times its outside diameter measured on the centerline of the tubing provided an inside mandrel is used during bending. The bend radius must be increased to two and one-half times the tubing diameter if no mandrel is used.
5. When making a bend at the end of a piece of tubing, allow sufficient metal for trimming; otherwise, the tubing will flatten.
6. Allow for metal springback when planning a bend. Use a bending form with a radius slightly smaller than the required radius. As springback varies with metal thickness, sample bends may have to be made to determine the proper size bending form needed.
7. Study the instruction book for the machine being used.

METL-FORMER

The METL-FORMER, Fig. 27-25, is a modified machinist's vise to which forming rolls have been adapted. The design provides accurate control of the work. Various interchangeable accessories permit the tool to be used to bend, shape and form tubing, rods and sheet into intricate shapes.

HOSSFELD UNIVERSAL BENDER

The HOSSFELD BENDER, Fig. 27-26, is designed to permit bar, angle iron, rod and pipe

Fig. 27-25. The Metl-Former. (Swayne, Robinson & Co.)

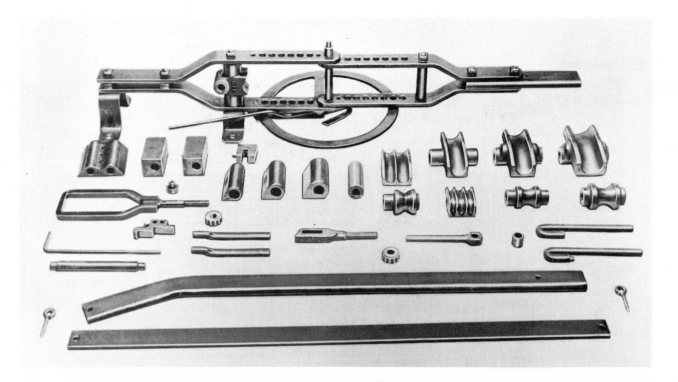

Fig. 27-26. Universal Bender with a few of the attachments available. (Hossfeld Mfg. Co.)

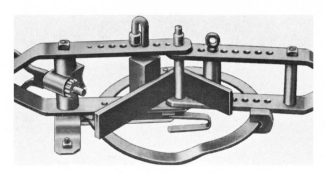

Fig. 27-27. Technique used to bend flat stock.

Fig. 27-28. Bending flat stock into a radius.

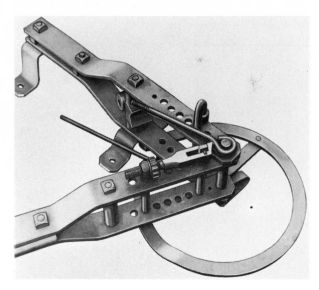

Fig. 27-29. Setup for bending an eye.

sizes and shapes.

Bender setup for making various bends are illustrated in Figs. 27-27, 27-28, and 27-29.

DI-ACRO BENDER

DI-ACRO BENDERS, both hand and power operated, have identical operating character-

to be bent into many and varied shapes. No tool changes are needed to bend the various

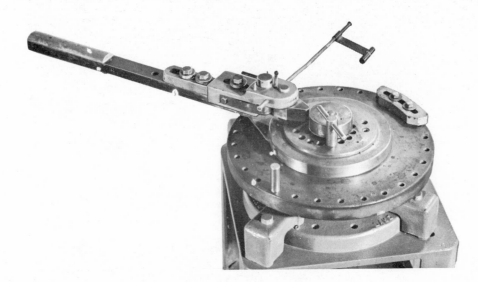

Fig. 27-30. The DI-ACRO Bender.

Fig. 27-31. Accessory blocks for the DI-ACRO Bender. Top left - Grooved radius block (for bending tubing). Bottom left - Zero radius block. Center - Radius collar. Top right - Scroll block. Bottom right - Radius collar.

istics. Fig. 27-30, illustrates the basic parts of the machine series.

These machines can be adapted to produce a variety of bends, and handle different shapes of metal by interchanging the various radius forming accessories and forming noses, Fig. 27-31. Special attachments are available for tube bending. Several of the accessories are shown in use in Figs. 27-32, 27-33, 27-34, and 27-35.

ASSEMBLING WROUGHT IRON WORK

Wrought-iron pieces may be assembled by various methods depending on the design of the piece and the facilities available.

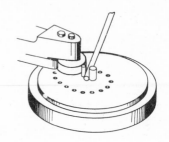
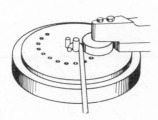
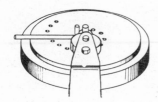

Fig. 27-32a. Using Di-Acro bender for off-center eye bending.

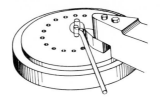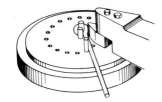

Fig. 27-32b. Alternate methods of centered eye bending.

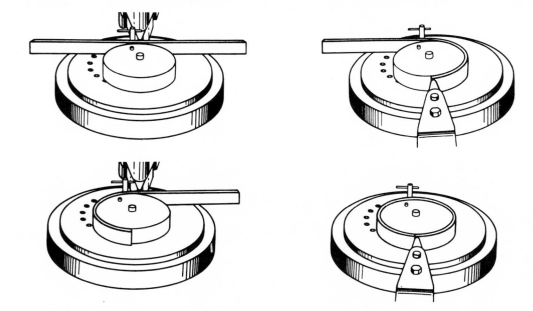

Fig. 27-33. Using Di-Acro bender for bending circles.

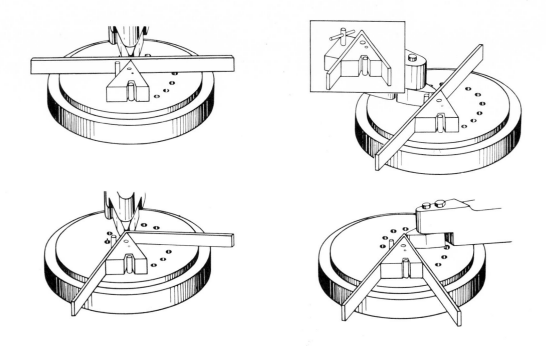

Fig. 27-34. Forming sharp zero radius bends.

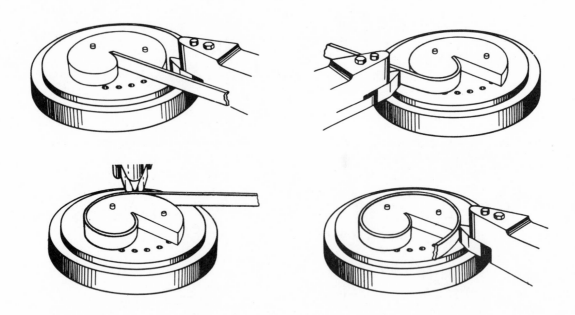

Fig. 27-35. Scrolls and other shapes of irregular radii can be formed with bender, by using collar having same contour as the shape to be formed.

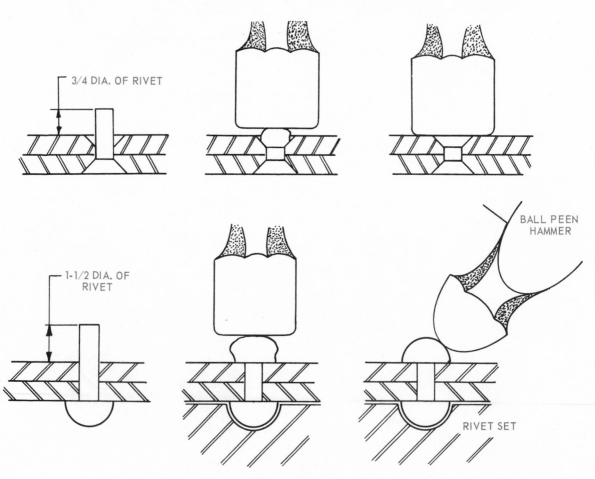

3/4 DIA. OF RIVET

1-1/2 DIA. OF RIVET

BALL PEEN HAMMER

RIVET SET

Fig. 27-36. Setting Rivets.

RIVETING

Rivets are frequently used to assemble this kind of work. Fig. 27-36, illustrates riveting techniques. Note how the length of the rivet shank differs between the round and flat head rivet styles.

Fig. 27-37. Close-up of a peened surface.

WELDING

Oxyacetylene and electric arc welding are also widely used to assemble modern wrought iron work. Welding procedures are explained in detail in UNIT 30.

FINISHING

Originally, wrought iron work acquired a surface texture (finish) when the rough iron pieces were forged to useable sizes before shaping. With the availability of a large range of standard sizes, it no longer became necessary to forge rough stock to size before shaping. The resulting smooth surfaces brought about the development of peening to apply surface texture, Fig. 27-37. While peening is not an honest finish (a surface acquired during the sizing and shaping of the rough metal), it has received considerable acceptance and is widely used as the surface treatment on contemporary iron work.

Most work of this nature is finished with a flat black lacquer or paint. These produce an acceptable effect without the trouble or mess of the older scorched oil finishes.

TEST YOUR KNOWLEDGE, Unit 27

1. Wrought ironwork is also known as __ __ __.
2. Metal up to____in. thick can usually be bent cold.
3. An allowance of_____ _____the thickness of the metal must be added to the length of the piece for each bend.
4. Wrought metal sections are twisted:
   a. To permit a suitable point of attachment.
   b. For additional stiffness.
   c. To break the monotony of a long flat section.
   d. All of the above.
   e. None of the above.
5. The scroll is widely used for decorative purposes. True or false?
6. A full-size pattern should be made before attempting to form a scroll or other curved section. True or false?
7. Wire rings are made by bending wire around a rod, and cutting the resulting coil along its length. True or false?
8. Bending machines use manual and mechanical power to perform the bending operation. True or false?

RESEARCH AND DEVELOPMENT

1. Visit a nearby museum and make sketches of slides of early wrought ironwork. Develop a bulletin board display around the sketches.
2. Prepare a display panel showing the proper sequence followed when developing and making a double end scroll.
3. Secure catalogs from historic developments (Williamsburg, Cooperstown, Greenfield Village. Old Sturbridge Village, etc.) and develop wrought-iron projects adaptable to the school shop based on the drawings and photos presented in them.
4. Investigate the use of metal benders in local industries. Secure samples of their work and devise ways to duplicate them in the school shop.

This aircraft wing spar is believed to be the world's largest forging. The giant part is 23 ft. long.   (Aluminum Co. of America)

Unit 28

FORGING

Forging is the process of using pressure to shape metal. The pressure is usually applied with a hammering action. The metal is heated (but not to the melting point) to make it easier to shape. HAND FORGING is one of the many aspects of this metal shaping technique and was in use long before man started to keep written records.

EQUIPMENT FOR HAND FORGING

As with other metalworking processes, special tools, peculiar to hand forging, have been devised.

FORGE

The forge, Fig. 28-1, is used to heat the metal prior to forging. It may be fired by gas or coal. However, since gas is readily available in most areas and is cleaner to use, it has replaced coal to a great extent.

ANVIL

Heated metal is shaped on an anvil, Fig. 28-2. The HORN is used to shape circular sec-

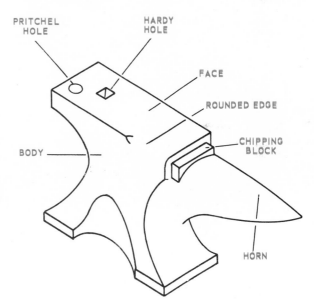

Fig. 28-2. Anvil used for hand forging with parts identified.

tions. Various tools may be mounted in the HARDY HOLE. The PRITCHEL HOLE is used for punching holes and for bending small diameter rods.

The anvil must be mounted on a solid base.

TONGS

Tongs are used to hold the hot metal while it is being formed. They are manufactured in many shapes and sizes. The tongs most frequently used

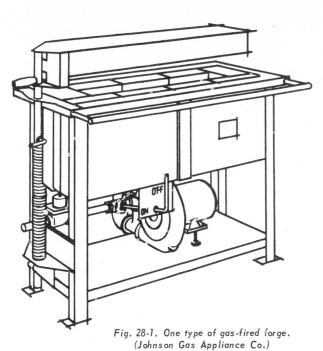

Fig. 28-1. One type of gas-fired forge.
(Johnson Gas Appliance Co.)

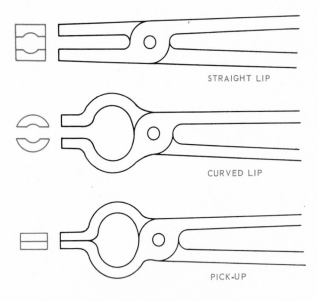

STRAIGHT LIP

CURVED LIP

PICK-UP

Fig. 28-3. Forging tongs.

the anvil. The HARDY, Fig. 28-6, is useful for cutting hot and cold metal. The square shank is placed in the hardy hole, and the metal to be cut is placed on the cutting edge and struck with a hammer. Nick the metal on both sides, and

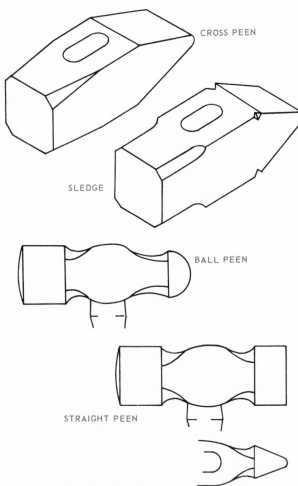

CROSS PEEN

SLEDGE

BALL PEEN

STRAIGHT PEEN

Fig. 28-5. Forging hammers.

are shown in Fig. 28-3. It is important to use tongs that fit the work, Fig. 28-4.

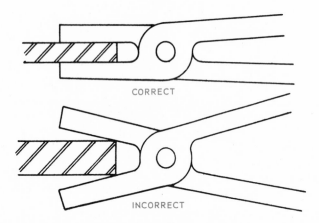

CORRECT

INCORRECT

Fig. 28-4. Use the correct tongs.

HAMMERS

Hammers of many shapes and sizes are used in hand forging, Fig. 28-5. A 1-1/2 - 2 lb. hammer is suitable for light work while a larger 3 lb. hammer will be satisfactory for larger work. Do not "choke-up" on the handle because too much power is wasted when the hammer is held in this manner.

ANVIL TOOLS

Numerous anvil tools are available. Many of them are designed to fit into the hardy hole of

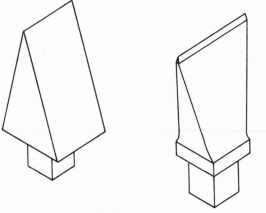

Fig. 28-6. Hardies.

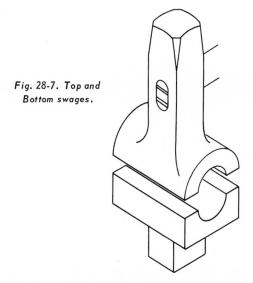

Fig. 28-7. Top and
Bottom swages.

Holes can be made in hot metal with a PUNCH, Fig. 28-10. Punches are made in many sizes and shapes.

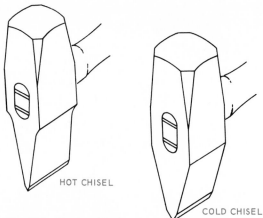

HOT CHISEL

COLD CHISEL

Fig. 28-9. Forging chisels.

bend it back and forth until it breaks. Metal thicker than 1/2 in. should be cut hot.

SWAGES, Fig. 28-7, are used to smooth round rods and rounded surfaces.

FULLERS, Fig. 28-8, are forming tools which come in different shapes and sizes, and can be manipulated to make grooves and hollows.

CHISELS, Fig. 28-9, are used to cut metal in much the same manner as the hardy, however, they have handles for safer and easier manipulation.

The HOT CHISEL is thinner than the COLD CHISEL and, as the name implies, is used to cut metal in the heated state.

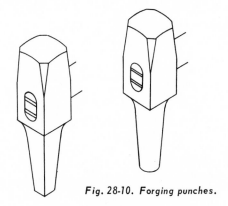

Fig. 28-10. Forging punches.

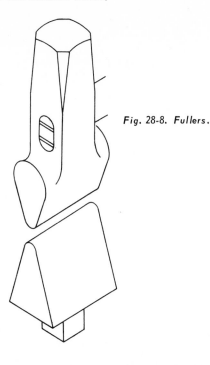

Fig. 28-8. Fullers.

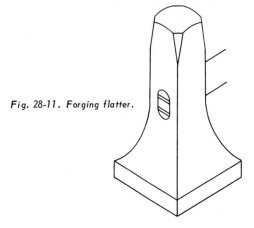

Fig. 28-11. Forging flatter.

The FLATTER, Fig. 28-11, has a smooth flat face and is used to smooth and flatten hammered surfaces. It is placed on the work and struck with a hammer.

HOW TO LIGHT A FORGE

The following procedure is recommended to safely light a gas forge:
1. Open the forge door if it is fitted with one and check to make sure that the gas valve is closed.
2. Start the air blower and open the air valve slightly.
3. Apply the lighter and turn on the gas. CAUTION: Stand to one side and do not look into the forge when you start it.
4. When the gas has ignited, adjust the air and gas valves for the best combination.

FORGING

The metal must be heated to the correct temperature before it can be forged properly. A bright red heat is needed for most mild steels. Tool steel must not be heated to more than a dull red; otherwise, it may lose many of its desirable characteristics. Never permit the metal to come to a white heat where sparks fly from the piece.

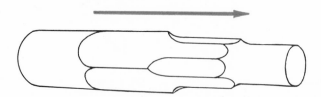

Fig. 28-12. Drawing out sequence.

HOW TO DRAW OUT METAL

Drawing out means that the metal is stretched or lengthened by the forging operation. Round stock is drawn out as shown in the sequence in Fig. 28-12. Square stock must be rounded off as the first step in the drawing out process; if this is not done, it has a tendency to split or crack on the edges, or become distorted.

Round stock can be pointed as shown in Fig. 28-13.

HOW TO BEND A METAL

A bend can be made in a piece of stock by several methods. In all, however, the metal must be heated until it is red:
1. Place the work over the anvil face so that the point of the bend is located where the

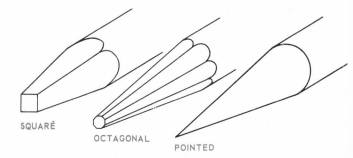

Fig. 28-13. Drawing out a point.

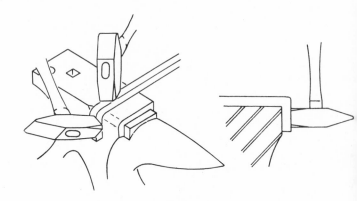

Fig. 28-14. Bending on the anvil.

face edge is rounded, Fig. 28-14. Strike the extended portion until it assumes the desired angle.
2. Place the heated metal into the hardy or pritchel hole and bend with tongs, Fig. 28-15. Square off the bend over the anvil edge.

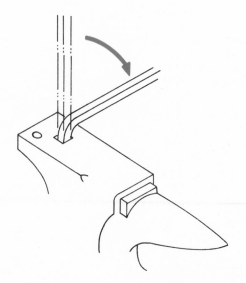

Fig. 28-15. Making a bend using the Hardy hole.

28-4

3. Thin metal can be bent in the vise without heating. Heavier sections must be heated. A pipe may be fitted over the extended portion of the metal for additional leverage.

4. Curved sections are formed over the anvil horn. Place the heated metal over the horn at the most suitable point, and shape by striking hammer blows as shown in Fig. 28-16.

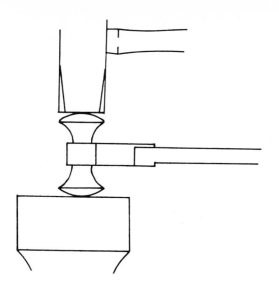

Fig. 28-16. Forming a circular section on anvil horn.

HOW METAL IS UPSET

Upset is the term used to describe the forging operation that thickens or bulges the piece and, at the same time, shortens it. Upsetting is the opposite of drawing. The procedure is as follows:

1. Heat the metal to the proper temperature.
2. Short pieces can be upset on the anvil face, Fig. 28-17.

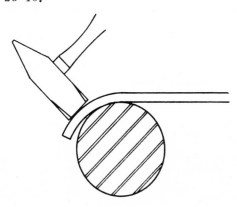

Fig. 28-17. Upsetting on the anvil.

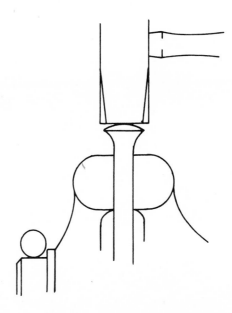

Fig. 28-18. Upsetting in a vise.

3. Longer pieces can be held in a vise for the upsetting operation. The heated section extends above the vise jaws and is hammered to increase its size, Fig. 28-18.

4. Long and heavy bars can be enlarged by ramming the heated end against the anvil face.

INDUSTRIAL APPLICATIONS

In the forging process, Fig. 28-19, the metal is heated to improve its plasticity before pressure is applied. The process is one of the few that improves the physical characteristics of most metals. That is, a forged piece is stronger than an identical piece machined from a solid bar of stock.

The flat hammer and anvil of the SMITH or OPEN DIE FORGE, are shown in Fig. 28-20. In open die forging, the work is manipulated by hand. A skilled operator can do acceptable work if close tolerances are not required. This is used mostly for "rough" work that needs additional forging or machining.

The DROP FORGE, Fig. 28-21, is a refinement of the open die technique. In drop forging, dies replace the hammer and anvil and can shape the metal to much closer tolerances. Several methods have been devised to apply the pressure. The simplest is gravity. This system operates by the alternate lifting to a set height and gravity drop of the hammer, or in the case of the drop

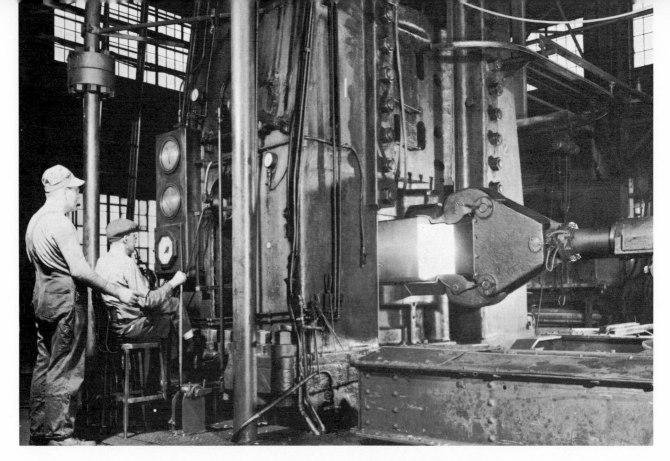

Fig. 28-19. A mechanical manipulator handling an aluminum ingot on a 3000-ton press.
(Aluminum Co. of America)

Fig. 28-20. A smith or open die forging press.
(Mueller Brass Co.)

Fig. 28-21. A drop forge and die shaping a blank of aluminum.
(Mueller Brass Co.)

forge, the upper die block. In the latter, the lower half of the die block is positioned between rails that guide the upper die block. The force of the blow is determined by the weight of the hammer, or the assembly that houses the upper die block, and the height from which it drops. This, and because only uniform blows can be obtained, gravity drop is limited to making small forgings.

A large portion of the forgings made today are such that they require variable blows, or, are so large that they require more pressure to shape them than can be delivered by the gravity forging hammer. For these forgings, the STEAM and AIR DROP HAMMER, Fig. 28-22, has been developed. Steam or air pressure is used to drive

Fig. 28-22. This 35,000 lb. steam hammer is used to produce aircraft parts and conventional forgings. Here, an aircraft engine crankcase is being made.

the upper die assembly against the metal blank in the lower die. The operator is able to control the amount of pressure and the distance of drop. This enables him to vary the force of the blow for blocking, shaping and finishing as required for the job at hand.

DIES, used as shown in Fig. 28-23, are made from specially hardened high strength steel. In

Fig. 28-23. A forging die. (Mueller Brass Co.)

addition to the cavity which forms the finished forging, part of it is in each half of the die, there may be additional cavities included to shape the piece gradually. To assure complete filling of the die, the forging blank is purposely increased in volume. The surplus metal forms a "flash" at the parting line of the dies and must be removed.

PRESS FORGING, Fig. 28-24, also known as "pressing," "no-draft forging," or, "precision forging," is a variation of conventional forging in that the metal is shaped by the gradual application of pressure rather than by impact. It is sometimes used in conjunction with drop forging to bring the work to final size when a smooth finish and close tolerances are specified. This is expensive compared to conventional forging because the process is slow, requires costly precision dies, and relatively long development time.

Forgings are used in applications where high strength and minimum material volume are required. The process is used widely in the automotive and aircraft industries, Fig. 28-25. Forgings of almost any shape or material may be produced except those having undercuts or holes that are parallel to the parting line of the dies.

INTRAFORM MACHINING

INTRAFORM (Cincinnati Milling Machine Co., Trademark), Fig. 28-26, is a recent development in "chipless machining" and is closely akin to forging except that it is possible to form

Fig. 28-24. Two giant forging presses for making aluminum forgings. A 50,000 ton press is in the foreground and a 35,000 ton press in the background. (Aluminum Co. of America)

Fig. 28-25a. Aircraft that uses the wing spar forging, shown in Fig. 28-25b. It is the T-39 Sabreliner, a twin jet utility plane developed for the Air Force. (North American Aviation Co.)

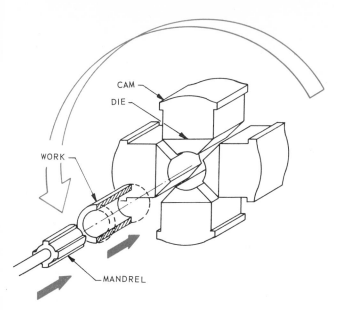

Fig. 28-25b. Straightening finished giant size aluminum forging (23 ft. long) after it has been stress relieved. The forging will serve as a wing spar for a twin jet plane as shown in Fig. 28-25a.

Fig. 28-26. Work ready to be formed by Intraform process.

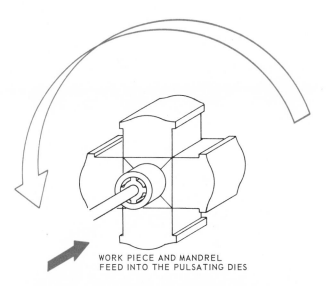

WORK PIECE AND MANDREL
FEED INTO THE PULSATING DIES

Fig. 28-26a. Work and mandrel between INTRAFORM dies. Contact with rotating dies causes free wheeling work (and mandrel) to revolve at about 80 per cent of die RPM. Work feeds over mandrel. Reduction in work diameter is evident in formed area.

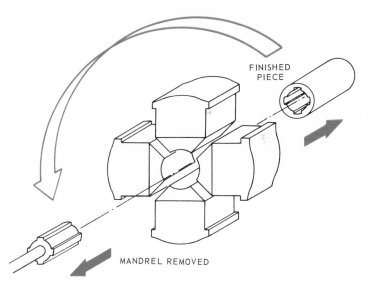

FINISHED
PIECE

MANDREL REMOVED

Fig. 28-26b. When the operation is completed the mandrel is retracted. The next piece feeds into position and ejects the completed part.

profiles on the inside diameter of cylindrical pieces that are extremely difficult and expensive to produce by other means.

The process works like this: A piece of hollow cylindrical stock, is placed over a steel MANDREL, Fig. 28-27, and is squeezed by rapidly pulsating DIES, Fig. 28-28. At the completion of the operation, the profile of the mandrel has been produced on the inside diameter of the part,

Fig. 28-27. Two-piece Intraform mandrel used in the production of automotive starter clutch housings. (Meta-Dynamics Div., Cincinnati Milling Machine Co.)

Fig. 28-28. Dies used in the production of automotive starter clutch housing.

Fig. 28-29. As Fig. 28-30 shows, four forming dies pulsate rapidly around the outside diameter of the work. The tops of the cams are shaped

to permit a smooth continuous squeezing action on the dies. Since the cams never lose contact with the rollers as they revolve, there is no hammering effect. And even though the work is being squeezed by the dies more than 1000 times per minute, noise and vibration are not a problem. A cross section of the Intraform machine is shown in Fig. 28-31.

Intraform has proven to be a practical method of producing rifle barrels. Predrilled steel blanks are fed into the machine which forms the chamber and rifling. In addition to improving the surface finish of the bore, the operation also improves the physical characteristics of the metal.

Fig. 28-29. Automotive starter clutch housing and sectioned part showing helical spline and cam clutch profile which was formed in one operation, at a production rate of 220 parts per hour.

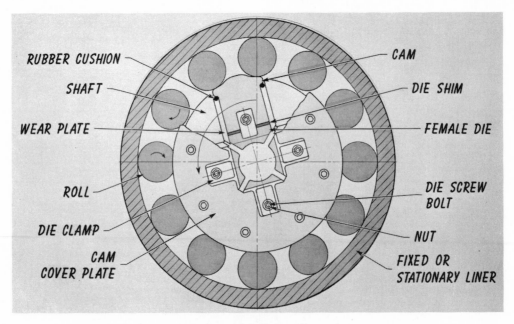

Fig. 28-30. A drawing of the die head of the Intraform machine, in open position.

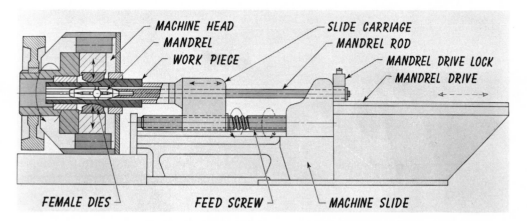

Fig. 28-31. A sectional view of the Intraform machine.

TEST YOUR KNOWLEDGE, Unit 28

1. Hand forging is one small segment of the forging process. True or false?
2. Forging makes use of pressure to shape metal. True or false?
3. Metal to be forged is heated to just above its melting point. True or false?
4. The anvil horn is used to bend sharp angles. True or false?
5. Small diameter rods are bent in the pritchel hole of the anvil. True or false?
6. A bright red heat is needed to forge mild steel. True or false?
7. Tool steel is heated to the same temperature as mild steel for forging. True or false?
8. Drawing out a piece of metal means that:
   a. It has been shortened.
   b. It has been bulged or enlarged.
   c. It has been stretched or lengthened.

9. Upsetting means:
   a. The opposite of drawing out.
   b. It has been stretched or lengthened.
   c. It has been forged to a circular shape.
   d. None of the above.
10. Forging _____ the physical characteristics of most metals.
11. In open die forging, the work is _____ _____ _____ .
12. In the drop forge technique _____ replaces the hammer and anvil of the open die forge.
13. Forgings are used where _____ _____ and minimum material is required.
14. Forgings are widely used by the _____ and _____ industries.
15. The Intraform process is an excellent method of producing _____ .

RESEARCH AND DEVELOPMENT

1. What does the term "plasticity," as applied to the forging process, mean?
2. How does the forging process improve the physical characteristics of many metals?
3. Experiment with the forging process by making a cold chisel.
   a. How does the metal work if forged cold?
   b. How does the metal work when heated properly?
   c. What happens if the metal is overheated?
4. Secure forgings and compare them with castings. Contact a concern that produces forgings and request information on the technique the industry uses to make etched cross sections of forged pieces to show grain flow and structure.
5. Make a chart with an automobile as the center theme. Around the drawing list various parts of the auto that are made by forging. Run colored cord or twine from part name to location it is used. Why are these parts forged?
6. Secure samples of forgings made from brass, aluminum, and steel. Locate and mark the die parting lines.

Unit 29

SOLDERING AND BRAZING

Soldering is a method of joining metals with a nonferrous metal filler without having to heat them to a point where the base metals melt. It is carried out at temperatures lower than 800 deg. F.

As the strength of solder is relatively low, a well designed soldered joint should employ a lock seam or fold.

SOLDERING CONDITIONS

Before two metals can be joined by soldering, several conditions must be met:
1. The correct solder alloy must be used.
2. The proper flux must be applied.
3. An adequate source of heat must be available.
4. The surfaces to be soldered must be clean.

SOLDER

Solders are tin-lead alloys. A 50-50 alloy, that is, 50 per cent tin - 50 per cent lead (tin is always the first figure mentioned) is most commonly used. It melts at about 420 deg. F. A 60-40 solder is suited for electrical work. A higher percentage of tin results in a lower melting temperature alloy.

Solder is available in solid wire, acid or resin core wire and bar form, Fig. 29-1.

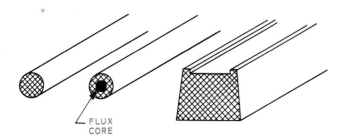

FLUX CORE

Fig. 29-1. Solder is available in solid wire, acid or resin core wire, and bar form.

FLUXES

All metals oxidize to some extent when exposed to the atmosphere. This film of tarnish or rust must be eliminated before the solder will adhere to the work surface.

A chemical mixture, called FLUX, is applied to the joint to remove the oxides, prevent further

Fig. 29-2. A soldering copper of the type that must be heated by external means.

oxides from forming while the metal is heated to soldering temperature, and lowers the surface tension of the molten solder enabling it to cover the area and to alloy with the work.

Fluxes fall into two categories, CORROSIVE and NONCORROSIVE. Corrosive fluxes (acid) are more effective for some purposes, however, after soldering the residue encourages oxidation that may cause the eventual failure of the soldered joint. Joints soldered using corrosive fluxes should be cleaned with hot water after soldering.

Resin is a noncorrosive flux that works best on tin plate, solder coated surfaces, brass and tin.

Aluminum can be soldered when a flux specifically designed for this material is used. Regular fluxes will not work.

It is advisable to use commercially prepared fluxes because of their consistent results rather than trying to prepare them in the shop.

SOLDERING DEVICES

There are many ways of applying heat to the metal surface:
1. SOLDERING COPPER, Fig. 29-2. A sol-

dering copper is a square or octagonal shaped piece of copper with a four sided tapered point. It is heated by a blowtorch or a gas fired SOLDERING FURNACE, and is available in a range of sizes or weights. A one-half pound copper is suitable for light work. A one-pound copper is best suited for most work. Soldering coppers are usually purchased in pairs - one heats while the other is in use.

2. ELECTRIC SOLDERING COPPER, Fig. 29-3. This type is preferred if current is available, because it maintains a uni-

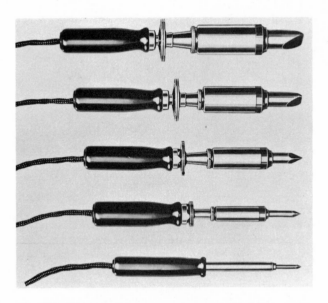

Fig. 29-3. Electric soldering coppers are available in a wide range of sizes. (Americal Electrical Heater Co.)

Fig. 29-3a. A soldering gun.

form heat. A 200-watt electric copper is suitable for most sheet metal work. The electric gun, Fig. 29-3a, is used mostly for electric/electronic work.

3. GAS TORCH, Fig. 29-4. This self-con-

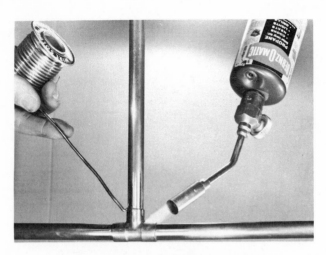

Fig. 29-4. The gas torch makes it possible to solder directly with heat.
(Bernz-O-Matic Corp.)

tained heating unit makes it possible to solder directly without using the usual soldering copper.

CLEANLINESS

A dirty or oxidized surface cannot be soldered. Oily or greasy surfaces should be cleaned with a liquid cleaner. Oxidized surfaces are cleaned with abrasive cloth until they are bright.

HOW TO TIN A SOLDERING COPPER

A soldering copper is tinned or coated with solder, so molten solder will adhere to it. This makes the handling of the solder easier. See Fig. 29-5.

Fig. 29-5. A properly tinned soldering copper.

Clean the copper tip with a file, if it is badly oxidized and pitted. Heat it until it will melt solder freely and do one of the following:

1. Rub the tip on a sal-ammoniac block on which a few drops of solder have been dropped, Fig. 29-6. This will clean the tip and cause the solder to adhere.

2. Apply flux cored solder to the point.

Remove the excess solder by wiping the tip with a clean cloth.

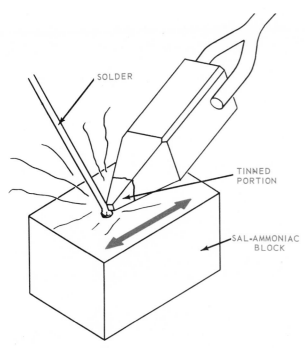

Fig. 29-6. Tinning a soldering copper on a sal-ammoniac block.

SAFETY

1. Use care when storing the soldering copper after use. Improper storage can result in serious burns or a fire.
2. Wash your hands thoroughly after using soft solder.
3. Protect your eyes from splattering solder and do not get flux in your eyes.
4. Have cuts and burns treated promptly.
5. Tin the soldering copper in a well-ventilated area.
6. Do not touch joints that have just been soldered.
7. Because of the temperatures reached and the composition of silver brazing alloys, good ventilation is a must. The fumes are poisonous and should be removed at the point of origin.
8. Use care when handling objects that have just been brazed.
9. Wear goggles when cleaning surfaces with an acid solution or with a wire brush.
10. Pour acid into the water slowly, never water into the acid, when preparing the solution.
11. Double check to be certain that all gas valves have been turned off after completing the job.

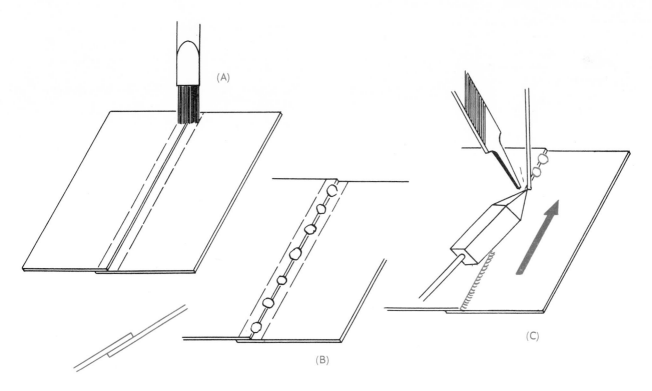

Fig. 29-7. Soldering a lap joint. (A) Apply flux; (B) Tack the joint with drops of solder; (C) Use a metal object such as a file tang to hold the joint together until the solder hardens.

HOW TO SOLDER A LAP JOINT

1. Clean the area to be soldered, apply flux and place the pieces to be soldered on a piece of asbestos sheet, Fig. 29-7(A).
2. Clean, heat and tin the soldering copper. Never let it become red hot.
3. Hold the seam together and tack it with small amounts of solder at several points across the joint, Fig. 29-7(B). Apply the solder directly in front of the soldering copper tip rather than on it.
4. Return to the starting point. With the copper flat on the work, Fig. 29-8, and with

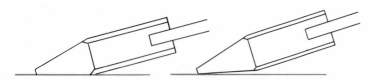

Fig. 29-8. The proper way (left) and improper way (right) to use a soldering copper on a joint.

the seam pressed together with a file tang, start moving the copper slowly toward the far end of the joint as soon as the solder melts and begins to flow, Fig. 29-7(C). As the copper advances, follow it with the file tang as soon as the solder hardens.

5. Clean the seam with hot water and neutralize any corrosive flux residue by brushing on a thin mixture of baking soda and water. This only needs to be done if an acid flux is used.

HOW TO SOLDER A SEAM JOINT

1. Make the seamed joint desired, Fig. 29-9.
2. Clean and prepare the area to be soldered as previously described.
3. Apply drops of solder along the edge of the

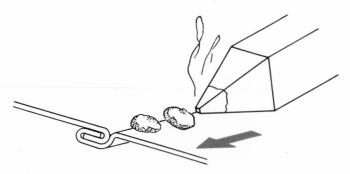

Fig. 29-9. A typical seamed joint.

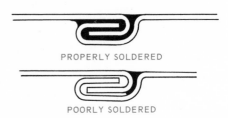

PROPERLY SOLDERED

POORLY SOLDERED

Fig. 29-10. The solder flows through a properly soldered joint.

seam. Whenever possible, solder seam joints on the inside.

4. Place the copper flat on the seam until the solder begins to melt and flow into the joint, then draw the copper along the seam slowly so the solder will flow into the joint, Fig. 29-10.

HOW TO SWEAT SOLDER A JOINT

Sweat soldering is done when two or more pieces must be assembled and no solder is to be seen after assembly.

1. Clean the surfaces and apply flux. Each surface is then coated with a thin layer or coating of solder.
2. Clip the prepared pieces together and apply heat until the solder melts and joins the pieces together.

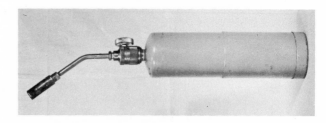

Fig. 29-11. The gas torch is a self-contained unit.

HARD SOLDERING

In hard soldering or silver brazing, alloys are used which melt at a much higher temperature than soft solder, and a stronger joint is produced. In silver brazing, the temperatures needed range between 800 and 1400 deg. F. More heat is required than can be furnished by the conventional soldering copper. While various types of torches are available for different fuel combinations oxyacetylene, city or natural gas and air may be used for silver brazing (the torch and fuel combination depends upon the size of the pieces to be joined), the familiar

Fig. 29-12. Hard soldering is well suited for production work. Here, cooling fans are being assembled to their hubs by this method, on a production line. (Handy & Harman)

self-contained torch and gas cylinder unit, Fig. 29-11, will handle most small jobs. Silver brazing is well suited for production techniques, Fig. 29-12.

Most ferrous metals, copper, brass and silver can be joined by this method.

SOLDERS

Hard or silver solder is available in many alloy combinations. It is commonly designated by three grades:

1. EASY FLOW (flow point up to 1300 deg. F.) is used when only one joint is required.
2. MEDIUM (flow point to 1360 deg. F.) is used to solder the first joint when two joints must be made. Easy flow is used for the second joint.
3. HARD (flow point ot 1460 deg. F.) makes the best joint. Care must be taken when using the alloys in the upper temperature ranges to join sterling silver because the flow point is very close to its melting point.

In addition to the many alloys, silver solder is also available in a large range of forms and sizes, Fig. 29-13.

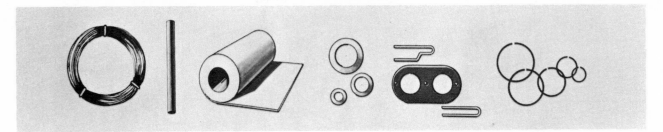

Fig. 29-13. Hard (silver) solder may be purchased in a variety of shapes, sizes and alloys. (Handy & Harman)

FLUXES

Fluxes are needed to clean the surfaces to be joined because the brazing alloy cannot wet or flow over dirty or oxidized areas. A mixture of borax thinned to a heavy paste with water

1. GOOD FIT AND PROPER CLEARANCE, Fig. 29-14. Thin films make the highest strength joints. A clearance of 0.001 to 0.003 in. provides the necessary capillary action to flow a thin film of alloy throughout the joint.

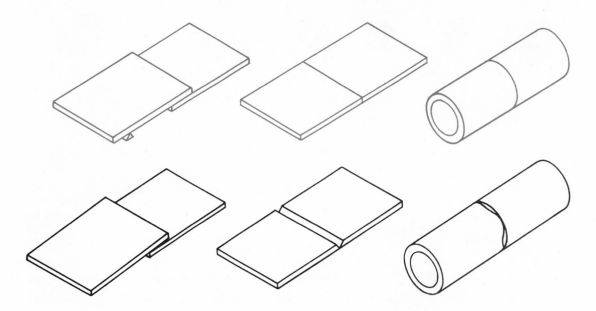

Fig. 29-14. Above. Good joint design. Below. Poor joint design.

makes a suitable flux. However, a commercially prepared flux usually gives more consistent results.

Fluxing should be done just prior to brazing; otherwise, it will dry and flake or be knocked off in handling.

HOW TO SILVER BRAZE

Silver brazing is a relatively simple process. Strong joints are obtained by following six steps. Each is important and none should be overlooked or eliminated.

2. CLEAN METAL, Fig. 29-15. The metal surfaces to be joined must be cleaned. This may be done mechanically with emery cloth, steel wool or a fine file, or chemically by pickling. Oil and grease may be removed with a suitable solvent. Clean the pieces just prior to brazing time.
3. PROPER FLUXING, Fig. 29-16. A good flux is essential because it protects the metals from oxidation while the joint is being heated, dissolves any existing oxides and assists the flow of the brazing alloy. Apply the flux evenly to all surfaces to be

joined, and to the brazing alloy. This should be applied just prior to brazing.

4. ASSEMBLING AND SUPPORTING. Joints should be assembled soon after fluxing.

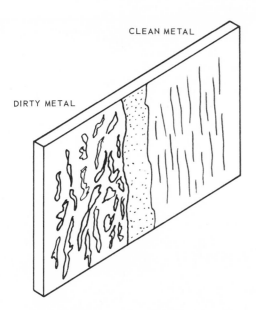

Fig. 29-15. Surfaces must be cleaned before applying flux.

As dry flux will chip off during assembly leaving areas that will oxidize when heated. The joints should be supported to prevent the pieces from shifting until the brazing job has been completed.

Fig. 29-16. The joint must be properly fluxed. Make sure the flux is distributed evenly.

5. HEATING AND FLOWING THE ALLOY. Use a neutral to reducing flame, to apply the heat, Fig. 29-17. Heat the joint to slightly above the flow point of the brazing alloy by keeping the torch in motion to apply a uniform heat, Fig. 29-18. Large surfaces to be joined should be heated well away from the joint. If a heavy

section is to be joined to a lighter section, concentrate the heat on the heavy section.

As the joint approaches brazing temperature, watch the flux and the color of the metal. The following will give an indication of the temperature:

900 deg. F. - The first visible red appears in the metal.
1200 deg. F. - A dull red appears.
1400 deg. F. - The metal takes on a cherry red color.

The flux will become a clear, thin fluid as the metal turns to a dull red. Bright

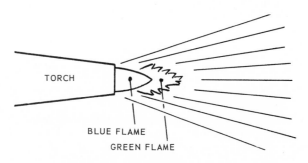

Fig. 29-17. Use a neutral to reducing flame. A greenish "feather" extending from the tip of the inner cone indicates a slightly reducing flame.

lighting conditions may deceive you so that another method of judging temperature will have to be used. Bring the brazing alloy under the torch and drop a small amount of alloy on the joint. If it balls up and solidifies, the joint is not hot enough. When the proper temperature has been reached, the brazing alloy will flow

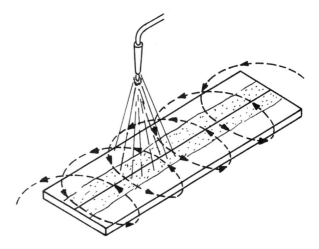

Fig. 29-18. Avoid hot spots. Keep the torch in motion. Bring both parts of a joint to brazing heat at the same time.
(Handy & Harman)

into the joint by capillary action.

6. FINAL CLEANING. All surfaces must be cleaned after brazing too. Some fluxes can be removed with hot water. If a large quantity of oxides have been dissolved in the flux, its removal becomes more difficult and a small amount of acid may have to be added to the water, or the contaminated flux will have to be removed by mechanical means.

Use slightly more brazing alloy than is necessary to fill the joint. It may be applied to the joint as a preform or small pieces placed along the joint in the flux.

HOW TO SILVER BRAZE MORE THAN ONE JOINT ON THE SAME PIECE

It is often necessary to silver braze several joints on the same piece. The first joint is made with high temperature brazing alloy and the remainder with lower temperature alloys. If only one alloy is available, the first joint is made and then covered with flux. This will help to keep it from melting when the remaining joints are brazed. The flux, plus the fact that it requires 15 to 20 deg. higher temperature to remelt a silver brazed joint prevents it from coming apart when the other joints are made.

TEST YOUR KNOWLEDGE, Unit 29

1. Soldering is a method of:
   a. Joining metals by fusing the base metals.
   b. Joining the metals with a nonferrous metal filler.
   c. Joining metals that are similar to welding.
   d. None of the above.
2. List four requirements for a satisfactory soldered joint:
   a. _____.
   b. _____.
   c. _____.
   d. _____.
3. Soldered seams should employ a lock seam or a fold in its design because _____.
4. _____ is always the first figure mentioned when the solder alloys are mentioned.
5. _____-_____ solder is most commonly used.
6. Flux is used to _____.
7. _____ and _____ are the two categories

of fluxes used for soft soldering.
8. Joints soldered when using a _____ flux must be washed with hot water to remove the flux residue.
9. Silver brazing resembles _____ more closely than _____ _____.
10. List the three grades of silver brazing alloys.
    a. _____ b. _____ c. _____
11. What are three uses of a flux in silver brazing?
    a. _____.
    b. _____.
    c. _____.
12. Six steps must be followed if a solid joint is to result by silver brazing. List them in their proper sequence:
    a. _____.   d. _____.
    b. _____.   e. _____.
    c. _____.   f. _____.

RESEARCH AND DEVELOPMENT

1. Make up samples of well made and poorly made seams or joints by the soft soldering method. Mount them on a display panel and label to indicate what constitutes a good solder joint and a poorly made joint.
2. Secure samples of commercially made products assembled by the soft solder technique. Display them in such a way to permit the solder seams to be seen and compared.
3. Visit local industries that produce objects that are assembled with soft solder. Prepare a short report on the methods used, and how they vary from those used in the school shop.
4. Demonstrate the correct method to silver braze a joint.
5. Prepare a display panel that illustrates properly and improperly made silver brazed joints.

Unit 30

WELDING

Welding is a method of joining metals by heating to a suitable temperature to cause them to melt and fuse together. This may be with or without the application of pressure, and with or without the use of filler material of a similar

sistance welding, will be discussed in the first portion of this unit. Recent welding developments with INDUSTRIAL APPLICATIONS will be covered in limited detail in the second portion of this unit.

Fig. 30-1. Welding plays a very important part in modern manufacturing.
(Lincoln Electric Co.)

composition and melting point as the base metal.

Many different welding processes have developed since the days of the simple welding done by the blacksmith in his forge (forge welding). Today, welding in its many modern forms is a very important facet of modern fabricating techniques, Fig. 30-1.

Welding methods may be divided into many categories, Fig. 30-2. Gas, simple arc and re-

GAS WELDING

Gas welding includes a group of welding processes that make use of burning gases, such as acetylene or hydrogen mixed with oxygen, to produce heat as required to cause the metal to melt and fuse. Filler material of a similar composition and melting temperatures as the base metal may or may not be used.

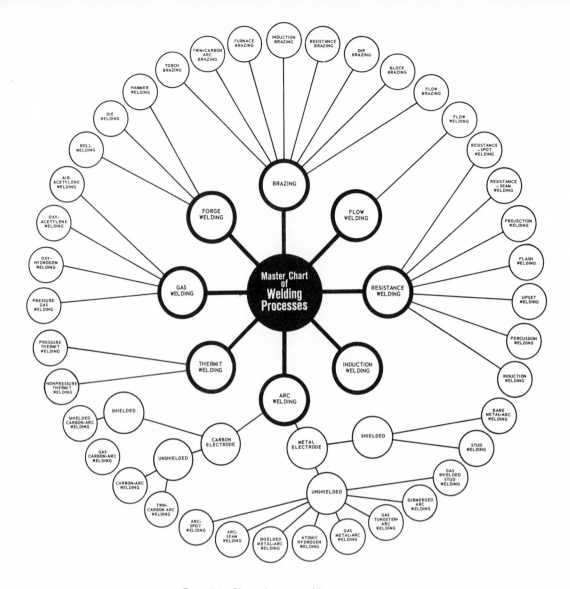

Fig. 30-2. Chart showing welding processes.

Acetylene and oxygen mixed in correct proportions are most commonly used for gas welding in the school shop. They burn with an extremely hot flame (6300 deg. F.); more than ample for doing an adequate job of joining most weldable metals.

Fig. 30-3. Typical oxyacetylene welding outfit. (Marquette Mfg. Co.)

EQUIPMENT

Basically, oxyacetylene welding equipment, Fig. 30-3, consists of:

1. A source of supply of the two gases (gas cylinders), Fig. 30-4.

Fig. 30-4. Left. Acetylene cylinder. Right. Oxygen cylinder.

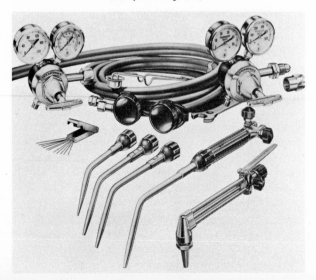

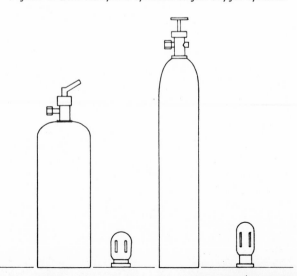

2. A mechanism for reducing the pressure and controlling the gases as they come from the cylinders (oxygen regulator and acetylene regulator).

3. A method for transferring the gases to the point of use (oxygen hose and acetylene hose-for easy identification, the oxygen hose is green and the acetylene hose is red).

4. A device to mix and control the gases in proper proportion when welding (welding torch).

In addition to the above, a wrench that fits the various connections, a spark lighter, Fig. 30-5, for lighting the torch, and a pair of suitable goggles are needed.

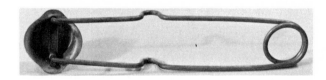

Fig. 30-5. Spark or friction lighter should be used in place of matches to light the torch. (Linde Co.)

Torches are manufactured in a variety of sizes with a wide range of tip sizes. The basic elements of a welding torch are shown in Fig. 30-6.

CARE OF REGULATORS

1. Clean cylinder valve outlets with a clean, dry cloth and blow dust from the outlet by opening the valve before connecting the regulator. This is known as "cracking" the valve.

2. Release the regulator adjusting screw before opening the cylinder valve.

3. Prevent the high pressure gases in the cylinders from surging by opening the cylinder valves very slowly.

4. Check gauges regularly to assure correct readings.

5. Turn the adjusting screws in slowly to prevent the regulator from being damaged by a sudden surge of high pressure gas.

6. Always use the correct size wrench on the fittings. Never force a threaded fitting.

7. Never use oil or grease on regulator or fitting. Use lubricant specified by manufacturer.

8. Use soapy water free of oils and greases to check for suspected leaks.

9. Have all equipment repaired by trained persons. Use only factory approved parts.

CARE OF TORCHES

1. Keep all oil and grease away from torches.

2. Never clamp a torch in a vise. The internal passages may be damaged.

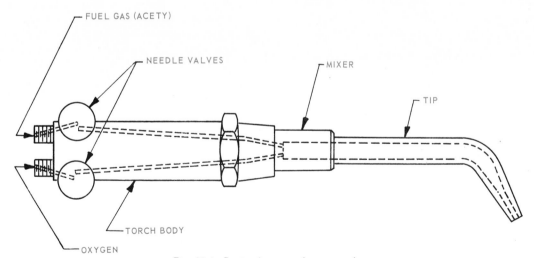

FUEL GAS (ACETY)

NEEDLE VALVES

MIXER

TIP

TORCH BODY

OXYGEN

Fig. 30-6. Basic elements of a gas torch.

CARE OF EQUIPMENT

Gas welding equipment, while extremely rugged, requires that certain precautions be taken for safe operation.

3. If the needle valve does not shut off when tightened in a normal manner, do not force it. Blow foreign matter from the valve seat. If this cannot be done, remove the stem assembly and wipe the seat clean with a lint-

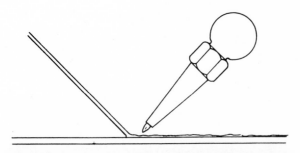

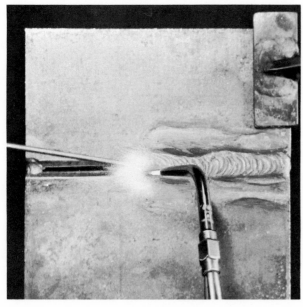

Fig. 30-7. Adding filler rod to the weld. (Linde Co.)

free cloth. Reassemble the unit.

4. Check the torch carefully each time you use it.

GENERAL SAFETY PRECAUTIONS

1. Wear suitable goggles when welding. The lenses are made in different degrees of density; select the lenses that are best suited for you.
2. Never light the torch with matches. Use a sparklighter.
3. Do not allow anyone to watch you weld unless they wear suitable goggles.
4. It is only necessary to turn off the torch if you are going to reposition the work; however, the entire unit should be turned off if the welding job is completed. Carefully hang up the torch.
5. Never light the torch with both valves open.
6. For added protection, wear welder's gloves, leather apron, and sleeves when welding.
7. Never attempt to blow dirt off your clothing

with gas pressure. The clothing will become saturated with oxygen and/or acetylene and will literally explode if a spark comes in contact with it.

WELDING RODS

Often, metal from a filler rod is added to the joint during welding, Fig. 30-7, to build it up and make it as strong as the base metal. A steel filler rod having a very low carbon content will prove satisfactory for most gas welding operations on ferrous metal in the school shop. This rod is available in a number of sizes (diameters) and is copper plated to prevent rusting.

The following rod sizes are recommended for oxyacetylene welding:

Metal Thickness	Rod Diameter
18 gauge	1/16
16 gauge	1/16 to 3/32
10 gauge	3/32 to 1/8
1/8	3/32 to 1/8
3/16	1/8 to 5/32
1/4 and up	3/16 to 1/4

Cast-iron filler rod is a high grade cast rod with a square cross section. To produce a satisfactory joint, it must be clean and free of all dirt, grease, oil and oxidation. A flux must be used with this rod.

Brazing rod must be of high quality and purity to obtain good results. It is made of brass or bronze; however, bronze filler rod is preferred because of its superior strength. A flux must also be used with this rod.

Brazing rod and fluxes for joining some aluminum alloys are available. However, as aluminum gives no warning by change of color prior to melting, extreme care must be taken when it is brazed. For best results, carefully follow the instructions furnished by the rod and flux manufacturer.

FLUXES

Fluxes must be used on most nonferrous and cast-iron welds. Flux cleans the metal, prevents oxidation and other forms of corrosion and promotes a better weld. Unless the metal is free of all oxides, it is difficult to make a good weld. A flux should not be used as a substitute for cleaning the base metal during joint preparation.

Borax can be used as a brazing flux; however, commercial fluxes are superior and should ordinarily be used. Aluminum and cast-iron welds require fluxes made especially for them.

PREPARING AND ADJUSTING THE EQUIPMENT AND LIGHTING THE TORCH

A careful study should be made of the manufacturer's recommended operational procedures that were furnished with the welding equipment, if available. The following should be observed:

1. Carefully check the equipment. If it must be assembled, ask your instructor to demonstrate how this is accomplished.

2. Select the proper tip size for the job to be done. The tips are usually made of copper because its high thermal conductivity reduces the danger of it burning up at high temperatures. Use the guide furnished with the torch to determine the tip best suited. Clean the tip with a tip cleaner, Fig. 30-8, if necessary - NEVER with a piece of wire. Attach the tip to the torch.

3. Turn the adjusting screws on both regulators out until they are loose.

4. Open the oxygen cylinder VERY SLOWLY until the high pressure gauge shows its maximum rating, then continue to turn the valve until it seats against the top of the valve cylinder. The valve has a double seat and turning it all of the way out prevents oxygen leakage.

5. Secure the proper size wrench and SLOWLY open the acetylene cylinder valve 1 to 1-1/2 turns - NEVER MORE. It is good practice to stand to one side of the regulator gauges when the cylinder valves are opened.

6. Open the oxygen valve on the torch about one turn and turn in the adjusting screw on the oxygen regulator until the low pressure indicates the pressure needed for the tip being used. Turn off the oxygen valve on the torch.

7. Repeat the sequence for acetylene.

8. Open the acetylene valve on the torch about 1/4 turn. Permit the gas to flow long enough to blow any air in the unit out before igniting with a scratch lighter. Hold the torch away from the cylinders and pointed away from the body, Fig. 30-9.

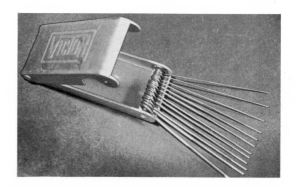

Fig. 30-8. Torch tip cleaner.

Fig. 30-9. Hold torch away from cylinders and pointed away from the body when lighting it. (Linde Co.)

9. Adjust the acetylene valve on the torch until the flame jumps away from the tip slightly. Open and adjust the oxygen valve on the torch until you get a NEUTRAL FLAME, Fig. 30-10. This flame is best for most

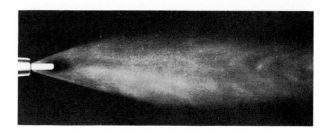

Fig. 30-10. Neutral flame is obtained by burning an approximately one-to-one mixture of acetylene and oxygen. The pale blue core of the flame is known as the inner cone. The oxygen required for the combustion of the carbon monoxide and hydrogen in the outer envelope of the flame is supplied from the air. (Linde Co.)

welding. An excess of acetylene produces a CARBURIZING FLAME, Fig. 30-11. A sharp hissing sound indicates that there is an excess of oxygen, and an OXIDIZING FLAME, Fig. 30-12, is the result.

10. If the torch is to be idle for only a few minutes, it is necessary to turn off only the torch valves. However, if the job is com-

pleted and the torch is not to be used for sometime, it is best that the unit be shut down completely. The proper technique for this is as follows:

a. Close the valves on the torch. The acetylene is closed first to prevent a slight

Fig. 30-11. The carburizing flame results when the one-to-one mixture is varied to give an excess of acetylene. (Linde Co.)

backfire or "pop" and to prevent the carbon smudge that burning acetylene makes.

b. Close the cylinder valves tightly.

c. Open the valves on the torch to release any gas in the hose and regulator.

d. When all gauges read zero, turn the adjusting screws on both regulators all of the way out.

e. Close the torch valves and store the torch in a suitable place. Never hang the torch and hose over the regulators. The weight may damage them.

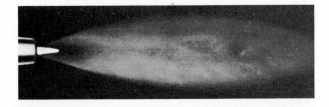

Fig. 30-12. The oxidizing flame is the result of too much oxygen in the mixture. The whole flame will be smaller, and hotter, than the other two flame adjustments because the combustible gases will not have to search so far to find the necessary amount of oxygen. (Linde Co.)

MAKING A WELD

After the proper tip has been installed on the torch, a welding table is made ready, Fig. 30-13. The table shown is steel with a fire-brick top which is not affected by the high welding temperatures. If this is the first welding job attempted, a careful study of the various welding joints and how the torch is handled to make them should be made.

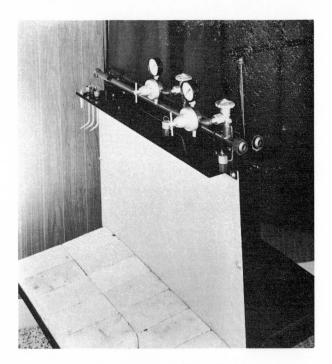

Fig. 30-13. Gas welding table. (Marquette Mfg. Co.)

TYPES OF WELDING JOINTS

Joint preparation is of paramount importance before a sound weld can be made. The type of preparation is dependent upon the thickness, kind of material to be welded and type of joint required. In addition, rust, scale and other impurities must be removed from the base metal.

In general, there are five basic types of joints and they are common to both gas and arc welding.

BUTT JOINT

The butt joint, Fig. 30-14, is the most common of the welded joints. Metals up to 1/8 in.

Fig. 30-14. Butt joint.

thick can be welded from one side. Up to 3/8 in., the joint should be welded from both sides. Heavier plate must be beveled before welding to secure a solid joint.

TEE JOINT

The tee joint, Fig. 30-15, is frequently used. Joint preparation is similar to that used for the butt joint.

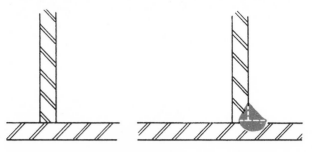

Fig. 30-15. Tee joint.

LAP JOINT

The lap joint, Fig. 30-16, consists of lapping a metal piece over the piece to which it is to be welded. It is important that the pieces fit together tightly and the weld is made on a flat surface.

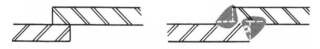

Fig. 30-16. Lap joint.

EDGE JOINT

Welding the edge joint, Fig. 30-17, differs somewhat from making other joints in that it is not necessary to use filler rod. The base metal serves as filler material.

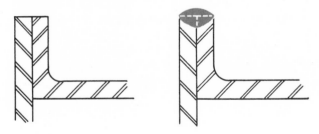

Fig. 30-17. Edge joint.

CORNER JOINT

The open corner joint, Fig. 30-18, is used when welding heavier plate. For additional strength, a light bead is often added to the inside.

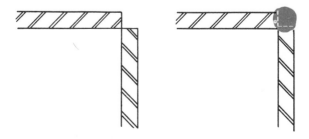

Fig. 30-18. Corner joint.

In general, welding without the use of filler rod is not considered good welding technique. Maximum strength is not always achieved because the thickness of the metal is reduced along the weld.

To weld with filler rod, bring the torch to the point to be welded and melt a small "puddle" on the surface of the work. Bring the filler rod close to the torch and as it becomes white hot dip it into the molten puddle. Never heat the rod directly and allow the molten metal to fall into the molten puddle. Add enough filler rod material to create a slight crown on the joint.

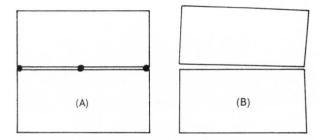

Fig. 30-19. Welded joints will become distorted if allowances are not made for contraction as the weld cools. (A) Tack weld the joint at intervals, (B) Position the work so that one end is slightly wider than the other (end where weld starts).

Expansion and contraction of the base metal during welding must be taken into consideration and planned for; otherwise, the piece will warp and twist out of shape as it cools. Fig. 30-19 illustrates two ways of allowing for contraction as the metal cools.

TORCH WELDING

FOREHAND WELDING is used for joining thin metal. The torch and filler rod are positioned as shown in Fig. 30-20. The flame is in the direction in which the weld is progressing.

BACKHAND WELDING, Fig. 30-21, is used for joining heavier sections. The torch is held at an angle of 30 to 45 deg. with the flame being directed back over the portion being welded. This permits the weld to cool more slowly, helping to relieve the stresses that develop in the metal during welding.

PUDDLING

It is suggested that a student welding for the first time should practice "puddling." The puddle is the molten spot that is produced by the torch

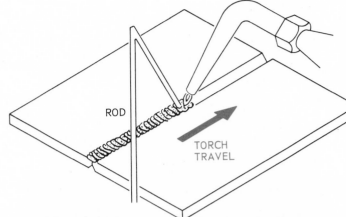

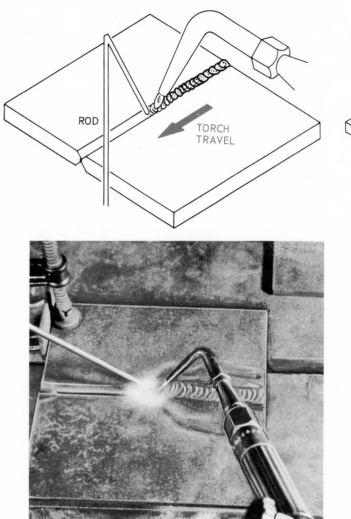

Fig. 30-20. For a forehand weld, the welding action progresses from right to left. The flame is between the completed weld and the welding rod. (Linde Co.)

Fig. 30-21. In the backhand technique, the weld progresses from left to right and the welding rod is between the completed weld and the blowpipe flame.

flame. It spans the metals being welded causing them to fuse. This is basic to both gas and electric arc welding. As the puddle forms, and filler metal is added, move the torch in a circular or oscillating motion, Fig. 30-22. Whatever motion is used, be careful not to allow the inner cone of the flame to go outside the puddle perimeter. Fig. 30-23 illustrates some of the problems encountered by the novice welder.

BRAZING OR BRONZE WELDING

This welding technique is widely used for repair work. The resulting joints, if properly made, are almost as strong as a conventional welded joint; however, they are quicker and more

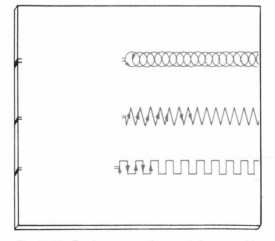

Fig. 30-22. Torch movement for a satisfactory weld.

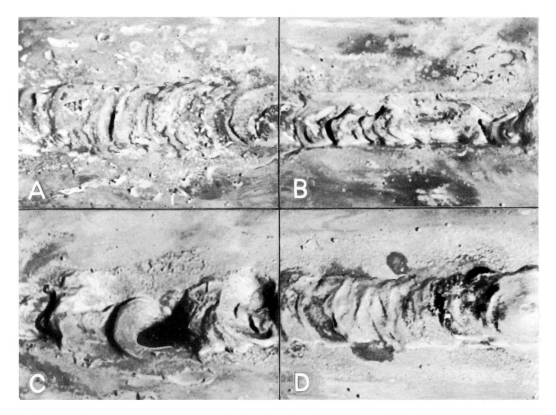

Fig. 30-23. In these four views are shown (A) an oxidized weld, (B) poor fusion and lack of reinforcement because insufficient heat was used, (C) holes burned through the plate because of the use of too much heat, and (D) the appearance of a satisfactory weld. (Linde Co.)

economical to make. See Fig. 30-23a. Bronze filler rod is preferred to brass because it makes a stronger joint.

It is essential that the surfaces to be joined

Fig. 30-23a. Here is an example of a properly deposited layer of bronze. During bronze-welding the blowpipe and rod should be held at angles of about 45 deg. to the plate surface, with the flame at the forward edge of the puddle.

be clean. Clamp the pieces into position and heat them. If one section is heavier than the other, apply more heat to it. As the metal heats up, use care to prevent burning through. Heat the filler rod and stick it into the flux. The fluxed end is held slightly ahead of the torch and, as the proper

temperature is reached, allow the rod to melt and flow onto the base metal. Never melt the rod directly with the torch. Be careful not to overheat the resulting joint.

ARC WELDING

Arc welding is a joining process that makes use of an electric arc to produce the heat necessary to cause the metals to melt and fuse together, Fig. 30-24. Filler metal in the form of an ELECTRODE, Fig. 30-25, may be added to the joint.

Today, there is hardly an industry or a business which does not depend in some way upon arc welding.

ARC WELDING EQUIPMENT AND ACCESSORIES

Like most other manufacturing equipment, arc welders are available in a large range of sizes (ratings). Arc welders are rated according to their current output. Most of those used in the

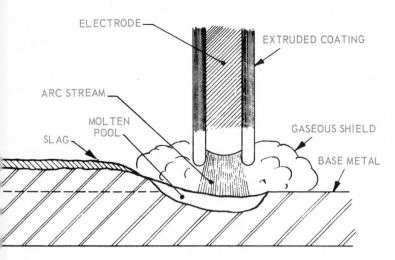

Fig. 30-24. *Close-up showing electric welding procedure.*

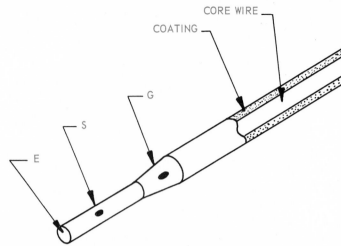

Fig. 30-25. *Electrode.*

average school shop range from 100 to 250 amperes.

Welding machines are of two basic types: those that provide DIRECT WELDING CURRENT (DC), Fig. 30-26, and those that provide ALTERNATING WELDING CURRENT (AC), Fig. 30-27. COMBINATION WELDERS, are also available that produce both AC and DC welding current.

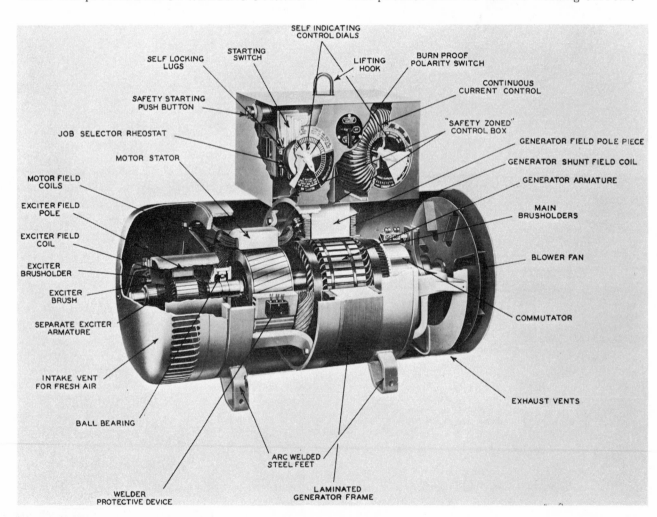

Fig. 30-26. *DC welding machine.*
(Lincoln Electric Co.)

The DC welding machine has some advantages over the AC welders. It is better for welding sheet metal and uses a wider variety of electrodes. Output can be controlled more precisely, and gasoline powered models permit the welders to be used where there are no power lines.

Safe and efficient welding procedures require the use of many accessories. No welding should be attempted unless the equipment is in first-class condition.

Arc welding requires the use of TWO CABLES to carry the current through a complete circuit.

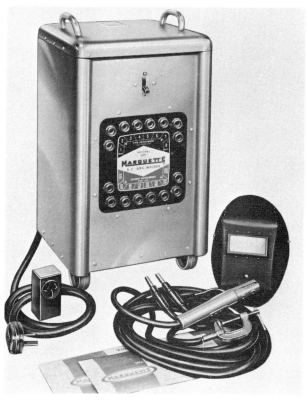

Fig. 30-27. AC welding machine.

Size and length of the cables is determined by the capacity of the machine. One cable is attached to the ELECTRODE HOLDER, Fig. 30-28. This holds the electrode during the welding operation. The second cable is attached to the GROUND CLAMP, Fig. 30-29. The clamp is attached to the work or, if the table has a cast-iron top, to the WELDING TABLE.

A HEAD SHIELD, Fig. 30-30, protects the face and eyes of the operator from the rays of the electric arc and spatter of molten metal. Never attempt to weld unless a shield is used.

The rays can cause serious and often permanent eye damage.

GAUNTLET TYPE GLOVES, a LEATHER APRON and SLEEVES should be worn for addi-

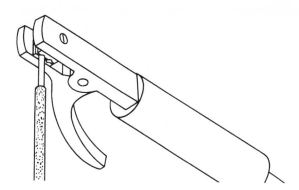

Fig. 30-28. Electrode holder.

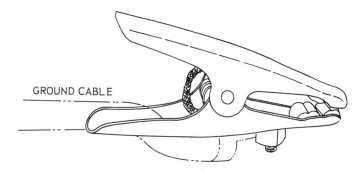

GROUND CABLE

Fig. 30-29. Ground clamp.

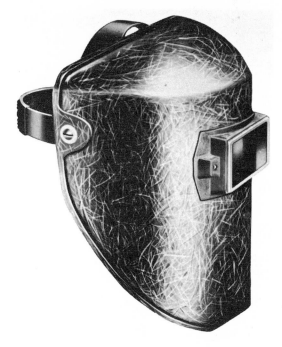

Fig. 30-30. Head shield. (Marquette Mfg. Co.)

tional protection. A WIRE BRUSH and CHIPPING HAMMER, Fig. 30-31, are necessary for removing slag and cleaning the weld bead. Be sure to wear goggles when chipping and wire brush-

Fig. 30-31. Combination chipping hammer and wire brush.

ing. TONGS or pliers should be available to handle hot metal. A WELDING TABLE, Fig. 30-32, will prove helpful for practice and small jobs. An assortment of clamps, punches, and small tools will help to make the job easier.

Fig. 30-32. Arc welding table. The curtains are to protect nearby workers from the arc. (Marquette Mfg. Co.)

ELECTRODES

Electrodes are metal rods covered with a baked flux coating. Rods are used to support the welding arc and to provide filler metal to the joint. The flux melts under the high temperatures and cleans the oxides from the base metal and acts as insulation, slowing down the cooling of the joint. This helps to relieve the internal strains which develop from the sudden changes of temperature.

When using a DC welder, it is necessary to know the correct terminal (pole) on the machine to attach the electrode cable. The current flow on the DC welder flows constantly in one direction, or has a definite polarity. Electrodes are designed to take advantage of this condition, Fig. 30-33. When the electrode is POSITIVE (+), the arc is forceful and digs into the base

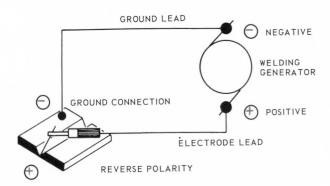
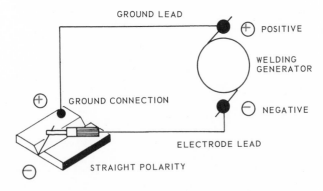

Fig. 30-33. Two methods of setting up a DC welder to take advantage of desirable electrode characteristics.

metal for deep penetration. When the electrode is NEGATIVE (-), the arc is not as forceful, however, the metal is deposited about a third faster.

The electrode polarity in DC welding is determined by the flux coating. A specific polarity must be used for some electrodes while others may be used with either polarity. Polarity instructions are given on the electrode container.

Store electrodes where they will be dry. Moisture destroys the desirable characteristics of the flux coating.

A uniform system of classifying electrodes has been established by the American Welding Society. The chart, Table 1, lists the most commonly used mild steel electrodes for general welding.

PREPARING TO WELD

Check the machine to be sure that all connections are tight and clean. As the heat of the arc is determined by the amount of the current (amperes) used, it is suggested that you set the machine to the middle of the recommended range for the electrode being used. Make a few trial beads and raise or lower the setting until you

ARC WELDING
Table 1 – Common Mild-Steel Electrodes

AWS No.	Welding Current	End (E) Secondary (S) Color Marking	Welding Position	Penetration and Characteristics	Application
E-6010	DC, reverse polarity	none	all	Deep penetration; thin slag, easy to remove; forceful arc	Building construction, pipe lines, pressure tanks, bridges, ship building, storage tanks, machinery frames
E-6011	AC or DC, reverse polarity	blue (S)	all	Deep penetration; thin slag, easy to remove; forceful arc	Same as E-6010 For use on AC welding current; Not all are usable with limited-input welders
E-6012	DC straight polarity or AC	white (S)	all	Medium penetration; heavy slag; soft arc	Work with poor fit-up; high speed welding; light gauge welding; build-up
E-6013	AC or DC, straight polarity	brown (S)	all	Medium to shallow penetration; light slag, easy to remove; soft arc	Mild steel repair, sheet metal, auto bodies, general farm welding and repair with limited-input welders
E-6014	AC or DC	brown (S)	all	Iron powder coating; medium to shallow penetration; drag technique; exceptionally easy to operate; little spatter; heavy slag almost self-removing	High speed welding; for ease of operation in all general welding; this is an E-6013 electrode with iron powder added to the coating
E-6016	DC reverse polarity or AC	Orange (S)	all	Medium to deep penetration; forceful arc; medium to heavy slag	Higher carbon steels, alloy steels, armor plate, auto bumpers. Not usable with limited input welders

1. NEVER arc weld or watch arc welding being done without using a protective shield. Gas welding goggles or sun glasses are not satisfactory.
2. Wear goggles when chipping slag.
3. Wear suitable clothing for welding.
4. Do not weld where solvent or paint fumes may collect. Remove all flammable materials from the welding area.
5. Weld only in a well-ventilated area.
6. Treat any cuts or burns promptly.
7. Wear goggles under the shield for additional protection.
8. Do not weld containers until you can determine whether they stored flammable liquids. If they have, get them steam cleaned or fill them with water before welding.

get a satisfactory weld; that is, one that does not burn through and gives sufficient penetration, Fig. 30-34.

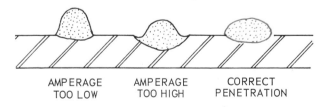

Fig. 30-34. Weld characteristics.

STRIKING THE ARC

1. Clean and prepare the joint.
2. Position the metal. Use clamps if necessary.
3. Attach the ground cable securely.

4. Set the welder to the desired amperage.
5. Put on protective clothing and head shield.
6. Clamp the electrode in the electrode holder. It should be at an angle of 90 deg. to the jaws, Fig. 30-35.
7. Keep the electrode and holder clear of the work area and turn the machine to "ON."

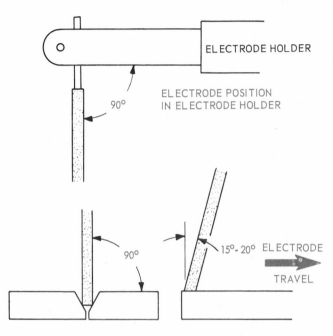

Fig. 30-35. Electrode position when running flat weld.

Fig. 30-36. Use two hands to grasp the electrode holder whenever possible. (Lincoln Electric Co.)

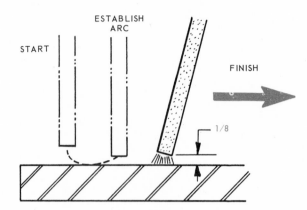

Fig. 30-37. The scratch method for starting the weld.

8. Grasp the electrode holder with a comfortable grip. Use two hands whenever possible, Fig. 30-36. Lower the electrode to about 1 in. above the base metal. Lean the electrode at a 15 - 20 deg. angle from the vertical in the direction of travel, Fig. 30-35.
9. Lower your head shield and strike the arc. The SCRATCH METHOD, Fig. 30-37, is suggested. The tip of the electrode is scratched over the face of the base metal as you would strike a match. As the arc starts, lift the electrode 1/8 in. and maintain the arc. Keep the electrode moving while starting the arc or it will "freeze" or stick to the base metal.
10. Once the arc is established, it is important that the correct arc length be maintained. Hold a short arc - 1/16 to 1/8 in. As the electrode burns down, keep feeding it to the work to maintain the correct arc length.
11. Maintaining correct welding speed is important. Watch the puddle of molten metal directly behind the arc. Do not watch the arc. The looks of the puddle and the ridge where the molten metal solidified, Fig. 30-38, indi-

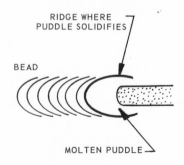

Fig. 30-38. The correct welding speed is indicated by the looks of the puddle and ridge of the bead.

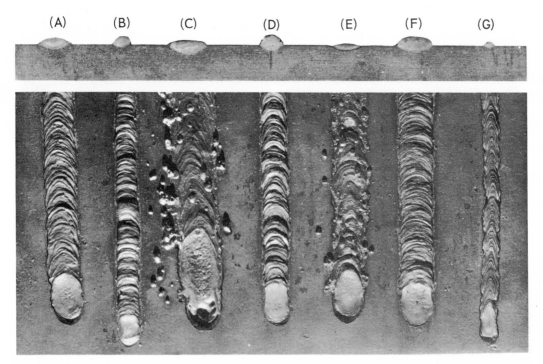

Fig. 30-39. *Characteristics of welds made under Various conditions. The conditions are accentuated to illustrate differences. A. Current, voltage and speed normal. B. Current too low. C. Current too high. D. Arc length too short. E. Arc length too long. F. Speed too low. G. Speed too high.   (Lincoln Electric Co.)*

cates correct welding speed. The ridge should be about 3/8 in. behind the electrode. Most beginners weld too rapidly, resulting in a shallow, uneven bead. Fig. 30-39, shows various types of beads.

For general welding, it is not necessary to move the electrode in any but a straight di-

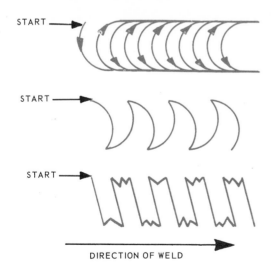

Fig. 30-40. *Electrode travel when covering wide, beveled joint.*

rection and an even pace. A weaving motion, Fig. 30-40, is necessary when covering a wide, beveled joint.

MAKING VARIOUS WELDS

The joints illustrated in Figs. 30-14 to 18 also apply to arc welding.

When making a butt joint, place the two metal

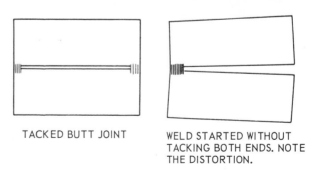

TACKED BUTT JOINT

WELD STARTED WITHOUT TACKING BOTH ENDS. NOTE THE DISTORTION.

Fig. 30-41. *Tack plates to be joined at both ends to prevent them from pulling apart as they are welded.*

pieces side by side with a 1/16 in. space between - 1/8 in. for heavy plate. Tack the plates at both ends to prevent them from pulling apart as they are welded, Fig. 30-41. Take care to distribute the weld evenly on both pieces.

Fillet welds are made by holding electrodes in the electrode holder at a 45 deg. angle to the jaws, Fig. 30-42.

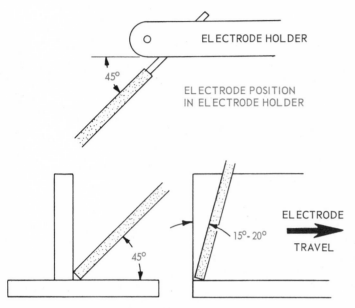

Fig. 30-42. Position of electrode in holder for making fillet welds.

Welds must penetrate close to 100 per cent; otherwise, they will be weaker than the base metal. Get the deepest penetration possible. It may be necessary to bevel the joint edges for best penetration in heavier sections, Fig. 30-43.

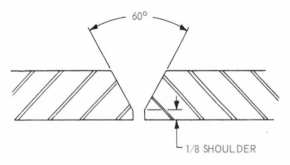

Fig. 30-43. A joint that has been beveled in preparation for welding.

ARC WELDING ALUMINUM WITH THE CARBON ARC TORCH

Aluminum and other nonferrous metals like copper and brass can be electric welded almost as easily as ferrous metals. About the only apparatus needed, in addition to an AC welding

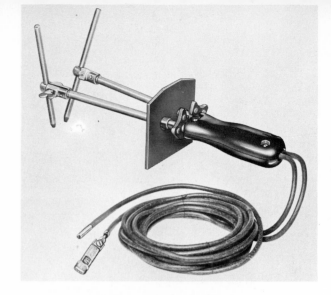

Fig. 30-44. Carbon arc torch. (Lincoln Electric Co.)

machine and its normal related equipment, is an arc torch, Fig. 30-44, and electrodes developed for the metal being welded.

TORCH ADJUSTMENTS

In using a carbon arc torch, the distance between the carbons and the work controls the amount of heat going into the work. Fig. 30-45, indicates the carbon diameter and amperage setting for various metal thicknesses.

RECOMMENDED CURRENTS AND CARBONS

Thickness of base metal	Approximate current setting	Carbon Diameter
1/16 in.	50 - 60 amps.	1/4 in.
1/8 in.	70 - 80 amps.	5/16 in.
1/4 in.	90 - 100 amps.	3/8 in.
over 1/4 in.	110 - 125 amps.	3/8 in.

Fig. 30-45. Table of recommended currents and carbon diameters for carbon arc torch applications. (Lincoln Electric Co.)

Extend the carbons 2 - 2-1/2 in. beyond the torch jaws, Fig. 30-46. Adjust the arc length (distance between carbons) as often as necessary to keep the arc going smoothly and to concentrate the flame in a small cone. As the carbons burn away, adjust the arc by manipulating the carbons with the thumb control on the torch handle.

SAFETY

The rays of the carbon arc torch are just as dangerous as those developed during conventional arc welding and a head shield and protective clothing are required.

Always turn the welder off when adjusting the carbons. This will prevent arcing should they touch during adjustment. The resulting flash could cause serious burns or damage your eyes.

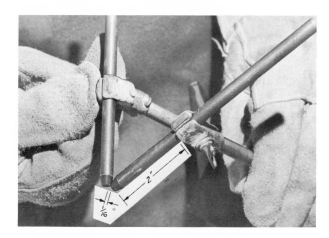

Fig. 30-46. Carbon adjustment.

2. Use a 1/8 in. diameter aluminum electrode as a filler rod. Hold it in the left hand.
3. Ignite the torch by bringing the carbons together and adjusting until the arc is going smoothly.
4. Keep the torch parallel to the joint as shown in Fig. 30-48. Observe the welding process by looking between the two carbons.
5. Preheat the joint by running the flame 3 or 4 in. up and down. This will improve the weld by helping the bead to flow more smoothly.
6. Begin the weld by moving the torch to the start of the joint.

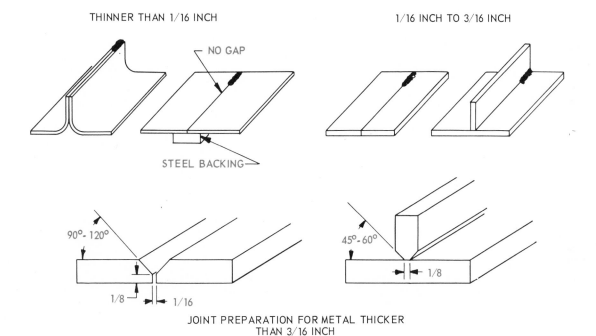

THINNER THAN 1/16 INCH

NO GAP

STEEL BACKING

1/16 INCH TO 3/16 INCH

90° - 120°

45° - 60°

1/8

1/8   1/16

1/8

JOINT PREPARATION FOR METAL THICKER
THAN 3/16 INCH

Fig. 30-47. Preparation for welding aluminum.

JOINT PREPARATION

The thickness of the metal being welded will determine how the joint must be prepared, Fig. 30-47. It is recommended that all welds be made in the horizontal downhand position even though this may require rotating the pieces.

MAKING THE WELD

The following sequence is recommended for welding aluminum:
1. Set the welder to the current recommended in Fig. 30-45.

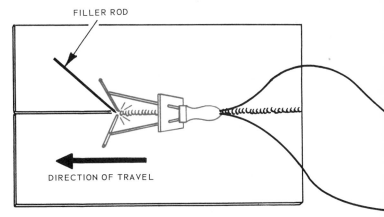

FILLER ROD

DIRECTION OF TRAVEL

Fig. 30-48. Keep the torch parallel to the joint.

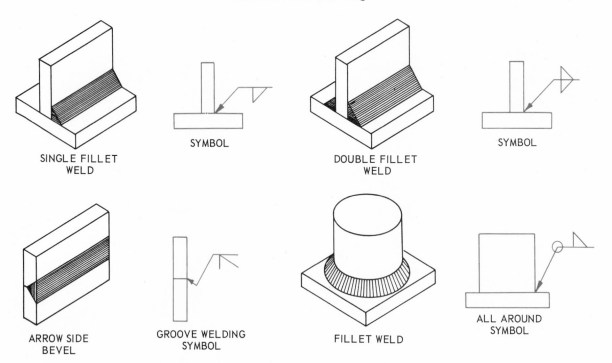

SINGLE FILLET
WELD

SYMBOL

DOUBLE FILLET
WELD

SYMBOL

ARROW SIDE
BEVEL

GROOVE WELDING
SYMBOL

FILLET WELD

ALL AROUND
SYMBOL

Fig. 30-49. Typical welding symbols and what they indicate.

7. Place the tip of the electrode in the arc. If the coating melts off and flows into the joint easily, the metal is hot enough and ready for welding. Let the filler metal melt and fuse into the joint.

8. Move the arc torch slowly along the joint adding filler metal into the molten puddle as needed.

WELDING SYMBOLS

The American Welding Society has developed a series of symbols to give the welder specific welding instructions. The symbols, Fig. 30-49, are included on drawings where the assemblies require some sort of welding.

RESISTANCE WELDING

SPOT WELDING is the best known of the resistance welding techniques. The weld is produced by heat obtained from the resistance of the work to a flow of electric current and by the application of pressure, Fig. 30-50. The outstanding advantages are economy and weight savings as the welds do not require the addition

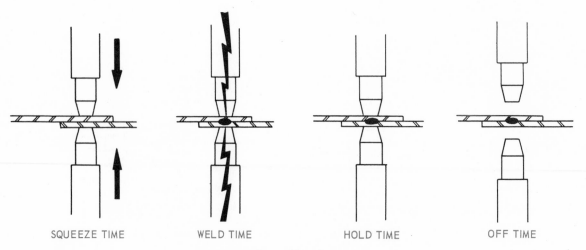

SQUEEZE TIME

WELD TIME

HOLD TIME

OFF TIME

Fig. 30-50. Spot welding sequence.

of filler metal. The welds are made directly between the metal parts being joined.

Spot welding, whether done by a portable unit, Fig. 30-51, or a larger manually controlled unit,

2. Weld time - Time electric current flows
3. Hold time - Forging time
4. Off time   - Release of electrode

Fig. 30-51. Portable spot welder unit. (Miller Electric Mfg. Co.)

Fig. 30-52, depends upon four definite time stages in the welding cycle:
1. Squeeze time - Application of electrode force

Fig. 30-52. Manually controlled spot welding unit. (Taylor-Winfield)

Fig. 30-53. Left. Tungsten inert-gas (TIG) welding equipment. Below. Tungsten inert-gas welding technique.

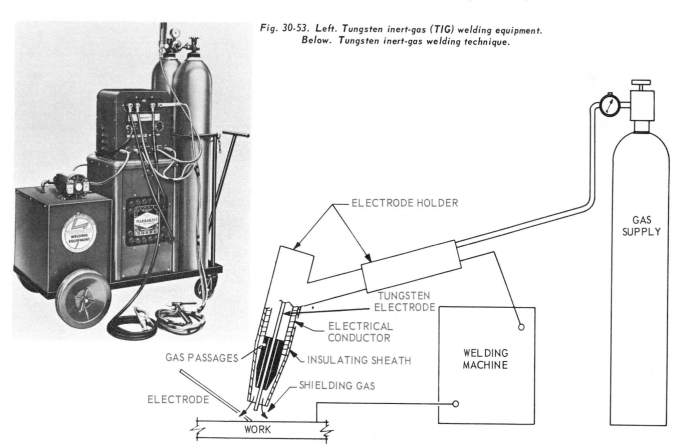

The cycles are regulated by controls on the spot welding machine. Tables for calculating the exact time of each stage for different kinds and thicknesses of metal are furnished with each machine.

INDUSTRIAL APPLICATIONS

All areas of welding have made significant advances in recent years. The use of "exotic" metals for space and aircraft applications has resulted in improved equipment and the development of new welding techniques.

Tungsten inert-gas (TIG), metal inert-gas (MIG), electron beam (EB), resistance (RW), and submerged arc welding processes are being used more and more nor production applications.

TIG AND MIG

These gas-shielded arc welding techniques are accomplished with a permanent electrode, that is, an electrode that is not consumed in the welding process (TIG), Fig. 30-53, or a consumable metal electrode that melts and contributes filler metal to the joint (MIG), Fig. 30-54. The electrode, arc and molten pool of the weld are protected from atmospheric contamination by a soft stream of inert gas (helium or argon) that is directed to the weld area by a

Fig. 30-53a. Close-up of torch end of *TIG* unit. *Filler rod is being used in this application.* (Lincoln Electric Co.)

tube that surrounds the electrode.

The gas-shielded arc gives an unobstructed view of the slag free weld permitting the operator to observe the flow and qualities of the molten weld metal. When done properly, a solid joint that requires little additional finishing is accomplished.

ELECTRON BEAM WELDING

The electron beam welding process, Fig. 30-55, makes use of a beam of fast moving electrons to supply the energy to melt and fuse the base metal. Welds must be made in a vacuum of 10^{-3} to 10^{-5} mm Hg, which practically eliminates the contamination of the weld metal by atmospheric gases. This requires the use of a

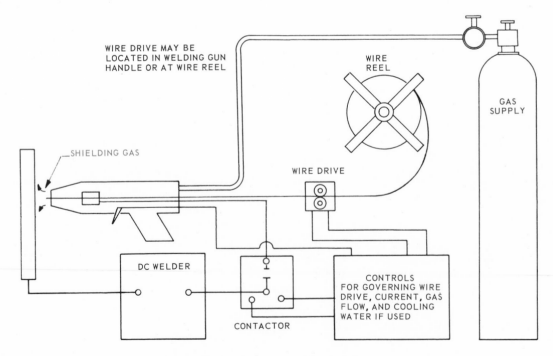

WIRE DRIVE MAY BE LOCATED IN WELDING GUN HANDLE OR AT WIRE REEL

WIRE REEL

GAS SUPPLY

SHIELDING GAS

WIRE DRIVE

DC WELDER

CONTACTOR

CONTROLS FOR GOVERNING WIRE DRIVE, CURRENT, GAS FLOW, AND COOLING WATER IF USED

Fig. 30-54. Metal inert-gas welding technique.

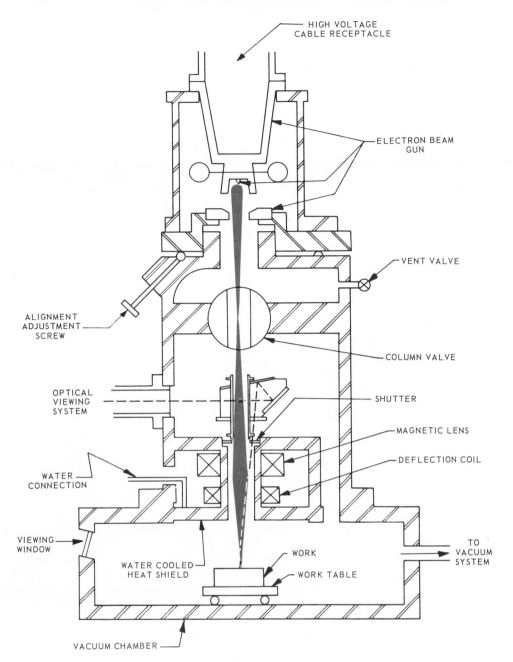

HIGH VOLTAGE
CABLE RECEPTACLE

ELECTRON BEAM
GUN

VENT VALVE

ALIGNMENT
ADJUSTMENT
SCREW

COLUMN VALVE

OPTICAL
VIEWING
SYSTEM

SHUTTER

MAGNETIC LENS

DEFLECTION COIL

WATER
CONNECTION

VIEWING
WINDOW

TO
VACUUM
SYSTEM

WATER COOLED
HEAT SHIELD

WORK

WORK TABLE

VACUUM CHAMBER

Fig. 30-55. Cross section of electron beam welder.

vacuum chamber which, at present at least,
limits the size of the unit that can be welded.

The electron beam is capable of melting any
known material. This makes it possible to join
high melting temperature metals like molybdenum (4760 deg.) and tungsten (6170 deg.)
needed for space and missile applications.

RESISTANCE WELDING

The design and size of modern aircraft have
placed unusual demands on the techniques used
to join both its primary and secondary struc-
tures. The precision joining of each part is of
utmost importance.

Fig. 30-55a. Electron beam welder.
(Hamilton Standard, Div. United Aircraft Corp.)

Many of the fastening needs are met by electrical resistance welding of the highest quality, Fig. 30-56.

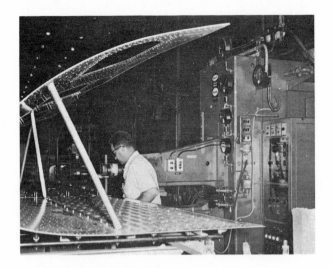

Fig. 30-56. Spot welding the leading edge of jet mainliner wing. Each weld will be X-rayed for soundness. (Sciaky Bros., Inc.)

SUBMERGED ARC WELDING

This welding technique is also known as "squirt welding." The process produces no smoke, arc rays, radiant heat or spatter. The welding machine, Fig. 30-57, consists of a wire reel case, control box with wire feed motor, welding gun and the necessary cables. Current is supplied by a separate power source.

Submerged arc is really a misnomer as it implies that the welding is done under water. Rather, it might better be called hidden arc welding as the welding process takes place hidden by a mound of flux. A bare electrode wire is coiled on a reel of 60 to 200 lbs.

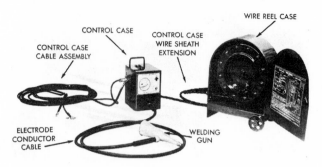

Fig. 30-57. Submerged arc welder. (Lincoln Electric Co.)

To weld, Fig. 30-58, the operator fills the flux cones, points the gun into the joint, allows a pile of flux to accumulate and then strikes the arc under the flux with the electrode. Once the arc is struck, the electrode automatically feeds into the arc as the gun is moved over the work.

Fig. 30-58. Preparing to weld by the submerged arc process.

TEST YOUR KNOWLEDGE, Unit 30

1. Welding is a method of joining metals by heating to a suitable temperature to cause them to_____ _____ _____ _____.
2. When welding, filler metal (welding rod) must be added. True or false?
3. When welding, filler metal (welding rod) does not necessarily have to be added. True or false?
4. Oxyacetylene welding is one of two types of gas welding. True or false?

5. Oxyacetylene welding equipment consists of:

_____ - stores the gases.

_____ - regulates and controls gas flow.

_____ - carries the gases to the point of use.

_____ - mixes and controls the gases when welding.

6. The acetylene hose is colored_____,

the oxygen hose is colored_____.

7. The torch is lit with a_____ _____ NEVER a match.

8. Gas welding rod is frequently copper plated to prevent it from_____.

9. Brazing rod is made of brass or_____.

10. Flux is needed when brazing to_____ _____.

11. List the five basic types of weld joints. Draw a sketch which shows the principles involved in each.
    a._____.
    b._____.
    c._____.
    d._____.
    e._____.

12. The torch may be held in one of two different positions:
    a. _____, usually used for joining thin metal:
    b. _____, for joining heavier sections.

13. Arc welding makes use of an_____ _____ to produce the necessary welding temperature.

14. A head shield must be worn to protect the _____ and_____from the harmful rays of the arc.

15. Electrodes are:
    a. Metal rods.
    b. Copper plated metal rods.
    c. Metal rods covered with a baked-on flux.
    d. None of the above.

16. Weld control can best be maintained by watching the shape and size of the arc. True or false?

17. Weld control can best be maintained by watching the molten metal puddle and the ridges where the molten metal has solidified rather than the electric arc. True or false?

18. _____ _____is accomplished by the resistance of the metal to the flow of an electric current and by the application of pressure.

19. The above process is the best known of the _____ _____ techniques.

Place the letter of the sentence that best describes the word in the blank space at the right of the word.

20. ____Brazing

21. ____Flux

22. ____Electrode

23. ____TIG and MIG

24. ____Resistance welding

25. ____EB

26. ____MIG

27. ____TIG

a. Shields the weld and arc with a stream of inert gas.

b. Is economical and weight saving because no filler rod is needed.

c. Must be done in a vacuum chamber.

d. The electrode is not consumed.

e. A flux covered rod.

f. The filler rod forms the electrode.

g. Cleans the base metal, prevents oxidation and slows down the cooling rate of the weld.

h. Widely used for repair work.

RESEARCH AND DEVELOPMENT

1. Secure samples of welded and brazed joints and mount them on a display board. Label the samples according to the process used to make them.

2. Prepare samples of the five basic weld joints.

3. Make a teaching aid that shows the appearance of gas welds:
    a. Made with excessive heat.
    b. Made with insufficient heat.
    c. Satisfactory welds.

4. Contact a local industry that makes use of welding in its manufacturing cycle and secure X-ray photos of an acceptable welded joint and also a defective joint.

5. Secure a weld fillet gauge and demonstrate its use to the class. If one cannot be found, make a large drawing that shows how it is used.

6. Visit a local industry that makes extensive use of welding and get information on the following welding processes:
    a. Stud welding.
    b. Electric slag welding.
    c. Plasma arc welding.
    d. Laser beam welding.

7. Invite a professional welder to the school shop to demonstrate the safe and proper way to gas weld and electric arc weld.

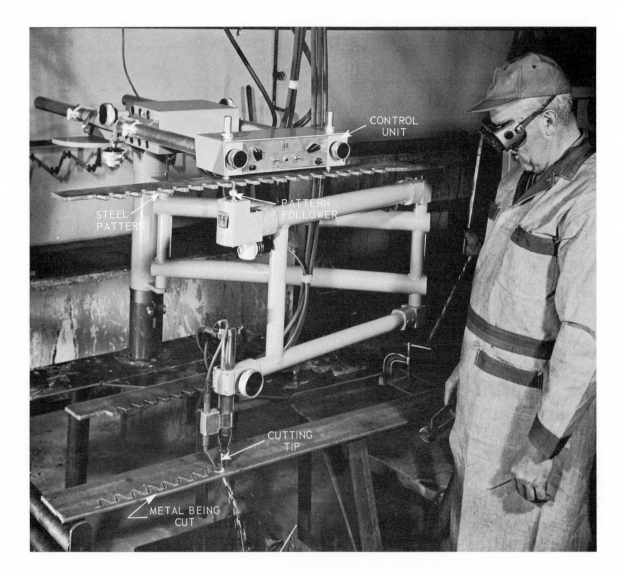

CONTROL
UNIT

STEEL
PATTERN

PATTERN
FOLLOWER

CUTTING
TIP

METAL BEING
CUT

Industry photo--An automatic single torch cutting machine. The template is mounted above the metal to be cut. A magnetic tracer is in vertical alignment with the cutting tip. Electronic controls and positioning motors move the tracer and the torch to produce a unit identical to the template. (Heath Engineering Co.)

Unit 31

HEAT TREATMENT
OF METALS

HEAT TREATMENT includes a number of processes involving the controlled heating and cooling of a metal, or an alloy, for the purpose of obtaining certain desirable changes such as toughness, hardness and resistance to shock in its physical characteristics. See Fig. 31-1. Also, it can be used to soften (anneal) metals to make them easier to machine, or to produce a hard exterior surface (caseharden) on steel for better resistance to wear.

Steel and its alloys are hardenable. Aluminum, magnesium, copper, berrylium and titanium are also capable of being treated.

HEAT TREATMENT is done by heating the metal to a predetermined temperature, then quenching (cooling rapidly) in water, brine, oil or in a blast of cold air. Because the desired qualities do not always prevail after quenching, the material may have to be reheated to a lower temperature, followed by another cooling cycle to develop the proper degree of hardness and toughness.

The heat treatment of metals may be divided into two major categories. One is concerned with FERROUS metals, the other with NONFERROUS metals. Because each area is so broad, it is

Fig. 31-1. Certain desirable changes can be made in the physical characteristics of many metals by heat treatment. (Lindberg Steel Treating Co.)

beyond the scope of this text to include more than basic information on heat treating of steel.

In describing the heat treatment of steel, it must be remembered that the carbon content of the metal is crucial, not only to what can be done to improve a particular part, but in determining how to do it.

Changes in the physical characteristics of steel and its alloys can be effected by six basic types of heat treatment:

STRESS RELIEVING

Stress relieving, Fig. 31-2, is done to reduce stresses that have developed in parts which have been cold worked, machined or welded. The parts

Fig. 31-2. Stresses that develop in metals when they are machined or welded, may be removed by stress relieving.

are heated to 1100-1200 deg. F., held at this temperature for one hour per inch of thickness, and then slowly cooled.

ANNEALING

Annealing, Fig. 31-3, is the process of reducing the hardness of a metal to make it easier to machine or work. The metal is heated to above its normal hardening temperature; the time it is

Fig. 31-3. Annealing machine parts in a hydrogen atmosphere. The hydrogen atmosphere prevents the formation of scale and other surface defects that sometimes form during heat treatment.

to be held at this temperature depends upon the shape and thickness of the piece, after which it is allowed to cool slowly in some insulating material like ashes or vermiculite.

NORMALIZING

Normalizing is a process closely related to annealing.

CASEHARDENING

Low carbon steel cannot be hardened to any great degree by conventional heat treatment. However, a hard shell or case can be put on the surface by heating the piece to a red heat and introducing small quantities of carbon or nitrogen to its surface. This can be done by one of the following methods:

1. PACK METHOD, Fig. 31-4. Often referred to as CARBURIZING. The part is buried in a container of carbonaceous material and placed in the furnace for 15 minutes to one hour, depending upon the depth of the case required. The part is quenched upon removal from the furnace.
2. LIQUID-SALT METHOD, Fig. 31-5. This technique is also known as CYANIDING and involves heating the part in a molten

cyanide salt bath and then quenching. The immersion period is usually less than one hour.

Fig. 31-4. Packing part to be casehardened in a container of carbonaceous material.

Fig. 31-5. Battery of carburizing salt baths such as used for heat treating a wide range of jet aircraft parts. (A. F. Holden Co.)

Fig. 31-6. Molds for plastic bowling pins being placed in a furnace for casehardening by gas method.
(Lindberg Steel Treating Co.)

3. GAS METHOD, Fig. 31-6. NITRIDING is another term for this process. It involves placing the parts in a special airtight heating chamber where ammonia gas is introduced at high temperature and decomposes into nitrogen and hydrogen. The nitrogen enters the steel to form nitrides which give an extreme hardness to the surface.

Fig. 31-7. A railroad rail being flame hardened.

SURFACE HARDENING

Surface hardening, Fig. 31-7, is the process that permits the surface of high carbon and alloy steels to be hardened without affecting the internal structure. FLAME HARDENING and INDUCTION HARDENING are used to attain these characteristics. Flame hardening involves the rapid heating of the surface with the flame of an acetylene torch, and then quenching the heated surface. Induction hardening makes use of a high frequency electrical current to heat the material. It is very rapid and ideal for production hardening.

Fig. 31-9. Aircraft structural members being lowered into tempering pit of gantry furnace. (Lindberg Steel Treating Co.)

TEMPERING or DRAWING OPERATION, Fig. 31-9. This involves heating the piece to below critical temperature (300-1300 deg. F.), and allowing it to cool in still air. With the internal stresses released, the toughness and impact resistance increases. As the temperature is increased, the ductility increases but there is a decrease in hardness and strength.

FURNACES

The furnace must be capable of reaching and maintaining the temperatures needed for heat

Fig. 31-8. Tray of seat belt buckles ready for heat treating.

HARDENING

Hardening, Fig. 31-8, is a process normally used to obtain the optimum physical qualities in steel. It is accomplished by heating the part to a predetermined temperature for a predetermined length of time. The temperature at which steel will harden is called the CRITICAL TEMPERATURE and may range from 1400 to 2400 deg. F., depending on the carbon and alloy content. After heating, the part is quenched in water, brine, oil or a blast of cold air. Water or brine is used to quench plain carbon steel, while oil is used to quench alloy steel. Blasts of cold air are used for the high alloy steels.

Quenching leaves the steel hard and brittle, and it may fracture if exposed to a sudden change in temperature. For most purposes, this brittleness and hardness must be reduced by a

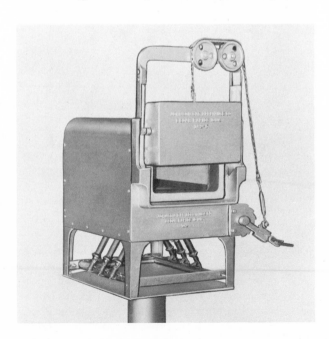

Fig. 31-10. Box or muffle type heat treating furnace.

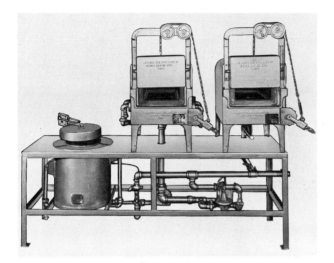

Fig. 31-11. Unit of two muffle type furnaces, and pot type heat treating furnace.

treatment. They are of two distinct types: the BOX or MUFFLE TYPE, such as shown in Fig. 31-10, and the POT TYPE, Fig. 31-11. A PY-ROMETER, Figs. 31-12 and 31-13, must be used for accurate control of temperatures. Industry makes use of many variations of the two types

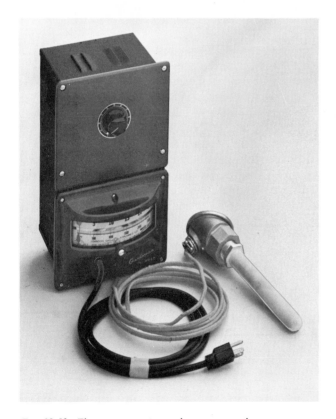

Fig. 31-12. The pyrometer is used to measure the temperatures in the furnaces. (Johnson Gas Appliance Co.)

of furnaces. Some have a continuous belt for high production rates. Others may be several stories high while still others can be sealed and flooded with inert gases (gases that do not oxidize the surface of the metal). A furnace of this type is shown in Fig. 31-15. Furnaces are heated by gas or oil, or electric power.

HOW TO HARDEN CARBON TOOL STEEL

The exact critical temperature and quenching procedure for the various kinds of steel will be found in information sheets furnished by steel manufacturers on hardening and tempering, and in machinist's handbooks.

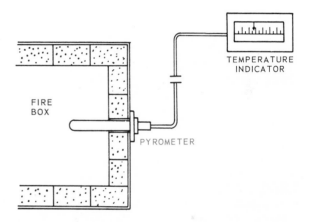

Fig. 31-13. Cross section of a furnace with a pyrometer in place.

Accurate temperatures are obtained by the use of a pyrometer. This instrument accurately measures the furnace temperature. If the furnace is not equipped with such a device, it becomes necessary to judge the temperature by the color of the steel as it heats up.

The following procedure is recommended when hardening steel:

1. Light the furnace, following the manufacturer's instructions.
   CAUTION: Stand to one side and do not look into the furnace when you start it. When the gas has ignited, adjust the air and gas valves for the best combination.
2. Heat the metal to its critical temperature and let it soak at this temperature until the work is heated evenly throughout.
3. Preheat the jaws of the tongs and remove the piece from the furnace.
4. Quench the piece in water or oil depending upon the type of steel used. Water quench-

ing causes very rapid cooling and creates strains that may cause the metal to develop cracks. Only certain steels may be quenched in water. Oil cools the metal more slowly and therefore creates fewer stresses in the metal. Steels are usually classed as WATER HARDENING or OIL HARDENING, according to the process recommended for use with them. The quenching technique is critical. To secure an even hardness throughout the piece, long slender pieces are dipped straight down into the quenching medium with an up and down motion. Avoid a circular motion as this may cause the piece to warp. Other pieces should be moved around in such a manner to permit them to cool quickly and evenly.

Steel that has been hardened properly will be "glass hard" and too brittle for much use. Hardness may be checked by trying to file the surface of the work. A file will not score the surface if it has been hardened properly. DO NOT USE A NEW FILE FOR TESTING.

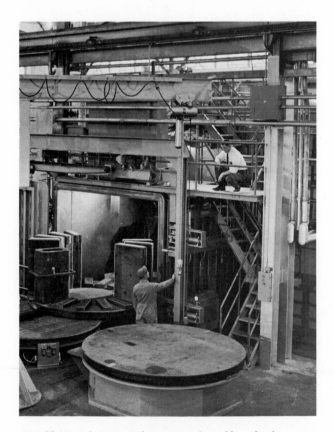

Fig. 31-14. A furnace used to prepare the molds and to heat treat large investment castings.
(Austenal Co., Div. of Howe Sound Co.)

HOW TO TEMPER CARBON STEEL

Tempering should follow immediately after hardening as the "glass hard" piece may crack

Fig. 31-15. A hydrogen atmosphere high temperature furnace.
(Allegheny Ludlum Steel Corp.)

if it is exposed to a sudden change in temperature. Tempering should be done as follows:

1. Polish the hardened piece with abrasive cloth.
2. Reheat to the correct tempering temperature. Use the color scale as a guide. Apply heat evenly. When the proper color has been reached, quench the piece in oil.
3. Small tools are best tempered by placing them on a steel plate that has been heated red hot. Have the point of the tool extending beyond the edge of the plate. Watch the temper color as the piece heats up. Quench when the proper color has reached the tool point.

HOW TO CASE HARDEN STEEL

Of the several methods of casehardening, probably the simplest and requiring a minimum of equipment, is CARBURIZING using a non-poisonous compound such as KASENIT. CYANIDING is not recommended for the school shop because potassium cyanide is a deadly poison and VERY DANGEROUS to use under any but ideal conditions.

There are two methods recommended for using Kasenit:
METHOD #1
1. Light and adjust the furnace.
2. Heat the work to a bright red - 1650-1700

deg. F., Fig. 31-15. Use a pyrometer to measure the temperature, Fig. 31-16.

3. Dip, roll or sprinkle the powder on the piece, Fig. 31-17. The powder will melt and adhere to the surface forming a shell.

4. Reheat to a bright red and hold at this temperature for a few minutes.

5. Quench in clean, cold water.

The second method is used when a deeper case is required:

METHOD #2

1. Secure a container large enough to hold the work. A tin can may be used if care is taken to burn off the tin coating before use.

2. Completely cover the job with compound, Fig. 31-4.

3. Place the entire unit in the furnace and heat to a red heat. Hold the temperature for 5 to 30 min. depending on the depth of the case required.

4. Quench the job in clean, cool water using dry tongs for handling.

Fig. 31-16. A pyrometer should be used to maintain the recommended heat (1650 - 1700°F.).

Fig. 31-17. Dip, roll or sprinkle Kasenit on the work to be case-hardened, until a shell of the powder is formed.

Fig. 31-18. Brinell Hardness Tester. (Detroit Testing Machine Co.)

HARDNESS TESTING

Hardness testing is a process used to make certain that the metal is brought to the best condition of heat treatment or cold work, or a combination of the two, for its particular use.

The more commonly used method is concerned with the distance a steel ball or special shaped diamond penetrates into the metal under a specific load. BRINELL and ROCKWELL testing machines, known as INDENTATION HARDNESS TESTERS, are used. The HARDNESS NUMBER indicates the degree of hardness of the material.

BRINELL HARDNESS TESTER

The Brinell Hardness Tester, Fig. 31-18, makes use of a steel ball which is forced into the metal. A given load is applied for 30 seconds, and upon removing the load, the diameter of the impression produced is measured with a microscope containing a graduated scale. The microscope reading is compared with a table that gives the hardness number. The narrower the indentation, the harder the metal and the higher the hardness number.

ROCKWELL HARDNESS TESTER

The Rockwell Hardness Tester, Fig. 31-19, utilizes a steel ball and a diamond penetrator to measure the degree of hardness. The diamond penetrator is used for testing all heat treated

Fig. 31-19. Rockwell Hardness Tester.
(Wilson Mechanical Instrument Div.)

steel, while the ball is used for other materials. A light load is applied to the ball or cone, after which a dial gauge on the machine is set to zero. A major load is added and removed. The dial gauge then indicates the Rockwell hardness directly.

SHORE SCLEROSCOPE

A hardness tester that operates on a different principle is known as the Shore Scleroscope, Fig. 31-20. A diamond-faced hammer is dropped within a glass tube on the surface of the piece being tested. The height of the rebound indicates the degree of hardness. This tester does not mar the surface tested and can be used to test very large pieces.

SAFETY

1. Heat treating involves metal heated to very high temperatures. Handle it with the appropriate tools.
2. Wear goggles and the proper protective clothing - gloves, apron (never one that is greasy or oil soaked).
3. Never look at the flames in the furnace unless you are wearing tinted goggles.

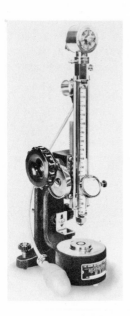

Fig. 31-20. The Shore Scleroscope.
(Shore Instrument & Mfg. Co.)

4. Do not try to light the furnace until you have been instructed in its operation. If you are not sure how it should be done ask for further instructions.
5. Be sure the area is properly ventilated.
6. DO NOT use potassium cyanide as a case-hardening medium.
7. Do not stand over the quenching bath when immersing work.

TEST YOUR KNOWLEDGE, Unit 31

1. Casehardening means that the metal has been:
   a. Properly tempered.
   b. Hardened only on its surface.
   c. Softened.
   d. Annealed.
2. _____ is the heat treating process that re-duces the hardness of the metal to make it easier to machine.
3. Tempering a piece of hardened steel makes it:
   a. Brittle.
   b. Tough.

c. Soft.
d. Flexible.
e. None of the above.

4. _____, _____ and blasts of cool air are used as quenching mediums.

5. A _____ must be used for accurate control of temperatures in the furnace. It is used to measure the temperature in the furnace.

6. List the three kinds of hardness testers:
   a._____.
   b._____.
   c._____.

7. _____ is not used for casehardening in the school shop because it is a deadly poison.

RESEARCH AND DEVELOPMENT

1. Secure pieces of material that have been heat treated by the various techniques. Mount them on a panel for easy observation and comparison of uses.
2. The METCALF Experiment is a simple way to show the grain structure of heat treated metal and the effect of heat on steel. How is it performed? Perform the experiment and mount the pieces that show the results on a panel for observation.
3. Secure pieces of heat treated nonferrous metals from industrial sources. How do their uses compare with the uses of the heat treated steel on the first display panel?
4. Prepare a metallic specimen that has been heat treated, for observation under a microscope. Do the same to an identical piece of steel cut from the same piece of stock, which has not been heat treated. Examine both under a microscope. What differences can be noted? Let the class examine the specimens under the microscope. What conclusions can be made?
5. Demonstrate the proper way to caseharden low carbon steel by carburizing. Use Kasenit as the source of carbon.
6. Demonstrate the proper way to temper a hardened piece of tool steel.

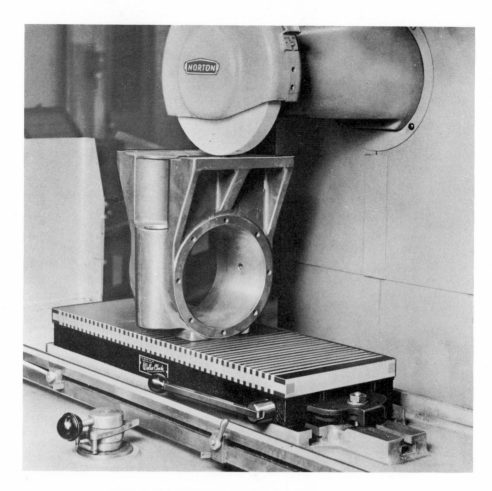

*Industry photo--Permanent type magnet chuck being used
to hold awkward-shaped piece for surface grinding.
(O. S. Walker Co.)*

Unit 32

METAL FINISHES

Finishes for metals and the methods used to apply them play an important part in the metal-working industry. They are applied for:

1. PROTECTION - All metals are affected to some degree by contaminants in the atmosphere and by abrasion.
2. APPEARANCE - More important than often realized. The sale of a product is often decided when its appearance is pleasing and gives the impression of quality.
3. IDENTIFICATION - Makes the product stand out over its competition, or to be inconspicuous and blend into its surroundings.

TYPES OF FINISHES

The finishes fall into several categories. However, regardless of the type which is applied, the metal surface must be clean of any oxidation, dirt and oil and grease. The oxidation may be removed mechanically or chemically. Oil and grease are removed with solvents.

MECHANICAL FINISHES

Mechanical finishes are most frequently applied to aluminum, copper base alloys, stainless steel and the precious metals. They include:

BUFFING, Fig. 32-1, is the brightest mechanical finish. A smooth bright finish is accomplished by two or more buffing operations with progressively softer buffs and/or finer abrasive compounds. Copper-base alloys must be protected by a clear lacquer or plastic to preserve the highly reflective surface.

WIRE BRUSHING, Fig. 32-2, produces a smooth satin sheen. Smoothness depends on wire size of the wheel, the thinner the wire the smoother the surface. Wheel brushes made with

Fig. 32-1. FINISHING - A smooth surface is given the spoon handle with fine abrasive, on a high-speed revolving buffing wheel. (International Silver Co.)

Fig. 32-2. Applying a satin finish to stainless steel sheet with a wire brush. (Osborn Mfg. Co.)

a combination of wire and fiber are often used for burr removal in addition to surface finishing, Fig. 32-3.

SANDBLASTING yields a matte finish. It is accomplished by spraying the surface with a fine abrasive.

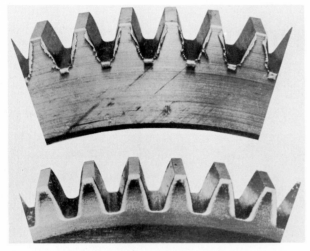

Fig. 32-3. Above. Gear with burrs. Below. Gear after burrs have been removed, using wire brush.
(Osborn Mfg. Co.)

METAL COATINGS

Metal coatings, with the exception of electroplating, are primarily applied to steel. They adhere to the steel surface tightly enough to offer protection from corrosion. The more commonly used techniques include:

HOT DIPPING, Fig. 32-4. The coating is applied by hot dipping the steel in molten aluminum, zinc, lead, tin or a lead-tin alloy. GALVANIZED STEEL is an example of this type finish. Copper can be hot dipped in tin, lead or a lead-tin alloy.

ELECTROPLATING, Fig. 32-5. A metal coating is deposited on a metal surface by the use of an electrical current. Practically any metal may be used as the coating. Coating thickness can be closely controlled and, unlike many other metal coating processes, can deposit wear resistant coatings as well as adding a coating that is attractive in appearance.

METAL SPRAYING. Metal wire or powder is heated to its melting point and sprayed by air pressure onto the work surface. This process is explained more completely in Unit 42.

ORGANIC COATINGS

A wide range of finishes fall into this category. Paints, varnishes, lacquers, enamels, the various plastic base and epoxies in both clear and pigmented formulas are the most common of the organic coatings. They set by the removal of their solvents. This may be accomplished by air drying or baking. A primer is often required

Fig. 32-4. Hot dipping steel pipe in molten zinc.
(American Hot Dip Galvanized Assoc., Inc.)

to secure a satisfactory bond between the metal and the finish. Castings may require a filler to smooth out the rough cast surface.

Organic coatings are applied by:

BRUSHING - At one time was a common method used to apply finishes.

SPRAYING - The finish is atomized and propelled to the work surface by air pressure, Fig. 32-6. Small pressure spray cans, offered in a wide range of colors, are available. Spraying is easily adapted to mass-production techniques, Fig. 32-6a.

Fig. 32-5. *SILVERPLATING - Forks rotate in plating tank containing cyanide solution and bars of pure silver. Amount of electric current and length of time pieces remain in tank determine amount of silver deposited on each piece.*
(International Silver Co.)

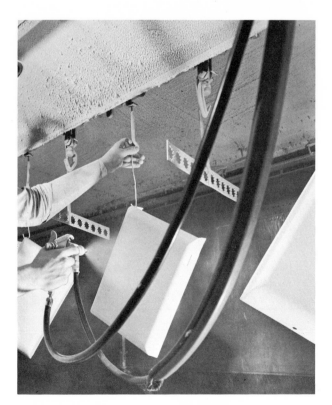

Fig. 32-6. *Spraying small parts.*

ROLLER COATING - Can be used only on flat surfaces. A low-cost system that can be mechanized.

DIPPING - The part is dipped into the finish, removed and allowed to dry. Widely used by the auto industry to apply body primer.

FLOW COATING - The part is flooded with the finish and allowed to drain while held in an atmosphere saturated with solvent vapor. Drying is then delayed until draining is complete.

INORGANIC COATINGS

Several well-known finishing materials fall under this classification. The most familiar are:

VITREOUS OR PORCELAIN ENAMELING - These are glass coatings that are fused to sheet

Fig. 32-6a. *Spraying is easily adapted to mass-production techniques. Here three spray guns are used to finish an electric mixer base. (DeVilbiss Co.)*

or cast metals to form an extremely hard coating that is smooth and easy to clean, Fig. 32-7. Available in a wide range of colors, they can be applied to most metals that remain solid, and do not oxidize too much at firing temperature. The coating is applied as a thin slurry known as "slip" and, after drying, is fired to about 1500 deg. until it fuses to the metal surface. Most kitchen and bathroom fixtures are protected with porcelain enamel. Fig. 32-8, shows porcelain enamel being applied to kitchen equipment.

ANODIZING - A process that applies an oxide coating to aluminum. It is done in a manner similar to electroplating. The coating produced can be dyed in a wide range of colors which becomes part of the surface of the metal.

OTHER FINISHES

The finishes in this group offer the least protection and durability. For this reason they are

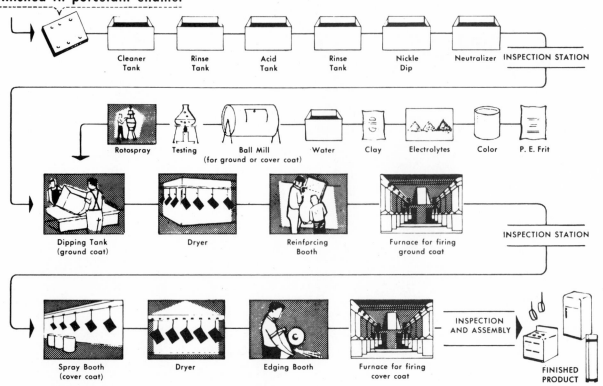

Steel parts or parts to be finished in porcelain enamel

Cleaner Tank — Rinse Tank — Acid Tank — Rinse Tank — Nickle Dip — Neutralizer — INSPECTION STATION

Rotospray — Testing — Ball Mill (for ground or cover coat) — Water — Clay — Electrolytes — Color — P. E. Frit

Dipping Tank (ground coat) — Dryer — Reinforcing Booth — Furnace for firing ground coat — INSPECTION STATION

Spray Booth (cover coat) — Dryer — Edging Booth — Furnace for firing cover coat — INSPECTION AND ASSEMBLY — FINISHED PRODUCT

Fig. 32-7. How porcelain enamel finishes are made.
(Porcelain Enamel Institute, Inc.)

Fig. 32-8. Porcelain enamel being sprayed on washer cabinets. Note the unusual protective gear worn by the men.   (DeVilbiss Co.)

seldom used by industry:

WAXING - This finish is simple to apply, but should only be used for indoor applications. A paste wax is applied to the metal surface which has been warmed slightly. Allow the waxed surface to cool before polishing with a soft cloth.

HEATING - The metal is heated until the desired temper color appears. It is then plunged into cool water. The finished surface must be protected with clear lacquer or plastic spray.

Fig. 32-9. A variable speed polishing and buffing lathe. (Osborn Mfg. Co.)

METAL BUFFING

Buffing should not be attempted until all tool marks and major scratches have been removed with abrasive cloth. After the surface has been prepared, select a buffing compound and wheel that will produce the surface required. The wheels are mounted on a polishing lathe, Fig. 32-9. Use a separate wheel for each step of the polishing operation.

Buffing is usually done in two operations. A hard wheel (made of many layers of cotton flannel, felt, canvas or leather, sewn or glued together to make the wheel face stiff but with some give) is charged with a greaseless abrasive such as tripoli or pumice in bar or cake form. The glue that holds the abrasive in shape melts when the bar is held against the wheel, causing the abrasive to stick to the wheel face. This abrasive-wheel combination is used to remove the scratches formed by the abrasive cloth.

A fine abrasive belt is frequently used in industrial applications for this operation, Fig. 32-10.

The final polishing is done with a loose wheel (made of many layers of flannel not sewn together) and a polishing compound. This compound consists of a soft abrasive such as rouge or whiting and a bonding agent of tallow, glue, oil or chemicals, that holds it in bar or cake

Fig. 32-10. EDGE POLISHING - Fine abrasive belts are used to polish edge surfaces of spoons and all other articles of flatware.

form. The bonding agent also enables it to stick to the buffing wheel.

One of the fundamental polishing techniques is the correct positioning of the work. Polishing is done best when the work is held below the centerline of the wheel, Fig. 32-11, Detail (A).

When considerable stock must be removed, best results can be obtained by pulling the work

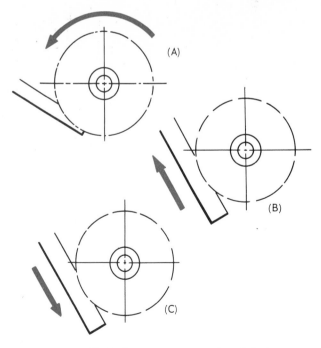

Fig. 32-11. Positioning piece to be polished.

against the rotation of the wheel, Detail (B). It is also safer because the hands are being pulled away from the wheel.

The final polish is obtained by making light downward passes on the wheel, Fig. 32-11, Detail (C).

Remove buffing residue with warm soapy water or a solvent.

SAFETY

1. Read instructions on finish container and follow them carefully.
2. Wash your hands after applying finish or using solvents to clean the work.
3. Examine the work for rough edges and burrs before attempting to clean it.
4. Use a well-ventilated area to apply finishes.
5. Keep open flames and sparks away from areas where finishes are being applied or solvents being used.
6. Use a filter mask when spraying finishes.
7. Wear goggles when buffing.
8. Secure immediate medical attention if solvents or foreign matter get into your eye.
9. Clean up any spilled solvents or finishes.
10. Dispose of used waste or wiping cloths by placing them in steel safety cans.

TEST YOUR KNOWLEDGE, Unit 32

1. Finishes are applied for what reasons?
   a._____ .
   b._____ .
   c._____ .
2. Buffing is a _____ finish usually applied to aluminum, copper base alloys, stainless steel and precious metals.
3. Before any finish can be applied the surface of the metal must be _____ .
4. _____ _____ produces a smooth satin sheen on the surface of the metal.
5. Galvanized steel is an example of ___ _____ .
6. Paints and varnishes may be applied by the following methods:
   a._____ .
   b._____ .
   c._____ .
   d._____ .
   e._____ .
7. Porcelain enamel is a _____ coating that is fused to the metal.
8. _____ and _____ are the easiest finishes to apply but offer the least protection and durability.

RESEARCH AND DEVELOPMENT

1. Visit a local body and fender shop and observe how an auto body is prepared for finishing, how the finish is applied and what is done to complete the job. Make a report to the class on what you observed.
2. Secure samples of metal finished by wire brushing, buffing and sandblasting. Label and mount them on a display panel.
3. Contact your science teacher for the equipment needed to demonstrate electroplating to the shop class.
4. Demonstrate hot dipping to the class. Use a lead-tin alloy (solder).
5. Prepare samples of metal sheet that have been finished by brushing, spraying, roller coating, dipping and flow coating. Label and mount them on a display panel for comparison purposes.

Unit 33

GRINDING

GRINDING, Fig. 33-1, is the operation that removes material by rotating an abrasive wheel against the work. It is often used for sharpen-

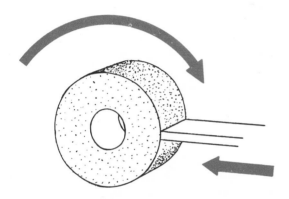

Fig. 33-1. How a typical grinder works.

ing tools, removing material that is too hard to be machined by any other method or when fine surface finishes and close tolerances are required.

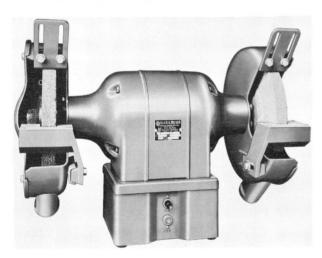

Fig. 33-2. The bench grinder. Eye shields have not been mounted. (Black & Decker Mfg. Co.)

BENCH AND PEDESTAL GRINDER

The familiar bench and pedestal grinders are the simplest and most widely used grinding machines. The grinding done on them is called OFFHAND GRINDING; that is, work that

Fig. 33-3. The pedestal grinder. (South Bend Lathe Inc.)

does not require great accuracy of size or shape is held in the hands and manipulated until ground to the desired shape.

The bench grinder, Fig. 33-2, is a grinder that is fitted to a bench or table. The grinding wheels mount directly onto the motor shaft; one is coarse for roughing, and the other is fine for finish grinding.

The pedestal grinder is usually larger than the bench grinder, and is equipped with a base (pedestal) that is fastened to the floor. The DRY

TYPE, Fig. 33-3, has no provisions for cooling the work during grinding other than a water container into which the tool may be dipped. In the WET TYPE, Fig. 33-4, a coolant system is built into the grinder and keeps the wheels

Fig. 33-4. Pedestal grinder with a built in coolant system. (Hammond Machinery Builders Inc.)

constantly flooded with fluid. The coolant washes away particles of loose abrasive and metal and keeps the work cool.

Bench and pedestal grinders can be dangerous if not used properly. They must never be used unless fitted with guards and safety glass EYE SHIELDS, Fig. 33-5. Even then, it is advisable to wear goggles. A TOOL REST is provided to support the work while grinding. It is recommended that the rests be adjusted to within 1/16 in. of the wheels. This will prevent

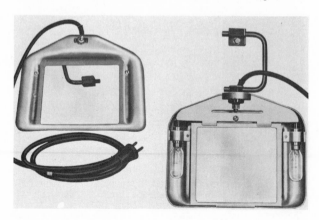

Fig. 33-5. Eye shields for bench and pedestal type grinders.

work from being wedged between the rest and the wheel. Turn the wheel by hand after adjusting the rest, to be sure there is sufficient clearance.

Grinding wheels can be another source of danger and should be examined frequently for eccentricity and soundness. A new wheel can be tested by suspending it on a string or wire and tapping the side of the wheel with a light metal rod. A solid wheel will give off a clear ringing sound. A wheel which does not give off such a sound must be assumed to be cracked and should be destroyed. Under no condition should it be used. Because it is not possible to check the wheels by this manner each time the grinder is used, it is considered safe practice never to stand in front of a grinder when it is first turned on.

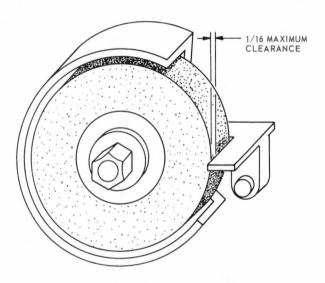

Fig. 33-6. A properly spaced tool rest.

The wheel must also run true and be balanced on the shaft. A WHEEL DRESSER, Fig. 33-7, should be used to bring abrasive wheels back to round and remove the glaze. The dresser is supported on the tool rest and is held firmly against the wheel with both hands, Fig. 33-7a. It is moved back and forth across the surface.

Maximum efficiency can be secured from the grinder if the following recommendations are heeded:

1. Use the face of the wheel, never the sides.
2. Move the work back and forth across the face of the wheel. Even wear will result and prevent the wheel from becoming grooved.
3. Keep the wheel dressed and the tool rests

Fig. 33-7. A mechanical wheel dresser. (Black and Decker Co.)

properly adjusted.

4. Soft metals like aluminum, brass and copper tend to load (clog) the abrasive wheel. If the grinder is to be used primarily for tool grinding, it is suggested that another grinder be secured for grinding soft metals, castings and weldments.

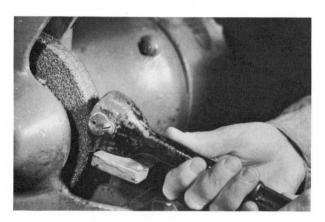

Fig. 33-7a. Using a wheel dresser.

FLEXIBLE SHAFT HAND GRINDERS

Flexible shaft hand grinders, Fig. 33-8, perform many grinding jobs from light deburring

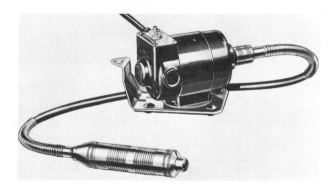

Fig. 33-8. A flexible shaft hand grinding unit. (Dumore Co.)

and polishing to light milling operations. They are used extensively on jobs such as finishing dies, Fig. 33-9.

Fig. 33-9. Finishing a die with a hand grinder.

SAFETY

1. Always wear goggles or an eye shield when performing any grinding operation.
2. Never put a wheel on the grinder before checking it for soundness. Destroy wheels that are not sound.
3. Because it is not always possible to check the wheel on the grinder each time you use it, it is considered good practice to stand to the side of the machine when it is first turned on and until it reaches operating speed. This will keep you clear of flying pieces if the wheel shatters.
4. Do not attempt to use a grinder unless the wheel guards are in place and securely fastened.
5. If the grinding operation is to be performed dry, do not forget to hook up the exhaust attachment before starting.
6. Check the machine thoroughly before using it. Lubricate it according to the manufacturer's specifications.
7. Keep your hands clear of the rotating grinding wheel. It is a cutting tool and can cause serious injuries.
8. Make sure that the tool rest is properly adjusted, but never adjust it while the machine is running.
9. Never force work against the grinding wheel.
10. Always stop the machine before making measurements or adjustments.
11. Make sure that the wheel is clear of the work before starting the machine.
12. If a magnetic chuck is used, make sure that it is holding the work solidly before starting to grind.
13. If an automatic feed is to be used, run the work through one cycle by hand to be sure that there is adequate clearance and that the dogs are adjusted properly.

Fig. 33-10. A close up of a cylindrical grinding operation.
(Cincinnati Milling Machine Co.)

14. Keep all tools clear of the work table.
15. Do not permit the wheel to become too badly glazed or loaded before dressing it.
16. Never operate a grinding wheel at speeds higher than that recommended by the manufacturer.
17. Remove your watch before using a magnetic chuck to prevent it from becoming magnetized.

PRECISION GRINDING

Precision grinding is a way to economically remove excess material and to finish hardened steel parts to very accurate sizes with extremely fine surface finishes. Tolerances as close as 1/100000 (0.00001) in. are possible using modern grinding techniques.

Precision grinding includes many specialized

Fig. 33-11. Traverse grinding — the work moves past the revolving grinding wheel. (Norton Co.)

Grinding

CYLINDRICAL GRINDING

In cylindrical grinding, the work is mounted between centers and rotates while in contact with the grinding wheel, Fig. 33-10. Straight, taper and form grinding can be done by this method. Two variations of cylindrical grinding are:

1. TRAVERSE GRINDING, Fig. 33-11. The revolving piece moves past the rotating grinding wheel. A fixed amount of metal is removed on each pass of the work. Traverse grinding permits work wider than the face of the grinding wheel to be ground.

2. PLUNGE GRINDING, Fig. 33-12. The work rotates while in contact with the grinding wheel but does not reciprocate past it, because the wheel is the same width as the area being ground. The infeed of the grinding wheel is continuous rather than intermittent.

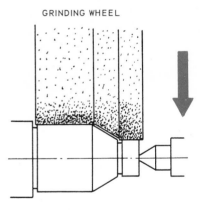

Fig. 33-12. Plunge grinding — the grinding wheel is fed into the rotating work. As the work is no wider than the grinding wheel, it is not necessary for it to be given a reciprocating motion.

CENTERLESS GRINDING

With centerless grinding, Fig. 33-13, it is not necessary to support the work between centers as it is rotated against the grinding wheel. Instead, the piece is positioned on a work support blade and is fed automatically between a regulating or feed wheel which causes the work to rotate, and the grinding wheel which

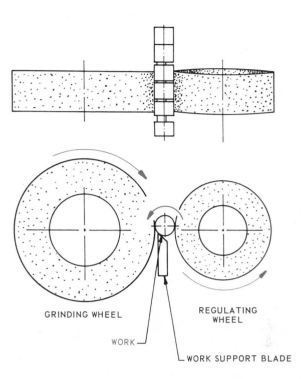

Fig. 33-13. How centerless grinding works.

does the cutting. Through feed is obtained by setting the regulating wheel at a slight angle.

Three variations of centerless grinding are:

1. THROUGH FEED GRINDING. Only simple cylindrical shapes can be produced by this method. The work is fed continuously by hand, or from a feed hopper, into the gap between the grinding wheel and the regulating wheel. The pieces drop off the work support blade when the grinding operation is completed. See Fig. 33-14.

Fig. 33-14. A centerless grinding machine. (Norton Co.)

2. INFEED GRINDING, Fig. 33-15. With this technique, the work is fed into the wheel gap until it reaches a stop. When the grinding operation is complete the work

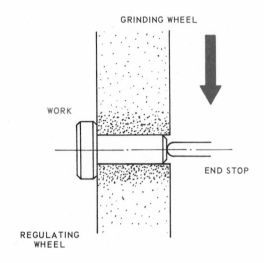

Fig. 33-15. Infeed centerless grinding.

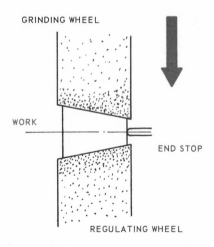

Fig. 33-16. End feed centerless grinding.

is ejected. The diameter of the work is controlled by the width of the gap between the regulating wheel and the grinding wheel. Infeed grinding is ideally suited for grinding work with a shoulder.

3. END FEED GRINDING, Fig. 33-16. End feed grinding is used for grinding spheres and short tapers. Both wheels are dressed to the required shape and the work is fed in from the side of the wheel to a end stop. The finished pieces are automatically ejected.

Fig. 33-17. Internal grinding operation being done on a universal grinding machine. (Norton Co.)

Centerless grinding is done when relatively large quantities of the same part are required. The production rate is high and the costs are low because there is no need to drill center holes nor to mount the work in a holding device.

INTERNAL GRINDING

Internal grinding, Fig. 33-17, is done to secure a fine surface finish and accuracy on internal diameters. The work is held in a chuck and rotates. The revolving grinding wheel moves in and out of the hole during the grinding operation. A special type internal grinding machine is used to finish holes in pieces too large to be rotated, Fig. 33-18. The hole diameter is controlled by regulating the diameter of the circle in which the grinding head moves.

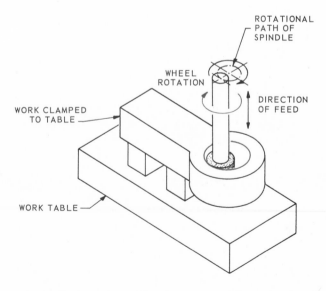

Fig. 33-18. Internal grinding of shapes too large to be rotated.

Fig. 33-19. Machine setup for sharpening a milling cutter. Before grinding operation is started, operator will wear goggles. (Norton Co.)

TOOL AND CUTTER GRINDING

Milling cutters, taps and reamers represent a considerable investment in the inventory of the average machine shop. Since much of their period of usefulness and efficiency depends on the keenness of their cutting edges, it is important that they be sharpened at the first sign or dullness, Fig. 33-18. Setting up a grinding machine is shown in Fig. 33-19.

FORM GRINDING

In form grinding, Fig. 33-20, the grinding wheel is shaped to produce the required design on the work. Thread grinding is an example of form grinding. A form (at top of illustration) is used to guide the cemented diamond particle wheel as it trues the wheel which grinds the required thread shape. The grinding machine compensates for any material removed from the grinding wheel.

SURFACE GRINDING

Flat surfaces are ground on a surface grinder. Two basic types of surface grinding machines are:

1. PLANER TYPE, Fig. 33-21. This machine makes use of a reciprocating motion

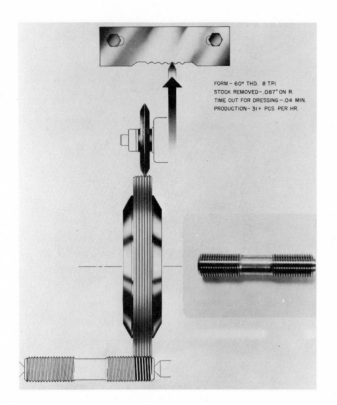

FORM – 60° THD. 8 T.P.I.
STOCK REMOVED – .087" ON R.
TIME OUT FOR DRESSING – .04 MIN.
PRODUCTION – 31+ PCS. PER HR.

Fig. 33-20. Form grinding precision threads on a special stud.
(Jones & Lamson Machine Co.)

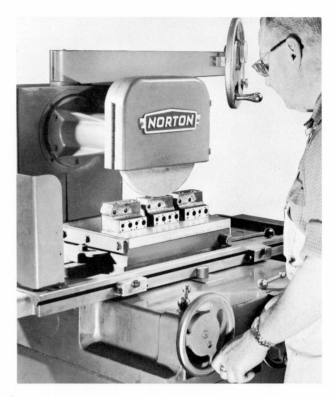

Fig. 33-21. Planer type surface grinder.

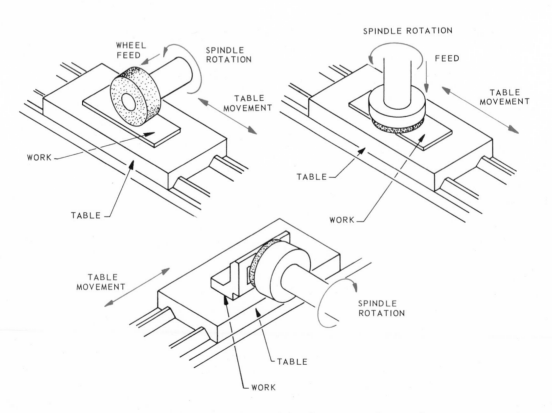

Fig. 33-22. Three variations of the planer type surface grinder.

to move the work table back and forth under the grinding wheel. Three variations of planer type surface grinding are illustrated in Fig. 33-22.

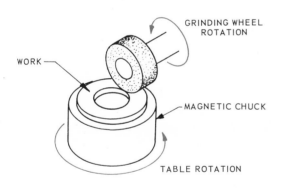

Fig. 33-23. The rotary type surface grinder. (Norton Co.)

2. ROTARY TYPE SURFACE GRINDER, Fig. 33-23. The machines in this category have circular work tables which revolve under the rotating grinding wheel. Two variations of this technique are shown in Fig. 33-24.

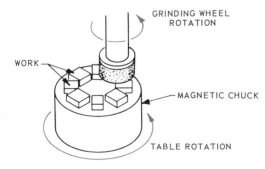

GRINDING WHEEL ROTATION

WORK

MAGNETIC CHUCK

TABLE ROTATION

GRINDING WHEEL ROTATION

WORK

MAGNETIC CHUCK

TABLE ROTATION

Fig. 33-24. Two variations of the rotary type surface grinder.

In a planer type surface grinder the reciprocating table movement can be controlled manually or by means of a mechanical or hydraulic drive. A manually operated machine is shown

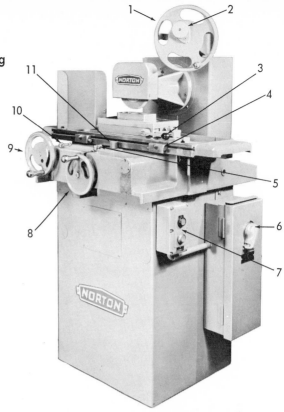

1. Grinding wheel downfeed handwheel... 1 turn equals 0.050 in.
2. Fine downfeed mechanism in increments of 0.0001 in.
3. Control handle for permanent magnetic chuck.
4. Table dog.
5. Cross-feed friction brake for "drag" or locking.
6. Master switch.
7. Electric motor controls.
8. Cross-feed handwheel... one turn equals 0.200 in.
9. Table traverse handwheel.
10. Table traverse friction brake for "drag" or locking.
11. Table traverse stop.

Fig. 33-25. A manually operated surface grinder. This is the type commonly found in the school shop. (Norton Co.)

in Fig. 33-25. A machine operated by automatic power feed is illustrated in Fig. 33-26.

Much of the work done on a surface grinder is held in position by a MAGNETIC CHUCK, Fig. 33-27. This holds the work by exerting magnetic force. Nonmagnetic materials can be ground by bracing with steel blocks or parallels to prevent them from sliding. The MAGNETIC CHUCK, Fig. 33-28, makes use of a permanent magnet, eliminating all cords and any danger of the electrical connection being broken accidentally, permitting the work to fly off.

The ELECTROMAGNETIC CHUCK, Fig. 33-29, makes use of an electric current to create the magnetic field.

Frequently, work mounted on a magnetic chuck becomes magnetized and must be demagnetized before it can be used. A DEMAGNETIZER as shown in Fig. 33-30, may be used to neutralize the piece.

Other ways to mount work on a surface

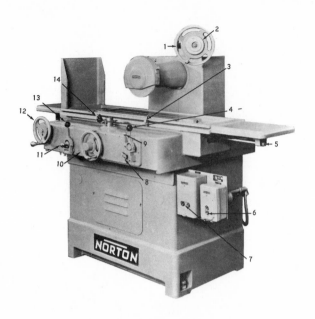

Fig. 33-28. Magnetic chuck with a permanent type magnet.
(O. S. Walker Co., Inc.)

1. Two-speed grinding wheel downfeed handwheel.
2. Fine wheel feed control, graduated to increments of 0.0001 in.
3. Table dog.
4. Power wheel truing control operates cross-feed.
5. Piston rod latches release piston to convert to manual from power traverse operation.
6. Electrical controls for hydraulic fluid pump.
7. Electrical controls for grinding wheel drive.
8. Cross-feed adjustment control.
9. Fast cross-feed control lever.
10. Cross-feed handwheel.
11. Table traverse rate control, 4 in. to 150 ft. per min.
12. Table start-stop lever.
13. Table traverse handwheel.
14. Table reverse lever.

Fig. 33-26. This grinder is fitted with automatic power feeds.
(Norton Co.)

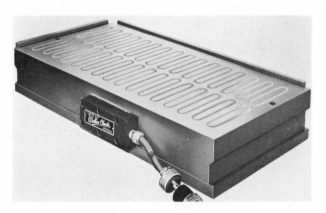

Fig. 33-29. Magnetic chuck which uses electric current to create magnetic field.

Fig. 33-27. Magnetic chuck being used to hold multiple pieces
for surface grinding. (Brown & Sharpe Mfg. Co.)

Fig. 33-30. A demagnetizer.
(L-W Chuck Co.)

grinder are to use a universal vise with index centers, Fig. 33-31, and to clamp it directly to the table, Fig. 33-32.

GRINDING WHEELS

The grinding wheel, with its thousands of abrasive grains, Fig. 33-33, might be compared with a many toothed milling cutter as each of the abrasive grains is actually a cutting tooth.

As the wheel cuts, the chips dull the abrasive grains and wear and cut away the bonding material (the material that holds the abrasive particles together). The ideal grinding wheel, of course, would be one in which the bonding medium wears away slowly enough to get maximum use from the individual abrasive grains, yet rapidly enough to permit the dulled particles to drop off and expose sharp new particles. Because so

Fig. 33-33. Closeup of abrasive grains that make up a typical grinding wheel, magnified about 50x. (Cincinnati Milling Machine Co.)

Fig. 33-31. Centers and an indexing head are used when the shape of the work permits. The indexing head is used in much the same manner as the dividing head in milling.

Fig. 33-34. Diamond tool being used to dress grinding wheel. (Norton Co.)

many factors govern the efficiency of the grinding wheel, the wheel eventually dulls and must be dressed with a DIAMOND DRESSING TOOL, Fig. 33-34. Failure to dress the wheels of a precision grinding machine in time, will result in the faces becoming loaded or glazed so they will not cut freely, Fig. 33-35.

Only man-made abrasives are suitable for modern high speed grinding wheels. The properties and the spacing of the abrasive grains and the composition of the bonding medium can be controlled to obtain the desired grinding performance.

To aid in duplicating grinding performance, a standard system of marking grinding wheels

Fig. 33-32. Work bolted directly to the table for grinding. (Brown & Sharpe Mfg. Co.)

was adopted by the Abrasive Industry. Five factors were considered:

1. ABRASIVE TYPE - manufactured abrasives fall into two main groups. Letter

usually ranging from 10 (coarse) to 600 (fine).

3. GRADE - the strength of the bond holding the wheel together ranging from A to Z

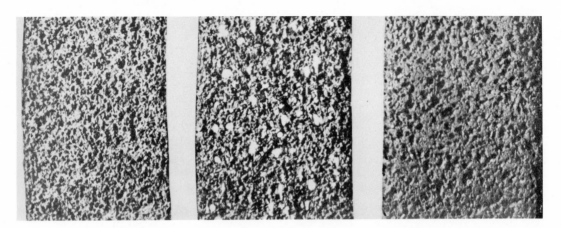

Fig. 33-35. Grinding wheels in various conditions: (A) Properly dressed. (B) Loaded. (C) Glazed. (Norton Co.)

symbols are used to identify them:

A - Aluminum Oxide
C - Silicon Carbide

A prefix number is used to designate a particular type of aluminum oxide or silicon carbide abrasive.

2. GRAIN SIZE - Indicated by a number

(soft to hard).

4. STRUCTURE - the grain spacing or the manner in which the abrasive grains are distributed throughout the wheel. It is numbered 1 to 12. The higher the number the "more open" the structure (wider grain spacing).

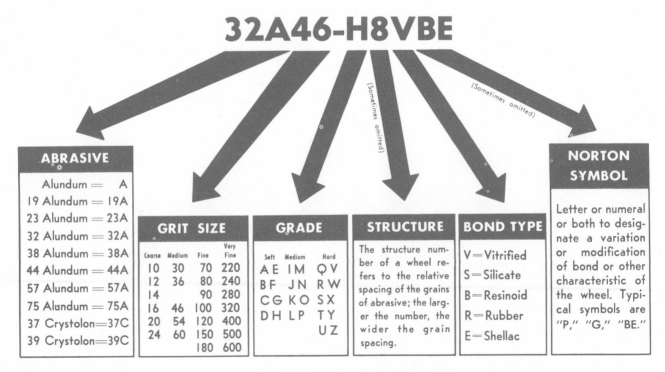

Fig. 33-36. Standard system for marking grinding wheels.

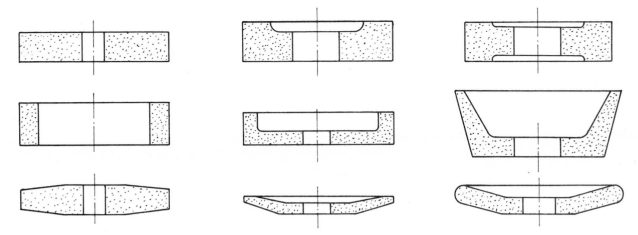

Fig. 33-37. Standard grinding wheel shapes.

5. BOND - the material that holds the abrasive grains together. Five types are used:
   V - Vitrified (carefully selected clays mixed with the abrasive particles are fired until the clay becomes molten and fuses to the abrasive grains.
   B - Resinoin (synthetic resins).
   R - Rubber.
   E - Shellac.
   S - Silicates.

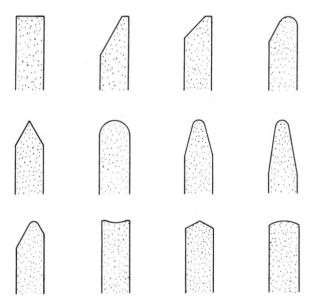

Fig. 33-38. Standard shapes of grinding wheel faces.

Most grinding wheels are made with a vitrified bonding medium.

The acceptance and adoption of the grinding wheel marking system has guaranteed, to a reasonable degree, duplication of grinding performance. The STANDARD SYSTEM FOR MARKING GRINDING WHEELS is given in Fig. 33-36.

GRINDING WHEEL SHAPES

Grinding wheels are made in nine standard shapes, Fig. 33-37, and while twelve basic face shapes are generally available, Fig. 33-38, the shape may be changed to suit the job. Wheels used for internal grinding are available in a large selection of shapes and sizes.

HOW TO MOUNT THE GRINDING WHEEL

Select a grinding wheel recommended for the material to be ground. Check it for soundness and mount it on the spindle. It is essential that

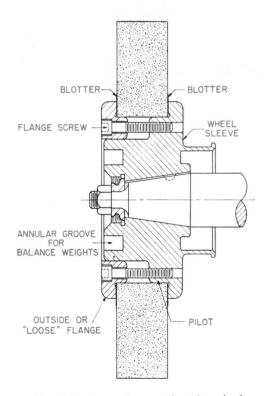

Fig. 33-39. A properly mounted grinding wheel.
(Norton Co.)

it be mounted properly or excessive strains will develop in it causing it to shatter during the grinding operation. Fig. 33-39 illustrates a properly mounted wheel.

TEST YOUR KNOWLEDGE, Unit 33

1. The bench and pedestal grinder are used to do _____ grinding.
2. This grinding technique is so named because:
   a. Can only be used on external work.
   b. The work is too hard to be machined by other means.
   c. The work is manipulated with the fingers until the desired shape is obtained.
   d. None of the above.
3. Name the two types of pedestal grinders:
   a. _____.
   b. _____.
4. The tool rest should be about _____ in. away from the grinding wheel for safety. This prevents the work from _____.
5. Grinding wheel soundness can be checked by _____.
6. As this cannot be done each time, it is recommended that operator _____ when first turning on the machine.
7. _____ grinding mounts the work between centers and rotates it while it is in contact with the grinding wheel.
8. With _____ grinding it is not necessary to support the work between centers as it is rotated against the grinding wheel.
9. The surface grinder is used to grind _____ surfaces.
10. Much work done on the surface grinder is held by a magnetic chuck. True or false?
11. Work held on a magnetic chuck sometimes becomes magnetized. True or false?
12. The magnetic chuck is the only work holding device that can be used safely on the surface grinder. True or false?
13. The grinding wheel actually produces metal chips. True or false?
14. The ideal grinding wheel will:
    a. Wear away as the abrasive particles become dull.
    b. Wear away at a predetermined rate.
    c. Wears away slowly to save money.
    d. None of the above.
15. List the five factors that are the distinguishing characteristics of a grinding wheel:
    a. _____.
    b. _____.
    c. _____.
    d. _____.
    e. _____.
16. Precision grinding is not as accurate as work done on the milling machine. True or false?
17. The major disadvantage of precision grinding is that it cannot be used to machine hard materials. True or false?
18. It is not necessary to wear goggles if the bench grinder is fitted with eye shields. True or false?
19. A solid wheel will give off a clear ringing sound when struck with a metal rod. True or false?
20. What two conditions will prevent a grinding wheel from cutting freely?
    a. _____.
    b. _____.

RESEARCH AND DEVELOPMENT

1. Abrasive machining is a relatively new machining technique. What is it and how does it differ from conventional precision grinding?
2. Prepare a specimen board that shows how a ground surface differs from a surface machined on the lathe, shaper, vertical milling machine and the horizontal milling machine.
3. Secure samples of products machined by precision grinding. Examine them carefully and list their distinguishing characteristics.

4. What is the MOHS SCALE? Prepare a chart showing the common abrasives in order of their hardness. Secure samples to mount on the chart.
5. How are natural sandstone grinding wheels made? Secure samples of natural sandstone and compare them with samples of the man-made abrasives. What, in your opinion, makes the man-made abrasive superior to the natural product.

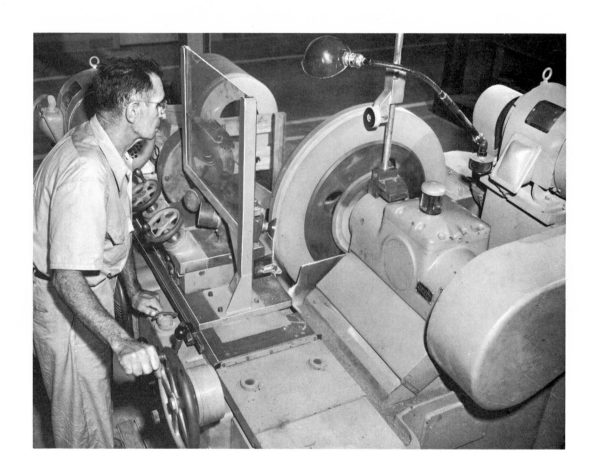

Truing abrasive wheel to required diameter. Note safety precautions being taken to protect the operator.

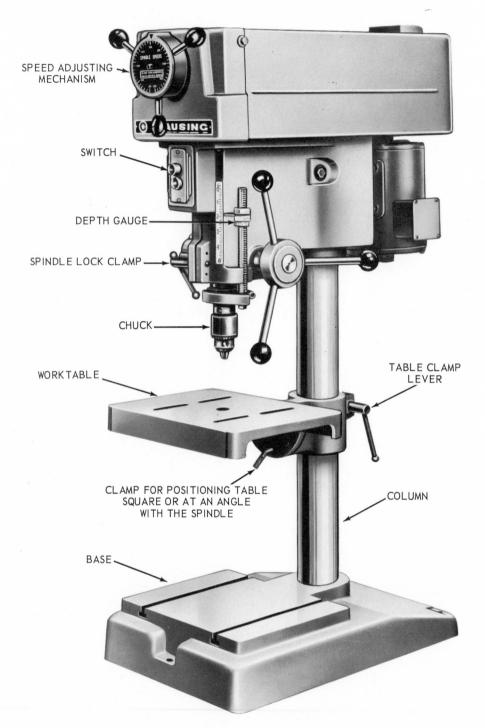

SPEED ADJUSTING
MECHANISM

SWITCH

DEPTH GAUGE

SPINDLE LOCK CLAMP

CHUCK

WORKTABLE

TABLE CLAMP
LEVER

CLAMP FOR POSITIONING TABLE
SQUARE OR AT AN ANGLE
WITH THE SPINDLE

COLUMN

BASE

Fig. 34-1. A bench model drilling machine.
(Atlas Press Co.)

Unit 34

DRILLS AND
DRILLING MACHINES

The drill press, such as shown in the photo, Fig. 34-1, is probably the best known of the machine tools. While it can be used for many different machining operations, the drill press is primarily used for cutting round holes.

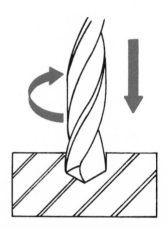

Fig. 34-2. How a drill works.

It operates by rotating a cutting tool, known as a DRILL, against the material with sufficient pressure to cause the drill to penetrate the material, Fig. 34-2.

The size of the drill press is determined by the largest diameter of a circular piece that can be drilled on center, Fig. 34-3. A 14-in. drill press can drill to the center of a 14-in. diameter piece. The center line of the drill is 7 in. from the column.

DRILLS

Common drills are known as TWIST DRILLS because most of them are made by forging or milling rough flutes, and then twisting to a spiral configuration. After twisting, the drills are milled to the desired size, Fig. 34-4, and heat treated.

Drills are made of HIGH SPEED STEEL (HS or HSS) or CARBON STEEL. High speed steel drills can be operated at much higher cutting speeds without danger of burning up.

TYPES OF DRILLS

Industry uses special drills to improve the accuracy of the drilled hole, to speed production

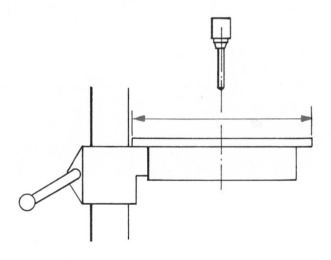

Fig. 34-3. How a drill press is measured.

and to improve drilling efficiency. The STRAIGHT FLUTE DRILL, Fig. 34-5, is designed for cutting brass and other soft metals. The OIL HOLE DRILL, Fig. 34-6, has coolant holes through its body to permit fluid or air to be forced to the point as a coolant or to eject chips from the hole while it is being drilled. THREE and FOUR FLUTE CORE DRILLS, Fig. 34-7, are used to enlarge core holes in castings. Special STEP DRILLS, Fig. 34-8, permit the elimination of one or more drilling operations in production work.

34-1

Fig. 34-4. A closeup of the flute milling operation in the manufacture of a large drill. (Chicago-Latrobe)

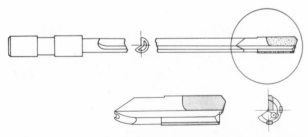

Fig. 34-5. The straight flute drill. The tip (circled) is shown in
larger scale. The shaded portion is tungsten carbide. The large
area does the cutting, the smaller pieces act as wear surfaces.

Fig. 34-6. The oil hole drill.

Fig. 34-7. The multi-flute core drill.

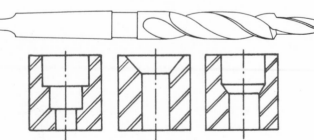

Fig. 34-8. A step drill.

DRILL SIZE

Drill sizes are expressed by the following series:

NUMBERS - #80 to #1 (0.0135-in. to 0.2280-in. diameters).

LETTERS - A to Z (0.234-in. to 0.413-in. diameters).

INCHES AND FRACTIONS THEREOF - 1/64-in. to 3-1/2-in. diameters.

METRIC - 3 mm (0.1181-in. diameter) to 76 mm (2.9921-in. diameter).

The DRILL SIZE CHART, Fig. 34-9, will give an idea of this vast array of drill sizes.

HOW TO MEASURE DRILLS

Most drills, with the exception of small number drills, have the diameter stamped on the shank. These figures frequently become obliterated with use and it is almost impossible to determine the drill diameter without measuring.

Inch	Mm.	Wire Gage	Decimals of an Inch
		80	.0135
		79	.0145
1/64			.0156
	.4		.0157
		78	.0160
		77	.0180
	.5		.0197
		76	.0200
		75	.0210
	.55		.0217
		74	.0225
	.6		.0236
		73	.0240
		72	.0250
	.65		.0256
		71	.0260
	.7		.0276
		70	.0280
		69	.0293
	.75		.0295
		68	.0310
1/32			.0313
	.8		.0315
		67	.0320
		66	.0330
	.85		.0335
		65	.0350
	.9		.0354
		64	.0360
		63	.0370
	.95		.0374
		62	.0380
		61	.0390
	1		.0394
		60	.0400
		59	.0410
	1.05		.0413
		58	.0420
		57	.0430
	1.1		.0433
	1.15		.0453
		56	.0465
3/64			.0469
	1.2		.0472
	1.25		.0492
	1.3		.0512
		55	.0520
	1.35		.0531
		54	.0550
	1.4		.0551
	1.45		.0571
	1.5		.0591
		53	.0595
	1.55		.0610
1/16			.0625
	1.6		.0630
		52	.0635
	1.65		.0650
	1.7		.0669
		51	.0670
	1.75		.0689
		50	.0700
	1.8		.0709
	1.85		.0728
		49	.0730
	1.9		.0748
		48	.0760
	1.95		.0768
5/64			.0781
		47	.0785
	2		.0787
	2.05		.0807
		46	.0810
		45	.0820
	2.1		.0827
	2.15		.0846
		45	.0860
	2.2		.0866
	2.25		.0886
		43	.0890
	2.3		.0906
	2.35		.0925
		42	.0935
3/32			.0938
	2.4		.0945
		41	.0960
	2.45		.0966
		40	.0980
	2.5		.0984
		39	.0995
		38	.1015
	2.6		.1024
		37	.1040
	2.7		.1063
		36	.1065
	2.75		.1083
7/64			.1094
		35	.1100
	2.8		.1102
		34	.1110
		33	.1130
	2.9		.1142
		32	.1160
	3		.1181
		31	.1200
	3.1		.1220
1/8			.1250
	3.2		.1260
	3.25		.1280
		30	.1285
	3.3		.1299
	3.4		.1339
		29	.1360
	3.5		.1378
		28	.1405
9/64			.1406
	3.6		.1417
		27	.1440
	3.7		.1457
		26	.1470
	3.75		.1476
		25	.1495
	3.8		.1496
		24	.1520
	3.9		.1535
		23	.1540
5/32			.1563
		22	.1570
	4		.1575
		21	.1590
		20	.1610
	4.1		.1614
	4.2		.1654
		19	.1660
	4.25		.1673
	4.3		.1693
		18	.1695
11/64			.1719
		17	.1730
	4.4		.1732
		16	.1770
	4.5		.1772
		15	.1800
	4.6		.1811
		14	.1820
		13	.1850
	4.7		.1850
	4.75		.1870
3/16			.1875
	4.8		.1890
		12	.1890
		11	.1910
	4.9		.1929
		10	.1935
		9	.1960
	5		.1969
		8	.1990
	5.1		.2008
		7	.2010
13/64			.2031
		6	.2040
	5.2		.2047
		5	.2055
	5.25		.2067
	5.3		.2087
		4	.2090
	5.4		.2126
		3	.2130
	5.5		.2165
7/32			.2188
	5.6		.2205
		2	.2210
	5.7		.2244
	5.75		.2264
		1	.2280
	5.8		.2283

Fig. 34-9. Decimal equivalents of tool sizes.

Inch	Mm.	Letter Sizes	Decimals of an Inch
	5.9		.2323
		A	.2340
15/64			.2344
	6		.2362
		B	.2380
	6.1		.2402
		C	.2420
	6.2		.2441
		D	.2460
	6.25		.2461
	6.3		.2480
1/4		E	.2500
	6.4		.2520
	6.5		.2559
		F	.2570
	6.6		.2598
		G	.2610
	6.7		.2638
17/64			.2656
	6.75		.2657
		H	.2660
	6.8		.2677
	6.9		.2717
		I	.2720
	7		.2756
		J	.2770
	7.1		.2795
		K	.2810
9/32			.2812
	7.2		.2835
	7.25		.2854
	7.3		.2874
		L	.2900
	7.4		.2913
		M	.2950
	7.5		.2953
19/64			.2969
	7.6		.2992
		N	.3020
	7.7		.3031
	7.75		.3051
	7.8		.3071
	7.9		.3110
5/16			.3125
	8		.3150
		O	.3160
	8.1		.3189
	8.2		.3228
		P	.3230
	8.25		.3248
	8.3		.3268

Inch	Mm.	Letter Sizes	Decimals of an Inch
21/64			.3281
	8.4		.3307
		Q	.3320
	8.5		.3346
	8.6		.3386
		R	.3390
	8.7		.3425
11/32			.3438
	8.75		.3345
	8.8		.3465
		S	.3480
	8.9		.3504
	9		.3543
		T	.3580
	9.1		.3583
23/64			.3594
	9.2		.3622
	9.25		.3642
	9.3		.3661
		U	.3680
	9.4		.3701
	9.5		.3740
3/8			.3750
		V	.3770
	9.6		.3780
	9.7		.3819
	9.75		.3839
	9.8		.3858
		W	.3860
	9.9		.3898
25/64			.3906
	10		.3937
		X	39.70
		Y	.4040
13/32			.4063
		Z	.4130
	10.5		.4134
27/64			.4219
	11		.4331
7/16			.4375
	11.5		.4528
29/64			.4531
15/32			.4688
	12		.4724
31/64			.4844
	12.5		.4921
1/2			.5000
	13		.5118
33/64			.5156
17/32			.5313
	13.5		.5315

Inch	Mm.	Decimals of an Inch
35/64		.5469
	14	.5512
9/16		.5625
	14.5	.5709
37/64		.5781
	15	.5906
19/32		.5938
39/64		.6094
	15.5	.6102
5/8		.6250
	16	.6299
41/64		.6406
	16.5	.6496
21/32		.6563
	17	.6693
43/64		.6719
11/16		.6875
	17.5	.6890
45/64		.7031
	18	.7087
23/32		.7188
	18.5	.7283
47/64		.7344
	19	.7480
3/4		.7500
49/64		.7656
	19.5	.7677
25/32		.7812
	20	.7874
51/64		.7969
	20.5	.8071
13/16		.8125
	21	.8268
53/64		.8281
27/32		.8438
	21.5	.8465
55/64		.8594
	22	.8661
7/8		.8750
	22.5	.8858
57/64		.8906
	23	.9055
29/32		.9063
59/64		.9219
	23.5	.9252
15/16		.9375
	24	.9449
61/64		.9531
	24.5	.9646
31/32		.9688
	25	.9843
63/64		.9844

Inch	Mm.	Decimals of an Inch
1		1.0000
	25.5	1.0039
1 1/64		1.0156
	26	1.0236
1 1/32		1.0313
	26.5	1.0433
1 3/64		1.0469
1 1/16		1.0625
	27	1.0630
1 5/64		1.0781
	27.5	1.0827
1 3/32		1.0938
	28	1.1024
1 7/64		1.1094
	28.5	1.1220
1 1/8		1.1250
1 9/64		1.1406
	29	1.1417
1 5/32		1.1562
	29.5	1.1614
1 11/64		1.1719
	30	1.1811
1 3/16		1.1875
	30.5	1.2008
1 13/64		1.2031
1 7/32		1.2188
	31	1.2205
1 15/64		1.2344
	31.5	1.2402
1 1/4		1.2500
	32	1.2598
1 17/64		1.2656
	32.5	1.2795
1 9/32		1.2813
1 19/64		1.2969
	33	1.2992
1 5/16		1.3125
	33.5	1.3189
1 21/64		1.3281
	34	1.3386
1 11/32		1.3438
	34.5	1.3583
1 23/64		1.3594
1 3/8		1.3750
	35	1.3780
1 25/64		1.3906
	35.5	1.3976
1 13/32		1.4063
	36	1.4173
1 27/64		1.4219
	36.5	1.4370

Page 2 of Fig. 34-9. Decimal equivalents of tool sizes (continued).

When a micrometer is used for measuring, the measurement is made across the drill margins. However, if the drill is worn, the measurement is made on the shank at the end of the flute, Fig. 34-10. The diameter can also be checked with a DRILL GAUGE, Fig. 34-11. Drill gauges are made for various drill series; however, 1/2-in. drills are the largest that can be checked by this method in the fractional series. New drills are checked at the points; worn drills at the end of the flutes.

ALWAYS CHECK THE DRILL'S DIAMETER BEFORE USING.

PARTS OF THE DRILL

The twist drill has been scientifically designed to produce an efficient cutting tool. It

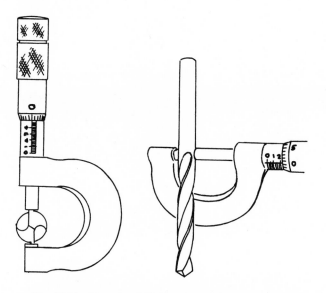

Fig. 34-10. *Measuring drill diameters with a micrometer.*

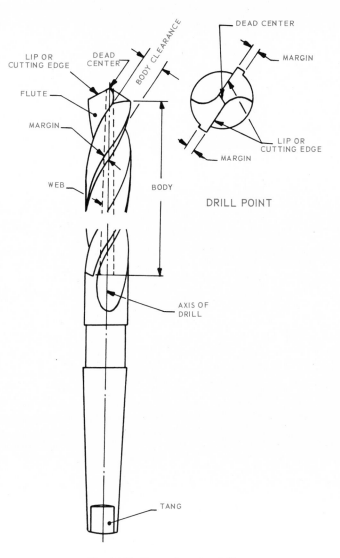

DRILL POINT

Fig. 34-12. *Parts of a twist drill.*

from the lips or cutting edge.

  d. LIP CLEARANCE. The amount the surface of the point is relieved back from the lips.

is composed of three principal parts, Fig. 34-12:

1. The POINT which is the cone-shaped end that does the cutting. The point consists of the following:

  a. DEAD CENTER. The sharp edge at the extreme tip of the drill. This should always be in the exact center of the drill AXIS.

  b. LIPS. The cutting edges of the drill.

  c. HEEL. The portion of the point back

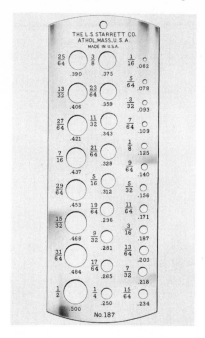

Fig. 34-11. *Drill gauge for measuring fractional size drills. Similar charts are available for measuring letter size, and number size drills.*

2. Twist drills are made with SHANKS that are either STRAIGHT or TAPERED, Fig. 34-13. Straight shank drills are used with a chuck. Taper shank drills have self-holding tapers (No. 1 to No. 5 Morse taper) that fit directly into the drill press spindle. Found on the taper shank is the TANG. This fits into a slot in the spindle, sleeve or socket and assists the shank in driving the tool. The tang also offers a means of separating the taper from the holding device.

3. The BODY is the portion between the point and the shank. The body consists of:
   a. FLUTES. Two or more spiral grooves that run the length of the drill body. The flutes do four things:
      1. Help form the cutting edge of the drill point.
      2. Curl the chip tightly within itself for easier removal.
      3. Form channels through which the chips can escape the hole being drilled.
      4. Allow the lubricant and coolant to get down to the cutting edge.
   b. MARGIN. The narrow strip extending back the entire length of the flute. It is the full diameter of the drill.
   c. BODY CLEARANCE. The part of the drill body that has been reduced in order to cut down friction between the drill and the wall of the hole.
   d. WEB. The metal column that separates the flutes. It gradually increases in thickness toward the shank to give added strength.

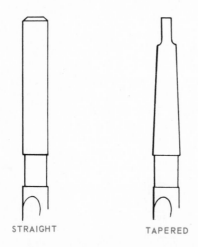

STRAIGHT   TAPERED

HOW TO HOLD DRILLS IN DRILL PRESS

A drill is held in the drill press by either of the following methods:
1. CHUCK. For drills with straight shanks, Fig. 34-14.
2. TAPERED OPENING IN THE DRILL PRESS SPINDLE. For drills with tapered shanks, Fig. 34-15. Drill chucks with tapered shanks make it possible to use straight shank drills when the drill press

Fig. 34-14. A drill chuck.

is fitted with a taper spindle opening.

When a chuck is used, the drill should be inserted and the chuck jaws tightened by hand. After a quick flip of the switch to determine that the drill is centered and running true, tighten the chuck with a CHUCK KEY. ALWAYS REMOVE THE KEY BEFORE TURNING ON THE MACHINE.

Taper shank drills should be wiped clean before inserting the shank into the spindle. Nicks in the shank can be removed with an oilstone otherwise the shank will not seat properly.

Most drill press spindles are made with No. 2 or No. 3 Morse tapers. A drill with a taper shank smaller than the spindle taper must

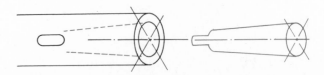

Fig. 34-15. Drill press spindle with tapered opening.

have its shank enlarged by fitting it with a SLEEVE, Fig. 34-16a. Drills with shanks larger than the opening in the spindle can often be used by fitting a SOCKET, Fig. 34-16b. The taper opening in the socket is larger than the taper on the shank.

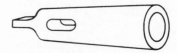

Fig. 34-16a. Drill sleeve.

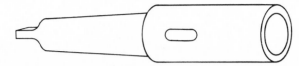

Fig. 34-16b. Drill socket.

Sleeves, sockets and taper shank drills are separated with a DRIFT, Fig. 34-17. To use the drift insert it in the slit with the round edge up, Fig. 34-18. A sharp rap with a lead hammer will cause the separation. NEVER USE A FILE TANG IN PLACE OF A DRIFT. IT WILL DAMAGE THE DRILL SHANK AND MACHINE SPINDLE.

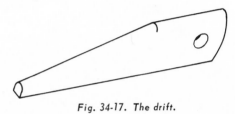

Fig. 34-17. The drift.

Hold the drill when removing it from the spindle to prevent it from falling to the floor. Falling may damage the drill point, and if the drill is large enough, injure your foot.

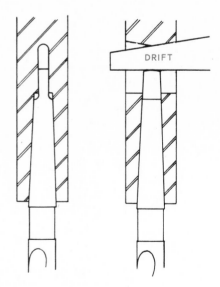

Fig. 34-18. Removing a tapered shank tool from a drill spindle with a drift.

WORK HOLDING DEVICES

Work must be clamped solidly to the drilling machine. When improperly clamped it will spring and move and cause drill damage or

breakage. Serious injury can result from work that becomes loose and spins about. To facilitate the process of holding work, the machinist has the following devices at his disposal.

Fig. 34-19. Above. A swivel vise. The base is designed to permit the vise to swivel through 180 deg. Below. Quick-acting vise. (L-W Chuck Co.)

VISES

Vises, Fig. 34-19, are widely used to hold work of regular size and shape. For best results the vise must be bolted to the drill table. A piece of wood or flat stock placed under the work will protect the vise when the drill breaks through the work. Parallels are often used for this purpose; however, as they are hardened,

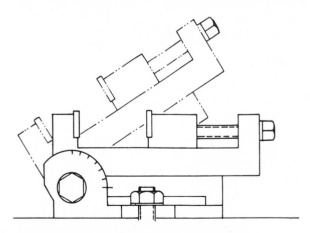

Fig. 34-20. The angular vise can be adjusted through 90 deg. to permit drilling on an angle without tilting the entire vise.

care must be taken to prevent the drill from making contact with them. Seat the work on the parallels by tightening the vise and tapping on the work with a mallet. Loose parallels indicate that the work is not seated properly.

The ANGULAR VISE, Fig. 34-20, permits angular drilling without tilting the drill press table.

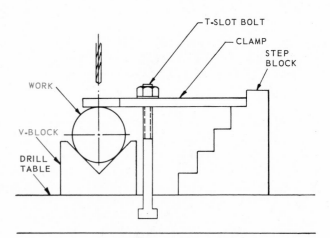

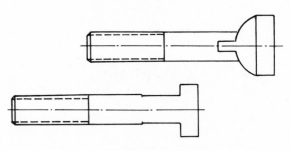

Fig. 34-22. Clamping work in V-Block, to drill press table.

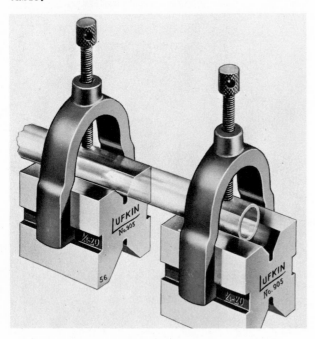

Fig. 34-21. A set of V-Blocks supporting work for drilling. (Lufkin Rule Co.)

V-BLOCKS

V-blocks, Fig. 34-21, support round work for drilling. These are made in many sizes, some are fitted with clamps to hold the work. The larger sizes must be clamped with the work, Fig. 34-22.

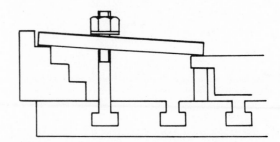

Fig. 34-23. T-Bolt.

T-BOLTS

T-bolts, Fig. 34-23, fit in the slots of the drill press table and fasten the work or clamping devices to the machine. A washer should always be used between the nut and the holding device. For convenience, having at hand an assortment of different length T-bolts is desirable. To reduce the chance of a set-up working loose, place the bolt as close to the work as possible, Fig. 34-24.

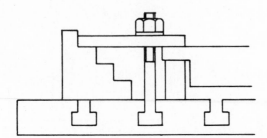

Fig. 34-24. Correct clamping technique is shown at the left. Note that the clamp is parallel and the T-Bolt is close to the work. Clamp slippage can be reduced by placing a piece of paper between the work piece and the clamp. The illustration at the right shows an unsafe method of clamping. The T-Bolt is too far from the work allowing the clamp to spring under pressure.

STRAP CLAMPS

Strap clamps, Fig. 34-25, make the clamping operation easier if a good assortment is available. The elongated slot permits some

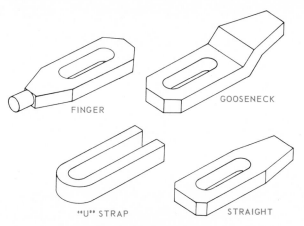

Fig. 34-25. Strap clamps.

adjustment without removing the nut. The U-strap clamp is used when the clamp must bridge the work. It can straddle the drill and not interfere with the drilling operation. The small round piece that projects from the FINGER CLAMP, permits the use of small holes or openings in the work to be used for clamping. Use a strip of copper to protect a machined surface that must be clamped.

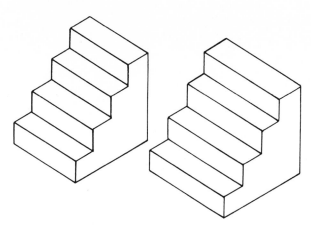

Fig. 34-26. Step blocks.

STEP BLOCKS

The step block, Fig. 34-26, supports the strap clamp opposite the work. The steps allow the adjustments necessary to keep the strap level, Fig. 34-24.

ANGLE PLATE

The angle plate, Fig. 34-27, is used when the work must be clamped to a support. The angle plate is then bolted to the machine table.

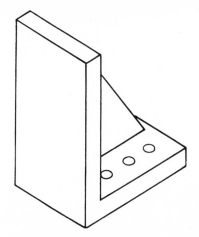

Fig. 34-27. An angle plate.

DRILL JIG

A drill jig, Fig. 34-28, is used when holes must be drilled in a number of identical pieces. It is a clamping device that supports and locks the piece in the proper position and with the use

Fig. 34-28. A typical jig for holding small parts for drilling. The front clamp is removed to show the part being drilled.

of bushings, guides the drill to the correct location. This makes it unnecessary to "lay-out" each individual piece for drilling. Quantity production requires the use of jigs.

PARALLELS

Parallels, Fig. 34-29, can be made from standard steel shapes or from special steel that is heat treated. The heat treated steel is then ground to size. These are helpful for raising work in the vise so that the drilling can be better observed. Parallels must be located so that the drill does not come in contact with them when the drill breaks through.

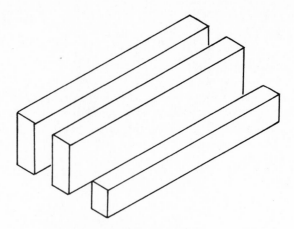

Fig. 34-29. Steel parallels.

CUTTING SPEEDS AND FEEDS

The speed that the drill rotates (CUTTING SPEED) and the distance that it is fed into the work with each revolution (FEED) are important considerations because they govern the time required to produce the hole.

Drill cutting speed, also known as PERIPHERAL SPEED, does NOT refer to the REVOLUTIONS PER MINUTE (RPM) of the drill, but rather to the distance the cutting edge travels, at its circumference, per minute.

FEED

Contrary to popular belief, the spiral of the drill flutes DOES NOT cause the drill to pull itself into the work piece. Constant pressure must

MATERIAL	CUTTING FLUID	SPEED FEET PER MINUTE	FEEDS PER REVOLUTION Over .040 Diameter**				
			Under 1/8	1/8 to 1/4	1/4 to 1/2	1/2 to 1	Over 1
Aluminum & Aluminum Alloys	Sol. Oil, Ker. & Lard Oil, Lt. Oil	200-300	.0015	.003	.006	.010	.012
Aluminum & Bronze	Sol. Oil, Ker. & Lard Oil, Lt. Oil	50-100	.0015	.003	.006	.010	.012
Brass, Free Machining	Dry, Sol. Oil, Ker. & Lard Oil, Lt. Min. Oil	150-300	.0025	.005	.010	.020	.025
Bronze, Common	Dry, Sol. Oil, Lard Oil, Min. Oil	200-250	.0025	.005	.010	.020	.025
Bronze, Soft and Medium Hard	Min. Oil with 5%—15% Lard Oil	70-300	.0025	.005	.010	.020	.025
Bronze, Phosphor, 1/2 hard	Dry, Sol. Oil, Lard Oil, Min. Oil	110-180	.0015	.003	.006	.010	.012
Bronze, Phosphor, Soft	Dry, Sol. Oil, Lard Oil, Min. Oil	200-250	.0025	.005	.010	.020	.025
Cast Iron, Soft	Dry or Airjet	100-150	.0025	.005	.010	.020	.025
Cast Iron, Medium	Dry or Airjet	70-120	.0015	.003	.006	.010	.012
Cast Iron, Hard	Dry or Airjet	30-100	.001	.002	.003	.005	.006
*Cast Iron, Chilled	Dry or Airjet	10-25	.001	.002	.003	.005	.006
*Cast Steel	Soluble Oil, Sulphurized Oil. Min. Oil	30-60	.001	.002	.003	.005	.006
Copper	Dry, Soluble Oil, Lard Oil, Min. Oil	70-300	.001	.002	.003	.005	.006
Magnesium & Magnesium Alloys	Mineral Seal Oil	200-400	.0025	.005	.010	.020	.025
Manganese Copper, 30% Mn.	Soluble Oil, Sulphurized Oil	10-25	.001	.002	.003	.005	.006
Malleable Iron	Dry, Soluble Oil, Soda Water, Min. Oil	60-100	.0025	.005	.010	.020	.025
Monel Metal	Sol. Oil, Sulphurized Oil, Lard Oil	30-50	.0015	.003	.006	.010	.012
Nickel, Pure	Sulphurized Oil	60-100	.001	.002	.003	.005	.006
Nickel, Steel 3-1/2%	Sulphurized Oil	40-80	.001	.002	.003	.005	.006
Plastics, Thermosetting	Dry or Airjet	100-300	.0015	.003	.006	.010	.012
Plastics, Thermoplastic	Soluble Oil, Soapy Water	100-300	.0015	.003	.006	.010	.012
Rubber, Hard	Dry or Airjet	100-300	.001	.002	.003	.005	.006
Spring Steel	Soluble Oil, Sulphurized Oil	10-25	.001	.002	.003	.005	.006
Stainless Steel, Free Mach'g.	Soluble Oil, Sulphurized Oil	60-100	.0025	.005	.010	.020	.025
Stainless Steel, Tough Mach'g.	Soluble Oil, Sulphurized Oil	20-27	.0025	.005	.010	.020	.025
Steel, Free Machin'g SAE 1100	Soluble Oil, Sulphurized Oil	70-120	.0015	.003	.006	.010	.012
Steel, SAE-AISI, 1000-1025	Soluble Oil, Sulphurized Oil	60-100	.0015	.003	.006	.010	.012
Steel, .30-.60% CARB., SAE 1000-9000							
Annealed 150-225 Brinn.	Soluble Oil, Sulphurized Oil	50-70	.0015	.003	.006	.010	.012
Heat Treated 225-283 Brinn.	Sulphurized Oil	30-60	.0025	.005	.010	.020	.025
Steel, Tool Hi. Car. & Hi. Speed	Sulphurized Oil	25-50	.0025	.005	.010	.020	.025
Titanium	Highly Activated Sulphurized Oil	15-20	.0025	.005	.010	.020	.025
Zinc, Alloy	Soluble Oil, Kerosene & Lard Oil	200-250	.0015	.003	.006	.010	.012

*Use Specially Constructed Heavy Duty Drills
**For drill under .040, feeds should be adjusted to produce chips and not powder with ability to dispose of same without packing.

Fig. 34-30. Drill speed and feed table.
(Chicago-Latrobe)

be applied and maintained to advance the drill point at a given rate. This advance is called FEED and is measured in decimal fractions of an inch.

Because so many variables affect results, there can be no hard and fast rule for determining EXACT cutting speeds and feeds for a given material. For this reason the DRILL SPEED AND FEED TABLE, Fig. 34-30, indicates only recommended speeds and feeds. The feed cannot be controlled accurately on a hand fed drill press so the machinist must become aware of the characteristics, such as uniform chips, that indicate whether the drill is being fed at the correct rate. A feed that is too light will cause the drill to scrape and "chatter" and dull rapidly. Chipped cutting edges, drill breakage and the drill heating up despite the application of coolant usually indicates that the feed is too great.

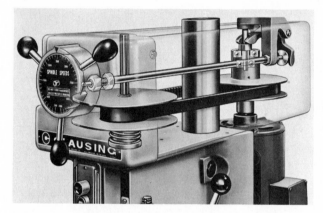

Fig. 34-31. *Split pulley speed control mechanism. The speed is dialed. (Atlas Press Co.)*

SPEED CONVERSION

A problem arises in setting the drill press to the correct speed inasmuch as its speed is given in revolutions per minute (RPM), while the recommended drill cutting speed (CS) is given in feet per minute (FPM).

The simple formula $RPM = \dfrac{CS}{0.250\,D}$ will determine the RPM to operate any diameter drill (D) at any specified cutting speed.

PROBLEM:

At what speed (RPM) must a drill press operate when drilling aluminum with a 1/2-in. diameter high speed steel drill?

STEPS IN SOLVING THE PROBLEM:
1. A glance at the SPEED AND FEED CHART, Fig. 34-30, will give the recommended cutting speed for aluminum, 250 FPM.
2. Convert the drill diameter (1/2) to a decimal fraction (0.500).
3. Set down the formula:
$$RPM = \frac{CS}{0.250\,D}$$
4. Substitute and solve:
$$RPM = \frac{250}{0.250 \times 0.500} = \frac{250}{0.125} = 2000\ RPM$$

DRILL PRESS SPEED CONTROL MECHANISMS

With some drill presses it is possible to dial the desired RPM, Fig. 34-31. However, on most conventional drilling machines it is not possible to set the machine at the exact speed and the machinist must settle for a speed nearest the desired RPM. The number of speed settings is limited by the number of pulleys in the drive mechanism, Fig. 34-32. An engraved metal chart showing spindle speeds is attached to many ma-

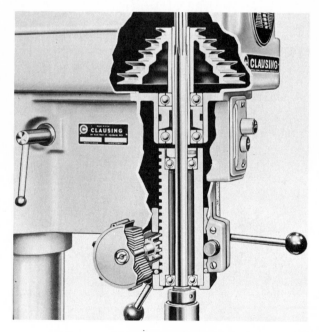

Fig. 34-32. *The step pulley speed control. The belt is transferred to different pulley ratios to change the speed. (Atlas Press Co.)*

chines. If not available, information on spindle speeds can be found in the operator's manual, or they can be calculated if the motor speed and pulley diameters are known.

CUTTING COMPOUNDS

Drilling at the recommended cutting speeds and feeds generates considerable heat at the cutting point. This heat must be dissipated as fast as it is generated or it will destroy the temper of the drill and cause it to dull rapidly.

Cutting compounds, usually oils, are applied to absorb the heat. These fluids not only cool the cutting tool but also act as a lubricant to reduce friction at the cutting edges, and to minimize the tendency of the chips to become welded to the lips. They improve the finish and aid in the rapid removal of chips from the hole.

Animal oils (lard oil), mineral oils (kerosene) and soluble oils make excellent cutting compounds. A soluble oil is made from an oily paste or concentrate that mixes readily with water.

Cutting fluids should be applied liberally as too little does no good. They cannot be used when drilling cast iron or other brittle material because they tend to cause the chips to pack and glaze the opening. Compressed air is used to cool the drill when working these materials.

SHARPENING DRILLS

A drill becomes dull with use and must be resharpened. Continued use of a dull drill may result in its breakage or cause it to burn up as it is forced into the metal. Improper sharpening will cause the same difficulties.

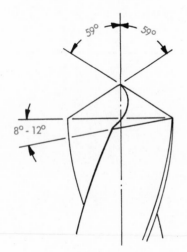

Fig. 34-33. Lip clearance.

Remove the entire point if it is badly worn or if the margins are burned or worn off near the point. If, by accident, the drill becomes over-

heated during grinding, DO NOT plunge it into water to cool. Allow it to cool in still air. The shock of sudden cooling may cause it to crack.

Three factors must be considered when repointing a drill:

1. LIP CLEARANCE, Fig. 34-33. The two cutting edges or lips are comparable to chisels. To cut effectively, the heel or that part of the point back of the cutting edge must be relieved. Without this clearance, it would be impossible for the lips to cut. If there is too much clearance cutting edges are weakened. Too little clearance results in the drill point merely rubbing without penetration. Gradually increase lip clearance toward the center - until the line across dead center stands at an angle of 120 to 135 deg. with the cutting edge, Fig. 34-34.

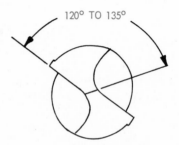

Fig. 34-34. Angle of the dead center.

2. LENGTH AND ANGLE OF LIPS, Fig. 34-33. The material to be drilled determines the proper point angle. The angles, in relation to the axis, must be the same - 59 deg. has been found satisfactory for most metals. If the angles are unequal only one lip will cut and the hole will be oversize, Fig. 34-35.

3. THE PROPER LOCATION OF THE DEAD CENTER, Fig. 34-36. Equal angles but lips of different lengths will result in oversize holes and the resulting "wobble" places tremendous pressures on the drill press spindle and bearings.

A combination of both faults can result in a broken drill and, if the drill is very large, permanent damage to the drilling machine. The hole produced, Fig. 34-37, will be oversize and often out-of-round.

The web of the drill increases in thickness toward the shank, Fig. 34-38. When the drill has been shortened by repeated grindings, the web must be thinned to minimize the pressures re-

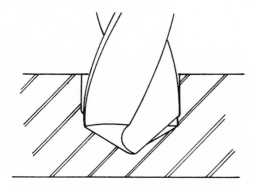

Fig. 34-35. Unequal drill point angles.

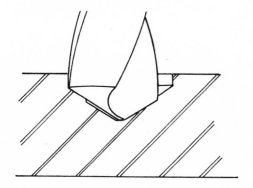

Fig. 34-36. Drill point off center.

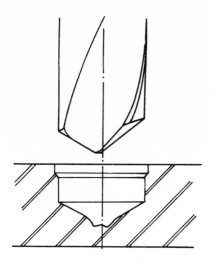

Fig. 34-37. A drill point with unequal point angles and with the drill point sharpened off center.

quired to make the drill penetrate the material. The thinning must be done equally to both sides of the web and care must be taken to insure that the web is centered.

The DRILL POINT GAUGE, Fig. 34-39, is the tool most frequently used to check the drill point during the sharpening operation.

HOW TO SHARPEN A DRILL

Use a coarse wheel for roughing out the drill point if much metal must be ground away. Complete the operation on a fine wheel.

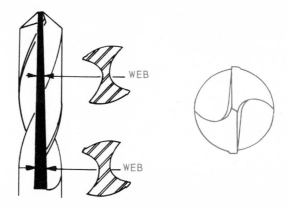

Fig. 34-38. The web of the drill, and how the drill point is relieved by grinding.

Many hand sharpening techniques have been developed. The following is recommended:
1. Grasp the drill shank with the right hand and the rest of the drill with the left hand.
2. Place the fingers of the left hand that are supporting the drill on the grinder tool rest. The tool rest should be slightly below center (about 1-in. on a 7-in. wheel).

Fig. 34-39. Using a drill point gauge.

3. Stand so the center line of the drill will be at a 59 deg. angle with relation to the centerline of the wheel, Fig. 34-40, and lightly touch the drill lip to the wheel in approximately a horizontal position.
4. Use the left hand as a pivot point and slowly lower the shank with the right hand. In-

crease pressure as the heel is reached to insure proper clearance.

5. Repeat the operation on each lip until the drill is sharpened. DO NOT QUENCH HIGH SPEED STEEL DRILLS IN WATER TO COOL. LET THEM COOL IN CALM AIR.

6. Check the drill tip frequently with the drill point gauge to assure a correctly sharpened drill.

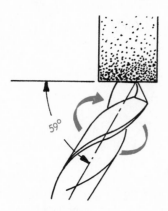

Fig. 34-40. The correct position of the drill at the start of the grinding operation. View is looking down on the grinder.

Secure a drill that is properly sharpened and run through the motions of sharpening it. When you have acquired sufficient skill, sharpen a dull drill. To test, drill a hole in soft metal and observe the chip formation. When properly sharpened, the chips will come out of the flutes in curled spirals of equal length. The tightness of the chip spiral is governed by the RAKE ANGLE, Fig. 34-41.

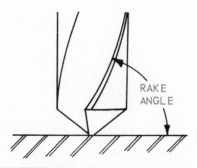

Fig. 34-41. Rake angle of drill for ordinary work.

The standard drill point has a tendency to stick in the hole when it is used to drill brass. When brass is to be drilled, the drill should be sharpened as shown in Fig. 34-42.

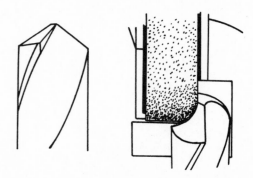

Fig. 34-42. Modified rake angle for drilling brass.

DRILL GRINDING ATTACHMENTS

A DRILL SHARPENING MACHINE is shown in Fig. 34-43.

An attachment for conventional tool grinders is shown in Fig. 34-44. In the machine shop where a high degree of hole accuracy is required and a large amount of sharpening is to be done, a machine or attachment is a must.

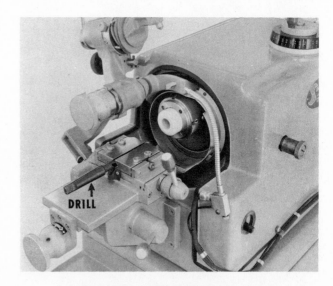

Fig. 34-43. A drill sharpening grinder. (Cincinnati Lathe and Tool Co.)

DRILLING HOLES

Accurate drilling is dependent on observing a few simple rules:

1. Carefully study the drawing to determine the hole location. Lay out the position and mark the intersecting lines with a prick punch.

2. Secure a drill of the size indicated and check it for size.

3. Mount the work on the machine solidly. DO NOT TRY TO HOLD IT BY HAND. It may be whipped out of your hand to cause what is known as a MERRY-GO-ROUND. This development can cause very serious injuries.

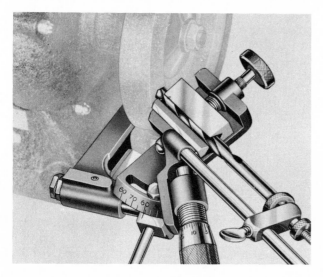

Fig. 34-44. A drill sharpening attachment mounted on a conventional bench grinder. (Atlas Press Co.)

4. Insert a WIGGLER or CENTER FINDER, Fig. 34-45, in the drill chuck. Turn on the power and center up the wiggler point with your fingers. Position the work until the revolving centered wiggler point does not "wiggle" when it is dropped into the punched location of the hole. If there is any point movement, additional alignment will be necessary because the work is not positioned properly.

5. Remove the wiggler and insert the drill. Check to determine whether it can go through the work. Adjust the table setting if necessary.

6. Calculate the correct cutting speed and adjust the machine to operate as closely as possible to this speed.

7. Start the machine and observe how the drill runs. If it wobbles, it may be bent or have been placed in the chuck off center. Tighten with a chuck key, when it runs true. REMOVE THE KEY BEFORE STARTING THE MACHINE.

8. Turn on the power, apply cutting fluid liberally and start the cut. Even pressure on the feed handle will keep the drill cutting freely.

9. Watch for signs that indicate a poorly cutting drill:
   a. A dull drill will squeak and overheat. Chips will be rough and blue and sometime clog in the flutes and cause the machine to slow down. Smaller drills will break.
   b. Infrequently, a chip will get under the dead center and act as a bearing preventing the drill from cutting. Remove by raising and lowering the drill in the hole several times.
   c. Chips packed in the flutes cause the drill to bind and slow the machine. Remove the drill from the hole and clean it with a brush that has been dipped in cutting fluid. DO NOT DO THIS WHEN DRILLING CAST IRON.

10. Clear chips and apply cutting fluid by removing the drill from the hole.

11. The most critical time of the drilling operation occurs when the drill starts to break through. Ease up on the feed pressure at this point to prevent the drill from digging in.

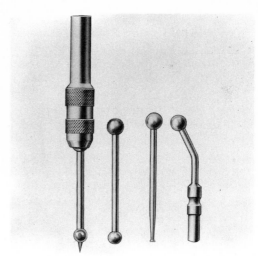

Fig. 34-45. It is difficult to align the drill with the centerlines by eye. To assist in this matter the center finder or "wiggler" is used. (Lufkin Rule Co.)

12. Remove the drill from the hole and turn off the power. DO NOT TRY TO STOP THE CHUCK WITH YOUR HAND. Clear the chips with a brush (NOT YOUR HAND). Unclamp the work and use a file to remove all burrs.

13. Clean chips and cutting fluid from the machine and return the drill to its proper place.

Observe extreme care in positioning the piece for drilling. A poorly planned setup may permit the drill to cut into the vise or drill table as it comes through the piece.

If a hole must be located precisely, certain additional precautions must be taken to insure that the hole is drilled where it should be. After the center point has been determined, a series of circles - PROOF CIRCLES - are scribed, Fig. 34-46(A). They will be reference points to help check whether the drill remains on center as it starts to penetrate the material. Even when

HOW TO DRILL IN ROUND STOCK

Holes are more difficult to drill in the curved surface of round stock. Many potential difficulties can be eliminated by holding the round material in a V-block, Fig. 34-21. The V-block can be clamped directly to the table, Fig. 34-22, or held in a vise.

It is a simple matter to center round stock in the V-block:

1. Locate the position of the hole on the stock. Prick punch the intersection of the lay-

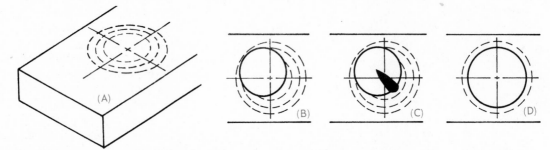

Fig. 34-46. *Bringing a drill back on center. (A) The proof circles. (B) The drill off center (exaggerated). (C) Cutting the groove to bring it back. (D) The drill back on center.*

work is properly centered, the drill may drift when starting the hole. Various factors can cause this - hard spots in the material, an improperly sharpened drill, etc. The drill cannot be brought back on center by moving the work, as it will follow the original hole. The condition, Fig. 34-46(B), must be corrected before the full diameter of the drill is reached. The tool is brought back on center by using a round nose cape chisel to cut a groove on the side of the hole toward where the drill must be drawn, Fig. 34-46(C). This groove will cause the drill point to cut in that direction. Repeat the operation until the hole being drilled is concentric with the proof circles, Fig. 34-46(D).

DRILLING LARGER HOLES

Drills larger than 1/2-in. diameter require considerable power and pressure to get started. Even then they may run off center. The pressure can be greatly reduced and accuracy improved by first drilling a PILOT or LEAD HOLE as shown in Fig. 34-47. The small hole permits pressure to come directly on the cutting edges of the large drill causing it to cut faster. The diameter of the pilot hole should be as large as, or slightly larger than, the width of the dead center.

out lines. Place the stock in the V-block making certain that the hole, if it is to go through the piece, will clear the V-block and there is ample clearance between the clamp and the drill chuck.

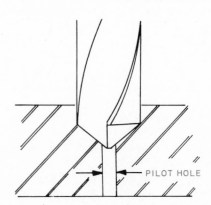

Fig. 34-47. *The pilot hole.*

2. To align the hole for drilling through center, place the work and V-block on the drill press table, or on a surface plate. Rotate the punch mark until it is upright. Place a steel square on the flat surface with the blade against the round stock as shown in Fig. 34-48. Measure from the blade to the punch mark, and rotate the

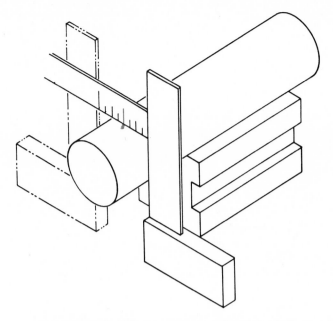

Fig. 34-48. Using V-block to center round stock for drilling.

stock until the measurement is the same when taken from both positions of the square.

3. From this point, the drilling sequence is identical with that previously described.

It may be desirable to make a DRILL JIG, as shown in Fig. 34-49, if a large number of

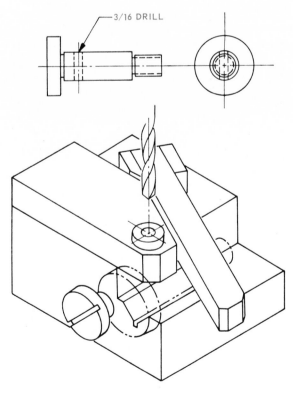

Fig. 34-49. A drill jig. The arm lifts to allow easy insertion and removal of the bolt.

identical pieces are to be drilled. The drill jig automatically positions and centers the piece for drilling.

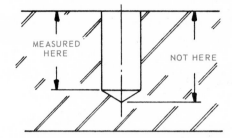

Fig. 34-50. How the depth of a blind hole is measured.

BLIND HOLES

A blind hole is a hole that is not drilled all of the way through the work. Hole depth is measured by the distance the full diameter goes into the work, Fig. 34-50. Using a drill press fitted with a DEPTH STOP or GAUGE, Fig. 34-51, is the most rapid means of securing the proper depth when drilling blind holes.

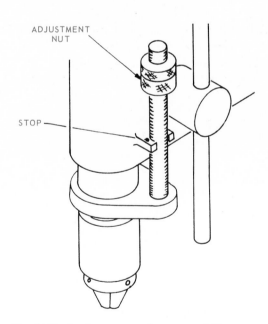

Fig. 34-51. Depth gauge attachment on a drill press.

OTHER OPERATIONS THAN CAN BE PERFORMED ON THE DRILL PRESS

The drill press is used to perform many operations other than drilling. As with drilling, they require a thorough knowledge of the machine and the cutting tools.

34-17

REAMING

Reaming is the operation that produces holes that are extremely accurate and have an exceptionally fine finish.

Machine reamers are made in a variety of sizes and styles. They are usually manufactured from high speed steel. Descriptions of a few of the more common machine reamers follow:

JOBBER'S REAMER

The jobber's reamer, Fig. 34-52, is identical to the hand reamer except that the shank is tapered and designed for machine operation.

Fig. 34-52. A jobber's reamer.

CHUCKING REAMER

The chucking reamer, Fig. 34-53, is manufactured with both straight and taper shanks. It is similar to the jobber's reamer but the flutes are shorter and deeper. It is available with straight or spiral flutes.

Fig. 34-53. A chucking reamer.

ROSE CHUCKING REAMER

A rose chucking reamer, Fig. 34-54, is designed to cut on its end. The flutes provide chip clearance and are ground to act only as guides. This reamer is best used when considerable metal must be removed and the finish is not critical.

Fig. 34-54. A rose chucking reamer.

EXPANSION CHUCKING REAMER

The expansion chucking reamer, Fig. 34-55, which has straight flutes, is available with either

Fig. 34-55. An expansion chucking reamer.

a straight or taper shank. Slots are cut in the body to permit the reamer to expand when the adjusting screw in the end is tightened.

Fig. 34-56. A shell reamer and its arbor.

SHELL REAMER

A shell reamer, Fig. 34-56, is mounted on a special arbor that can be used with several reamer sizes. It may have straight or spiral flutes and is also made in the rose style. The arbor shank may be straight or tapered. The hole in the reamer is tapered to fit the arbor which is fitted with drive lugs.

HOW TO USE MACHINE REAMERS

Reamers are precision tools and the quality of finish and the accuracy of the reamed hole will depend on how the tools are used.

1. Mount the work solidly.
2. Allow enough material in the hole to permit the reamer to cut rather than burnish. The following allowances are recommended:
   a. To 1/4-in. diameter allow 0.010 in.
   b. 1/4 to 1/2-in. diameter allow 0.015 in.
   c. 1/2 to 1.0-in. diameter allow 0.020 in.
   d. 1.0 to 1-1/2-in. diameter allow 0.025 in.
3. Use sharp reamers.
4. The cutting speed for a high speed steel reamer should be about two-thirds that of a similar size drill.
5. The feed should be as much as possible while giving a good finish and accurate hole size.
6. Check reamer diameter before using. If the diameter is critical, drill and ream a hole in a piece of similar material to check tool size.
7. When not in use, reamers should be stored in separate containers or compartments, to minimize the danger of chipping the cutting edges.

8. Use an ample supply fluid.
9. Remove the reamer from the hole before stopping the machine.

COUNTERSINKING

Countersinking, Fig. 34-57, is the operation that cuts a chamfer in a hole to permit a flat-head fastener to be inserted with the head flush with the surface, Fig. 34-58. The tool used is called a COUNTERSINK, Fig. 34-59, and is available with cutting edges of 60, 82, 90, 100, 110 and 120 deg. included angles. Countersinks may also be used for deburring holes.

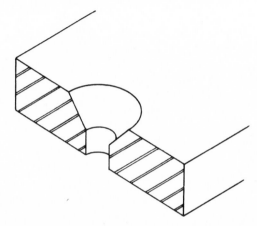

Fig. 34-57. Cross section of hole that has been countersunk.

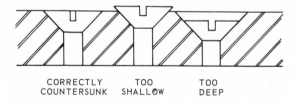

CORRECTLY COUNTERSUNK   TOO SHALLOW   TOO DEEP

Fig. 34-58. Correctly and incorrectly countersunk holes.

Fig. 34-59. The countersink tool.

HOW TO USE A COUNTERSINK

1. Use a cutting speed about one-half that recommended for a similar size drill. This will minimize the possibility of "chatter."
2. Feed the tool into the work until the

chamfer is large enough for the fastener head to be flush.
3. Use the depth stop if a number of similar holes must be countersunk.

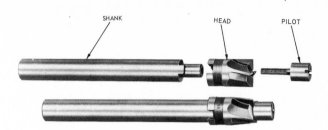

SHANK   HEAD   PILOT

Fig. 34-60. A straight shank interchangeable counterbore.

COUNTERBORING

The heads of fillister and socket head screws are usually set below the work surface. A COUNTERBORE, Fig. 34-60, is used to enlarge the hole to the proper depth and machine the square shoulder on the hole bottom to secure maximum clamping action from the fastener. The tool has a guide, called a PILOT, which keeps it positioned correctly in the hole.

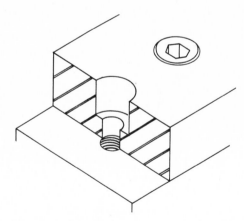

Fig. 34-60a. A sectional view of a hole that has been drilled and counterbored to receive a socket head cap screw.

Solid counterbores are available. However, counterbores with interchangeable pilots and cutters are commonly used, because they can be changed from one size cutter or pilot to another size. A drop of oil on the pilot will prevent it from binding in the hole.

SPOTFACING

Spotfacing, Fig. 34-61, is the term applied when a circular spot is machined on a rough surface to furnish a bearing surface for the head of a bolt or nut. A counterbore may be used for spotfacing, although a special tool is manufactured for inverted spotfacing.

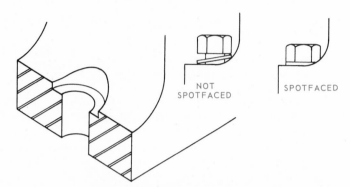

Fig. 34-61. *Sectional view of a casting with a mounting hole that has been spotfaced. Smaller drawings show a side view of the casting before and after spotfacing. Note that the bolt cannot be drawn down tightly until the mounting hole has been spotfaced.*

TAPPING

Tapping may be done by hand on the drill press by:

1. Drilling a hole of the correct size.
2. With the work still clamped in the machine, insert a small 60 deg. center in the chuck. The center holds the tap vertical.
3. Place the center point in the center hole of the tap.
4. Feed the tap into the work by holding down the feed handle and turning the tap with a tap wrench.

NEVER INSERT A TAP IN A DRILL PRESS CHUCK AND ATTEMPT TO USE POWER TO CUT THE THREADS. THE TAP WILL SHATTER THE SECOND POWER IS APPLIED.

Tapping can be done with power through the use of a TAPPING ATTACHMENT, Fig. 34-62. This device fits the standard drill press and has

Fig. 34-62. *Tapping attachment that fits to the drill press spindle. (Ettco Tool & Machine Co.)*

reducing gears that slows the tap to about one-third the drill press speed. A clutch arrangement drives the tap until it reaches the predetermined depth at which time the tap is reversed and runs out of the hole when the feed handle is raised.

POLISHING, GRINDING AND BORING

Polishing, grinding and boring can be done with a limited degree of success on the standard drill press. However, the machine does not always have the necessary rigidity or means to make fine adjustments to do these jobs as well as they can be done on more specialized equipment.

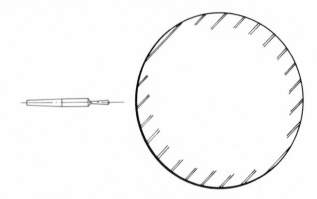

Fig. 34-63. *A micro-drill (left) compared with a human hair.*

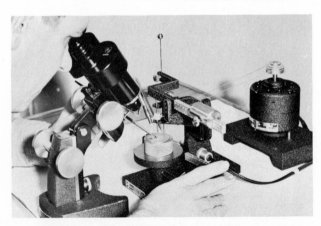

Fig. 34-64. *A skilled operator using a micro-drilling machine. The drilling operation is so small that he must use a microscope to see what he is doing. (National Jet Co.)*

INDUSTRIAL APPLICATIONS

Specialized drilling machines enable industry to drill holes as small as 1/10000 (0.0001) in. in diameter to as large as 3-1/2 in.

Fig. 34-65. The radial drill press.
(National Machine Tool Builders)

The machine used to drill these very small holes, so small as a matter of fact, that twenty-five holes could be drilled in the diameter of a human hair, Fig. 34-63, is called an ULTRA-SENSITIVE MICROSCOPIC PRECISION DRILLING MACHINE, Fig. 34-64. Micro-drilling is becoming increasingly more important in modern industry. The development of these techniques has made it possible to mass-produce such jobs as the precision fuel injection nozzle that is the heart of the modern diesel engine.

Fig. 34-66a. Electric hand or pistol drill being used for aircraft production. (Cessna Aircraft)

The RADIAL DRILL PRESS, Fig. 34-65, is at the other end of the drilling machine scale. This machine can handle very large work. The

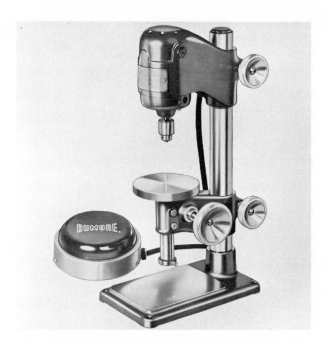

Fig. 34-66b. High speed sensitive drill press.
(Dumore Co.)

Fig. 34-66c. Deep hole drilling machine, tape controlled.

drill head is mounted in such a manner that it can be moved back and forth on the arm that extends from the massive column. The arm can be moved up, down and pivoted on the column.

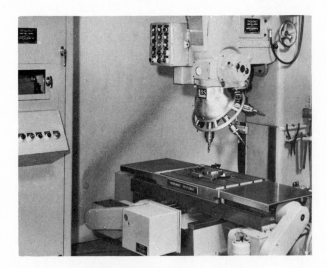

Fig. 34-66d. A tape controlled turret head drilling machine. The machine receives its instructions from perforations in a strip of tape. The work is positioned automatically, and the turret head rotates at the proper time to bring the desired drill into position. With the exception of mounting the work on the machine all operations are completely automatic.
(Control Instrument Div., Warner & Swasey Co.)

Often, a large pit is located along one side of this machine to permit the positioning of large, odd-shaped pieces. The pit is covered when not in use. It is not uncommon to drill holes 3-1/2

in. in diameter with this machine.

In between these two extremes are many drilling machines. The ELECTRIC HAND DRILL, the HIGH SPEED SENSITIVE DRILL PRESS, TAPE CONTROLLED TURRET HEAD and DEEP HOLE DRILLING MACHINES, the GANG and MULTIPLE SPINDLE and familiar FLOOR and BENCH DRILLING MACHINES, as illustrated in this Unit.

Fig. 34-66f. Gang of four drilling machines. Each machine is fitted with a different cutting tool. As the work moves from position to position a different operation is performed.
(Atlas Press Co.)

Fig. 34-66g. Battery powered hand drill for use in areas where there is no electric power. (Black & Decker Mfg. Co.)

DRILL PRESS SAFETY

1. Remove neckties and tuck in loose clothing so there is no chance of them becoming entangled with the rotating drill.
2. Check out the machine. Are all guards in place? Switches work? Does the machine

Fig. 34-66e. Multi-spindle attachment which fits standard drilling machine and enables the machine to drill several holes at one time.
(Ettco Tool & Machine Co., Inc.)

operate properly? Are the tools sharpened properly for the material being worked?

3. Clamp the work solidly. Do not hold it with your hands. A "merry-go-round" can inflict serious and painful injuries.

4. Wear goggles.

5. Place a piece of wood under drills being removed from the machine. Small drills are damaged in dropping and the larger tools can injure you if they fall on your foot.

6. Use sharp tools.

7. Clean chips from the work with a brush, not your hands.

8. Treat cuts and scratches immediately.

9. Always remove the key from the chuck be-

fore turning on the power.

10. Let the drill spindle stop of its own accord after the power had been turned off. Do not try to stop it with your hand.

11. Keep the work area clean of chips. Use a brush, not your hands.

12. Wipe up all cutting fluid that spills on the floor.

13. Never clean the tapered opening in the spindle while the machine is operating.

14. After using the drill, wipe it clean of chips and cutting fluid with a piece of cotton waste. Do not use your hands.

15. Place all oily and dirty waste in a closed container when the job is finished.

TEST YOUR KNOWLEDGE, Unit 34

1. Drill press size is determined by:
   a. The largest drill that will fit the machine.
   b. The largest piece of work that will fit on the drill table.
   c. The largest diameter work piece that can be drilled on center.
   d. None of the above.
   e. All of the above.

2. A drill made from _____ can be operated at higher speeds than a drill made from carbon steel.

3. Drill sizes are expressed by the following series:
   a._____.
   b._____.
   c._____.
   d._____.

4. List two commonly used methods of measuring drills if the drill size is worn from the shank.
   a._____.
   b._____.

5. What are the two different types of drill shanks?
   a._____.
   b._____.

6. _____ shank drills are used with a chuck.

7. _____ shank drills fit directly into the drill press spindle.

8. _____ are the spiral grooves that run the length of the drill body.

9. They are used to:
   a. Help form the cutting edge of the drill point.
   b. Curl the chips for easier removal.

   c. Form channels through which the chips can escape from the hole.
   d. None of the above.
   e. All of the above.

10. Tapered drill shanks too small to fit directly into the drill press spindle can be enlarged to fit properly by fitting it with a _____.

11. The item described above is removed from the drill shank with a _____. It is never removed with a file tang.

12. The material from which the drill is made must be taken into consideration when determining cutting speeds. True or false?

13. The drill flutes, because of their spiral, pull the drill into the work. True or false?

14. "Chatter" causes the drill to dull rapidly. True or false?

15. More drills are ruined by operating them at too slow a speed than are ruined by operating at too high a speed. True or false?

16. Cutting fluids are used to:
    a. Cool the drill.
    b. Improve the finish of the drilled hole.
    c. Aid in the rapid removal of chips.
    d. None of the above.
    e. All of the above.

17. The proper way to cool a drill that has become overheated while being sharpened is to plunge it into cold water. True or false?

18. The three factors that must be considered when repointing a drill are:
    a._____.
    b._____.
    c._____.

19. When the cutting lips of the drill are uneven

in length the drill will:

a. Drill a hole larger than the drill size.

b. Drill a hole smaller than the drill size.

c. Drill a hole the same size as the drill size.

d. None of the above apply.

e. All of the above apply.

20. When sharpening the drill, a coarse grinding wheel is used because it cuts faster. True or false?

21. The _____ _____ _____ should be used frequently during grinding to assure a correctly sharpened drill.

22. The included angle of a point sharpened for general drilling is _____ degrees.

23. The _____ is very useful for centering work for drilling.

24. Kerosene is the cutting fluid used when drilling cast iron. True or false?

25. Large drills require considerable power and pressure to get them started. They also have a tendency to drift off center. These conditions can be improved by first drilling a _____ _____. This hole should be as large as, or slightly larger than, the width of the _____ _____ of the drill point.

26. A blind hole goes completely through the work. True or false?

27. The depth of a drilled hole can be regulated by adjusting the _____.

28. Reaming is the same as drilling. True or false?

29. The _____ reamer is almost identical to the hand reamer except that the shank has been designed for machine use.

30. The _____ reamer is ideal for finishing holes that must be a few thousandths over standard size.

31. Reamers should be backed out by reversing the machine. True or false?

32. _____ is the operation that cuts a chamfer in a hole to permit it to receive a flat head screw.

33. The _____ is used to prepare a hole to receive a fillister or socket head screw.

34. _____ is the operation that machines a circular spot on a rough surface for the head of a bolt or nut.

RESEARCH AND DEVELOPMENT

1. Make for use as a teaching aid a large drawing of a twist drill. Label the various parts.

2. Prepare a research paper on early drilling devices. Include sketches. You may want to reproduce this on the spirit duplicator, or make a series of projectuals of these early tools for the overhead projector.

3. Make a series of tape recordings that indicate how drills in various conditions of sharpness sound while drilling.

4. Develop a research problem to investigate the effects of cutting compounds in drilling. This may be accomplished by recording the sounds of the tool drilling when different cutting fluids are used - or no cutting fluid is used. It may be shown visually by clamping two pieces of metal together and drilling at different points along the joint. Be sure the metal and drill are clean before starting the next hole.

5. Prepare teaching aid that will show samples of a drilled hole, reamed hole, countersinking, counterboring and spot-facing.

6. Borrow drill jigs from a local industry. Describe to the class how they are used.

7. Make a teaching aid that shows the parts of a chucking reamer. Label the various parts.

8. Demonstrate one of the following lessons to the class:

a. Centering round stock in a V-block.

b. The proper way to use a wiggler.

c. Sharpen a twist drill.

d. The correct way to clamp work on the drill press table.

9. Make a series of safety posters on the use of the drill press.

Unit 35

POWER SAWING

There are three principal types of metal-cutting power saws. One has a reciprocating (back and forth) cutting action and uses a blade similar to the one used in a hand hacksaw, only

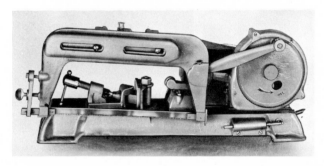

Fig. 35-1. A bench model reciprocating type power hacksaw. (Covel Mfg. Co.)

larger and heavier, Fig. 35-1. One uses a continuous or band-type blade, Fig. 35-2. The third type uses a circular blade, Fig. 35-12.

RECIPROCATING POWER HACKSAW

HOW TO SELECT THE BLADE

As in the use of the hand hacksaw, proper blade selection is important. The three-tooth rule (at least three teeth in contact with the work) still applies. Large pieces and soft materials require coarse teeth, while small or thin work and hard materials, require a fine tooth blade. For best cutting action, apply heavy feed pressure on soft materials and large work, and light pressure on soft materials and small work.

Blades are manufactured in two principal types, flexible back, or all-hard. The choice depends upon the use. Flexible back blades should be used where safety requirements demand a shatter-proof blade, or, for cutting odd-shaped work, Fig. 35-3, that cannot be mounted firmly

Fig. 35-2. Metal cutting band saw. (Kalamazoo Tank & Silo Co.)

Fig. 35-3. Initial finishing operation on large sand casting. Gates and risers are being removed by band sawing. (Aluminum Co. of America)

on the machine. For the majority of cutting jobs, the all-hard blade is first choice for straight accurate cutting under a variety of conditions.

Blades are manufactured from tungsten and molybdenum steel and with tungsten carbide teeth on alloy steel backs. The following rule-of-thumb can be followed for selecting the correct blade:

4-tooth blade for cutting large sections or readily machined metals.

6-tooth blade for cutting harder alloys and miscellaneous cutting.

10 and 14-tooth blades are used on the majority of light duty machines where work is limited to small sections and moderate and light feed pressures.

HOW TO MOUNT HACKSAW BLADE

The blade must be mounted to cut on the power stroke, Fig. 35-4, be perfectly flat against the mounting plates, and be properly tensioned, if long blade life and accurate cuts are to be achieved.

Many techniques have been developed for properly mounting blades. For best results, consult the manufacturer's literature. The recommended pressure can be secured by using a torque wrench. If this information is not available, the following method can be used:

Tighten the blade until a low toned musical ring is heard when the blade is tapped lightly. A tone too high in pitch indicates that the blade is too tight. A dull thud indicates that the blade is too loose.

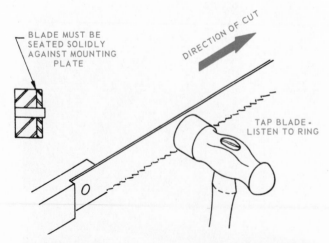

Fig. 35-4. Adjusting the blade on a reciprocating type power hacksaw. On band type machines bring up the tension just enough to eliminate the slack in the blade. If, upon checking, the blade is tracking properly; rotate the tensioning screw one more complete turn. (Capewell Mfg. Co.)

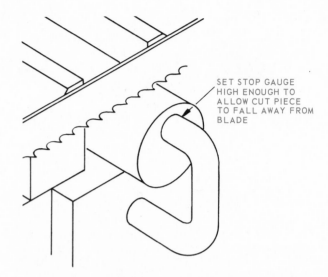

Fig. 35-5. The stop gauge is used when several pieces of the same length must be cut. Adjust it high to permit the work to fall free when it is cut through.

CUTTING

Measure off the distance to be cut, mark the stock, and firmly mount the work on the machine. If several pieces of the same size are to be cut, use a STOP GAUGE, Fig. 35-5. Use ample supplies of coolant if the machine is designed to use it.

HORIZONTAL BAND SAW

The band saw offers three advantages over the hacksaw:

1. FASTER. The long blade moves in only one direction, and being continuous, can be run at much higher speeds as the blade rapidly dissipates the heat generated in cutting.

2. PRECISION. The blade can be guided more accurately than the blade on the reciprocating type saw, and can utilize a finer blade for a given piece of material. It is common practice to cut directly to the line when band sawing.

3. LITTLE WASTE. The small cross section of the band saw blade makes smaller and fewer chips for a given length or thickness of material.

HOW TO SELECT BLADE

Select the best blade for the job. Band saw blades are made with the teeth RAKER SET or

WAVY SET, Fig. 35-6. The raker set is preferable for general use. The tooth pattern determines the efficiency of the blade in various materials.

The STANDARD TOOTH is best for cutting most ferrous metals. The SKIP TOOTH blade

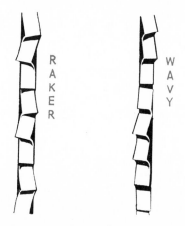

Fig. 35-8. The vertical band saw for metal machining. (DoALL Co.)

Fig. 35-6. Saw blade teeth are commonly made with the teeth RAKER SET or WAVY SET. The raker set teeth are preferred for general use and for cutting large solids or thick plate. (Capewell Mfg. Co.)

pattern is best suited for cutting aluminum, magnesium, copper and soft brass. The HOOK TOOTH is recommended for most nonferrous metallic materials, Fig. 35-7.

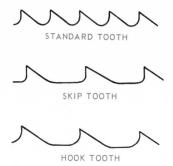

Fig. 35-7. STANDARD TOOTH blades, with their well rounded gullets, are usually best for most ferrous materials, hard bronzes and brasses. SKIP TOOTH blades provide for more gullet and better chip clearance without weakening the blade body. This one is desirable for aluminum, copper, magnesium and soft brasses. HOOK TOOTH blades offer two advantages over the skip tooth blade: The blade design makes it feed easier and its chip breaker design prevents gumming up.

HOW TO INSTALL BLADE

The blade must be installed carefully, if the saw is to work efficiently. The blade guides should be adjusted to permit the blade to cut true

and square with the work table. Follow the manufacturer's instructions for adjusting blade tension. Improper blade tension ruins blades and can cause early failure of the wheel bearings.

VERTICAL BAND SAW

A VERTICAL BAND SAW is shown in Fig. 35-8. With this type saw finish and accuracy can be held to within 0.010 to 0.015 in. to finished dimensions, Fig. 35-9. This accuracy eliminates or minimizes many secondary machining operations. Finishing operations can be performed

SAFETY

1. Get help when cutting heavy material.
2. Clean oil and grease from floor around the work area.
3. Burrs on cut pieces are sharp. Handle the pieces with care until the burrs can be removed.
4. Do not clean chips from the machine with your hands. Use a brush. Do not remove chips while the machine is in motion.
5. Follow the manufacturer's instructions for tensioning the blade. Too much tension could shatter the blade causing particles of flying steel.
6. Keep your hands clear of moving parts.
7. Stop the machine before making adjustments.
8. Have any cuts and scratches, even though minor, treated promptly.
9. Do not operate the machine unless all guards are in place.

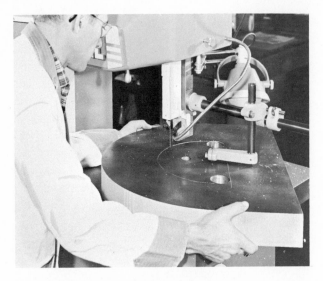

Fig. 35-9. Close-up showing how precision internal cuts can be made on a band saw. The band is threaded through holes drilled in the piece, welded, and the work is maneuvered along the prescribed line. (DoALL Co.)

with file and finishing bands. Abrasive and brittle materials, and the hardest steels can be cut rapidly and economically on the band saw by substituting a diamond-edge blade for the conventional blade.

The vertical band saw is manufactured in a

wide range of sizes, and has been adapted to do many kinds of band machining. The machine illustrated in Fig. 35-10, has been fitted with a closed circuit TV and a remote control console to permit the operator to perform hazardous or dangerous work. One such use has been for cutting radioactive materials, where it is desirable for the operator to control the machine from a distant point.

CIRCULAR TYPE METAL-CUTTING SAWS

Metal-cutting circular saws find limited but specialized use in industry. They are primarily production machines and are divided into three classifications:

1. ABRASIVE CUTOFF SAW. This saw cuts material by means of a rapidly revolving thin abrasive wheel, Fig. 35-11. Most materials, glass, ceramics and a long list of metals can be cut to close tolerances. Hardened steel does not have to be annealed to be cut. Abrasive cutting falls into two classifications - dry and wet. Wet abrasive cutting, while not quite as rapid as dry cutting, produces a finer surface finish and permits cutting to closer tolerances.

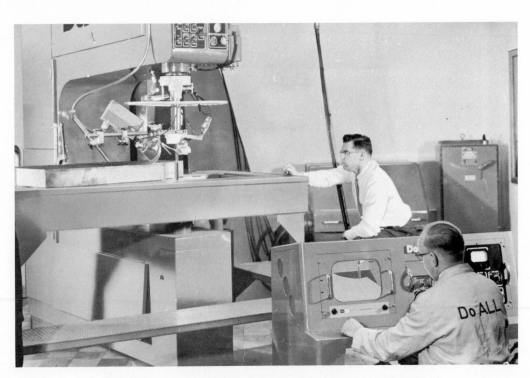

Fig. 35-10. A band-type machine fitted with a closed circuit TV and a remote control console. (DoALL Co.)

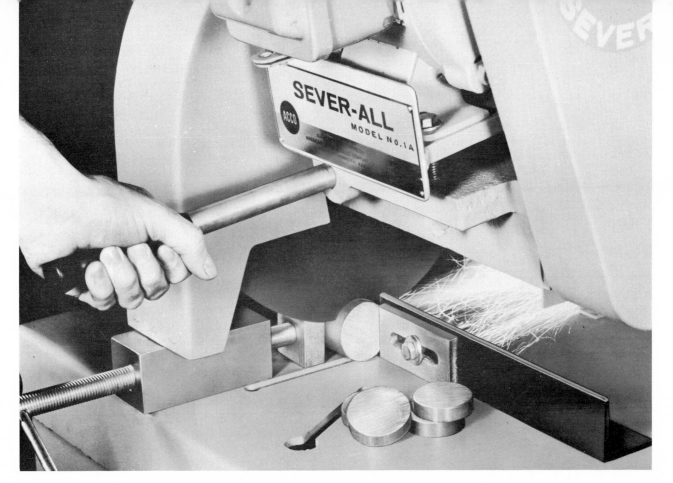

Fig. 35-11. A dry type abrasive cutoff saw. (Allison-Campbell Div., American Chain and Cable Co.)

2. COLD CIRCULAR SAW. This type machine makes use of a circular blade, Fig. 35-12. The toothed blade is capable of producing very accurate cuts with a finish that is comparable to that produced by milling. The larger machines are capable of rapidly severing metals up to 27-in. in diameter.

3. FRICTION SAW. The blade of this machine may or may not have teeth. The saw operates at a very high speed - 20 - 25,000 surface feet per minute and actually burns or melts its way through the metal. If teeth are on the blade, their primary use is to carry oxygen to the cut. These machines find wide use in steel mills to cut billets while they are still hot.

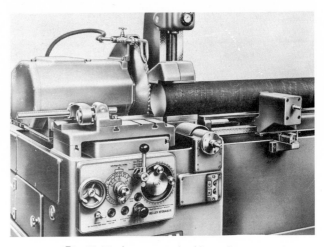

Fig. 35-12. An automated cold circular saw. (Motch & Merryweather Machinery Co.)

TEST YOUR KNOWLEDGE, Unit 35

1. The continuous blade power saw is actually a band saw. True or false?
2. The three-tooth rule for sawing means:
   a. That the blade teeth are in good condition.
   b. The blade should be adjusted frequently so that three consecutive teeth are always in good condition.
   c. At least three teeth in contact with the work at all times during the cutting sequence.
   d. None of the above.

3. The flexible back blade shatters easily if not used properly. True or false?
4. The continuous blade sawing machine offers three advantages over the other forms of power sawing:

    a._____.

b._____.

c._____.

5. List two methods of getting the proper tension on blade of a reciprocating type saw:

    a._____.

    b._____.

RESEARCH AND DEVELOPMENT

1. The abrasive cutoff wheel is also used to cut metal. How does its operation differ from conventional sawing? Make a display panel that shows a photograph or drawing of a cutoff machine, a sample of the abrasive wheel it uses and samples of materials for which it is better suited than the conventional saw.
2. Prepare models of the following blade types from suitable sheet aluminum. Secure samples and mount in hardwood blocks in such a manner that the tooth configuration can be observed with a magnifying glass.

    a. Raker and wavy set teeth.
    b. Standard tooth blade.
    c. Skip tooth blade.
    d. Hook tooth blade.
3. If the power hacksaw in your shop has seen considerable service, contact the manufacturer for a service manual and parts list. If time permits, and the machine can be spared, recondition it and paint it according to "color dynamics" specifications.
4. Design and produce a safety poster pretaining to the power saw.

Unit 36
METAL LATHE

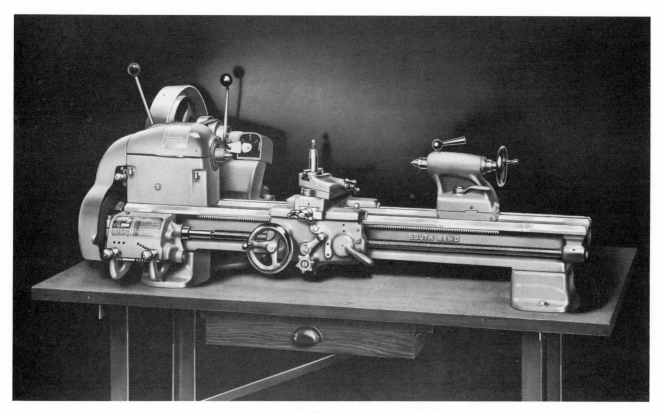

Fig. 36-1. The bench lathe.   (South Bend Lathe, Inc.)

A lathe is a machine tool in which the work is held and rotated, while being shaped by a cutting tool that is fed against the work. See Figs. 36-1, and 36-2.

LATHE SIZE

Lathe size is determined by the SWING and BED LENGTH, Fig. 36-3. The swing indicates the largest diameter of work that can be turned. The bed length is the entire length of the ways, and should not be mistaken for the maximum length of metal piece that can be turned.

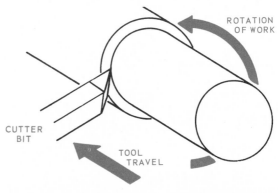

ROTATION OF WORK

CUTTER BIT

TOOL TRAVEL

Fig. 36-2. The operating principle of the lathe.

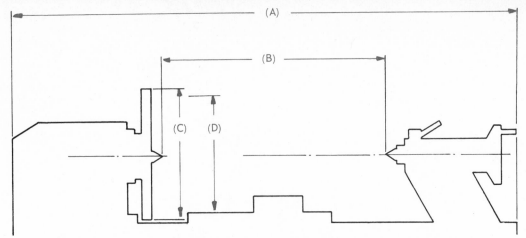

Fig. 36-3. How a lathe is measured. (A) Length of the bed. (B) Distance between centers. (C) Diameter of work that can be turned over the ways. (D) Diameter of work that can be turned over the cross slide.

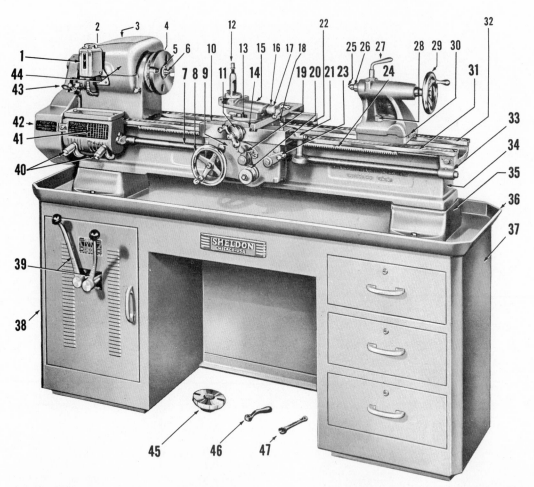

1	Motor Switch	**13**	Graduated Swivel Base	**25**	Center (tailstock)	**37** Cabinet
2	Back Gear Lever	**14**	Cross Feed tapered take-up Gib	**26**	Calibrated tailstock spindle	**38** Motor Drive (in Cabinet Leg)
3	Oiling Instruction Plate	**15**	Compound Rest	**27**	Tailstock Spindle back handle	**39** Speed Change Hand levers
4	Spindle Nose	**16**	Compound Rest tapered take-up Gib	**28**	Tailstock Clamp Nut	**40** Gear Box tumbler levers
5	Center Sleeve	**17**	Compound Micrometer Dial	**29**	Tailstock Handwheel	**41** Full Quick Change gear box
6	Center (Headstock)	**18**	Carriage Lock Nut	**30**	Tailstock Set-over Scale	**42** End Gear Cover
7	Precision Lead Screw	**19**	Power Feed Quadrant	**31**	Front "V" and "Flat" Ways	**43** Reversing Lever
8	Longitudinal Feed Hand Wheel	**20**	Power Feed Clutch	**32**	Rear "V" and "Flat" Ways	**44** Headstock
9	Apron	**21**	Thread Chasing Dial	**33**	Lead Screw End Bearing	**45** Dog Plate
10	Carriage	**22**	Felt Way Washer	**34**	Lathe Bed	**46** Tailstock Clamp Wrench
11	Micrometer dial on hand cross feed	**23**	Half-Nut Lever	**35**	Bench Leg	**47** Tool Post Wrench
12	Tool Post Assembly	**24**	Longitudinal hand feed rack	**36**	Chip Pan	

Fig. 36-4. The engine lathe and its major parts.
(The Sheldon Machine Co., Inc.)

Lathe

MAJOR PARTS OF THE LATHE

Each of the lathe parts, Fig. 36-4, fall into one of three functional categories:
1. DRIVING THE LATHE.
2. HOLDING AND ROTATING THE WORK.
3. HOLDING AND MOVING THE CUTTING TOOL.

LATHE BED

The lathe bed, Fig. 36-5, is the foundation or base to which the other parts of the lathe

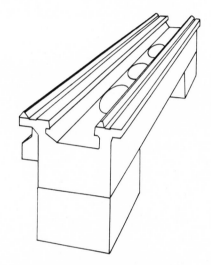

Fig. 36-5. The lathe bed.

are fitted. Carefully machined ways on top of the lathe bed, support and provide for precise alignment of the headstock and tailstock.

HEADSTOCK

The headstock, Fig. 36-6, contains the SPINDLE to which the various work holding attachments are fitted. The spindle is hollow

Fig. 36-6. The headstock. (Delta Power Tool Div., Rockwell Mfg. Co.)

with the front end tapered internally to receive tools and attachments with taper shanks, Fig. 36-7. The hole permits long stock to be turned and allows a KNOCKOUT BAR, Fig. 36-8, to be used to remove taper shank tools.

The spindle is usually fitted with one of two

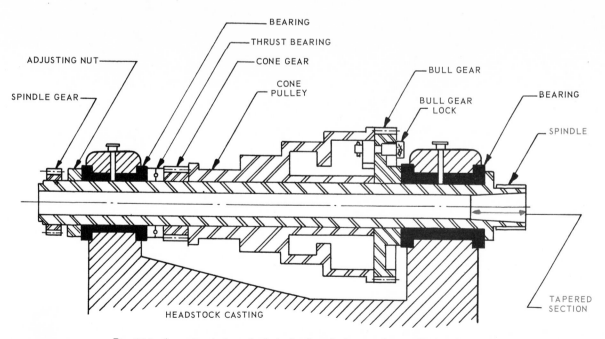

Fig. 36-7. A sectional view of a lathe headstock showing the spindle fitted in place.

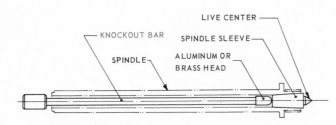

Fig. 36-8. The knockout bar is used to tap tapered shank lathe accessories from the spindle.

standardized tapered spindle noses, or with a threaded spindle nose, Fig. 36-9a, b, c.

Also found in the headstock is the SPEED CONTROL MECHANISM. Power supplied by an

Fig. 36-9a. Cam-lock type spindle nose. (South Bend Lathe, Inc.)

Fig. 36-9b. Long taper key spindle nose. (South Bend Lathe, Inc.)

electric motor is transmitted to the spindle by a series of belts or a gear train. Spindle speed is changed by moving the belts to positions on the pulleys or by changing the gear ratio.

Slower speeds on belt driven lathes are ob-

tained by engaging the BACK GEARS, Fig. 36-10. The large gear (BULL GEAR) is keyed to the spindle and is locked to the pulley with the BULL GEAR LOCK PIN. The back gears can be engaged by disconnecting the bull gear from the step pulley by releasing the bull gear lock pin.

DO NOT ENGAGE THE BACK GEARS WHILE THE SPINDLE IS ROTATING.

Fig. 36-9c. Threaded type spindle nose. (South Bend Lathe, Inc.)

Fig. 36-10. Back geared headstock. A. Back gear lever. B. Back gears. C. Step pulley. D. Bull gear lock pin. The guards have been removed for clarity.

TAILSTOCK

The tailstock, Fig. 36-11, can be adjusted along the lathe ways to accommodate different lengths of work. It mounts the "dead" center that supports the outer end of the work, and can be fitted with cutting tools for drilling, reaming

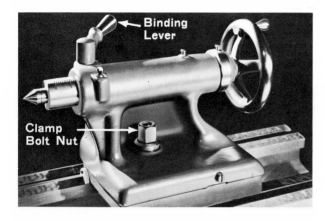

Fig. 36-11. The tailstock. (South Bend Lathe, Inc.)

and threading. The unit is clamped to the ways by tightening the CLAMP BOLT NUT. The spindle is positioned by rotating the HAND-WHEEL and is locked in position with the BINDING LEVER.

CARRIAGE

The carriage, Fig. 36-12, includes the SAD-DLE, APRON, CROSS and LONGITUDINAL

FEED and SCREW CUTTING MECHANISM. COMPOUND REST and TOOL POST. The cutting tool is supported and its actions controlled by the carriage which is moved along the ways by hand or power feed. The power feed mechanism is located in the apron, Fig. 36-13. A friction clutch controls longitudinal and cross power feed. Half-nuts are engaged for thread cutting.

SAFETY

1. Do not attempt to operate the lathe until you have been checked out on it and are thoroughly familiar with its operation.
2. Dress appropriately. Remove your necktie, sweater, wrist watch and rings. Wear an apron or a properly fitted shop coat. Safety goggles are a must.
3. Clamp all work solidly. Use the correct size tool or work holding device for the job. Get help if you must use heavy chucks or attachments.
4. Check your work frequently when it is being machined between centers. The work ex-

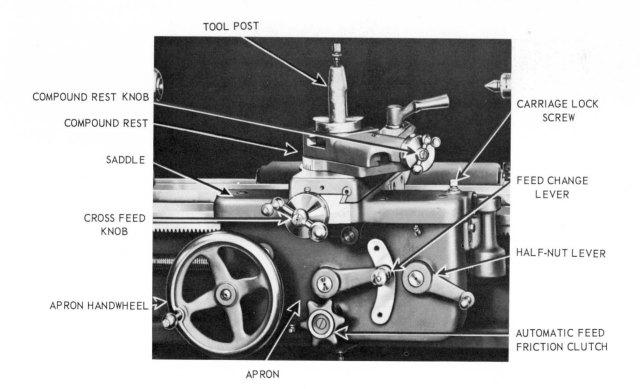

Fig. 36-12. The lathe carriage. (South Bend Lathe, Inc.)

pands as it heats up and could damage the tail center if it overheats.

5. Replace all guards before starting to work. The guards should only be removed to make adjustments, and then with the power turned off at the main electrical panel to prevent the machine from being turned on accidentally. Replace the guards immediately after the adjustments have been made.

6. Return all unnecessary tools to the proper storage area. Remove all other tools from the immediate work area.

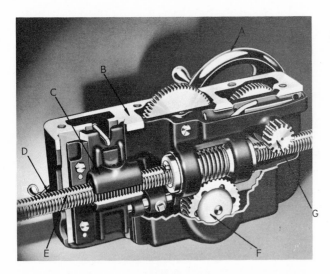

Fig. 36-13. The apron mechanism as seen with part of the apron casting cut away. A. Handwheel. B. Apron. C. Half-nut. D. Lead screw. E. Spline. F. Automatic feed clutch. G. Rack gear. (South Bend Lathe, Inc.)

7. Turn the chuck or faceplate by hand to be sure there is no binding or danger of the work striking any part of the lathe.

8. Stop the machine before making adjustments or measurements.

9. Remember that the chips are razor sharp. Do not attempt to remove chips with your fingers. Stop the machine and use pliers to remove them.

10. Support all work solidly. Do not permit small diameter work to project too far from the chuck without support from the tailstock center.

11. Be careful not to run the cutting tool into the chuck or dog. Check out any readjustment of work or tool to be sure there is ample clearance between the tool and the chuck or dog, when the tool has been moved left to the farthest point that will be machined.

Fig. 36-14. The feed mechanism. (Sheldon Machine Co., Inc.)

12. Do not use cotton waste or rags to wipe grease or oil from the work surface unless the machine is stopped. Keep brushes used for cleaning and to apply coolant, clear of work when knurling.

13. If work must be removed from the lathe, or repositioned in the chuck, always move the cutting tool clear of the work or reverse it in the tool post to prevent it from cutting you accidentally.

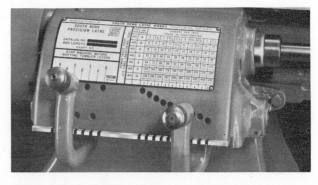

Fig. 36-15. The index plate. (South Bend Lathe, Inc.)

14. Do not talk to anyone, nor permit anyone to fool around the machine while you are operating it. You are the only one who should turn the machine on or off, or make adjustments to the lathe while you are operating it.

15. Never attempt to run the chuck on or off the spindle by using power. It is also a dangerous practice to stop the lathe by reversing its direction of rotation.

16. You should always be aware of the direction and speed of the carriage or cross-feed before engaging automatic feed.

Fig. 36-16. The lead screw.

17. Never leave the key in the chuck. Make it a habit never to let go of the key until it is out of the chuck and clear of the work area.

18. Tools must not be placed on the lathe ways. Use a tool board or place them on the lathe tray.

19. Do not wrap the cord around your hands when cleaning the lead screw. Grip it lightly between the fingers so if it catches on the screw it will slip safely out of your hand.

20. Never use a file without a handle.

21. Stop the machine immediately if some odd noise or vibration develops while you are operating it. If you cannot find what is causing the trouble, get your instructor. Under no condition should the machine be operated until the trouble has been found and corrected.

22. Remove all burrs and sharp edges from the piece before removing it from the lathe.

23. Plan your work thoroughly before starting. Have all of the tools that will be needed at hand before commencing work.

24. Be careful when you clean the machine. As stated before, chips and shavings are sharp and will cause serious cuts if you attempt to remove them with your hands. Use a cleaning brush, NOT A DUST BRUSH, for the job. NEVER USE THE AIR HOSE. The flying chips may injure someone.

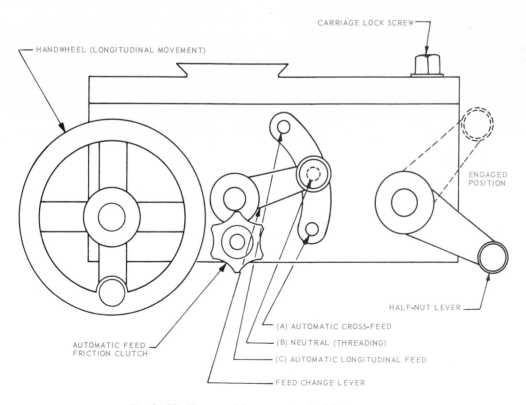

Fig. 36-17. The control levers on a typical lathe apron.

FEED MECHANISM

The feed mechanism, Fig. 36-14, transmits power through a train of gears to the QUICK CHANGE GEAR BOX, which regulates the amount of tool movement per revolution of the spindle. The feed mechanism also contains gears for reversing tool travel. Lettering on the INDEX PLATE, Fig. 36-15, tells how to position the levers for various thread cutting and feed combinations.

The LEAD SCREW, Fig. 36-16, transmits the power to the carriage through a gearing and clutch arrangement in the apron. The FEED CHANGE LEVERS on the apron, Fig. 36-17, control the operation of power feeds and when placed in neutral permit half-nuts to be engaged for threading operations.

Fig. 36-19. The carriage should be checked for binding by moving it along the ways.

6. Inspect the tailstock if it is to be used for any portion of the operation. Check it for alignment. Use a smooth dead center.
7. Place the proper work holding attachment on the headstock spindle. Clean the threads and apply a drop of oil.
8. Sharpen the cutter bit. Clamp it in the appropriate tool holder and mount it in the tool post.

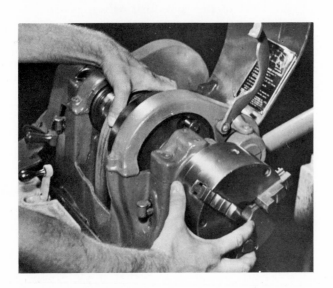

Fig. 36-18. Check to be sure the machine is not locked in back gear. Release belt tension before checking.

PREPARING THE LATHE FOR OPERATION

1. Clean and lubricate the lathe. Use the lubricants specified by the manufacturer.
2. Turn the spindle by hand to be sure it is not locked in back gear, Fig. 36-18. Set the drive mechanism to the desired speed and feed.
3. Place all guards in position.
4. Move the carriage along the ways, Fig. 36-19. There should be no binding.
5. Inspect the cross-feed and compound rest slides. Adjust the gibs if there is too much play, Fig. 36-20. Do not permit excessive overhang of the compound rest, Fig. 36-21.

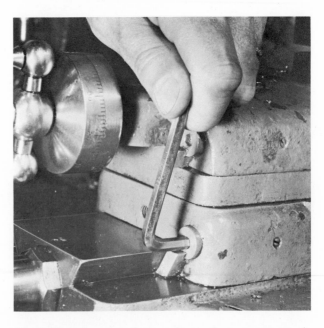

Fig. 36-20. Adjust the gibs according to the instructions in the manufacturer's handbook on the lathe if there is too much play in the unit.

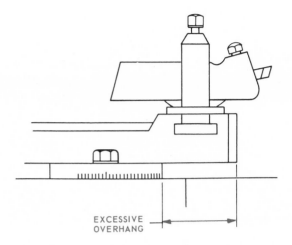

Fig. 36-21. Excessive compound rest overhang usually causes tool "chatter" with a poorly machined surface as the result.

For safety reasons goggles must be worn, sleeves rolled up and rings and jewelry removed. Measuring tools, wrenches, files, etc., should be kept on a LATHE BOARD, Fig. 36-22, and not on the ways.

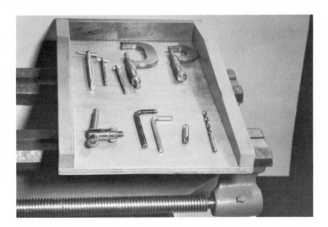

Fig. 36-22. The lathe board keeps tools within easy reach.

DO NOT ATTEMPT TO TAKE MEASUREMENTS OR CLEAN THE WORK. WHEN THE MACHINE IS RUNNING.

Use pliers to remove stringy chips. DO NOT USE YOUR FINGERS. Tool adjustment should permit machining to the desired point on the work without danger of running into the chuck or lathe dog.

HOW TO CLEAN THE LATHE

A lathe should be cleaned after each work period. Remove chips with a paint brush --

NOT YOUR HAND. Wipe all painted surfaces with a soft cloth. To complete the job, move the tailstock to the extreme right and use a soft cloth to wipe the remaining oil, chips and dirt from the machined surfaces. DO NOT USE COMPRESSED AIR TO REMOVE THE CHIPS. The flying chips are dangerous.

The lead screw needs an occasional cleaning too. This may be done by adjusting the lathe to rotate at a slow speed and using a piece of cord, as shown in Fig. 36-23. Permit the cord to feed along the threads. DO NOT WRAP THE CORD AROUND YOUR HAND because THE CORD MIGHT CATCH ON THE LEAD SCREW AND CAUSE SERIOUS INJURY.

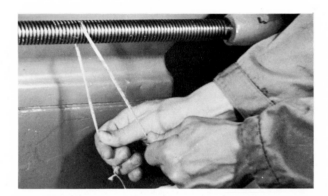

Fig. 36-23. Cleaning the lead screw with a piece of cord. DO NOT WRAP THE CORD AROUND YOUR HAND.

LATHE CUTTING TOOLS AND TOOL HOLDERS

Before a machinist can operate a lathe efficiently he must have a good understanding of cutting tools and how these should be sharpened to machine various materials.

CUTTING TOOLS

Carbon steel tool cutter bits formerly used have been almost entirely replaced by high speed steel (HSS) bits. These are, in all probability, the type cutting tools you will be using.

LATHE TOOL HOLDERS

In use a cutter bit is inserted in a TOOL HOLDER, Fig. 36-24, and tightened down with a setscrew. The tool holders are made in STRAIGHT, RIGHT-HAND and LEFT-HAND SHAPES. To differentiate between a right and

Fig. 36-24a. Straight tool holder. (J. H. Williams & Co.)

Fig. 36-24b. Right-hand tool holder. (J. H. Williams & Co.)

Fig. 36-24c. Left-hand tool holder. (J. H. Williams & Co.)

*Fig. 36-25. A turret type tool holder. Four cutter bits are fixed in the holder and can be brought into cutting position by loosening the lock (handle) and pivoting the desired cutter bit into cutting position and locking it in place.
(Allegheny Ludlum Steel Corp.)*

left-hand tool holder, hold the head of the holder in your hand and note the direction the shank points. The right-hand tool holder points to the right, the left-hand tool holder to the left.

On some lathes a turret type tool holder is used, Fig. 36-25.

CUTTING TOOL SHAPES

Parts of a cutter bit are shown in Fig. 36-26. Most cutter bits are ground to cut in one direction only. Some cutting tools for general

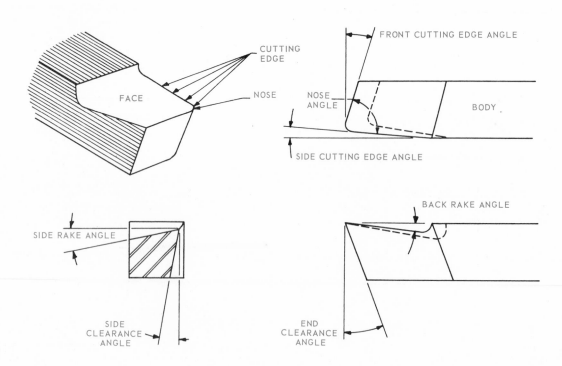

Fig. 36-26. The cutter bit and its parts.

turning are shown in Fig. 36-27. To get satisfactory results from a metal lathe, the tool bit must have a keen, properly-shaped cutting edge.

small rounded nose, permits deep cuts at heavier feeds. The slight side relief angle provides ample support to the cutting edges.

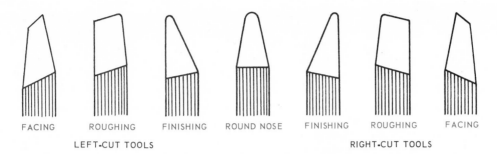

FACING   ROUGHING   FINISHING   ROUND NOSE   FINISHING   ROUGHING   FACING

LEFT-CUT TOOLS   RIGHT-CUT TOOLS

Fig. 36-27. Standard cutting tool shapes.

The shape to grind the bit depends on the class of work (roughing or finishing) and upon the metal to be cut.

LEFT-CUT AND RIGHT-CUT ROUGHING TOOLS

The left-cut roughing tool, Fig. 36-28(A), cuts most efficiently when it travels from left to right. The right-cut roughing tool, Fig. 36-28(B), operates just the opposite.

The tool shape, straight cutting edge with a

FINISHING TOOL

The finishing tool, Fig. 36-29, has a nose that is more rounded. Such a tool will produce a smooth finish, if the cutting edge is honed with a fine oilstone after grinding. A light cut with fine feed is used with this tool.

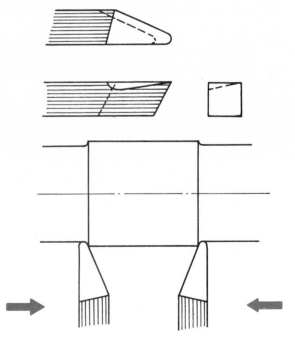

Fig. 36-29. Finishing tool.

FACING TOOL

The facing tool, Fig. 36-30, is ground to prevent interference with the tailstock center. The tool point is set at a slight angle to the work face with the point leading slightly.

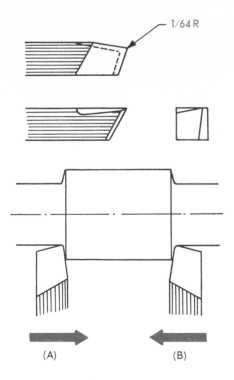

— 1/64 R

(A)   (B)

Fig. 36-28. Roughing tool.

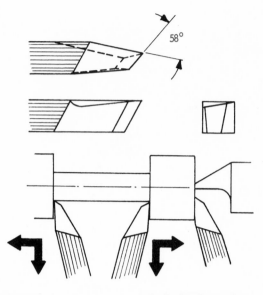

Fig. 36-30. Facing tool.

ROUND NOSE TOOL

The round nose tool, Fig. 36-31, is designed for lighter turning and is ground flat on the face (without back or side rake) to permit cutting in

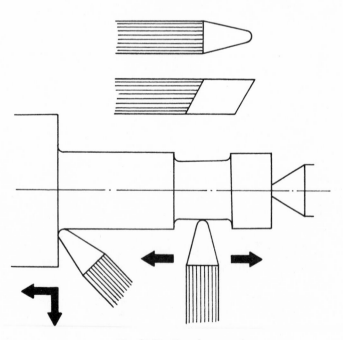

Fig. 36-31. Round nose tool.

either direction. A slight variation with a negative rake ground on the face is excellent for machining brass, Fig. 36-32.

Aluminum requires a different tool shape,

Fig. 36-33, from those previously described. The tool is set slightly above center to reduce any tendency to chatter (vibrate rapidly).

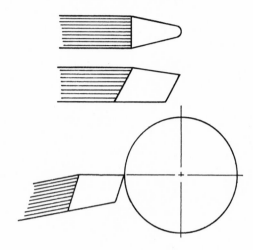

Fig. 36-32. Tool for brass.

HOW TO SHARPEN THE CUTTER BIT

When first attempting to grind a cutter bit, it may be desirable to use chalk and draw the shape of the desired point on the front portion

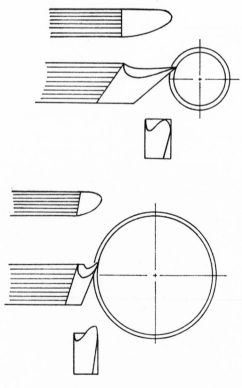

Fig. 36-33. Tools for aluminum.

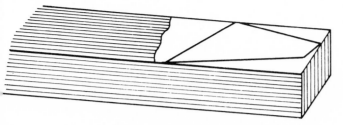

Fig. 36-34. Laid out cutter bit blank.

clearance, top clearance and end relief may be checked with a CLEARANCE AND CUTTING ANGLE GAUGE, Fig. 36-36.

CUTTING SPEEDS, FEEDS AND DEPTH OF CUT

The term CUTTING SPEED indicates the distance in feet per minute the work moves past

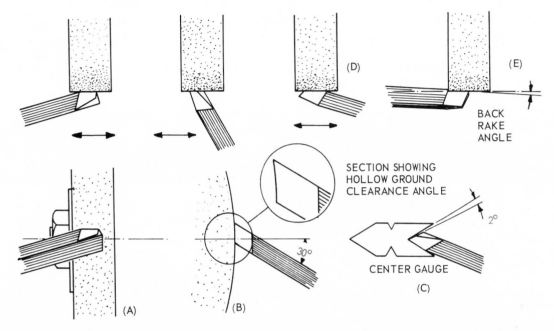

Fig. 36-35. Cutter bit grinding sequence.

of the blank, Fig. 36-34. In grinding, the chalk lines serve as a guide.

Fig. 36-35 shows the grinding sequence. Side

the cutting tool. Measuring is done on the circumference of the work.

To explain this differently, if a lathe were

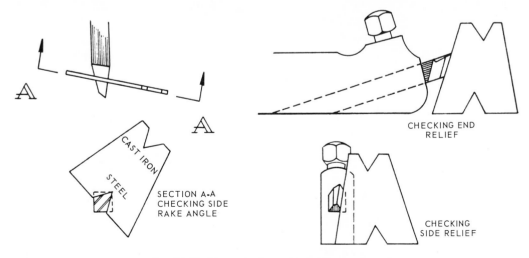

Fig. 36-36. The cutter bit gauge and how it is used.

to cut one long chip, the length of that chip in feet cut in one minute, would be the cutting speed of the lathe. Feed is the distance the cutter moves lengthwise along the lathe bed during one revolution of the work.

The specifications on the SPEED AND FEED CHART, Fig. 36-37, are intended for use with

Material	Roughing Cut 0.010 to 0.020 in. Feed	Finishing Cut 0.002 to 0.010 in. Feed
Cast Iron	80 FPM	100 FPM
Steel		
Low Carbon	130 FPM	160 FPM
Med. Carbon	90 FPM	100 FPM
High Carbon	50 FPM	65 FPM
Tool Steel (Annealed)	50 FPM	65 FPM
Brass - Yellow	160 FPM	220 FPM
Bronze	90 FPM	100 FPM
Aluminum*	600 FPM	1000 FPM

The speed for rough turning is offered as a starting point. It should be all the machine and work will withstand. The finishing feed depends upon the finish required.

* The speeds for turning aluminum will vary greatly according to the alloy being machined. The softer alloys can be turned at speeds upwards of 1600 FPM (Roughing) to 3500 FPM (Finishing). The high silicon alloys require a lower cutting speed.

Fig. 36-37. Suggested cutting speeds and feeds for turning (High Speed Steel Tools).

high speed steel cutter bits. These can be increased 50 percent if a coolant is used and another 300 to 400 percent if a tungsten carbide cutting tool is used.

Fig. 36-38a. The micrometer dials on the cross slide and compound rest. (South Bend Lathe, Inc.)

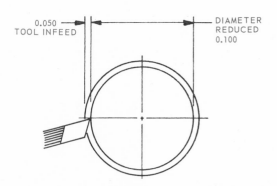

Fig. 36-38b. How material is removed on each cut.

HOW TO CALCULATE CUTTING SPEEDS

CUTTING SPEEDS (CS) are given in FEET PER MINUTE (FPM), while the WORK SPEED is given in REVOLUTIONS PER MINUTE (RPM); thus, the peripheral speed of the work (CS) must be converted to RPM in order to determine the lathe speed required. The following formula can be used:

$$RPM = \frac{CS \times 4}{D}$$

Where: RPM = Revolutions per minute
CS = Cutting speed of the particular metal being turned in feed per minute.
D = Diameter of the work in inches

EXAMPLE: What spindle speed is required to finish turn 4 inch diameter aluminum alloy.

$$RPM = \frac{CS \times 4}{D}$$ CS = 400 FPM for finish turning

$$RPM = \frac{400 \times 4}{4}$$ D = 4 in.

$$= 400$$

Adjust the speed control mechanism to a speed as close to this figure as possible.

ROUGHING CUTS

Roughing cuts are taken to reduce the work quickly to approximate size. The work is left 1/32 in. oversize for the finishing operation. As the finish of the roughing cut is not important, the highest speed and coarsest feed, consistent with safety and accuracy, should be used.

RAKE AND CLEARANCE ANGLE FOR LATHE TOOLS
(High Speed Steel)

	Cast Iron	Low Carbon Steel	High Carbon Steel
Back Rake	6 – 8°	8 – 12°	4 – 6°
Side Rake	10 – 12°	14 – 18°	8 – 10°
Clearance *	6 – 9°	8 – 10°	6 – 8°
	Alloy Steels	**Soft Brass**	**Aluminum**
Back Rake	5 – 8°	0 – 2°	25 – 50°
Side Rake	10 – 15°	0 – 2°	10 – 20°
Clearance *	6 – 8°	10 – 15°	7 – 10°
	Copper		
Back Rake	10 – 12°		
Side Rake	20 – 25°		
Clearance *	6 – 8°		

* The end and side clearance angles are usually the same.

FINISHING CUTS

The finish cut brings the work to the required diameter and surface finish. A sharp tool, used at high speed and fine feed, is used.

Fig. 36-39. Machining work mounted between centers.

Fig. 36-40. Turning work held in a 3-jaw universal chuck.

DEPTH OF CUT

Depth of cut refers to the distance the cutter has been fed into the work surface. The cutter can be set very accurately with a MICROMETER DIAL, Fig. 36-38a, on both the cross slide and compound rest. These dials are graduated in thousandths (0.001) in. which means that a movement of one graduation will move the cutting tool 1/1000 (0.001) in. into the work AND WILL CAUSE 2/1000 (0.002) IN. OF MATERIAL TO BE REMOVED, Fig. 36-38b.

WORK HOLDING ATTACHMENTS

The work is machined while supported by one of the following methods:
1. Between centers, Fig. 36-39.
2. Held in a chuck, Fig. 36-40.
3. Held in a collet, Fig. 36-41.
4. Bolted to faceplate, Fig. 36-42.

Fig. 36-41. Turning work held in a collet chuck.
(The Jacobs Mfg. Co.)

Fig. 36-42. Work bolted to a faceplate for boring.
(South Bend Lathe, Inc.)

Fig. 36-43. Lathe faceplates.

TURNING BETWEEN CENTERS

Considerable lathe work is done between centers. For this operation, a FACEPLATE, Fig. 36-43, is threaded to the spindle nose and a SLEEVE and LIVE CENTER, Fig. 36-44, is inserted in the headstock spindle. A DEAD CENTER is placed in the tailstock. The ends of the stock are drilled to fit the centers. The stock is connected to the faceplate with a DOG, Fig. 36-45.

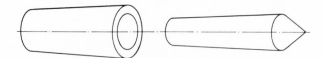

Fig. 36-44. The sleeve and head center.

Fig. 36-45a. Bent tail standard lathe dog. (Armstrong Bros. Tool Co.)

Fig. 36-45b. Bent tail safety dog. (Armstrong Bros. Tool Co.)

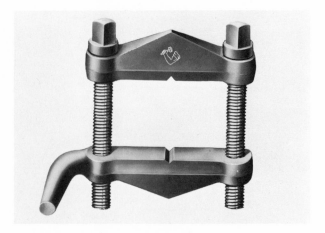

Fig. 36-45c. Clamp type lathe dog. (Armstrong Bros. Tool Co.)

DRILLING CENTER HOLES

Before work can be turned between centers, it is necessary to locate and drill a CENTER HOLE in each end of the stock. Fig. 36-46 illustrates several methods of locating the center of the stock.

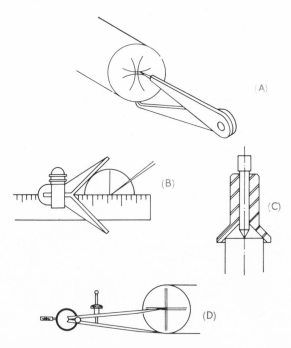

Fig. 36-46. Ways to locate the center of round stock. (A) With hermaphrodite caliper. (B) With center head of combination set. (C) With the bell center punch. (D) With dividers.

Center holes are drilled with a COMBINATION DRILL AND COUNTERSINK, Figs. 36-47a, b. They provide a reservoir for a lubricant. The center hole may be drilled on the drill press; on the lathe with the work centered in a chuck; or supported on the dead center with the center drill mounted in the headstock.

Fig. 36-47a. Plain type combination drill and countersink. (Standard Tool Co.)

CHECKING ALIGNMENT OF LATHE CENTERS

Accurate work requires centers that run true and in precise alignment. If the live center does not run true, the diameters will be eccentric,

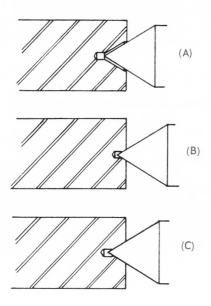

Fig. 36-47b. Center holes. (A) Hole drilled too deeply, center rides on lip of hole. Groove will wear on dead center. (B) Hole not drilled deeply enough. Not enough support, center point will burn off. (C) Properly drilled center hole.

Fig. 36-48, as the piece must be reversed to machine the entire length.

A tapered piece will result if the centers are not aligned.

Approximate alignment can be determined by:

1. Bringing the centers together and checking them visually, Fig. 36-49.
2. Checking the alignment of the two lines on the back of the tailstock, Fig. 36-50.

Extremely accurate machining requires a more precise method of checking center alignment. A test piece is machined and "miked" at

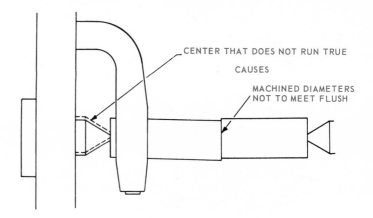

Fig. 36-48. Eccentric diameters will result if the live center does not run true and the piece must be reversed in the dog so that the stock can be machined its entire length.

several points along its length. If the piece tapers, the tailstock should be adjusted until the diameter is the same the entire length. Use the

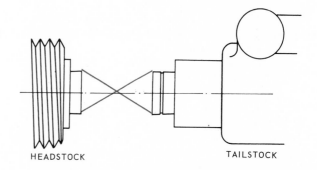

Fig. 36-49. Checking center alignment by bringing the center points together.

adjusting screws on the base of the tailstock.

Make the adjustments gradually. A common mistake is to move the setscrews too far and overshoot the mark.

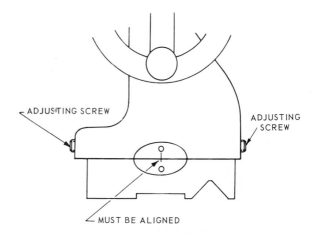

Fig. 36-50. Alignment of centers determined by checking witness marks on tailstock.

HOW TO MOUNT WORK BETWEEN CENTERS

Clamp a lathe dog on one end of the work. Place lubricant (white lead and oil, white lead, graphite and oil or a commercial center lubricant) in the center hole. Fit the work on the centers and adjust the tail center until the work is snug on the centers. Check the adjustment from time to time during the machining operation as the heat generated causes the piece to expand.

Be sure that the dog tail does not bind on the faceplate slot, Fig. 36-51.

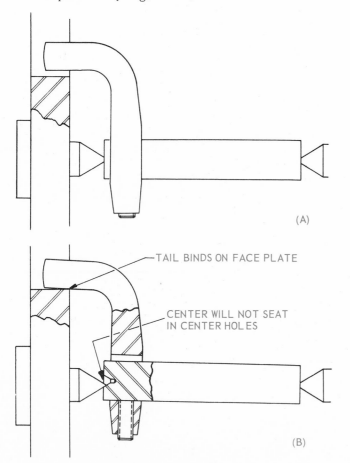

(A)

(B)

TAIL BINDS ON FACE PLATE

CENTER WILL NOT SEAT IN CENTER HOLES

Fig. 36-51. The diameter of the machined surface will not be concentric with the center holes if the center hole is not seated properly on the headstock center. A binding lathe dog is a common reason for this fault.

FACING STOCK HELD BETWEEN CENTERS

Facing is the operation of machining the end of the stock square and reducing it to a specific length.

There are times when considerable material

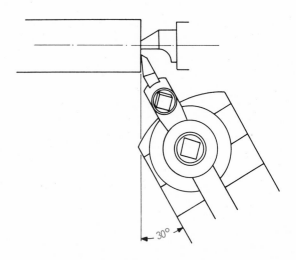

Fig. 36-52. The compound setting when facing stock to length.

must be removed. In normal practice, the work is left longer than finished size and the center holes are drilled deeper for better support during rough turning. The stock is faced to length before starting the finishing operation.

A RIGHT-CUT FACING TOOL is used. The point of the tool permits a slight clearance between the work face and the center. A HALF CENTER may be used for the facing operation. With the compound rest set at 30 deg., Fig. 36-52, bring the cutting tool up until it just touches the surface to be machined, and lock the carriage. Feed the cutter into the work, with the compound rest.

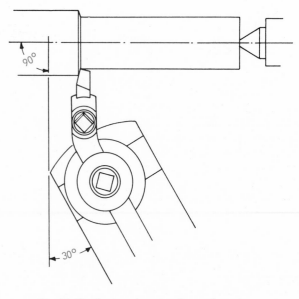

Fig. 36-53. Compound setting for rough turning.

ROUGH TURNING BETWEEN CENTERS

Rough turning is the operation that removes excess metal rapidly with little regard for the quality of the finish. The diameter is reduced to within 1/32 in. of required size by using coarse feed and deep cuts. The compound is set at 30 deg. to the work, Fig. 36-53. This permits the tool to cut as close as possible to the left end of the work without the dog striking the compound rest.

CHECK BEFORE STARTING THE MACHINE TO DETERMINE HOW FAR THE CARRIAGE CAN BE MOVED TO THE LEFT WITHOUT DANGER OF THE DOG STRIKING THE COMPOUND REST.

Use a LEFT HAND TOOL HOLDER to support the cutter bit. Position the tool post as far to the left in the compound rest T-slot as possi-

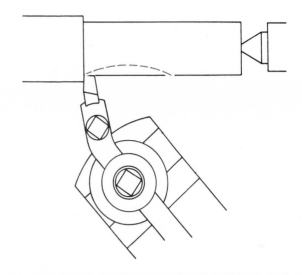

Fig. 36-55. An incorrectly positioned tool will cut deeper and deeper into the work if it should pivot in the tool post.

It is also important to have the tool holder in the correct position in the tool post. This is especially true when making heavy cuts. The side pressures developed sometimes cause the tool holder to turn in the tool post. If not positioned correctly, the cutting tool will be forced still deeper in the work, Fig. 36-55. The correct position permits the tool to swing away from the work, Fig. 36-56.

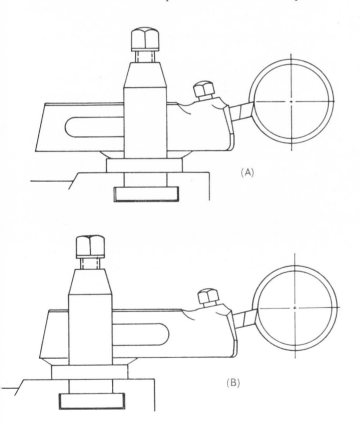

Fig. 36-54. (A) Tool holder and cutter bit in the proper position. (B) Too much overhang. Tool will "chatter" and cause a machined surface that is rough.

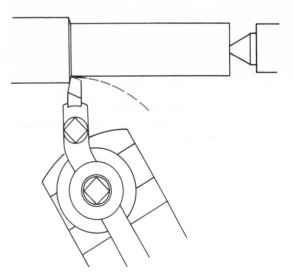

Fig. 36-56. A correctly positioned tool will swing clear of the work if the tool holder slips in the tool post.

ble. When mounting the tool holder, do not permit too much overhang, Fig. 36-54. The cutting edge of the tool should be about 1/16 in. above center for each inch of diameter.

Apply lubricant to the center hole each cut. A heavy-duty BALL BEARING CENTER (the center revolves in the unit) is ideal for rough turning, Fig. 36-57.

Fig. 36-57. A heavy-duty ball bearing center.
(Motor Tool Mfg. Co.)

FINISH TURNING

A RIGHT-CUT FINISHING TOOL is used for finish machining. Adjust the lathe for a faster spindle speed and a finer cut. Feed the cutting tool into the work until a very light cut is being made and engage the power feed. After a sufficient distance has been machined, disengage the power feed and stop the lathe. UNDER NO CONDITION SHOULD THE LATHE BE REVERSED TO STOP IT. Do not interfere with the cross slide setting. Measure the machined diameter with a micrometer. Calculate the additional material that must be removed to bring the piece down to size. Move the cutting tool clear of the right end of the work and feed it in ONE-HALF the amount that must still be removed. Make another cut about 1/2-in. wide, and remeasure. If to size, complete the cut, if not, reposition the cutter.

If the piece must be reversed to machine its entire length, protect the section under the lathe dog setscrew by inserting a piece of soft aluminum or copper sheet.

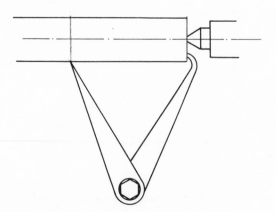

Fig. 36-58. Locating reference points on the work using an hermaphrodite caliper.

TURNING TO A SHOULDER

It is often necessary to machine several different diameters on a single piece of stock. Locate the points to which the different diameters are to be cut by scribing them with a hermaphrodite caliper set to the specified size, Fig. 36-58.

The machining is done as previously described with the exception of machining the SHOULDER. This is the point where the diameters change, and one of the shoulders illustrated in Fig. 36-59 is specified.

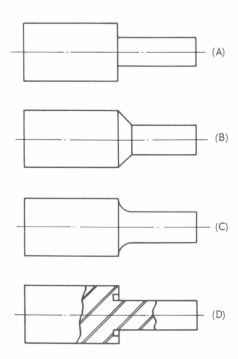

Fig. 36-59. Four kinds of shoulders: (A) Square. (B) Angular. (C) Filleted. (D) Undercut.

A RIGHT-CUT FACING TOOL is used to make the square and angular type shoulder. A ROUND NOSE TOOL, ground to the proper radius, is used to machine the filleted shoulder.

TURNING WITH CHUCKS

The CHUCK is the most rapid method of mounting work for turning. Operations such as drilling, reaming, boring and internal threading, can be done to work held in a chuck. Additional support can be secured by supporting the free end of work held in a chuck with the tailstock center.

Fig. 36-60. The 3-jaw universal chuck.
(L. W. Chuck Co.)

Fig. 36-62. The 4-jaw independent chuck.
(L. W. Chuck Co.)

The chucks most commonly used are:
1. 3-jaw Universal Chuck.
2. 4-jaw Independent Chuck.
3. Jacobs Chuck.
4. Draw-in Collet Chuck.

THE 3-JAW UNIVERSAL CHUCK

The 3-jaw universal chuck, Fig. 36-60, is designed to permit all jaws of the chuck to operate simultaneously. This automatically centers round or hexagonal shaped stock to within a few thousandths of an inch.

Two sets of jaws are normally provided with each universal chuck permitting a wide variety of work to be mounted, Fig. 36-61. Do not grip the work near the front of the jaws.

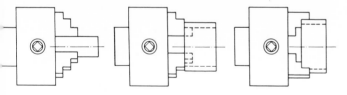

Fig. 36-61. Methods of holding work in the 3-jaw universal chuck.

THE 4-JAW INDEPENDENT CHUCK

As each jaw of the 4-jaw independent chuck, Fig. 36-62, can operate individually, irregular shaped castings and forgings can be centered.

The jaws can be reversed to hold different size work, Fig. 36-63.

The most accurate method of centering work in this type chuck makes use of a dial indicator, Fig. 36-64. Center the work approximately using the concentric rings on the chuck face as a guide. Bring to final adjustment using the dial indicator.

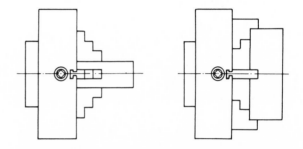

Fig. 36-63. The reversing feature of the jaws in the 4-jaw independent chuck makes it possible to turn work with extreme differences in diameter without difficulty.

BE SURE TO REMOVE THE CHUCK KEY
BEFORE TURNING ON THE MACHINE

The tool holder can also be used to position the work on approximate center, Fig. 36-65. Reverse it in the tool post and tighten it by hand. Rotate the chuck by hand. The high point of the work will push the tool holder back. Loosen the

Fig. 36-64. Centering work in the 4-jaw chuck
by using the dial indicator.

Fig. 36-65. Using the tool holder to center work in a 4-jaw independent chuck.

jaw opposite the high point and tighten the jaw on the high side. Repeat the sequence until the piece is centered.

JACOBS CHUCK

A Jacobs chuck, Fig. 36-66, can be used to hold small diameter and short work for turning.

Fig. 36-66a. Turning small diameter work in a Jacobs chuck.

A standard drill chuck can be used if fitted with a sleeve. Wipe the shank clean before inserting the sleeve.

DRAW-IN COLLET CHUCK

A draw-in collet chuck, Fig. 36-67, is used for holding comparatively small diameter work. The standard type collet has a circular hole for round stock, but collets for holding square, hexagonal and octagonal material are available. Their chief advantage lies in their ability to center work automatically and maintain accuracy over long periods of hard usage.

A collet chuck that makes use of steel segments bonded to rubber is shown in Fig. 36-68. An advantage of this chuck is that each collet has a range of 0.100 in., rather than being a single size like steel collets.

Fig. 36-66b. Turning work held in a Jacobs chuck.

Fig. 36-67. A collet chuck in use.

HOW TO MOUNT CHUCKS

Chuck accuracy is affected if it is not installed on the spindle nose correctly. Remove the center and sleeve by holding with one hand and lightly tap them loose with the knockout bar. Carefully wipe the spindle threads clean of chips

Fig. 36-68. The Rubber-Flex Collet in use. (The Jacobs Mfg. Co.)

and dirt and apply a few drops of lubricating oil. Clean the chuck threads with a SPRING CLEANER, Fig. 36-69.

Hold the chuck against the spindle nose with

the right hand and turn the spindle with the left hand. Screw the chuck on until it presses firmly against the shoulder. DO NOT SPIN IT ON OR USE POWER. Place a board on the ways under the chuck for protection. RELEASE BELT TENSION, IF POSSIBLE, TO ELIMINATE ANY CHANCE OF POWER BEING TRANSFERRED TO THE SPINDLE.

HOW TO REMOVE CHUCKS

There are several accepted methods for removing chucks from a lathe headstock spindle. The first step in all methods is to place a

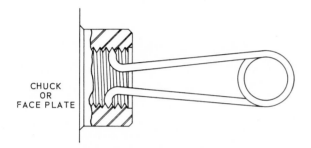

CHUCK
OR
FACE PLATE

Fig. 36-69. The spring cleaner for cleaning the threads in the chuck.

Fig. 36-70. A wooden cradle placed under the chuck will make removing the chuck from the spindle safer and easier.

wooden cradle across the ways beneath the chuck, Fig. 36-70. Then use one of the following techniques:

1. Lock the spindle in back gear and use the chuck key to apply leverage, Fig. 36-71.
2. Place an adjustable wrench of a suitable size on one jaw, Fig. 36-72, grasp the drive pulley with one hand or lock the

Fig. 36-71. Using the chuck wrench to loosen the chuck for removal.

Fig. 36-72. An adjustable wrench fitted to one of the jaws may be used to loosen the chuck on the spindle.

spindle in back gear, and apply pressure to the wrench.
3. If neither of the first two methods work, place a block of wood between the back lathe way and a chuck jaw. Engage the back gear and give the drive pulley a quick backward turn, Fig. 36-73.

HOW TO FACE STOCK HELD IN CHUCK

A ROUND NOSE CUTTING TOOL held in a straight tool holder is used to face stock held in a chuck. The tool is set up as shown in Fig. 36-74. Move the carriage into position and lock it.

A facing cut can be made in either direction; that is, the tool may be started in the center and fed out, or the reverse may be done. The usual

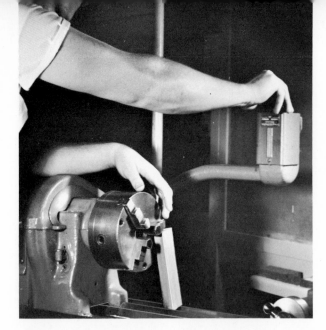

Fig. 36-73. Reversing the chuck against a block of wood is often used to remove a stubborn chuck.

practice is to start from the center and feed out. Use automatic feed if the material is over 1-1/2-in. in diameter.

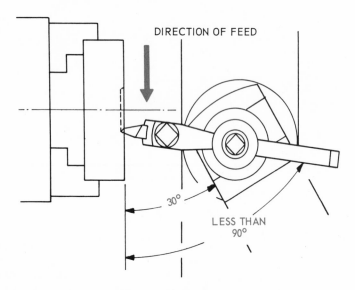

DIRECTION OF FEED

30°

LESS THAN 90°

Fig. 36-74. The tool and tool holder in the correct position for facing.

PLAIN TURNING AND TURNING TO A SHOULDER

Work mounted in a chuck is machined in the same manner as it is machined between centers. To prevent springing while it is being machined, long work should be center drilled and supported with the tailstock center.

PARTING OPERATIONS

Parting is the operation of cutting off material after it has been machined, Fig. 36-75.

Fig. 36-75. Cutting off a section after it has been machined.

This is one of the most difficult jobs performed on the lathe.

The cutting tool, Fig. 36-76, must be ground with the correct clearance (front, side and end) and is held in a STRAIGHT or OFFSET TOOL HOLDER. The blade is set at exactly 90 deg. to the work surface, Fig. 36-77. The cutting edge

Fig. 36-76. Parting tool holders. (Armstrong Bros. Tool Co.)

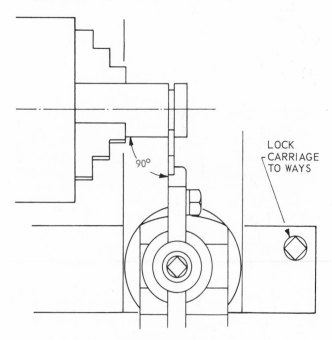

90°

LOCK CARRIAGE TO WAYS

Fig. 36-77. Close-up of parting tool cutting edge showing concave top rake.

---

is set on center when cutting off stock 1 in. or less in diameter and 1/16 in. above center for each additional inch in diameter. The tool must be lowered as the diameter is reduced, unless the center of the piece has been drilled out.

Spindle speed is about one-third the speed used for conventional turning. Use ample supplies of coolant. Whenever possible, hold the work close in the chuck.

DO NOT ATTEMPT TO CUT OFF WORK HELD BETWEEN CENTERS. IT CANNOT BE DONE SATISFACTORILY, Fig. 36-78.

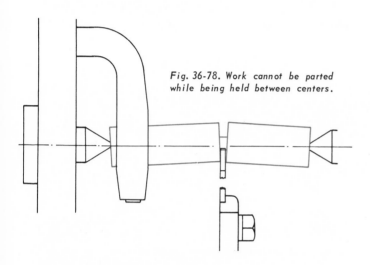

Fig. 36-78. Work cannot be parted while being held between centers.

HOW TO TURN A TAPER

There are four generally accepted methods of machining tapers on the lathe. Each has its advantages and disadvantages.
1. Using the compound rest.
2. By offsetting the tailstock.
3. If lathe is fitted with taper attachment use that attachment.

Fig. 36-79a. The cross slide and the compound rest. (South Bend Lathe, Inc.)

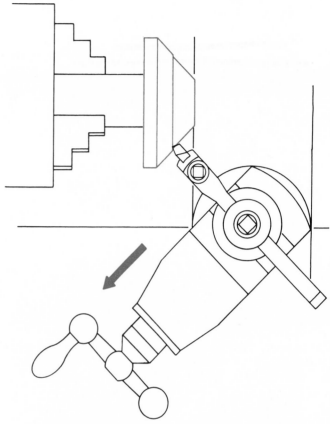

Fig. 36-79b. Turning a taper by using the compound rest.

4. Using cutting tool ground to the desired taper.

COMPOUND REST METHOD

The compound rest method of turning tapers, Fig. 36-79, is the easiest of the group. It can be used to cut internal and external tapers, however, the length of the taper is limited by the movement of the compound rest. The base of the compound rest is graduated in degrees.

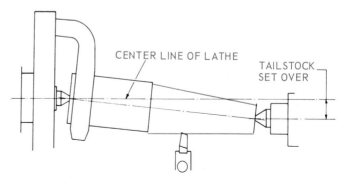

CENTER LINE OF LATHE
TAILSTOCK SET OVER

Fig. 36-80. Machining a taper by the offset tailstock technique.

OFFSET TAILSTOCK METHOD

The offset tailstock method, Fig. 36-80, also known as the tailstock setover method, is widely used in small shops for turning tapers. Any job that can be machined between centers can be tapered by this method. Only external tapers can be turned.

The lathe tailstock is constructed in two parts permitting the portion mounting the dead center to be moved off center, Fig. 36-81. This

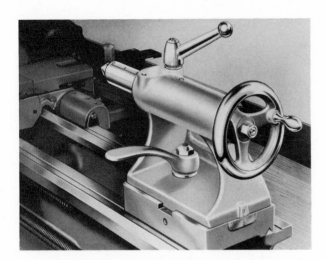

Fig. 36-81. The tailstock. (Delta Power Tool Div., Rockwell Mfg. Co.)

is accomplished by loosening the anchor bolt that locks the tailstock to the ways. There are adjusting screws on each side of the base.

CALCULATING THE SETOVER

Offset tailstock taper turning is not a precise art and requires some "trial and error" adjustment to produce an accurate piece. The approximate setover can be calculated when certain basic information is known.

The offset must be calculated for each job as the work length plays an important part in the figuring. When the length varies, different tapers will result with the same tailstock offset, Fig. 36-82.

The following terms are used when calculating tailstock setover, Fig. 36-83.

TPI = Taper per inch
TPF = Taper per foot
  D = Diameter at large end
  d = Diameter at small end
  l = Length of taper
  L = Total length of piece

CALCULATING THE SETOVER WHEN THE TAPER PER INCH IS KNOWN

Information needed: TPI = Taper per inch
L = Total length of piece

FORMULA USED: $Offset = \dfrac{L \times TPI}{2}$

EXAMPLE: What will be the setover for the following job?
TPI = 0.050
L = 8.000

$$Offset = \frac{L \times TPI}{2} = \frac{8.000 \times 0.050}{2} = 0.200 \text{ in.}$$

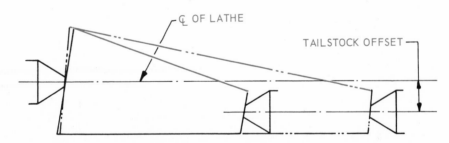

Fig. 36-82. Note how the length of the work varies the taper even though the tailstock offset remains the same.

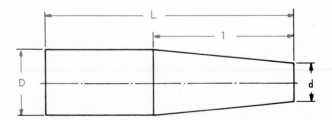

Fig. 36-83. Basic taper information: D - Diameter at large end. d - Diameter at small end. l - Length of taper. L - Total length of piece.

CALCULATING THE SETOVER WHEN THE TAPER PER FOOT IS KNOWN

When the taper per foot (TPF) is known, it must first be converted to taper per inch (TPI). The formula below takes this into account:

$$\text{Offset} = \frac{\text{TPF x L}}{24}$$

CALCULATING THE TAILSTOCK SETOVER WHEN THE DIMENSIONS OF THE TAPERED SECTION ARE KNOWN BUT TPF OR TPI ARE NOT GIVEN

Quite often the plans do not specify TPI or TPF but do give other pertinent information. Convert all fractions to decimals. All dimensions must be in inches.

FORMULA USED: $\text{Offset} = \dfrac{L \times (D - d)}{2 \times l}$

EXAMPLE: D = 1-1/4 in.
           d = 7/8 in.
           l = 3.000 in.
           L = 9.000 in.

$$\text{OFFSET} = \frac{L \times (D - d)}{2 \times l} = \frac{9 \times (1.250 - 0.875)}{2 \times 3}$$

$$= \frac{9 \times 0.375}{6} = 0.562$$

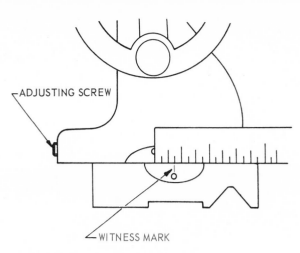

Fig. 36-84a. *Measuring offset by distance between witness marks on base of tailstock.*

MEASURING TAILSTOCK SETOVER

When an ample tolerance is allowed ($\pm$ 1/64 in.), the setover can be measured with a rule, Fig. 36-84.

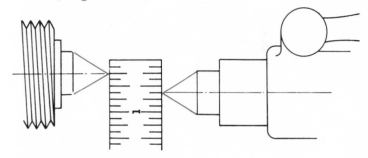

Fig. 36-84b. *Using center points for determining amount of tailstock offset.*

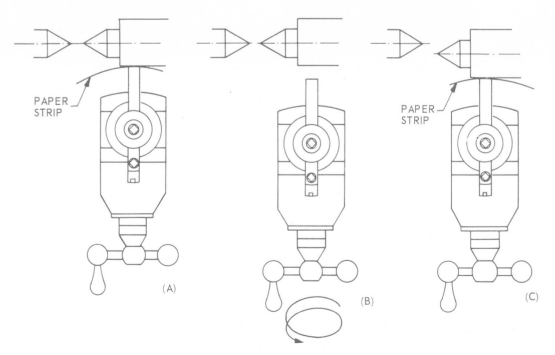

Fig. 36-85. *Using the micrometer collar of the compound rest to make the setover measurement.*

Accurate work requires more care in making the tailstock setover. This can be done using the compound rest and a strip of paper, Fig. 36-85. The compound rest is manipulated to remove all "play." It is fed against the tailstock spindle until it touches the paper strip. The compound rest is then backed out the required setover distance. The adjusting screws in the tailstock are moved until the spindle is brought out to contact the paper strip.

The dial indicator, Fig. 36-86, may also be used to measure the setover.

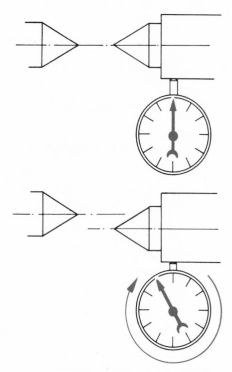

Fig. 36-86. Using the dial indicator to measure the amount of setover.

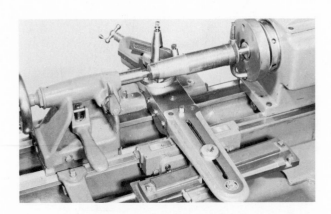

Fig. 36-87. A plain taper attachment. (Atlas Press Co., Clausing Div.)

TAPER ATTACHMENT METHOD

A taper attachment as shown in Fig. 36-87, is a guide that can be attached to most lathes. It provides an accurate way to cut tapers and offers some advantages over other methods. Internal and external tapers are possible. The work can be held by any conventional means. Once the attachment is set, the same taper can be machined on any length piece. The lathe does not have to be altered in any manner. It can be used for straight turning by simply locking the taper attachment out. It is not necessary to realign anything.

TAPER TURNING WITH SQUARE NOSE TOOL

This method is limited to the production of short tapers, Fig. 36-88. The cutter bit is ground with a square nose and is set to the correct angle with the protractor head and blade of the combination set. Be sure to set the tool on exact center.

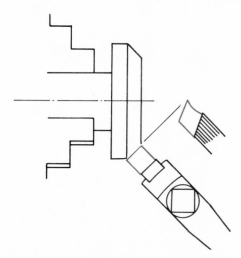

Fig. 36-88. Using a square nose tool for turning a taper.

MEASURING TAPERS

Two methods of testing the accuracy of tapers are:
1. A comparison method using taper plug and ring gauges.
2. Direct measurement of the taper. The direct measurement will be explained.

This technique makes use of a surface plate. The tapered section is placed on the surface plate, and two gauge blocks or parallels of the same height, are placed on opposite sides of the taper. Two cylindrical rods (drill rod sections

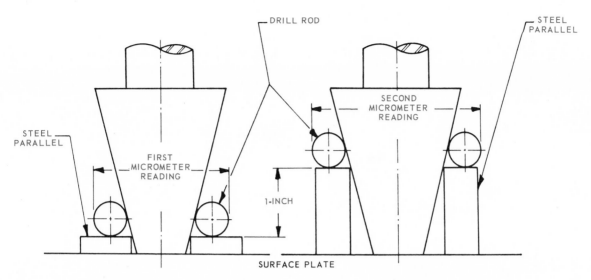

Fig. 36-89. *Measuring a taper using parallels, drill rod, micrometers and surface plate.*

are ideal) of the same diameter are placed on the blocks, Fig. 36-89. The distance across the rods is measured with a micrometer.

The second reading is made 1-, 3- or 6-in. above the first. The difference in measurement can be easily converted to the required information.

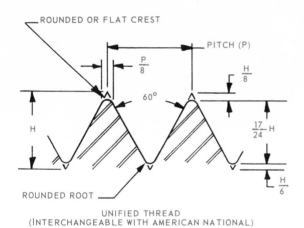

Fig. 36-90a. *Unified screw thread form: N = Number of threads per inch, P = Pitch = $\frac{1}{N}$, H = Depth of thread = $\frac{0.866}{N}$.*

CUTTING SCREW THREADS ON LATHE

Screw threads are used for many reasons, including:
1. Making adjustments.
2. Assembling parts.

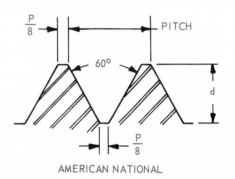

Fig. 36-90b. *American National screw thread form: N = Number of threads per inch, P = Pitch = $\frac{1}{N}$, d = Depth of thread = P x 0.6495.*

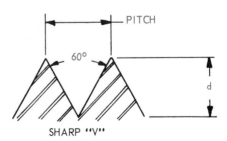

Fig. 36-90c. *Sharp "V" screw thread form: N = Number of threads per inch, P = Pitch = $\frac{1}{N}$, d = Depth of thread = $\frac{0.866}{N}$.*

3. Transmitting motion.
4. Applying pressure.
5. Making measurements (micrometer).

SCREW THREAD FORMS

The first machine-cut threads were square, but since that time several different thread forms have been developed: AMERICAN NATIONAL, SHARP "V," ACME, SQUARE and WORM THREADS. Each thread form has a particular use and formula for calculating its shape and size, Fig. 36-90.

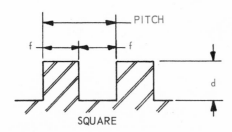

Fig. 36-90d. Square screw thread form: N = Number of threads per inch, P = Pitch =$\frac{1}{N}$, d = Depth of thread = $\frac{0.500}{N}$, f = Flat or space = $\frac{0.500}{N}$.

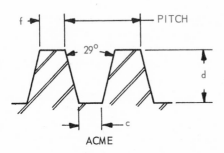

Fig. 36-90e. Acme screw thread form: N = Number of threads per inch, P = Pitch =$\frac{1}{N}$, d = Depth of thread = $\frac{0.500}{N}$ + 0.010, f = Flat = $\frac{0.3707}{N}$, c = Root = $\frac{0.3707}{N}$ + 0.0052.

THREAD FORMS

PITCH is the distance from one point on a thread to a corresponding point on the next thread. Fig. 36-91 shows the parts of a screw thread. LEAD is the distance a nut will travel in one complete revolution of the screw. On a single thread, the pitch and lead are the same. Double thread screws have a lead twice the pitch, etc.

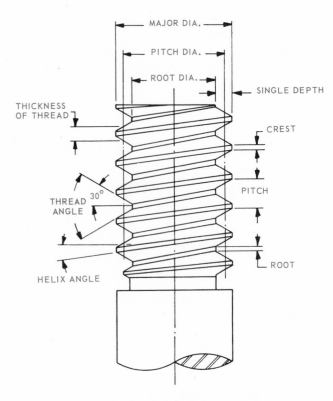

Fig. 36-91. The parts of the screw thread.

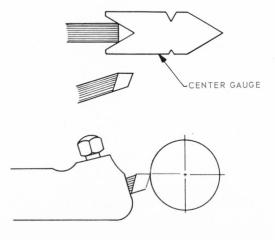

Fig. 36-92. A cutting tool properly ground for machining sharp "V" screw threads. The tool is set on center as shown.

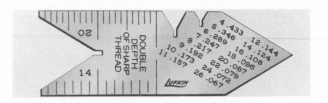

Fig. 36-93. The center gauge or "fish tail." (The Lufkin Tool Co.)

HOW TO CUT SHARP "V" THREADS ON THE LATHE

Sharpen the cutting tool to the correct shape including correct clearances. Grind the top flat with no side or back rake, Fig. 36-92. The CENTER GAUGE, Fig. 36-93, is used for grinding and setting the tool on the work.

The work is set up in much the same manner as for straight turning. If held between centers, the centers must be precisely aligned and the work must run true. Many machinists leave the stock slightly oversize and make a light truing cut to reduce the stock to size before cutting the threads.

A groove is frequently cut at the point where the thread terminates. It is cut equal to the depth of the thread, Fig. 36-94.

After making the proper gear and apron adjustments, pivot the compound rest 29 deg. to

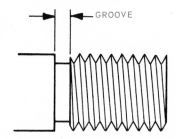

Fig. 36-94. Terminating a screw thread.

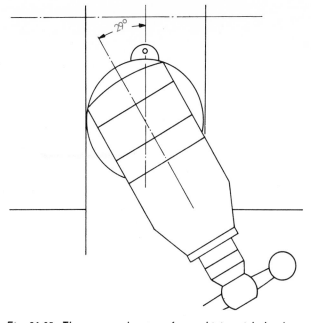

Fig. 36-95. The compound set up for machining right-hand external threads.

the right, Fig. 36-95, and set the threading tool in the tool post. It is essential that the tool be set on center and at 90 deg. to the centerline of the work. This is done by using a center gauge as shown in Fig. 36-96.

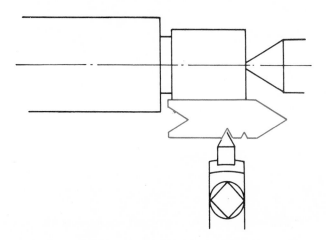

Fig. 36-96. Using the center gauge to position the tool for machining threads.

The compound rest is set at 29 deg. to permit the tool to shear the chip better than if it were fed straight in, Fig. 36-97.

As the tool must be removed from the work after each cut and repositioned before the next cut can be started, a THREAD CUTTING STOP, Fig. 36-98, may be used. After the point of the tool is set so that it just touches the work, the stop is locked to the saddle dovetail, with the ADJUSTING SCREW just bearing on the stop.

After a cutting pass has been made, move the tool back from the work with the cross slide screw. Move the carriage back to start another cut and feed the tool into the work until the adjusting screw again bears on the stop. Turn the compound rest screw in 0.002 in. and the tool will be in position for the next cut.

A THREAD DIAL, Fig. 36-99, is fitted to the carriage of many lathes. It meshes with the lead screw and is used to indicate when to engage the half-nuts to permit the cutting tool to follow in the original cut. The thread dial eliminates the necessity of reversing spindle rotation in order to bring the tool back to the starting point after each cut.

MAKING THE CUT

Set the spindle speed to about one-quarter that used for conventional turning. Feed the tool

Fig. 36-99. The thread dial. (South Bend Lathe, Inc.)

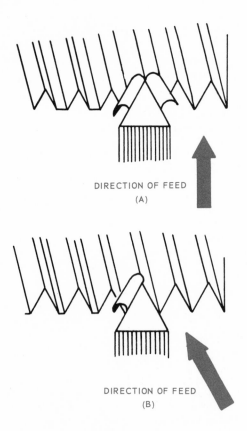

Fig. 36-97. The cutting action of the tool when: (A) Fed straight in. Note that both edges are cutting and the weakest part of the tool (the point) is doing the most work. (B) Fed in at a 29° angle. Note that only one edge is cutting and the cutting load is distributed across it evenly.

in until it just touches the work. After this it is moved beyond the right end of the piece and adjusted to make a cut of 0.002 in.

Turn on the power and engage the half-nuts when indicated by the thread dial. This cut will

be a check to see whether the machine has been set to cut the desired number of threads per inch, Fig. 36-100.

When this checks out, additional cuts in 0.005 in. increments (minute additions) are made until the thread is almost to size. The last few cuts should be no more than 0.002 in. deep.

A liberal application of lard oil or cutting oil, before each cut, will help to produce a smooth finish.

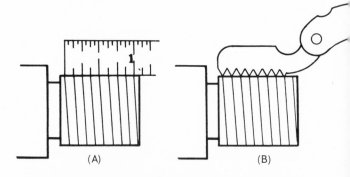

Fig. 36-100. Checking the pitch after the first light cut has been made: (A) With a rule. (B) With a screw pitch gauge.

HOW TO MEASURE THE THREAD

Measure the thread at frequent intervals during the machining operation. Probably the easiest way to check the thread is to fit it to a threaded hole or nut. Closer tolerances require the use of a THREAD MICROMETER, Fig. 36-101. This gives the true pitch diameter which is equal to the outside diameter less the depth of one thread.

The THREE WIRE METHOD OF MEASURING

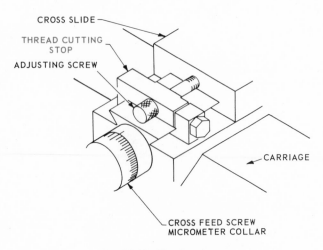

Fig. 36-98. The thread stop.

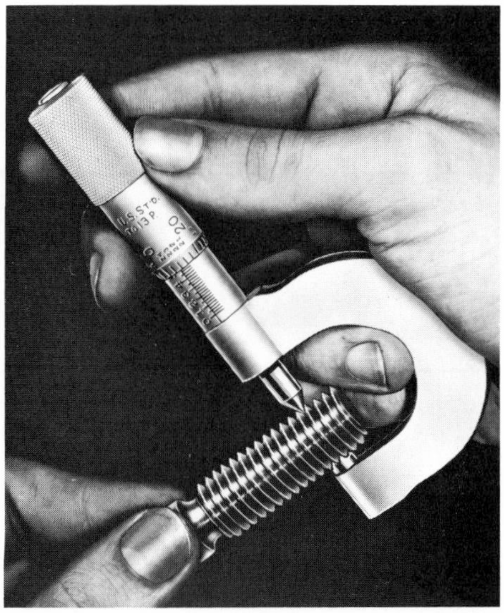

Fig. 36-101. The thread micrometer. (The L. S. Starrett Co.)

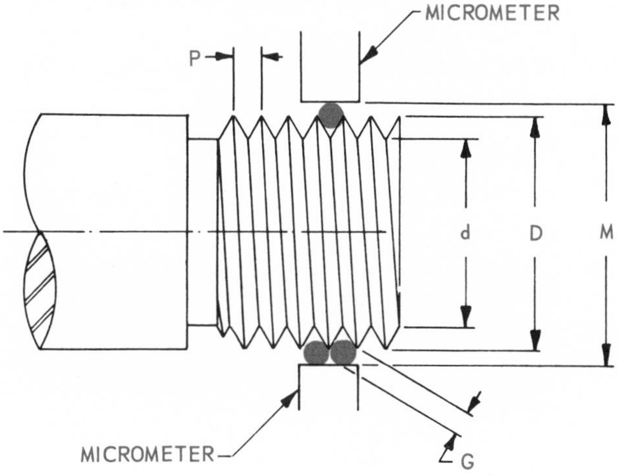

Fig. 36-102. The 3-wire method of measuring screw threads.

THREADS, Fig. 36-102, has proven to be quite satisfactory. A micrometer measurement is made over three wires of a specific diameter that are fitted into the threads. The formula, Fig. 36-103, is used to calculate the correct measurement over the wires.

HOW TO CUT LEFT-HAND THREADS

Left-hand threads are cut in basically the same manner as right-hand threads. The major difference involves pivoting the compound rest to the left and changing the rotation of the lead screw so that the carriage will travel toward the tailstock.

Fig. 36-103. The 3-wire thread measuring formula (below).

$$M = D + 3G - \frac{1.5155}{N}$$

Where: M = Measurement over the wires
D = Major diameter of thread
d = Minor diameter of thread
G = Diameter of wires
P = Pitch $= \frac{1}{N}$
N = Number of threads per inch

The smallest wire size that may be used for a given thread –

$$G = \frac{0.560}{N}$$

The largest wire size that can be used for a given thread –

$$G = \frac{0.900}{N}$$

The 3-wire formula will work only if "G" is no larger or smaller than the sizes determined above. Any wire diameter between the two extremes may be used. All wires must be the same diameter.

HOW TO CUT INTERNAL THREADS

Internal threads, Fig. 36-104, are made with a conventional boring bar and a cutting tool sharpened to thread shape.

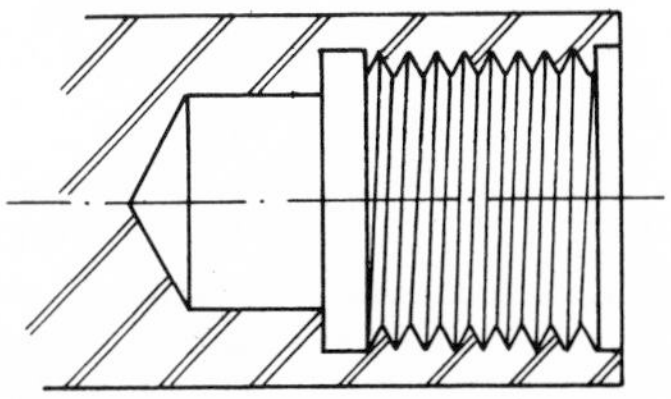

Fig. 36-104. Internal screw threads.

A hole is drilled and bored to the correct size for the minor diameter. A recess is machined with a square nose tool at the point where the thread terminates, Fig. 36-105. The recess diameter is equal to major diameter of thread.

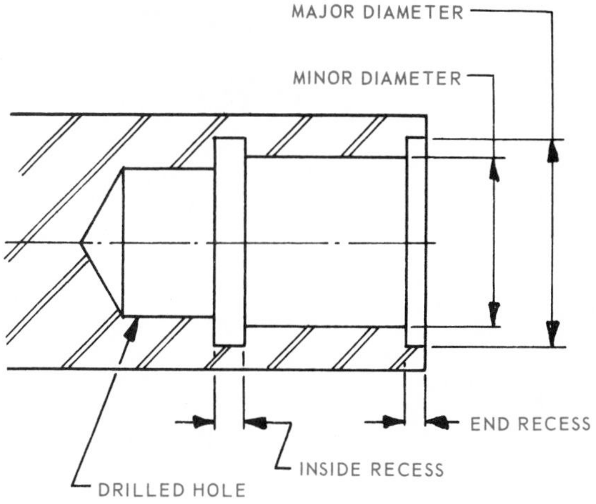

Fig. 36-105. Machining the opening for internal screw threads.

Pivot the compound rest 29 deg. to the left for cutting right-hand threads. Mount the tool on center with a center gauge, Fig. 36-106. Machine as you would external threads.

IN CUTTING INTERNAL THREADS REMEMBER THAT TOOL FEED AND REMOVAL FROM THE CUT ARE EXACTLY THE REVERSE OF THOSE USED FOR CUTTING EXTERNAL THREADS.

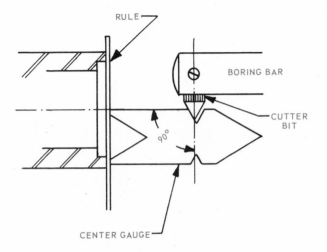

Fig. 36-106. Positioning the cutting tool for machining internal screw threads.

HOW TO BORE ON THE LATHE

Boring, Fig. 36-107, is an internal machining operation where a single-point cutting tool is used to enlarge a hole. Boring is done to enlarge a hole to exact size when a drill or reamer

Fig. 36-107. Boring (machining internal surfaces on the lathe). (Allegheny Ludlum Steel Corp.)

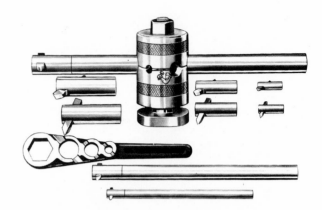

Fig. 36-108a. Interchangeable type boring bar permits the machinist to use the stiffest bar for the job. The body replaces the tool post. (Armstrong Bros. Tool Co.)

of the proper size is not available. Its main purpose, however, is to produce a hole that is exactly concentric with the outside diameter of the work.

The size of the hole to be bored determines the type and size of boring bar to be used, Fig. 36-108. Always use the largest bar possible as this gives maximum support to the tool. The bar

Fig. 36-108b. Boring tool holder and bars for light work. (Armstrong Bros. Tool Co.)

Fig. 36-108c. Boring tool holder and bar with interchangeable end caps. (Armstrong Bros. Tool Co.)

should extend from the holder only far enough to permit the tool to cut to the proper depth, Fig. 36-109.

Set the tool on center or slightly below with the bar parallel to tool travel. Check for adequate clearance when the tool is at maximum depth in the hole. Make your cuts in much the same manner as you would for external work.

HOW TO DRILL AND REAM ON THE LATHE

The lathe can be used to perform many operations other than turning and boring.

DRILLING

The usual method is to hold the work in a chuck and mount the drill in the tailstock spindle. For holes less than 1/2 in., the drill should be

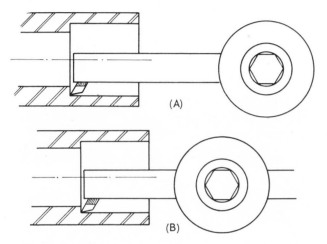

Fig. 36-109. Keep the cutting tool as close to the tool post as possible for maximum support. (A) Boring bar projects too far from the tool post. Vibration may result. (B) Properly positioned boring bar.

held in a Jacobs chuck. Larger drills with taper shanks are fitted directly into the spindle, Fig. 36-110.

Drills with taper shanks too large to fit the tailstock spindle can be held with a dog, with the tailstock center pressed into the center hole on the drill shank, Fig. 36-111. Otherwise, a commercial holder may be used as shown in Fig. 36-112a, b.

Greater accuracy requires an exactly cen-

Fig. 36-110a. Drills that are larger than 1/2-in. in diameter are usually fitted with a self-holding taper that fits into the tailstock spindle.

Fig. 36-110b. Drilling with a straight shank drill held in a Jacobs chuck.

tered starting point for the drill. A starting point made with a center drill is adequate.

Holes over 1/2 in. require pilot holes. The

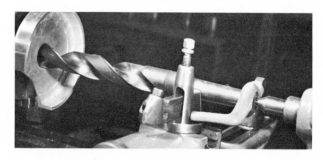

Fig. 36-111. The setup used when the drill shank is too large to be fitted in the tailstock. The lathe dog, with its tail supported by the compound, prevents it from revolving during the drilling operation.

drill used for this purpose should have a diameter equal to the web thickness of the larger drill. Ample clearance must be provided in the back, to permit the drill to break through without striking the chuck or headstock spindle.

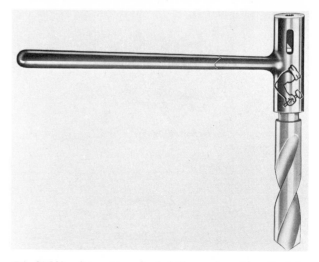

Fig. 36-112a. Large taper shank drills can be used on the lathe by fitting them in this drill holder. (Armstrong Bros. Tool Co.)

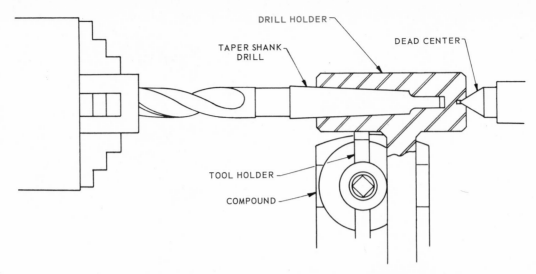

Fig. 36-112b. This illustration shows how the commercial drill holder is used.

HOW TO REAM ON THE LATHE

A hole is reamed when a high degree of accuracy in diameter and finish are required, Fig. 36-113. The hole is first drilled allowing suf-

Fig. 36-113. Using a chucking reamer supported in a Jacobs chuck.

ficient stock for reaming. Do not apply power if a hand reamer is used, Fig. 36-114. Use regular hand reaming procedures, however, feed the reamer into the hole with the tailstock handwheel.

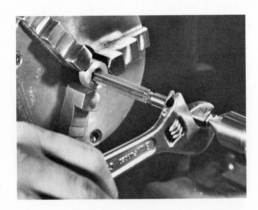

Fig. 36-114. DO NOT use power when using a hand reamer.

KNURLING

Knurling, Fig. 36-115, is the process of forming horizontal or diamond-shaped serrations on the circumference of the work to pro-

Fig. 36-115. A handwheel being knurled.

Fig. 36-116. Knurling tool. (J. H. Williams & Co.)

vide a gripping surface. It is done with a KNURLING TOOL that is mounted in the lathe tool post, Fig. 36-116. The knurl pattern is raised by rolling the knurls against the metal to raise the surface. STRAIGHT and DIAMOND PATTERN KNURLS, Figs. 36-117a, b, can be produced in COARSE, MEDIUM and FINE PITCH.

Fig. 36-117a. Diamond knurl pattern in coarse, medium and fine pattern. (J. H. Williams & Co.)

HOW TO USE KNURLING TOOL

The knurling tool must be set up correctly, so the knurls will track properly and will not dull rapidly. Use this procedure:

1. Mark off the section to be knurled.
2. Adjust the lathe to a slow back gear speed and a fairly rapid feed.
3. Place the tool in the tool post and set it up to the work. Both wheels must bear evenly on the work with the wheel faces parallel with the work surface.
4. Start the lathe and force the knurls slowly into the work surface until a pattern begins to form. Engage the automatic feed and let the tool feed across the work. When it reaches the proper position, stop the machine but do not disengage the feed. Reverse the spindle rotation and, at the same time, apply additional pressure and permit the tool to move back to the starting point. Repeat the operation until a satisfactory knurl is formed. Flood the surface with cutting fluid during the operation.

FILING AND POLISHING ON THE LATHE

Lathe filing is done to remove burrs, improve the surface finish by removing tool marks, round off sharp edges and finish off slight irregularities on tapers. When filing is used to finish a job, the diameter of the stock should be left oversize to the extent of 0.002 to 0.003 in. A file is useful on many jobs but should not be expected to do the work of a properly sharpened cutting tool.

HOW TO FILE ON THE LATHE

When filing on the lathe, do not hold the file stationary but move it constantly across the work. If held in one position, it will "load" and score the work surface.

The ordinary mill file will produce satis-

Fig. 36-117b. Straight knurl pattern in coarse, medium and fine pattern. (J. H. Williams & Co.)

Fig. 36-118. Right-hand method of filing. Note how the left hand and arm must be over the revolving chuck.

factory results, but the long angle lathe file produces superior results without "chatter." Operate the lathe at a high spindle speed and use long even strokes, releasing the pressure on the return stroke.

FILE SAFETY

1. Move the carriage out of the way and remove the tool post.
2. There are two schools of thought on how to hold the tool for lathe filing. In the RIGHT-HAND METHOD, Fig. 36-118, the file handle is held in the right hand, putting the left hand over the revolving dog or chuck. The LEFT-HAND METHOD, Fig. 36-119, involves holding the handle in the left hand

Fig. 36-119. Left-hand method of filing.

and is usually the recommended procedure.
3. Remove rings and wrist watch, and roll up your sleeves.

HOW TO POLISH ON THE LATHE

Polishing is the operation that produces a fine finish on the work. A strip of abrasive cloth,

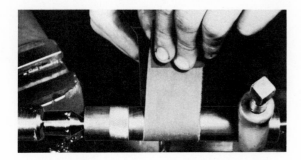

Fig. 36-120. Polishing with abrasive cloth held by the hands. Keeps them clear of the rotating dog or chuck.

Fig. 36-122. The mandrel in use.

suitable for the material to be polished, is cut to length. It can be grasped between the fingers and held across the work, Fig. 36-120. If more pressure is required, mount the abrasive cloth on a strip of wood or file, Fig. 36-121. Use a high spindle speed.

Fig. 36-121. More pressure can be applied if the cloth is supported by a file or block of wood.

The finer the abrasive the finer the resulting finish. A few drops of machine oil on the abrasive will improve the finish. For the final polish, reverse the abrasive cloth so the cloth backing is in contact with the work.

CLEAN THE MACHINE THOROUGHLY AFTER POLISHING. THE ABRASIVE CHIPS FROM THE CLOTH WILL CAUSE RAPID WEAR OF THE MOVING PARTS OF THE MACHINE.

HOW TO USE LATHE MANDRELS

It is sometimes necessary to machine the outside diameter of a piece concentric with a hole that has been previously bored or reamed. This is a simple operation if the material can be held in the lathe by conventional means. There are, however, times when the piece cannot be gripped satisfactory to permit accurate machining. In such cases, the work is mounted on a MANDREL and turned between centers, Fig. 36-122.

A mandrel is a cylindrical piece of hardened steel that has been machined with a very slight

Fig. 36-123. The arbor press. (Dake Corp.)

Fig. 36-124. The tool post grinder. (The Dumore Co.)

36-38

taper. The arbor press, Fig. 36-123, is used to press the mandrel into the work. The arbor press is also excellent for straightening bent shafts, pressing pieces together, etc.

GRINDING ON THE LATHE

The tool post grinder, Fig. 36-124, permits the lathe to be used for both internal and external grinding. With a few simple attachments, the lathe can be used to sharpen reamers and milling cutters in addition to grinding shafts and truing lathe centers.

It is important that the lathe be protected with cloth or canvas during the grinding operation for protection from the resulting abrasive dust and grit, Fig. 36-125.

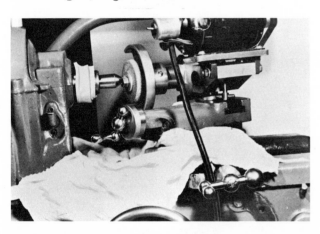

Fig. 36-125. The ways and other bearing surfaces of the lathe should be carefully protected before performing grinding operations.

Fig. 36-126. Milling on the lathe.

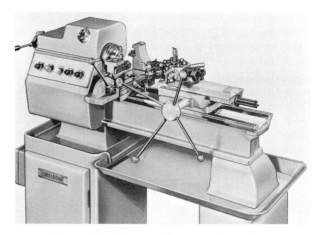

Fig. 36-127a. The manually-operated turret lathe. (The Sheldon Machine Co., Inc.)

Fig. 36-127b. Larger and more versatile models of the turret lathe. (The Warner & Swasey Co.)

MILLING ON THE LATHE

Many small shops are not equipped with a milling machine. To meet this need, lathe manufacturers have developed attachments that permit milling to be performed on the lathe, Fig. 36-126.

The cutters are mounted on an arbor or held in a chuck fitted to the headstock spindle. The cut is controlled by carriage and cross slide movements.

INDUSTRIAL APPLICATIONS

When the part to be produced requires several turning, drilling, facing, reaming and threading operations, and the quantity desired is sufficient to justify the tooling expenses, variations of the basic lathe are used.

For limited production runs, 100 to 5000

pieces, the manually-operated TURRET LATHE, Figs. 36-127a, b, is generally used. This is a lathe equipped with a six-sided tool holder called

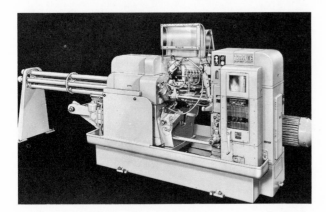

Fig. 36-128. A multiple spindle automatic screw machine for high speed precision production. (The Warner & Swasey Co.)

a turret, to which a number of different cutting tools are fitted. Stops control the length of tool travel and rotate the turret to bring the next cutting tool into position automatically. A cross

slide unit is used for turning, facing, forming and cut off operations.

The SCREW MACHINE, Fig. 36-128, another variation of the lathe, was developed for the high

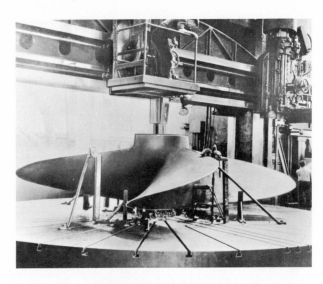

Fig. 36-129. A propeller for a destroyer being machined on a boring mill. (National Machine Tool Builders' Assoc.)

Fig. 36-130. The modern lathe is manufactured in a wide range of sizes from the tiny jewelers' lathe (used to manufacture watch and instrument parts) to the large machines that machine the forming rolls used in steel mills. Some idea of the size of the latter type can be gained by comparing it with the machinist in the photo.

speed production of large numbers of identical parts. These machines have been designed to perform the maximum number of operations, either simultaneously, or in rapid sequence.

Work too large or too heavy to be machined in a horizontal position, can be machined on a VERTICAL BORING MACHINE, Fig. 36-129.

These huge machines, also known as BORING MILLS, are capable of turning and boring work with diameters up to 40 ft.

Conventional metalworking lathes are manufactured in a large range of sizes from the tiny jeweler's lathe to large machines that machine forming rolls for the steel industry, Fig. 36-130.

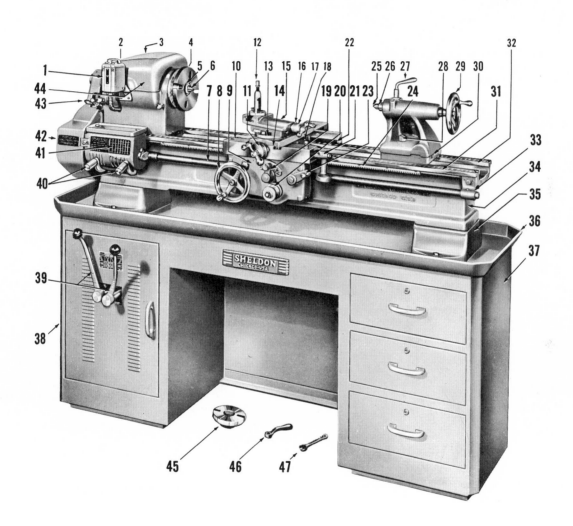

TEST YOUR KNOWLEDGE, Unit 36

Refer to the numbered photo above and answer the following questions. Place the number of the question on a separate answer sheet (do not write in this book) and the letter - a, b, c, d, or e, representing the correct answer, after it.

1. If Item #41 is changed, the cutting tool will - (assume that power is being transmitted through the gear box):
   a. Cut deeper.

   b. Move faster or slower.
   c. Cut better.
   d. Move faster or slower if the carriage is engaged to the lead screw.
   e. Do none of the above.

2. Item #39 does one of the following:
   a. Reduces or increases motor speed.
   b. Increases power to the spindle.
   c. Puts tension on the belt.

d. Changes spindle speed.
e. None of the above.

3. Item #7 transmits power from the quick change gear box to the:
a. Tailstock.
b. Headstock.
c. Spindle.
d. Back gears.
e. None of the above.

4. Item #4:
a. Is removed with a hammer.
b. Supports the work.
c. Is lubricated each day.
d. Makes the centers line up.
e. None of the above.

5. Items #31 and 32 guide the:
a. Chucks.
b. Carriage.
c. Power feed.
d. Back gears.
e. None of the above.

6. Item #15 is called the:
a. Apron.
b. Carriage.
c. Cross-feed.
d. Compound rest.
e. None of the above.

7. Item #12 is called a:
a. Tool post assembly.
b. Tool post ring.
c. Tool post wedge.
d. Tool holder adjuster.
e. None of the above.

8. Item #18 is called the:
a. Saddle.
b. Guide.
c. Carriage.
d. Apron.
e. None of the above.

9. Item #23 does one of the following:
a. Causes the cutter bit to move in and out.
b. Engages the half-nuts for threading.
c. Engages the clutch for automatic power feed.
d. Locks the unit to the ways.
e. None of the above.

10. Item #20 does one of the following:
a. Locks the unit to the ways.
b. Engages the clutch for automatic power feed.
c. Engages the half-nuts for threading.
d. Causes the cutter bit to move up and down.
e. None of the above.

11. Item #8 does one of the following:

a. Moves the entire unit right and left on the ways.
b. Moves the cutter bit in and out.
c. Engages the unit for threading.
d. Locks the unit to the ways.
e. None of the above.

12. The lathe removes material by:
a. Rotating the work against the cutter; the tool remains stationary.
b. Rotating the cutter against the work; the work moves against the cutter.
c. Rotating the work against the cutter; the tool travels or feeds into or across it.
d. Rotating the cutter as it feeds into the work; the work remains stationary.
e. None of the above.

13. To remove 0.028 in. from the diameter of a piece being turned on the lathe, feed the cutter into the work:
a. 0.0014 in.
b. 0.014 in.
c. 0.140 in.
d. 0.0028 in.
e. None of the above.

14. When setting up a lathe to turn material:
a. Cut the material to the correct size.
b. Carefully check over and lubricate it.
c. Plug it in.
d. Make sure that it is clean.
e. None of the above.

15. The compound on the lathe can be used to cut:
a. A hole.
b. A taper.
c. Threads.
d. A ring.
e. None of the above.

16. The 4-jaw lathe chuck is called:
a. An independent chuck.
b. A universal chuck.
c. A Jacobs chuck.
d. A metal chuck.
e. None of the above.

17. The 3-jaw lathe chuck is called:
a. An independent chuck.
b. A universal chuck.
c. A Jacobs chuck.
d. A metal chuck.
e. None of the above.

18. Item #23 engages:
a. The automatic power feed.
b. The half-nuts for threading.
c. The automatic power cross-feed.
d. Locks the unit to the ways.
e. None of the above.

19. Item #7 is the:
    a. Lead screw.
    b. Lengthwise feed screw.
    c. Compound feed screw.
    d. Cross-slide feed screw.
    e. None of the above.
20. Which of the following does not belong:
    a. Compound.
    b. Offset tailstock.
    c. Taper attachment.
    d. Cross-slide.
    e. All of the above.
21. The _____ guides the carriage when it is moved.
22. Name four ways to hold work in the lathe.
    a. _____ .
    b. _____ .
    c. _____ .
    d. _____ .
23. What three chucks may be used to hold work for turning?
    a. _____ .
    b. _____ .
    c. _____ .
24. The chuck is fitted to the headstock _____ .
25. List four methods used to cut tapers on the lathe.
    a. _____
    b. _____
    c. _____
    d. _____

The following list is of the matching type. Place the question number on your answer sheet and the letter of the work that describes it correctly, beside it.

26. Ways
27. Tool post
28. Tool post wedge
29. Lead screw
30. Knurl
31. Center gauge
32. Dead center
33. Apron
34. 4-jaw chuck
35. 3-jaw chuck
36. Lead
37. Boring tool

A. Supports the tool holder.
B. The distance a thread in one revolution.
C. Used to position the threading tool for the sharp "V" thread.
D. Positions the tool holder by permitting it to be raised or lowered in the tool post.
E. Transmits power from the quick change gear box to the carriage.
F. The tailstock center.
G. Universal chuck.
H. Guides the carriage.
I. For internal machining.
J. Independent chuck.
K. The carriage front.
L. A diamond or straight pattern pressed into the surface of the work piece.

Calculate the correct rpm for machining the following materials: Round your answer off to the nearest 50 rpm.
38. Aluminum - 3-1/2-in. in diameter.
39. Mild steel - 1-1/4-in. in diameter.
40. Tool steel - 2-3/8-in. in diameter.

Using the 3-wire method measuring screw threads, calculate the correct measurement over the wires for the following threads. Use the wire size given in the problem:
41. 1/2-20NF   (wire size 0.032 in.)
42. 1/4-20NC   (wire size 0.032 in.)
43. 3/8-16NC   (wire size 0.045 in.)
44. 7/16-14NC (wire size 0.060 in.)

Using the formulas previously presented, find the tailstock setover when the following information is known:
45. Taper per in.   = 0.008 in.
    Length of piece = 7.250 in.
46. Large diameter = 2.000 in.
    Small diameter = 1.000 in.
    Length of taper = 3.000 in.
    Length of piece = 9.000 in.
47. Taper per foot = 0.123 in.
    Length of piece = 6.330 in.
48. Large diameter = 1.000 in.
    Small diameter = 0.075 in.
    Length of taper = 2.000 in.
    Length of piece = 8.000 in.

RESEARCH AND DEVELOPMENT

1. Demonstrate milling on the lathe.
2. Plan and produce a series of 35mm. color slides showing how to prepare the lathe for turning.
3. Make a model of a tree lathe.
4. Make wooden models of the seven basic cutting tool shapes. They should be cut-away models to permit the various clearance angles to be seen easily.
5. Prepare a comparison test using carbon

steel, high speed and cemented carbide cutting tools. Make the tests on mild steel (annealed), tool steel (heat treated) and aluminum. Use the recommended cutting speeds and feeds and make a graph that will show the times needed by the various tools to perform an identical machining operation.

6. Prepare models of the sharp "V," Acme and square thread forms.

7. Prepare a series of six posters on safe lathe practices.

8. Make an appointment with a skilled machinist. Ask him for the shortcuts and unusual techniques he uses when operating the lathe. Evaluate them with the class for safety, good work habits, time saved and adaptability to the school shop.

9. Invite the manager of the State or Federal Employment Agency in your area to discuss with the class the work opportunities in metalworking in your community.

10. Make arrangements to tour a local plant that uses automatic screw machines and turret lathes in manufacturing their products. Prepare a short paper describing your impressions of these machines in action.

11. Prepare a paper, with illustrations if possible, on how the first screw threads were made. What does the term "chasing" mean in reference to first threads cut on a metalworking lathe.

12. Demonstrate to the class the proper method of machining screw threads. Illustrate how the tool can be repositioned and how to use the 3-wire thread measuring technique to measure threads.

Unit 37

PLANING MACHINES

The SHAPER, Fig. 37-1, is used to machine flat surfaces which may be horizontal, vertical or angular planes. While primarily used to machine flat surfaces, a skillful machinist can manipulate a shaper to cut curved and irregular shapes, slots, grooves and keyways. Because of

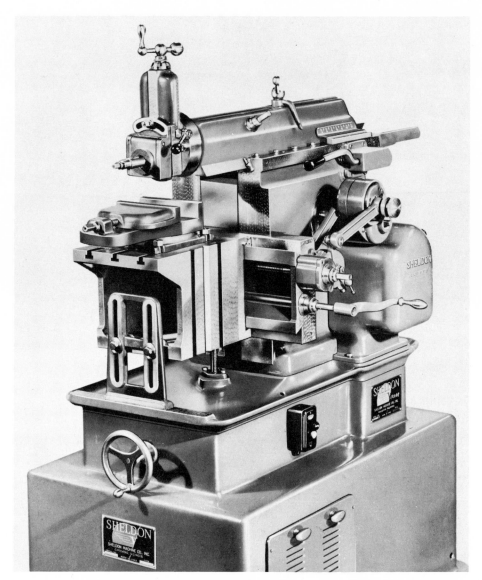

Fig. 37-1. The shaper. (Sheldon Machine Co., Inc.)

the way the machine operates - the cutting tool travels back and forth over the work, Fig. 37-2, the cutting stroke is limited to a maximum length of 36 in. on heavy duty shapers.

A shaper, typical of the type used in school shops is illustrated in Fig. 37-3. The various components and adjustment points are designated.

Before any machine tool is used, the operator should be thoroughly familiar with the tool and its limitations. It should be checked out and carefully inspected to be sure that it is in satisfactory

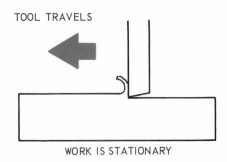

Fig. 37-2. Diagram showing how the shaper operates. The work is stationary and the cutting tool moves against it.

Fig. 37-3. 7-in. shaper with parts identified.
(South Bend Lathe Inc.)

A – Clapper Box	F – Ram	L – Motor Cradle	Q – Cross Feed Crank	V – Work Table
B – Down-feed Handle	G – Switch Box	M – Tension Release Lever	R – Cross Rail	W – Vise
C – Head	H – Hand Wheel	N – Eccentric	S – Base	X – Lamp
D – Head Swivel Lock Screw	J – Drive Pulley Guard	O – Feed Rod	T – Work Table Support	Y – Tool Post
E – Ram Clamping Handle	K – Motor	P – Table Elevating Crank	U – Support Locking Handle	Z – Tool Holder

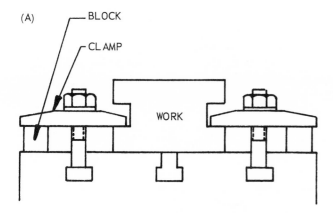

(A) BLOCK
CLAMP
WORK

(B)
PLANER JACK
WORK
ANGLE PLATE
C-CLAMP

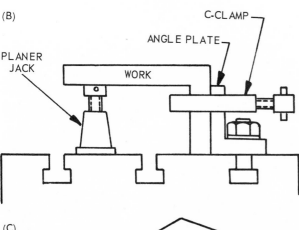

(C)

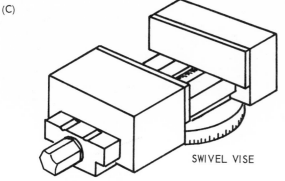

SWIVEL VISE

Fig. 37-4. Three methods used to mount work for machining on the shaper. The work should be held solidly.

operating condition. The machine should be lubricated, following the manufacturer's lubrication chart as the guide.

SHAPER SIZE

Shaper size is determined by the maximum length of material that the tool can machine in one setup. A 7-in. shaper has a stroke (the distance the tool travels) that is sufficient to machine a surface 7 in. long.

HOW TO MOUNT WORK

The work must be mounted solidly to the shaper if accuracy is to be maintained during the machining operation. Of the many methods the machinist has at his disposal, Fig. 37-4, the SWIVEL VISE is most commonly used. The vise body swivels or rotates on the base which is graduated in degrees, Fig. 37-5.

Fig. 37-5. A swivel vise showing the graduated base. (South Bend Lathe, Inc.)

For work that requires extreme accuracy, the vise must be checked for squareness with the stroke of the ram. This is done with the aid of a dial indicator, machinist's square and parallels, with the vise being adjusted until there is no difference in readings from one end of the square to the other or across the parallels, Fig. 37-6.

Much vise held work is rested on steel PARALLELS, Fig. 37-7. These are precisely made steel bars that have been hardened and ground to size.

HOLD DOWNS, Fig. 37-8, are another method of mounting work on the shaper. The pressure of the vise jaws against the hold downs forces the work firmly onto the parallels. Hold downs are especially useful for holding thin work which cannot be supported above the vise jaws.

To mount the work, place it in the vise on the parallels and tighten the jaws. If the work is

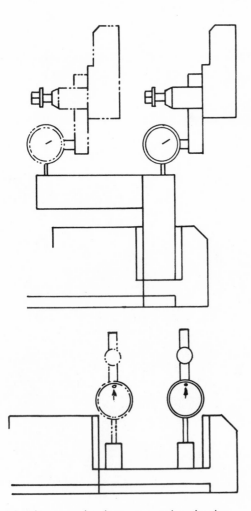

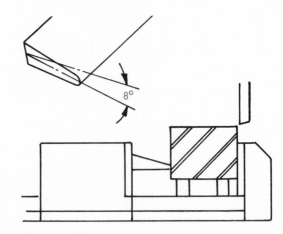

for the vise jaw to hold it securely, it is sometimes possible to clamp it tightly by placing the flat side against the fixed jaw and using a metal

Fig. 37-8. Hold downs are another method of mounting work in a shaper vise. They are particularly useful in holding thin work.

Fig. 37-6. After a vise has been remounted on the shaper, or the work to be machined requires close tolerances, the vise should be checked for levelness with a dial indicator, parallels and a precision machinist's square.

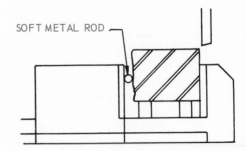

Fig. 37-9. Using paper strips to check whether the work piece is in the vise solidly. (South Bend Lathe, Inc.)

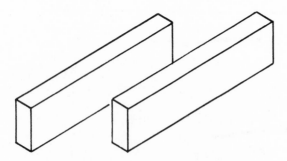

Fig. 37-7. Parallels are accurately made steel bars. They come in a large variety of sizes. The bars are hardened to reduce wear that would affect accuracy of the parallels.

Fig. 37-10. A soft metal rod is sometimes used to hold work that has an uneven surface.

too large to permit the use of parallels, strips of paper, Fig. 37-9, are used to check whether the work is resting firmly and squarely on the vise body.

If one side of the work is not square enough

rod against the rough or unsquare surface and the movable jaw, Fig. 37-10.

Another condition that must be considered,

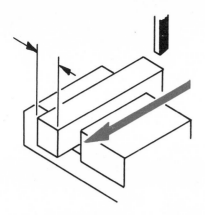
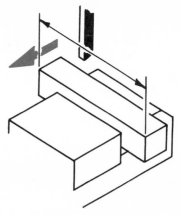

Fig. 37-11. The position of the vise is an important consideration when using the shaper. It should be positioned so that the machining can be done in the shortest possible time. Assuming that the cutter is making the same number of strokes per minute the setup shown in the drawing at the left will permit the work to be machined in about a third of the time needed to machine the work in the setup at the right.

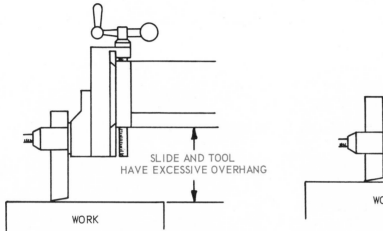

SLIDE AND TOOL
HAVE EXCESSIVE OVERHANG

WORK

SHORT OVERHANG

WORK

Fig. 37-12. Left. Excessive overhang of the slide and the tool may cause "chatter." Right. Keep the slide up and the grip on the tool short for rigidity.

is to position the vise to permit the work to be machined in the shortest time, Fig. 37-11.

HOW TO ADJUST THE SHAPER FOR CUTTING

Several shaper adjustments must be made before cutting can begin. Hold the tool as short as practical to avoid excessive overhand which can cause "chatter" - another way of describing a rough cut. Fig. 37-12, illustrates incorrect and correct setup.

For additional support and rigidity, the WORK TABLE SUPPORT, Fig. 37-13, is locked into position by tightening the locking screw.

A lathe tool holder or a UNIVERSAL TOOL HOLDER, Fig. 37-14, supports the cutting tool. It is clamped in the tool post which is attached to the CLAPPER BOX. The entire unit, Fig. 37-15, is held firmly in place during the cutting stroke, and is hinged to lift on the return stroke, Fig. 37-16. This permits the cutter bit to return across the work with a minimum of "drag" and prevents the cutting edge from being damaged or dulled on the return stroke.

Fig. 37-13. Locking the work table support will eliminate "spring" in the work during the cutting operation. (South Bend Lathe, Inc.)

SHAPER SAFETY

1. Be sure you understand the operation of the machine thoroughly before you attempt to operate it.
2. Getting caught between the work and the tool is one of the most common injuries around the shaper. Don't let this happen to you. Turn off the power before you attempt to make any adjustments in this area of the machine.
3. Wear goggles to protect your eyes from flying chips.
4. Keep out of line of the stroke of the shaper if it is throwing chips. The chips are hot and while they will not cause serious burns, they can be uncomfortable.
5. Use a brush to remove accumulated chips and shavings. It will greatly diminish the danger of getting caught between the tool and the work and of receiving a serious cut from the sharp chips.
6. Handle the cutter bit with care. If it will cut hard steel you can be sure that it can also cut you.
7. Making too deep a cut or not securely clamping work in the vise may result in the work dropping to the floor and a serious foot injury.

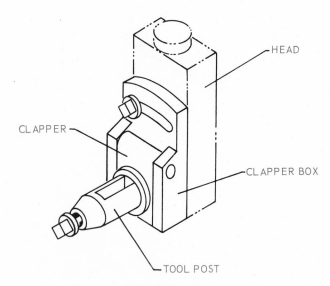

Fig. 37-15. A close-up of the parts of the clapper box assembly. The clapper should lift smoothly but not sloppily.

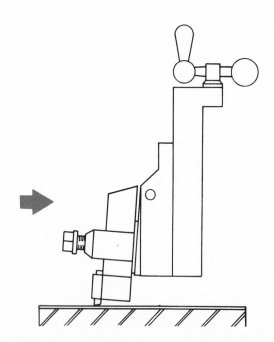

Fig. 37-16. The cutter bit lifts slightly to be drawn back over the work with only a slight rubbing action rather than a binding action which would dull the cutter bit.

HOW TO ADJUST AND POSITION THE STROKE

The stroke length is determined by the width of the work surface to be machined plus 3/4 in. - 1/4 in. at the end of the stroke to allow ample chip clearance and 1/2 in. at the start of the stroke to permit the clapper box to drop back to normal position for the start of the next stroke, Fig. 37-17.

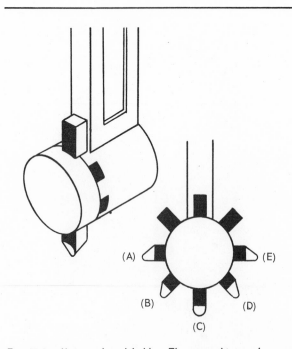

Fig. 37-14. Universal tool holder. The cutter bit can be set to five different positions. (A) and (E) – Vertical Cutting; (B) and (D) – Angular Cutting; and (C) – Horizontal cutting.

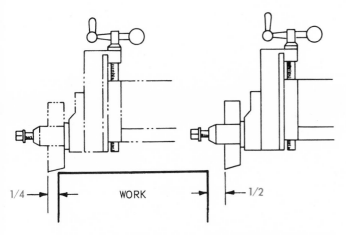

Fig. 37-17. The 1/4 in. allowance at the end of the stroke gives ample chip clearance while 1/2 in. allowance permits the cutter to drop back into position for the next cutting stroke.

While the stroke is adjusted for the correct length, it may not be located at the correct position, Fig. 37-18. The ram must be located to allow for chip clearance and repositioning of the clapper box.

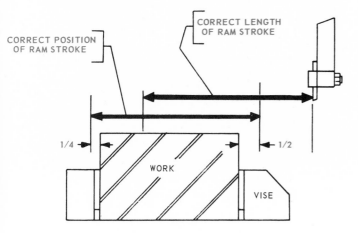

Fig. 37-18. After the ram stroke has been adjusted to the correct length the ram may have to be positioned on the work.

Stroke length and ram positioning is done according to the manufacturer's recommendation for the shaper to be used. Check with your instructor if you are not sure how it is done.

HOW TO MACHINE A HORIZONTAL SURFACE

Machining a horizontal surface requires a tool holder setting that is as close to vertical as possible so that the cutting tool will turn out and away rather than digging into the work should a mishap occur, Fig. 37-19.

CUTTING SPEED AND FEED

The speed is the number of cutting strokes the ram makes per minute and the feed is the distance the work travels or moves after each cutting stroke. Generally the following should be observed:

1. The harder the metal or the deeper the cut the slower the cutting speed.
2. The softer the metal or the lighter the cut the faster the cutting speed.
3. Coarse feed, deep cut and slow cutting speed for the roughing cut.
4. Fine feed, light cut and fast cutting speed for the finishing cut.

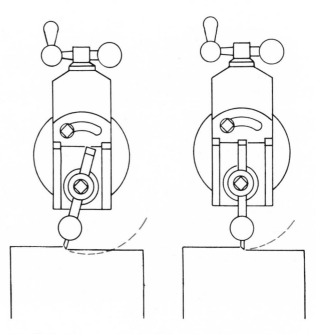

Fig. 37-19. The cutter bit should be adjusted to a vertical position to prevent the tool from "digging in" during the machining operation.

The shaper is capable of making heavy cuts, Fig. 37-20, if it is properly adjusted and the cutter bit is sharpened correctly. As with many other machine tools, the beginner has a tendency to operate the machine with feed too light, cutting speed to slow and too light.

In setting up a shaper, setting the horizontal travel (feed) of the work for automatic or power feed is one of the last steps. A good "rule-of-thumb" to follow in adjusting the feed and depth of cut is that it is usually safe to use as much feed and speed as possible without producing a rough finish. The feed mechanisms on some shapers must be adjusted in a specific way

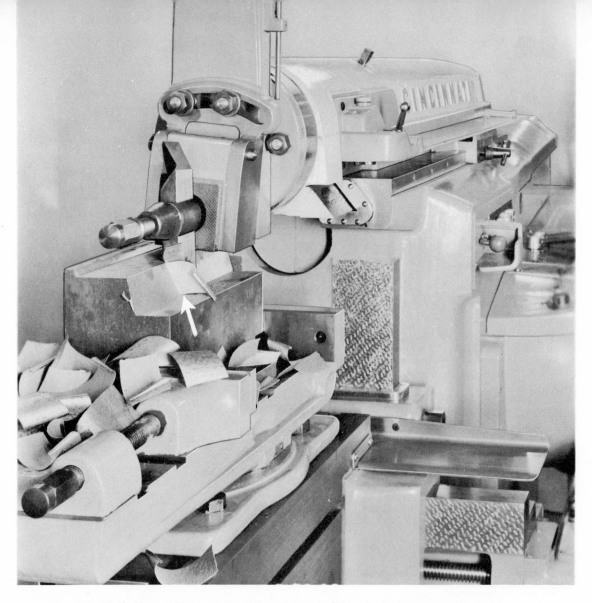

Fig. 37-20. Shaper taking a cut that is 2 in. deep and 1/32 in. thick. (Cincinnati Shaper Co.)

or the work will advance on the cutting stroke rather than when the ram is on the return stroke as it should.

CAUTION: TURN THE MACHINE OVER BY HAND BEFORE TURNING ON THE POWER TO BE SURE THE RAM WILL NOT STRIKE THE WORK.

Turn on the power and advance the work by turning the CROSS FEED CRANK (see Fig. 37-3(Q), page 37-2), until the work is in position with the cutting tool, then turn the DOWN-FEED HANDLE, Fig. 37-3(B), until the cutting tool is taking a cut 1/16 to 1/8 in. deep. Lock the HEAD, Fig. 37-3(C), and engage the automatic feed to start the first cut. If the cutter bit is properly ground, steel and aluminum will produce a curled chip while cast iron will have a crumbly chip. A light brushing of cutting oil

on the work surface will help to produce a better finished surface on all materials but cast iron. This must be cut dry.

CAUTION: IF IT BECOMES NECESSARY TO STOP THE MACHINE BEFORE THE CUT IS COMPLETED, DISENGAGE THE AUTOMATIC FEED BEFORE TURNING OFF THE POWER. THIS WILL AVOID STOPPING THE TOOL BEFORE THE CUT IS COMPLETED WHICH COULD DAMAGE THE CUTTING EDGE OF THE TOOL.

Make the roughing cut to within 0.010 to 0.015 in. of size, then readjust the machine for a faster speed and a finer feed to get a smooth finished surface.

CAUTION: ALWAYS STOP THE MACHINE BEFORE RETURNING THE WORK FOR THE NEXT CUT.

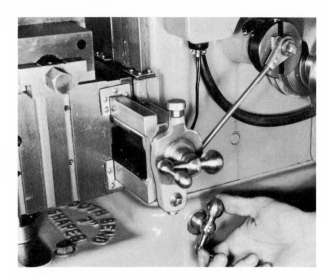

Fig. 37-21. *The machinist is shown elevating the work by rotating the* TABLE ELEVATING CRANK. *(South Bend Lathe, Inc.)*

HOW TO MACHINE A VERTICAL SURFACE

Machining a vertical surface may be necessary to square up the end of a piece of stock with the other surfaces, or to machine a shoulder on the work. Most of the preliminary setup adjustments are similar to those for machining a horizontal surface. It will be necessary to turn the vise so that the jaws are at right angles to the ram stroke, if it is not already in this position. Also, as the adjusting levers are operated from the right side of the machine, it will be more convenient if the material is placed in the vise to permit machining from the right side of the vise.

There are two ways that a vertical cut can be made. The cutter bit can be fed down on the

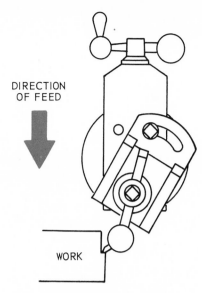

Fig. 37-22. *The correct position of the clapper box for making vertical cuts. By pivoting as shown, the cutter will not "drag" on the work on the return stroke.*

work by means of the DOWN-FEED HANDLE, Fig. 37-3(B), or the work can be fed up into the tool by means of the TABLE ELEVATING CONTROL, Fig. 37-21.

CAUTION: IF THE LAST METHOD IS USED, BE CAREFUL THAT THE WORK IS NOT ELEVATED TOO FAR OR THE RAM WILL STRIKE IT.

Regardless of which method is used to feed the work into the cutter, it will be necessary to swivel the top of the clapper box away from the surface to be machined, Fig. 37-22. This will permit the tool to swing out and away from the work on the return stroke.

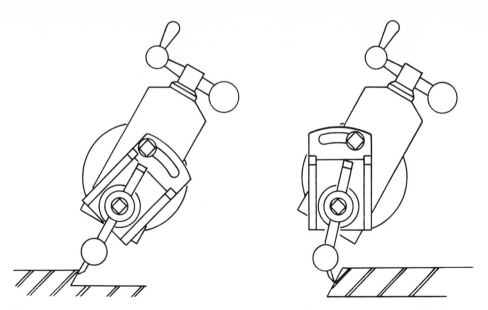

Fig. 37-23. *Angular cutting requires the clapper box to be positioned differently to eliminate "drag" on the return stroke.*

Modern Metalworking

HOW TO MACHINE ANGULAR SURFACE

Machining an angular surface will not present new difficulties if reasonable care is used to set up the machine. If possible, set up the angular surface parallel with the top of the vise so that it can be machined as a horizontal surface. Should this not be possible, the HEAD, Fig. 37-3(C), must be pivoted to the desired angle and the clapper box swiveled into the correct position, Fig. 37-23, to permit the cutting tool to swing out and away from the work on the return stroke. The cutter bit must be fed into the work by the down-feed handle.

On large shapers, it is possible to make angular cuts by setting the UNIVERSAL VISE - a vise that can be set at any angle on any plane, to the correct angle, Fig. 37-24.

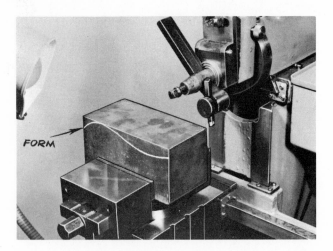

Fig. 37-25. The shape of the desired form or contour is carefully drawn on the work piece. (South Bend Lathe, Inc.)

setting up the machine to cut a conventional horizontal surface. Most of the excess metal is removed with roughing cuts. A LEFT-HAND CUTTING TOOL is used to remove the metal from the right side and a RIGHT-HAND CUTTING TOOL to remove the metal from the left side. When the work has been roughed to approximate shape, a BLUNT ROUNDNOSE CUTTING TOOL, which allows a gradual slope to the finishing cut, is inserted in the tool holder.

Fig. 37-24. Universal vise on large shaper being used to cut an angle on a job. Notice how the vise is pivoted on several planes. (Cincinnati Shaper Co.)

CAUTION: BE CAREFUL THAT THE HEAD AND CLAPPER BOX DO NOT STRIKE THE SHAPER BODY ON THE RETURN STROKE WHEN THEY ARE IN THE EXTREME DOWN POSITION.

HOW TO DO CONTOUR OR FORM CUTTING

Contour or from cutting is accomplished by laying out the contour or form, Fig. 37-25, and

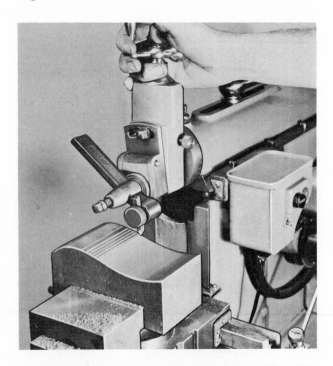

Fig. 37-26. The machinist is shown adjusting the position of the cutting tool as the work piece moves to the right on automatic feed. (South Bend Lathe, Inc.)

Planing Machines

Engage the automatic feed and follow the contour line by feeding the cutting tool up and/or down as it progresses across the work, Fig. 37-26. Practice will make this seemingly difficult job easy.

Large modern shapers are available with hydraulic duplicating attachments that machine contours by "tracing" the required shape from a template as the table progresses horizontally by automatic feed, Fig. 37-27.

Fig. 37-27. Tracer unit on modern production shaper. (Cincinnati Shaper Co.)

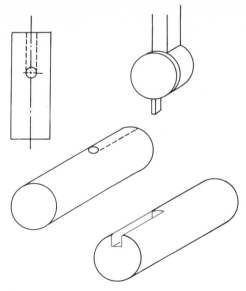

Fig. 37-28. Steps in machining an open end keyway.

HOW TO MACHINE KEYWAYS

Machining keyways often requires the cuts to be stopped at some point in the metal. A hole with the same diameter as the keyway width is drilled at the end of the stroke to prevent a build up of chips that will eventually break the cutting tool, Fig. 37-28. A keyway closed at both ends requires a series of holes - one at the end of the stroke and two at the start, to allow the cutter bit to drop back into position after the cutting stroke, Fig. 37-29.

HOW TO MACHINE SERRATIONS

Serrating is the process of cutting a series of equally spaced grooves on the surface of a piece, Fig. 37-30. It may consist of two sets of grooves that cross each other and leave small

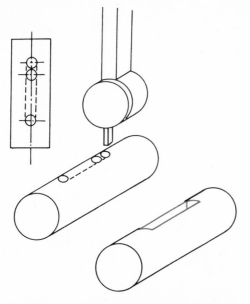

Fig. 37-29. Steps in machining a keyway closed at both ends.

regularly spaced areas between them. Pivot the vise 30 deg. to the right and mount the work. A V-shaped tool bit is fed slowly into the work until the desired depth is attained. It is backed out and the table is moved a previously determined distance and the next groove is made. This sequence is followed until the first series of serrations are made. The vise is pivoted 30 deg. to the left. The cycle is repeated until the job is completed.

HOW TO SQUARE STOCK

A specific sequence must be followed to square stock, Fig. 37-31. The first surface is machined and rotated in the vise so that it is

Fig. 37-30. Serrating is the process of cutting a series of equally spaced grooves upon the surface of a piece.
(South Bend Lathe, Inc.)

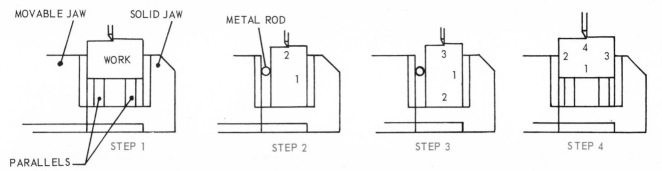

Fig. 37-31. *Proper sequence for squaring a piece of stock. Note that a machined surface is against the solid vise jaw after Step 1.*

against the solid jaw of the vise. It may be necessary to use a soft metal rod to help to seat the first surface machined solidly against the vise jaw. Side 2, is then machined, as is side 3. However, side 3 must be machined to dimension as must side 4. Machine the ends as explained in HOW TO MACHINE A VERTICAL SURFACE.

CUTTING TOOLS

The finest metal shaper machine is worthless without high-quality cutting tools. The tool's RAKE, CUTTING ANGLE and CLEARANCES, Fig. 37-32, are governed by the material being cut. The tool shape, Fig. 37-33, depends upon the shape of the cut, the degree of finish desired and the material to be machined.

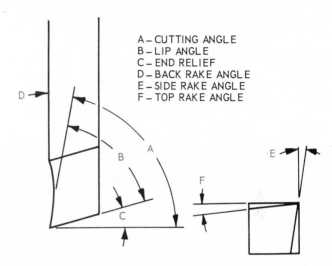

A – CUTTING ANGLE
B – LIP ANGLE
C – END RELIEF
D – BACK RAKE ANGLE
E – SIDE RAKE ANGLE
F – TOP RAKE ANGLE

Fig. 37-32. *The cutter bit must be ground to provide the correct clearance angles if it is to cut properly and have a long life.*

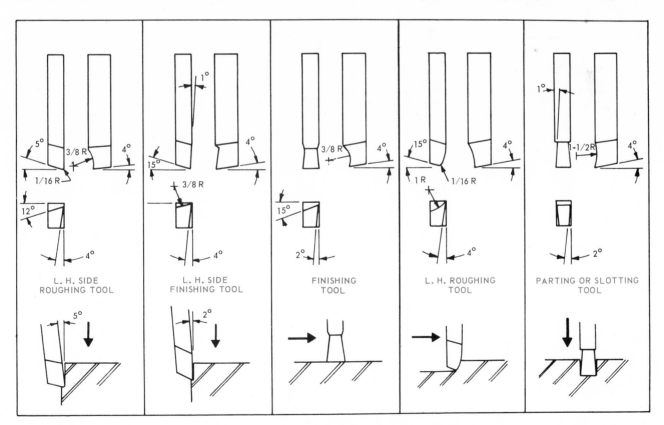

Fig. 37-33. *Cutting tool shapes recommended for mild steel.*

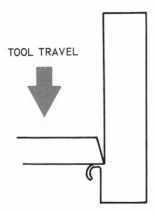

Fig. 37-34. *Diagram of the operation of a vertical shaper (slotter).*
The machine operates in a manner similar to the shaper, how-
ever, the tool moves vertically rather than in a horizontal motion.
The work is held stationary.

Fig. 37-35. *Job being done on a vertical shaper or slotter.*

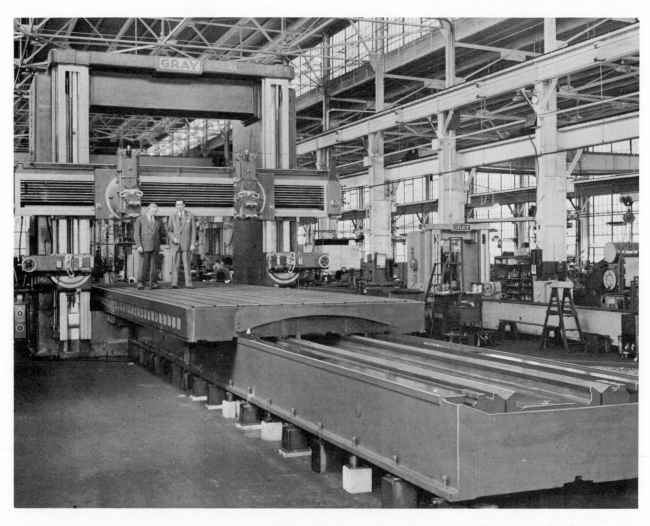

Fig. 37-36. *A photograph of a 144 x 126 in. x 40 ft. double housing planer. The two men will give some idea of the*
machine's size. (G. A. Gray Co.)

INDUSTRIAL APPLICATIONS

Where the LATHE is used to shape metal to a circular cross section, the PLANING MACHINE TOOLS - the SHAPER, SLOTTER, PLANER and BROACH, are used to machine flat surfaces.

The SHAPER is considered too slow to be used for many modern mass-production jobs. Much of

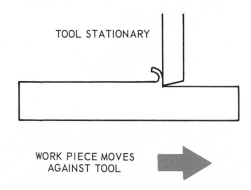

TOOL STATIONARY

WORK PIECE MOVES AGAINST TOOL

Fig. 37-37. A diagram showing how the planer works. The tool remains stationary while the work moves against it.

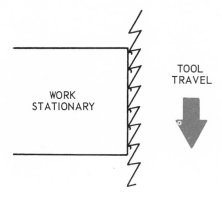

WORK STATIONARY

TOOL TRAVEL

Fig. 37-38. A diagram showing the operation of a broach. A multitooth cutter moves against the work. The operation may be vertical or horizontal.

the work that was formerly done on the shaper is being done faster and more economically on the milling machine and the broaching machine.

The chief difference between the shaper and SLOTTER is the direction of the cutting action. The slotting machine is classified as a VERTICAL SHAPER. It is used to cut slots, keyways - both internal and external, and for jobs such as machining internal and external gears. The vertical shaper and the manner it cuts are illustrated in Figs. 37-34 and 37-35.

The PLANER, Fig. 37-36, differs from the shaper in that the work piece travels back and

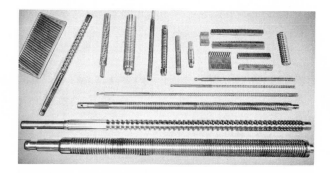

Fig. 37-39. A selection of broaching cutters. Note the many teeth on each cutter.

forth while the cutter remains stationary, Fig. 37-37. A planer is used to handle work that is too large or impractical to be machined on the milling machine. Planers are in themselves large pieces of equipment; some of them are very large because they must handle and machine surfaces up to 20 feet wide and often twice as long.

BROACHING is similar to shaping, but instead of a single cutting tool advancing slightly after each stroke across the work, the broach is a long tool with many cutting teeth, as shown in Figs. 37-38 and 37-39. Each tooth has a cutting edge that is a few thousandths of an inch higher

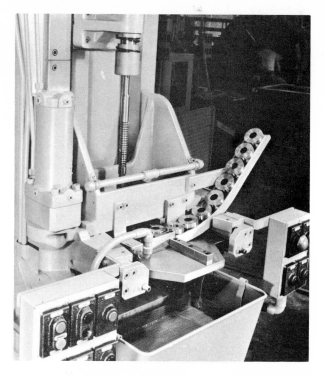

Fig. 37-40. Work moving into position on a modern broaching machine. (Sundstrand Corp.)

than the one before and increases in size to the exact finished size required.

The broach is pushed or pulled over the surface to be finished, Fig. 37-40, and can be used for internal machining - keyways, splines and irregular-shaped openings like the slots that hold the buckets on a jet engine turbine, and for facing automobile engine blocks. It provides an economical way of doing certain finish machining operations.

TEST YOUR KNOWLEDGE, Unit 37

1. The cutting tool on the shaper:
   a. Is stationary and the work moves against it.
   b. Moves across the work which is stationary.
   c. Is pulled or pushed across the work.
   d. Is moved across the work which in turn moves at a slower speed in the opposite direction.
   e. None of the above.
   f. All of the above.
2. The cutting tool on the planer:
   a. Is stationary and the work moves against it.
   b. Moves across the work which is stationary.
   c. Is pulled or pushed across the work.
   d. Is moved across the work which in turn moves at a slower speed in the opposite direction.
   e. None of the above.
   f. All of the above.
3. The shaper is used to machine _____ surfaces.
4. Shaper size is determined by the maximum length that can be machined in one setup. True or false?

5. The body of a swivel vise pivots on its base. True or false?
6. It is possible to machine work on the shaper that is not square on all sides. True or false?
7. The universal tool holder is the same as a conventional lathe tool holder. True or false?
8. The clapper unit lifts on the return stroke to_____.
9. The harder the metal or the deeper the cut the_____the cutting speed.
10. The softer the metal or the lighter the cut the_____the cutting speed.
11. _____ feed,_____cut and_____cutting speed for the roughing cut.
12. _____feed, _____cut and_____cutting speed for the finishing cut.
13. The roughing cut is made to within_____ to_____in. of final size.
14. _____ are a series of equally spaced grooves on the surface of the work.
15. List the sequence followed to square a piece of stock.
    a._____.
    b._____.
    c._____.
    d._____.
    e._____.

RESEARCH AND DEVELOPMENT

1. Make a working teaching aid that demonstrates the drive mechanism of the shaper.
2. Secure samples of work done by the four planing type machines. Label them according to the machine used in each production job.

3. Prepare a display of photos, drawings or magazine illustrations that illustrate the four planing type machine tools. Use photos, drawings, magazine pictures or actual samples of work done on them in your display.

Unit 38

MILLING MACHINES

With the exception of the lathe, the milling machine is the most versatile machine tool used in the machining of metal. Metal is removed by a rotating multi-tooth cutter that is fed into the work, Fig. 38-1.

TYPES OF MILLING MACHINES

It is difficult to classify the various categories of the milling machine because their designs tend to merge into one another. However, for practical purposes, milling machines may be classified into two large families:

1. FIXED BED TYPE.
2. COLUMN AND KNEE TYPE.

FIXED BED TYPE MILLING MACHINE

The fixed bed milling machine, Fig. 38-2, is a production type machine. The table is mounted at a fixed height and is restricted to

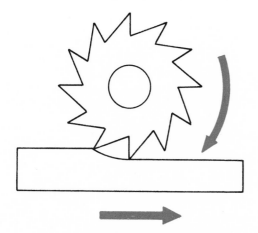

Fig. 38-1. How the milling machine works.

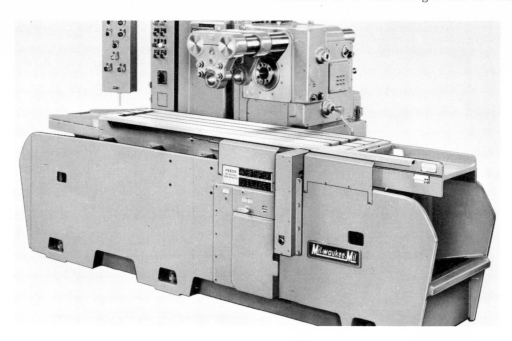

Fig. 38-2. The Simplex fixed bed milling machine makes use of one cutting head.
(Kearney & Trecker Corp.)

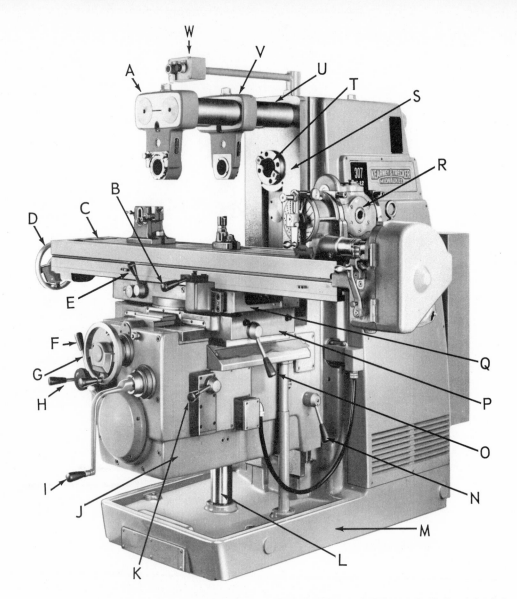

Fig. 38-3. Parts of the milling machine: A-Arbor support, B-Table feed lever, C-Table, D-Table handwheel, E-Table clamp lever, F-Saddle power feed lever, G-Saddle handwheel, H-Knee power feed lever, I-Knee handcrank, J-Knee, K-Rapid traverse lever, L-Telescopic coolant return and elevating screw, M-Base, N-Knee clamp lever, O-Saddle clamp lever, P-Saddle, Q-Saddle plate, R-Universal dividing head, S-Column, T-Spindle, U-Overarm, V-Inner arbor support, W-Spindle start-stop and master switch (the arm engages the clutch).
(Kearney & Trecker Corp.)

longitudinal (back and forth) movement. Vertical (up and down) and cross Traverse (in and out) movements are obtained by cutter head movement.

COLUMN AND KNEE TYPE MILLING MACHINE

The column and knee type milling machine, Fig. 38-3, is so named because the components that provide movement to the work consists of a COLUMN that supports and guides the KNEE in vertical movement. The knee supports the mechanism for obtaining cross traverse and longitudinal table movements.

There are three types of column and knee type milling machines:

1. PLAIN MILLING MACHINE   }Horizontal
2. UNIVERSAL MILLING MACHINE} spindle
3. VERTICAL SPINDLE MILLING MACHINE

Fig. 38-4. The plain type milling machine.
(Greaves Machine Tool Div., J. A. Fay & Egan Co.)

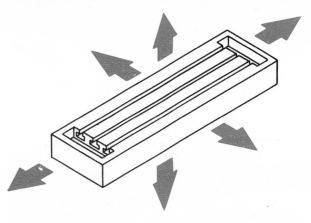

Fig. 38-5. *Table movements of the plain type milling machine.*

UNIVERSAL MILLING MACHINE

The universal milling machine, Fig. 38-6, is similar to the plain milling machine but the table has a fourth movement. On this machine,

Fig. 38-6. *The universal type milling machine. (Greaves Machine Tool Div., J. A. Fay & Egan Co.)*

the table can be swiveled on the saddle through an angle of 45 deg. or more, Fig. 38-7, making it possible to produce spiral gears, splines and similar work.

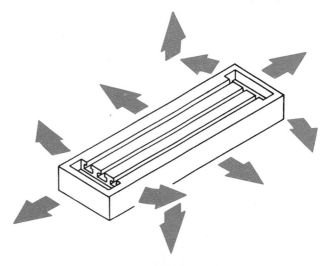

Fig. 38-7. *Table movements of the universal type milling machine.*

SAFETY

1. Do not attempt to operate the machine until you are thoroughly familiar with it. When in doubt, secure additional instructions.
2. Wear appropriate clothing and goggles.
3. Get help to move any heavy attachment like the vise, dividing head, rotary table, etc.
4. Never handle a cutter with bare hands. Use a piece of heavy cloth for protection.
5. Use a small brush to remove chips - NEVER BRUSH WITH YOUR HAND.
6. Stop the machine before attempting to remove chips.
7. Never reach over or near the rotating cutter.
8. Make sure the holding device is mounted solidly to the table, and the work held firmly. Spring or vibration can cause thin cutters like the slitting saw to jam and shatter.
9. Do not talk to anyone while operating the machine, nor allow anyone to turn on your machine for you.
10. No adjustments should be made while the cutter is rotating. Stop it before making measurements, removing chips, etc.
11. Keep the floor around the machine clear of chips and wipe up spilled cutting fluid immediately.
12. Be thoroughly familiar with the STOP lever.
13. Treat any small cuts and skin punctures as potential infections. Clean them thoroughly, apply antiseptic and cover with a bandage. Report any injury, even though minor, to your instructor.
14. Do not permit your work clothes to become saturated with oil and cutting fluids. Greasy clothing is a fire hazard.
15. Put all oily rags used to wipe down the machine in a metal container that can be closed tightly.
16. Do not fool around while operating the mill. Keep your mind on your job and be ready for any emergency.

PLAIN MILLING MACHINE

The work table of the plain milling machine, Fig. 38-4, has three movements: VERTICAL, CROSS and LONGITUDINAL, Fig. 38-5. The cutter spindle projects horizontally from the column.

VERTICAL SPINDLE MILLING MACHINE

The vertical spindle milling machine, Fig. 38-8, differs from the plain and universal machines by having its cutter spindle in a vertical

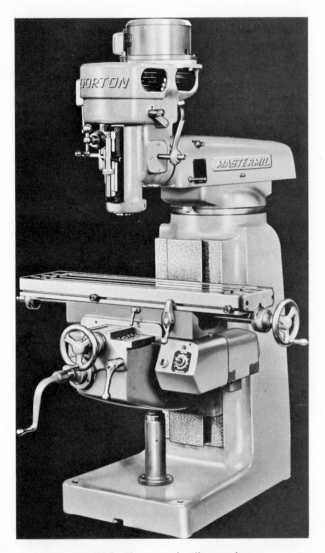

Fig. 38-8. The vertical milling machine.
(George Gorton Machine Co.)

axis, at right angles to the worktable top. The cutter head can be raised and lowered by hand or power feed, and, on some models, pivoted for angular cuts.

METHODS OF CONTROL

The method used to control table movement is another way of classifying milling machines, and, in general, all machine tools. Basically

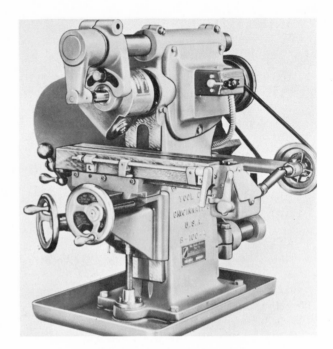

Fig. 38-9. An example of a bench mill.
(U. S. Burke Machine Tool Corp.)

there are three methods of control:
1. MANUALLY - All movements are made by hand lever control.
2. SEMI-AUTOMATIC - Movements can be controlled by hand or power feeds.
3. FULLY AUTOMATIC - A complex hydraulic feed arrangement follows two or three dimensional templates to guide the cutter automatically; or specifications are programmed on punch cards, magnetic tape or perforated tape which guides the cutter through the machining operation.

Machines used in the school shop are ordinarily of the type controlled manually or are semi-automatic. Smaller machines, like the BENCH MILL, Fig. 38-9, have only longitudinal table movement fitted with power feed. Other movements must be controlled manually.

MILLING OPERATIONS

All milling operations fall into two main categories:
1. FACE MILLING - The surface being machined is parallel with the face of the cutter, Fig. 38-10. Large flat surfaces are machined by this method.
2. PERIPHERAL MILLING - The surface being machined is parallel with the periphery of the cutter, Fig. 38-11.

Fig. 38-10. Face milling. (Lovejoy Tool Co., Inc.)

MILLING CUTTERS

Milling cutters, Fig. 38-12, cannot be readily ground for a particular job as can the lathe

Fig. 38-11. Peripherial milling.

Fig. 38-12. Standard milling cutters. How many can you identify?
(Browne & Sharpe Mfg. Co.)

Fig. 38-13. With the exception of the cutter in the back row, these
are solid milling cutters. How many can you identify?
(Brown & Sharpe Mfg. Co.)

cutter bit; therefore, they are made in a large
number of stock shapes, sizes and kinds to
meet many requirements.

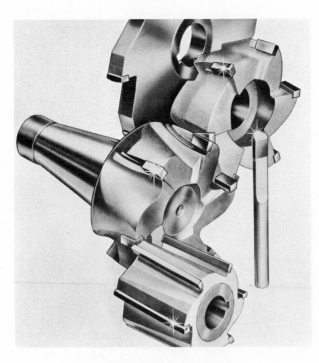

Fig. 38-14. Inserted tooth cutters.
(Brown & Sharpe Mfg. Co.)

TYPES OF MILLING CUTTERS

Milling cutters are made in two general types:
1. SOLID CUTTER - The shank and body are
   made in one piece, Fig. 38-13.
2. INSERTED TOOTH CUTTER - The teeth
   are made of special cutting material and
   are brazed or clamped in place, Fig.
   38-14. Badly worn or broken teeth can
   be replaced.

HOW CUTTERS ARE CLASSIFIED

Cutters are frequently classified by the
method used to mount them in the machine:
1. ARBOR CUTTERS - There is a suitable
   hole for mounting on an arbor, Fig. 38-15.

Fig. 38-15. An arbor type cutter.

2. SHANK CUTTERS - They have either a
   straight or taper shank, Fig. 38-16. Shank

Fig. 38-16. Shank type cutters.

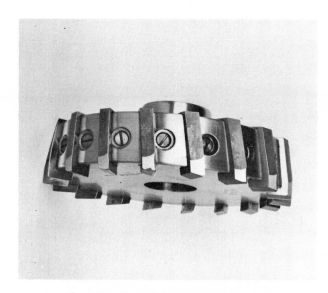

Fig. 38-17. A facing type cutter.
(Brown & Sharpe Mfg. Co.)

cutters are held in sleeves or collets.
3. FACING CUTTERS - Cutters that can be mounted directly to the spindle nose, or, on a stub arbor, Fig. 38-17.

KINDS AND USES OF MILLING CUTTERS

The more commonly used milling cutters and the work to which they are best adapted are:

PLAIN MILLING CUTTER

Plain milling cutters are cylindrical with teeth around the circumference. Plain cutters less than 3/4 in. wide are made with straight teeth. Wider plain cutters, called SLAB CUTTERS, are made with helical teeth.
1. LIGHT-DUTY PLAIN MILLING CUTTER- Used chiefly for light slabbing cuts and cutting shallow slots, Fig. 38-18.

Fig. 38-18. Light-duty plain milling cutters.

2. HEAVY-DUTY PLAIN MILLING CUTTER - Recommended for heavy cuts when a considerable amount of metal must be removed, Fig. 38-19.

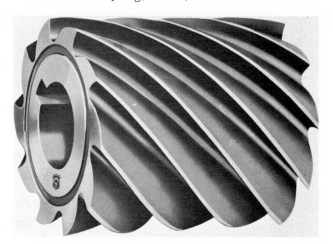

Fig. 38-19. Heavy-duty plain milling cutter.
(Standard Tool Co.)

3. HELICAL PLAIN MILLING CUTTER - Can be operated at a higher speed and produces an exceptionally smooth finish, Fig. 38-20.

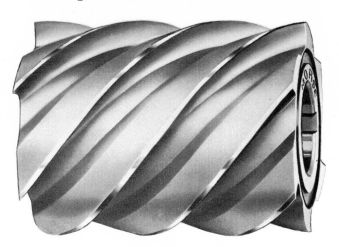

Fig. 38-20. Helical plain milling cutter.
(Morse Cutting Tools)

SIDE MILLING CUTTERS

Side milling cutters have cutting edges on the circumference and on one or both sides.
1. PLAIN SIDE MILLING CUTTER - Used for side milling, straddle milling and slotting, Fig. 38-21.
2. STAGGERED TOOTH SIDE MILLING CUTTER - Has alternate right-hand and

Fig. 38-21.

Plain side milling cutter.

left-hand helical teeth and are used primarily for deep slotting operations, Fig. 38-22.

Fig. 38-22.

Staggered tooth side milling cutter.

3. HALF SIDE MILLING CUTTERS - Side teeth on one edge only. Manufactured as right- and left-hand cutters, and are recommended for heavy straddle milling, Fig. 38-23.

Fig. 38-23. Half side milling cutters. (Standard Tool Co.)

4. INTERLOCKING SIDE MILLING CUTTERS - Cutters ideally suited for milling slots, bosses and other cuts that must be held to close tolerances. The two cutters have interlocking teeth that can be adjusted to the required slot width by separating them with spacers or collars, Fig. 38-24.

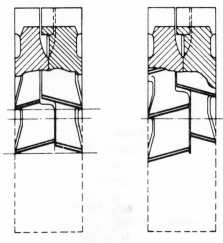

Fig. 38-24. Interlocking side milling cutters. (Morse Tool Co.)

ANGLE CUTTERS

Angle cutters differ from other cutters in that the cutting edges are neither parallel, nor at right angles to the cutter axis.

1. SINGLE ANGLE CUTTER - Suitable for cutting dovetails, ratchet wheels and the like. Made in either right-hand or left-hand angles and with angles of 45 or 60 deg., Fig. 38-25.

2. DOUBLE ANGLE CUTTER - Used for milling threads, notches, serrations and

Fig. 38-25.

Single angle milling cutter.

similar work. Manufactured with included angles of 45, 60 and 90 deg., Fig. 38-26.

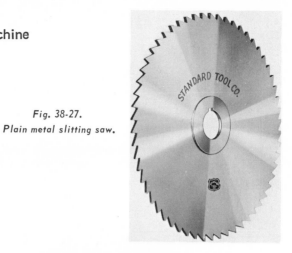

Fig. 38-27.
Plain metal slitting saw.

Fig. 38-26.
Double angle milling cutter.

METAL SLITTING SAWS

Metal slitting saws are thin milling cutters that resemble circle saw blades. They are used for narrow slotting and cut-off operations.

1. PLAIN METAL SLITTING SAW - This is essentially a thin plain milling cutter and is used for ordinary slotting and cutoff operations, Fig. 38-27.

2. SIDE CHIP CLEARANCE SLITTING SAW - This cutter is especially suited, because of ample chip clearance for deep slotting and sawing, Fig. 38-28.

Fig. 38-28.
Side chip clearance slitting saw.

END MILLS

End mills are designed for milling slots, keyways, pockets and similar work, Fig. 38-29,

Fig. 38-29. End milling a slot.

where ordinary arbor type milling cutters cannot be used. Solid end mills may have straight or helical flutes, Figs. 38-30 and 38-30a, and

Fig. 38-30. Straight flute end mill (inserted tooth type). (Brown & Sharpe Mfg. Co.)

Fig. 38-30a. Helical fluted end mill.

taper or straight shanks, Fig. 38-31. Straight shank end mills are available in single and double end styles, Fig. 38-32. A cut with a depth equal to one-half the diameter can generally be taken in solid stock.

1. TWO FLUTE END MILL - Can be fed into

Fig. 38-31. Above. Straight shank end mill. Below. Taper shank end mill.

Fig. 38-32. Single and double end style end mills.

Fig. 38-33. Two-flute double end style end mill. (Brown & Sharpe Mfg. Co.)

the work like a drill, Fig. 38-33.

2. MULTI-FLUTE END MILL - Have a longer life and produce a better finish than a two flute end mill when run at the same speed, Fig. 38-34.

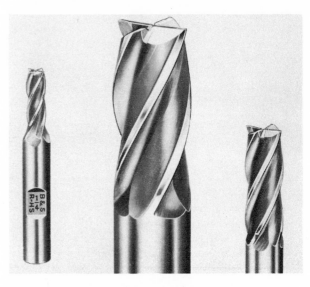

Fig. 38-34. Multi-flute end mills.

Fig. 38-35. Shell end mill. (Greaves Machine Tool Div., J. A. Fay & Egan Co.)

3. SHELL END MILL - Has teeth similar to the multi-flute end mill but is mounted on a stub arbor. Can be used for face and end milling, Fig. 38-35.

The Milling Machine

FACE MILLING CUTTERS

Face mills, Fig. 38-36, are intended for machining large flat surfaces parallel to the face of the cutter. The teeth are designed to make the roughing and finishing cuts in one operation.

Fig. 38-36. Face mill.

Fig. 38-37. Concave cutter.

Fig. 38-38. Convex cutter. (Standard Tool Co.)

FORMED MILLING CUTTERS

Formed milling cutters are used to accurately duplicate a required contour. A wide range of shapes can be machined with the standard cutters available. Included in this cutter class are the CONCAVE CUTTER, Fig. 38-37, CONVEX CUTTER, Fig. 38-38, CORNER ROUNDING CUTTER, Fig. 38-39, and the GEAR CUTTER, Fig. 38-40.

Fig. 38-39. Corner rounding cutter (available as left- and right-hand cut).

Fig. 38-40. Gear cutter. (Standard Tool Co.)

MISCELLANEOUS MILLING CUTTERS

Included in this category are cutters that do not fit into any of the previously mentioned groups.

1. T-SLOT MILLING CUTTER - Used to mill the bottom of T-slots after the slot has been cut with a side cutter, Fig. 38-41.
2. WOODRUFF KEYSEAT CUTTER - Mills the circular keyway required for Woodruff keys, Fig. 38-42.

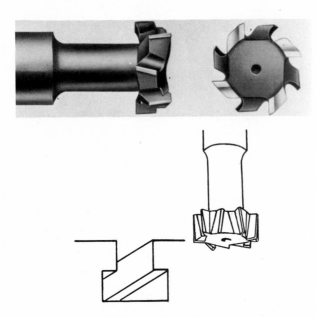

Fig. 38-41. T-Slot milling cutter.
(Morse Cutting Tools)

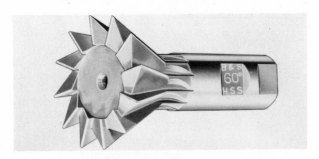

Fig. 38-42. Woodruff keyseat cutter.
(Standard Tool Co.)

3. DOVETAIL CUTTER - Used to machine dovetail type ways in the same manner as the T-slot cutter, Fig. 38-43.

Fig. 38-43. Dovetail cutter.
(Brown & Sharpe Mfg. Co.)

METHODS OF CUTTING

Milling operations fall into two distinct methods:

1. CONVENTIONAL or UP-MILLING, Fig. 38-44. The work is fed into the rotation of the cutter. The chip is at minimum thickness at the start of the cut, and is so slight that the cutter has a tendency to slide until sufficient pressure is built up to make it bite into the work.

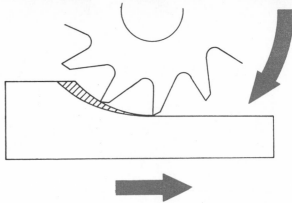

Fig. 38-44. Conventional milling.

2. CLIMB or DOWN MILLING, Fig. 38-45. The work moves in the same direction as the rotation of the cutter. Full engagement of the tooth is instantaneous. The sliding action of conventional milling is eliminated resulting in a better finish and a longer life.

Climb milling is not recommended on light milling machines because lack of rigidity and light support offsets any advantages of the technique.

CARE OF MILLING CUTTERS

Milling cutters are very expensive and are easily ruined if care is not taken in their use and storage. These precautions should be observed:

1. Support the cutter properly and hold the work rigid.

2. Use the correct cutting speed and feed.
3. An ample supply of cutting fluid is essential.
4. Use the correct cutter for the job.
5. Store cutters in individual compartments

Fig. 38-46. *Suggestions for storing cutters. Cutters should be stored so that they cannot come in contact with other cutters.*

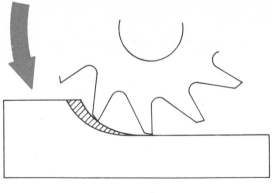

Fig. 38-45. *Climb milling.*
(Brown & Sharpe Mfg. Co.)

or on wooden pegs, Fig. 38-46.
6. Clean cutters before storing.
7. Never hammer a cutter on the arbor, Fig. 38-47. Examine the arbor for burrs or nicks if the cutter does not slip on easily.
8. Place a board under the end mill when removing it from the vertical milling ma-

Fig. 38-47. *Never hammer a cutter on the arbor.*

Fig. 38-48. It is a good idea to place a board under the end mill before removing it from its holder.

chine to prevent damage to its cutting edges, in case it is accidentally dropped, Fig. 38-48.

9. Use sharp cutters.

HOLDING AND DRIVING CUTTERS

The most common method of holding and driving milling cutters is the ARBOR. Arbors are made in a number of sizes and styles. In

Fig. 38-49. Arbor with self-holding taper.

addition to arbors made with SELF-HOLDING TAPERS, Fig. 38-49, for use on small hand millers, there are three arbor styles in general use:

1. STYLE A, Fig. 38-50. It is fitted with a small pilot that runs in a bronze bearing in the arbor support.
2. STYLE B, Fig. 38-51. This arbor is characterized by the large bearing that

Fig. 38-50. Style A arbor. (Kearney & Trecker Corp.)

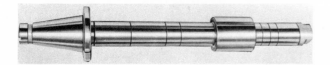

Fig. 38-51. Style B arbor.

can be positioned to any location on the arbor to localize support.

3. STYLE C, Fig. 38-52. Used to hold the smaller sizes of shell end mills and face mills that cannot be bolted directly to the spindle nose.

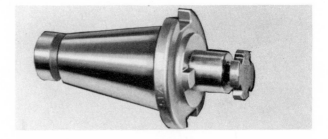

Fig. 38-52. Style C arbor.

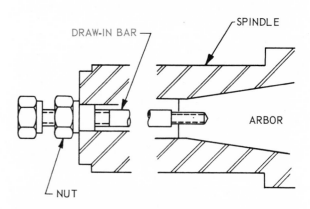

Fig. 38-53. Draw-in bar.

Fig. 38-54. Spindle drive keys. (Kearney & Trecker Corp.)

It is advisable to use the shortest arbor possible which permits adequate clearance between the arbor support and the work.

SPACING COLLARS are used to position the cutter on the arbor. They are made in a variety of thicknesses and permit the accurate spacing of two or more cutters for gang or straddle milling.

A DRAW-IN BAR, Fig. 38-53, fitted through the spindle, screws into the arbor and holds it

Fig. 38-58. In tightening nut on arbor, it is important to use wrench of correct type and size.

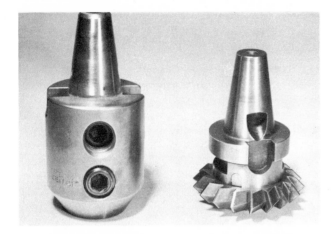

Fig. 38-55. Milling adapters. The adapter on the left permits an end mill to be used. The one on the right permits an arbor type cutter to be used on a vertical milling machine.

Fig. 38-56. Spring collets to hold end mills in milling machine.

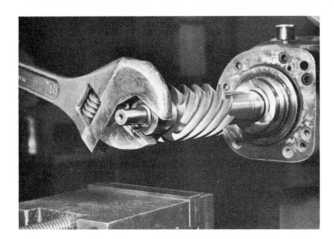

Fig. 38-57. Tightening or loosening the arbor nut without the arbor support in place may spring the arbor.

firmly in the spindle. DRIVE KEYS on the spindle nose, Fig. 38-54, fit into corresponding slots in the arbor flange to provide positive (non-slip) drive.

ADAPTERS, Fig. 38-55, permit a wide variety of milling cutter types and sizes to be mounted on the spindle.

SPRING COLLETS, Fig. 38-56, accommodate straight shank end mills and drills. Most collets are designed for use with a COLLET HOLDER.

CARE OF CUTTER HOLDING AND DRIVING DEVICES

To maintain accuracy during the machining operation it is necessary to prevent damage to the cutter holding and driving devices:

1. Keep the taper of the arbor free of nicks.
2. Clean and lubricate the bearing sleeve and arbor support bearing before use.
3. Clean the spacing collars before placing them on the arbor; otherwise, cutter run-out will occur.
4. Store arbors separately and in a vertical position.
5. Never loosen or tighten the arbor nut unless the arbor support is locked in place, Fig. 38-57.
6. Use a wrench of the correct type and size, Fig. 38-58.
7. Do not tighten the arbor nut by striking the wrench with a hammer or mallet. This may crack the nut or distort the threads.
8. To remove an arbor or adapter from the machine:
   a. Loosen the nut on the draw-in bar a few turns. DO NOT remove it from the arbor completely.
   b. Tap the draw-in bar head with a lead hammer to loosen the arbor from the spindle.
   c. Hold the loosened arbor with one hand and unscrew the draw-in bar with the other.
   d. Remove the arbor from the spindle, clean and store it.

CUTTING SPEEDS AND FEEDS

The time required to complete a milling operation and the quality of the finish of the machined surface is almost completely governed by the CUTTING SPEED and FEED of the cutter.

CUTTING SPEED

Cutting speed refers to the distance, measured in feet, a point (tooth) on the circumference moves in one minute. It is expressed in terms of FEET PER MINUTE (FPM) and is directly dependent on the REVOLUTIONS PER MINUTE (RPM) of the cutter.

FEED

Feed is the rate the work moves into the cutter and is given as FEED PER TOOTH PER

Material	H.S.S. Cutter	Carbide Cutter
Aluminum	550 - 1000	2200 - 4000
Brass	250 - 650	1000 - 2600
Low Carbon Steel	100 - 325	400 - 1300
Free Cutting Steel	150 - 250	600 - 1000
Alloy Steel	70 - 175	280 - 700
Cast Iron	45 - 60	180 - 240

Reduce speeds for hard materials, abrasive materials, deep cuts and high alloy materials.

Increase speeds for soft materials, better finishes, light cuts and frail work pieces and setups.

Start at mid-point on the range and increase or decrease speed until best results are obtained.

Fig. 38-59. *Recommended cutting speeds for milling (Speed in Surface Feet per Minute (SPM).*

RECOMMENDED FEED IN INCHES PER TOOTH
(High Speed Steel Cutters)

TYPE OF CUTTER	MATERIAL				
	ALUMINUM	BRASS	CAST IRON	FREE CUTTING STEEL	ALLOY STEEL
End Mill	0.009 0.022	0.007 0.015	0.004 0.009	0.005 0.010	0.003 0.007
Face Mill	0.016 0.040	0.012 0.030	0.007 0.018	0.008 0.020	0.005 0.012
Shell End Mill	0.012 0.030	0.010 0.022	0.005 0.013	0.007 0.015	0.004 0.009
Slab Mill	0.008 0.017	0.006 0.012	0.003 0.007	0.004 0.008	0.001 0.004
Side Cutter	0.010 0.020	0.008 0.016	0.004 0.010	0.005 0.011	0.003 0.007
Saw	0.006 0.010	0.004 0.007	0.001 0.003	0.003 0.005	0.001 0.003
Form Cutter	0.006 0.010	0.005 0.009	0.004 0.007	0.004 0.006	0.003 0.005

Increase or decrease feed until the desired surface finish is obtained.

Feeds may be increased 100% or more, depending upon the rigidity of the machine and the power available, if carbide tipped cutters are used.

Fig. 38-60. *Recommended feed in inches per tooth (High Speed Steel Cutters).*

REVOLUTION (FTR). The selection of the proper feed is probably the most difficult thing for the machinist to determine. In view of the many variables: width of cut, depth of cut, condition of the machine and cutter, etc., feed should be as coarse as possible, consistent with the desired finish.

CALCULATING CUTTING SPEEDS AND FEEDS

Considering the previously mentioned variables, the SPEEDS listed in Fig. 38-59, and FEEDS in Fig. 38-60, are suggested. The usual procedure is to start with the mid-range figure

RULES FOR DETERMINING SPEED AND FEED

TO FIND	HAVING	RULE	FORMULA
SPEED OF CUTTER IN FEET PER MINUTE (FPM)	DIAMETER OF CUTTER AND REVOLUTIONS PER MINUTE	DIAMETER OF CUTTER (IN INCHES) MULTIPLIED BY 3.1416 (π) MULTIPLIED BY REVOLUTIONS PER MINUTE, DIVIDED BY 12	$FPM = \dfrac{\pi D \times RPM}{12}$
REVOLUTIONS PER MINUTE (RPM)	FEET PER MINUTE AND DIAMETER OF CUTTER	FEET PER MINUTE, MULTIPLIED BY 12, DIVIDED BY CIRCUMFERENCE OF CUTTER (πD)	$RPM = \dfrac{FPM \times 12}{\pi D}$
FEED PER REVOLUTION (FR)	FEED PER MINUTE AND REVOLUTIONS PER MINUTE	FEED PER MINUTE, DIVIDED BY REVOLUTIONS PER MINUTE	$FR = \dfrac{F}{RPM}$
FEED PER TOOTH PER REVOLUTION (FTR)	FEED PER MINUTE AND NUMBER OF TEETH IN CUTTER	FEED PER MINUTE (IN INCHES) DIVIDED BY NUMBER OF TEETH PER MINUTE (NUMBER OF TEETH IN CUTTER x REVOLUTIONS PER MINUTE)	$FTR = \dfrac{F}{T \times RPM}$
FEED PER MINUTE (F)	FEED PER TOOTH PER REVOLUTION, NUMBER OF TEETH IN CUTTER, AND RPM	FEED PER TOOTH PER REVOLUTIONS MULTIPLIED BY NUMBER OF TEETH IN CUTTER, MULTIPLIED BY REVOLUTIONS PER MINUTE	$F = FTR \times T \times RPM$
FEED PER MINUTE (F)	FEED PER REVOLUTION AND REVOLUTIONS PER MINUTE	FEED PER REVOLUTION MULTIPLIED BY REVOLUTIONS PER MINUTE	$F = FR \times RPM$
NUMBER OF TEETH PER MINUTE (TM)	NUMBER OF TEETH IN CUTTER AND REVOLUTIONS PER MINUTE	NUMBER OF TEETH IN CUTTER MULTIPLIED BY REVOLUTIONS PER MINUTE	$TM = T \times RPM$

RPM = REVOLUTIONS PER MINUTE   TM = TEETH PER MINUTE
T = TEETH IN CUTTER   F = FEED PER MINUTE
D = DIAMETER OF CUTTER   FR = FEED PER REVOLUTION
π = 3.1416 (PI)   FTR = FEED PER TOOTH PER REVOLUTION
FPM = SPEED OF CUTTER IN FEET PER MINUTE

Fig. 38-61. Rules for determining speed and feed.

and increase or reduce speeds until the most satisfactory setting is obtained.

Refer to the RULES FOR DETERMINING SPEEDS AND FEEDS, Fig. 38-61, to calculate the cutting speed and feed for a specific material.

FOR EXAMPLE:

PROBLEM: Determine the proper speed and feed for a 6-in. diameter side cutter (HSS) with 16 teeth, milling aluminum.

INFORMATION AVAILABLE

Recommended cutting speed
for aluminum . . . . 750 FPM
(mid-point on range)
Recommended feed per tooth . . . 0.015 in.
(mid-point on range)
Diameter of cutter . . . . 6 in.
Number of teeth on cutter 16

TO DETERMINE SPEED SETTING (Cutter RPM)

Referral to Figure 38-61 gives the following:

RULE: Divide the feet per minute (FPM) by the circumference of the cutter, expressed in feet.

FORMULA: $RPM = \dfrac{FPM \times 12}{\pi D}$

$$= \dfrac{750 \times 12}{3.14 \times 6} = \dfrac{1500}{3.14} = 478*$$

TO DETERMINE FEED SETTING (Feed in inches per minute = F)

RULE: Multiply feed per tooth per revolution by number of teeth in cutter and by speed (RPM).

FORMULA: $F = FTR \times T \times RPM =$
$0.015 \times 16 \times 478 = 117*$

*The speeds and feeds are only approximate. Set machine to closest setting.

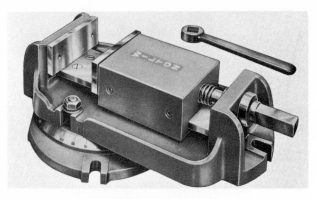

Fig. 38-63. A swivel vise. (Wilton Tool Mfg. Co.)

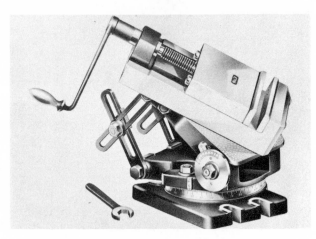

Fig. 38-64a. A universal vise. (Brown & Sharpe Mfg. Co.)

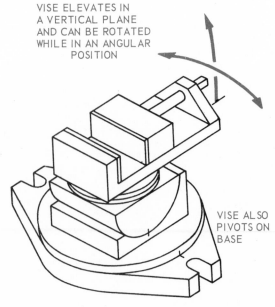

VISE ELEVATES IN A VERTICAL PLANE AND CAN BE ROTATED WHILE IN AN ANGULAR POSITION

VISE ALSO PIVOTS ON BASE

Fig. 38-64b. Another style of universal vise.

Fig. 38-62. A flanged vise.

CUTTING FLUIDS

Cutting fluids serve several purposes. They carry away the heat generated during the machining operation; act as a lubricant and prevent the chips from sticking or fusing to the cutter teeth; and flush away chips. The lubricating qualities also influence the quality of the finish of the machined surface.

RECOMMENDED CUTTING FLUIDS FOR VARIOUS MATERIALS

Aluminum and its Alloys. . . . . . Kerosene, Kerosene and Lard Oil, Soluble Oil
Plastics . . . . Dry
Brass, Soft . . . . Dry, Soluble Oil, Kerosene and Lard Oil
Bronze, High Tensile. . . . . . . Soluble Oil, Lard Oil, Mineral Oil, Dry
Cast Iron. . . . . Dry, Air Jet, Soluble Oil
Copper . . . . Soluble Oil, Dry, Mineral Lard Oil, Kerosene
Magnesium. . . . . Low Viscosity Neutral Oils
Malleable Iron . . . . Dry, Soda Water
Monel Metal. . . . . Lard Oil, Soluble Oil
Slate. . . . . Dry
Steel, Forging. . . . . Soluble Oil, Sulphurized Oil, Mineral Lard Oil
Steel, Manganese. . . . . Soluble Oil, Sulphurized Oil, Mineral Lard Oil
Steel, Soft . . . . Soluble Oil, Mineral Lard Oil, Sulphurized Oil, Lard Oil
Steel, Stainless. . . . . Sulphurized Mineral Oil, Soluble Oil
Steel, Tool. . . . . Soluble Oil, Mineral Lard Oil, Sulphurized Oil
Wrought Iron . . . . Soluble Oil, Mineral Lard Oil, Sulphurized Oil

WORK HOLDING ATTACHMENTS

One of the more important features of the milling machine is its adaptability to a large number of work holding attachments, each of which increases the usefulness of the machine.

VISE

The Vise is probably the most widely used method of holding work for milling. The jaws are hardened and ground for accuracy and wear resistance. It is keyed to the table with LUGS.

The FLANGED VISE, Fig. 38-62, has slotted flanges for fastening the vise to the work table. The slots permit the vise to be mounted parallel to or at right angles to the spindle.

The body of the SWIVEL VISE, Fig. 38-63, is similar to the flanged vise but is fitted with a circular base, graduated in degrees, permitting it to be pivoted on a horizontal plane and be locked at any angle to the spindle.

The TOOLMAKER'S UNIVERSAL VISE, Fig. 38-64, permits compound or double angles to be machined without complex or multiple setups.

The MAGNETIC CHUCK, as used in Fig. 38-65, is ideally suited for many milling operations. New chuck designs have made it a quick and easy tool to eliminate the time consuming use of hold-down clamps.

A ROTARY TABLE, Fig. 38-66, can perform a variety of operations such as cutting segments of circles, circular slots, locating angularly spaced holes or slots, cutting irregular shaped

Fig. 38-65. Milling machine using a magnetic chuck. (O. S. Walker Co., Inc.)

slots and similar operations. A dividing attachment can be fitted in place of the handwheel.

An INDEX TABLE, Fig. 38-67, permits the rapid positioning of the work for angular work.

The DIVIDING HEAD is one of the more important of the milling machine attachments. Its

Fig. 38-66a. Rotary table.
(Troyke Mfg. Co.)

Fig. 38-67. Indexing table.

Fig. 38-66b. Rotary table being used to produce a machine part.
(Greaves Mach. Tool Div., J. A. Fay & Egan Co.)

main function is to divide the circumference of a circular piece into equally spaced divisions. This makes the dividing head indispensable when milling gear teeth, cutting splines and spacing holes on a circle. It also makes possible the milling of squares, hexagons, octagons, etc., when required.

The dividing head consists of two parts: the dividing unit and the footstock, Fig. 38-68. The work may be mounted between centers, held in a chuck, or clamped in a collet.

The standard ratio for the dividing head is five turns of the index crank for one complete revolution of the spindle (5:1); or 40 turns of the index crank for one revolution of the spindle (40:1).

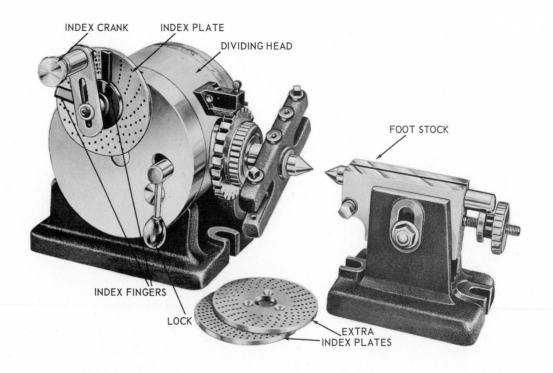

Fig. 38-68. A modern dividing head and footstock. (L-W Chuck Co.)

The ratio between the index crank turns and spindle revolution, plus the index plate with its series of equally spaced hole circles, makes it possible to divide the circumference of the work into the required number of equal spaces.

For example: If 10 teeth were to be cut in a gear, it would require 1/10 of 40 turns (assuming the dividing head has a 40:1 ratio), or four full turns of the index crank for each tooth.

For 28 teeth, the number of crank turns would be 1/28 of 40, or 1-12/28; or 1-3/7 turns of the crank for each tooth. This is where the holes in the index plate come into use: they allow fractional turns to be made accurately. On one such plate the circles have 46, 47, 49, 51, 53, 54 and 57 holes. In this situation, 49 is divisable by 7; then 3/7 of 49 or 21 holes on the 49 hole circle. It is not necessary to count 21 holes each time the work is repositioned after a tooth is cut. The two arms, called index fingers, are loosened. One is positioned until it touches the pin on the index crank; the other is moved clockwise until the arms are 21 holes apart (DO NOT COUNT THE HOLE THE PIN IS IN).

To index, rotate the crank one complete revolution, plus the section taken up by the index fingers. Drop the pin into the hole at this position and lock the dividing head. Move the index fingers in the same direction as crank rotation to catch up with the plunger. Repeat the operation after each cut, Fig. 38-69.

The dividing head can be elevated for cutting gears as shown in Fig. 38-70.

Fig. 38-69. Cutting a gear on the milling machine. Work is being held in a three-jaw universal chuck. Many machinists make a light cut at each tooth position to check whether the dividing head has been setup properly.

Fig. 38-70. Cutting a spiral gear. The universal dividing head is coupled to the automatic feed mechanism of the worktable. The operation is similar to cutting threads on the lathe.
(Kearney & Trecker Corp.)

MILLING OPERATIONS

The versatility of the milling machine permits many different machining operations to be performed by it. Because of space limitations, only those operations commonly performed in the school shop will be described in this text.

MILLING FLAT SURFACES

Flat surfaces may be milled with a plain or slab milling cutter mounted on an arbor (peripherial milling), and an inserted tooth or shell face milling cutter (face milling). The method used will be determined by the size and shape of the work. After the method has been decided, the following sequence of operations is recommended:

1. Check and lubricate the machine.
2. Use a vise if the work cannot be clamped directly to the table. Clean its base, and the worktable, and bolt the vise to the machine. Locate it as close to the column as the shape of the work and arbor support will permit. When possible, pivot the vise so that the solid jaw supports the work against cutting pressure, Fig. 38-71.

Fig. 38-72. The use of a dial indicator permits extreme accuracy in aligning the solid jaw.

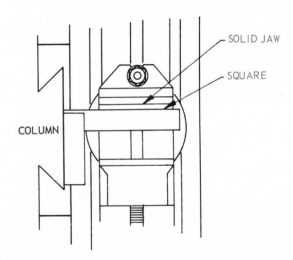

Fig. 38-73. Squaring solid vise jaw with column by using a steel square.

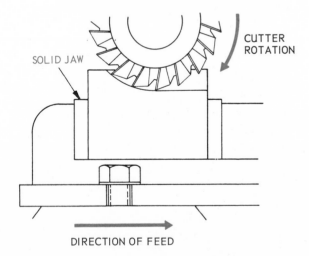

Fig. 38-71. The solid jaw of the vise should be in this position whenever the setup permits.

3. Align the vise with a dial indicator, Fig. 38-72, if extreme accuracy is required. Otherwise, a square, Fig. 38-73, or machine arbor, Fig. 38-74, will do.
4. Place the parallels in the vise with the work on them. Tighten the jaws and tap the work onto the parallels. Use paper

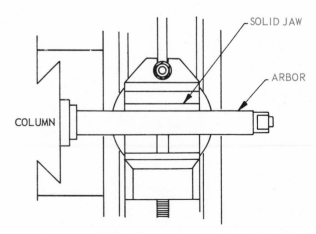

Fig. 38-74. Using arbor to align solid jaw of vise.

Fig. 38-75. Seating work on parallels.

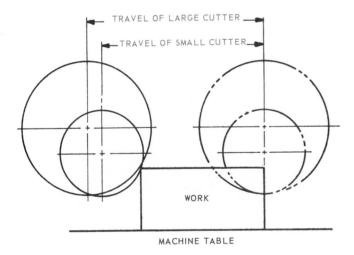

Fig. 38-76. A small cutter is more efficient because it travels less distance.

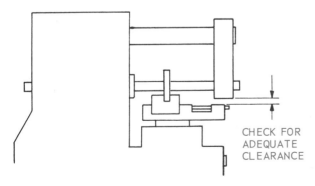

Fig. 38-77. Use as small a diameter cutter as possible but large enough for adequate clearance.

strips to check whether the work is on the parallels solidly, Fig. 38-75. Protect the vise jaws with soft metal strips if the work is rough.

5. Wipe the arbor taper and place it in the spindle and draw it in tightly with the draw-in bar.

6. Use the smallest cutter diameter possible, Fig. 38-76, but large enough to provide adequate clearance, Fig. 38-77. USE A PIECE OF CLOTH TO PROTECT YOUR HANDS FROM THE CUTTER TEETH, Fig. 38-78.

Fig. 38-78. It is advisable to use a cloth to protect hands when handling a cutter.

7. Place the cutter on the arbor and key it to the shaft. If a helical slab is used, mount it so the cutting pressure forces it toward the column, Fig. 38-79.

Fig. 38-79. Helical cutters should be mounted so that cutting pressures tend to force the cutter toward the spindle.

8. Swing the arbor support into place and tighten the arbor nut.

9. Adjust the machine to the proper cutting speed and feed.

10. Turn on the machine and check cutter rotation and direction of power feed. If satisfactory, loosen all worktable and knee locks, and position the work under the rotating cutter until it just touches the surface. Set the micrometer dial to

"0." Back the work away from the cutter and raise the table the required distance. Make the cut using ample cutting fluid.

Should additional material have to be removed from a machined surface, it will be best to set the cutter in the following manner. Hold a LONG, narrow strip of paper with its loose end between the work and the cutter, Fig. 38-80. Raise the table until the paper strip is pulled lightly from the fingers. CAUTION: PAY

Fig. 38-80. Setting the cutter by using a strip of paper. PAY ATTENTION WHEN POSITIONING THE CUTTER BY THIS METHOD.

CLOSE ATTENTION TO THIS JOB AND USE A PAPER STRIP THAT IS LONG ENOUGH TO KEEP YOUR FINGERS WELL CLEAR OF THE CUTTER. RELEASE IT AS SOON AS YOU FEEL THE CUTTER "GRABBING" AT IT.

After the cutter has been positioned, it is only necessary to move the cutter clear of the work and raise the table the required distance.

11. Tighten all locks and feed the work into the cutter. As soon as cutting starts, turn on the coolant and the power feed. Do not stop the work during the machining operation. To do so causes a slight depression to be made in the work surface, Fig. 38-81.

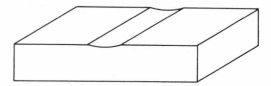

Fig. 38-81. A slight depression will be made in the work surface if the feed is stopped during the cut.

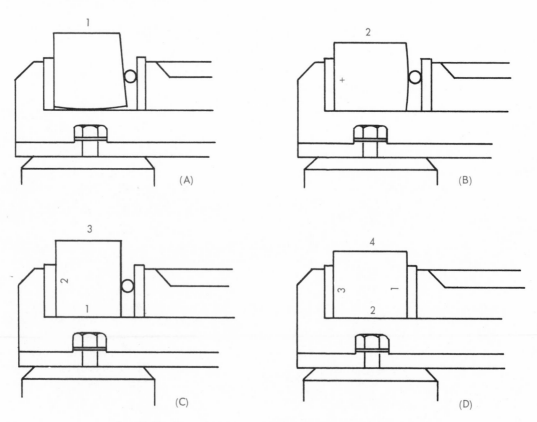

Fig. 38-82. The sequence for squaring work on the milling machine.

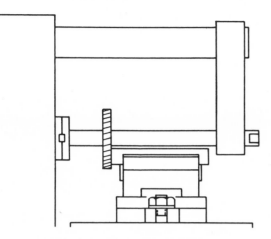

Fig. 38-83. One method of squaring work ends.

DO NOT ATTEMPT TO FEEL THE MACHINED SURFACE WHILE THE CUT IS IN PROGRESS OR WHILE THE CUTTER IS ROTATING.

12. Complete the cut. Stop the cutter and return the work to the starting position. NEVER FEFD THE WORK BACK UNDER THE ROTATING CUTTER.

13. Repeat the above operations if additional metal must be removed.

SQUARING STOCK

A definite sequence of operations must be followed to machine several surfaces of a piece square with one another.

The operations are very similar to those just explained:

1. Machine the first surface. Remove the burrs and place the first machined surface against the fixed vise jaw. Insert a length of soft metal rod between the work and the movable jaw if necessary, Fig. 38-82.

2. Machine the second surface.

3. Remove the burrs and reposition the work in the vise as shown in Fig. 38-82c, then machine the third side. This side must be machined to dimension. Take a light cut and "mike" for thickness. The difference between this measurement and the required thickness is the amount of material that must be removed.

4. Repeat the above operation to machine the fourth side.

5. If the piece is short enough, the ends may be machined by placing the piece in a vertical position; otherwise it may be machined with a side mill as shown in Fig. 38-83.

FACE MILLING

Face milling makes use of a cutter that machines a surface at right angles to the spindle axis and parallel to the face of the tool.

1. Select a cutter that is 3/4 to 1-in. larger in diameter than the width of the surface to be machined.

2. The work should project about 1 in. beyond the edge of the work table to provide clearance. Mount it to the table, or in a suitable holding device.

3. Adjust for correct speed and feed.

4. Slowly feed the work into the cutter until it starts to remove material. Roughing cuts up to 1/4 in. may be taken.

5. Use adequate cutting fluid.

6. Upon completion of the cut, stop the cutter and return the work to the starting position for additional cutting if needed.

7. Make the finishing cut and tear down the setup. Use a brush to remove chips.

SIDE MILLING

Side milling refers to any milling operation that makes use of the half-side and side milling cutters. When the cutters are used in pairs to machine two opposite sides of a piece at the same time, the setup is called STRADDLE MILLING, Fig. 38-84.

Fig. 38-84. Straddle milling.

Fig. 38-85. Gang milling makes use of several cutters.

GANG MILLING, Fig. 38-85, is a variation of straddle milling and involves mounting several cutters on the arbor to permit several surfaces to be machined in one pass. Gang milling is done when many similar pieces must be made.

HOW TO LOCATE A SIDE CUTTER FOR MILLING A SLOT

The machine setup is much the same as it was for milling flat surfaces. Indicate the vise jaw if the tolerances require this accuracy. A plain side milling cutter may be used if the slot is not too deep; otherwise, a staggered tooth side milling cutter should be used.

The cutter may be positioned by one of the following methods:

1. Lay out the end of the piece, Fig. 38-86, and position the cutter according to the lines.

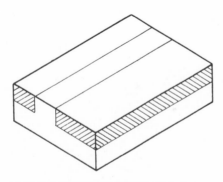

Fig. 38-86. Work laid out for milling.

2. Position the cutter with a rule, Fig. 38-87, and use a depth micrometer for depth.
3. Use the paper strip technique previously described and as shown in Fig. 38-88. REMEMBER TO USE A LONG STRIP OF

PAPER AND KEEP YOUR FINGERS CLEAR OF THE ROTATING CUTTER.

HOW TO LOCATE A SIDE CUTTER FOR MILLING A SLOT IN THE CENTER OF A ROUND PIECE

There are many situations that require keyways for the standard square keys to be cut in round pieces. The keyway must be exactly on center if it is to be in alignment with the keyway in the mating piece.

After the machine has been set up, cutter mounted and the work mounted in a vise, be-

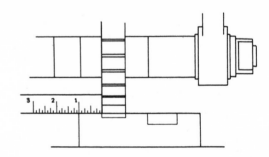

Fig. 38-87. Positioning the cutter with a steel rule.

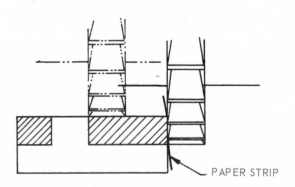

Fig. 38-88a. Using a paper strip to position the cutter.

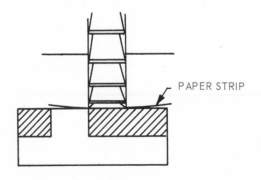

Fig. 38-88b. Using a paper strip to position the cutter for depth.

tween centers, in V-blocks or in a fixture, precise centering of the cutter may be accomplished by one of the following methods:

1. Center the cutter on the work visually. With a steel square and a rule, adjust the the table until both sides measure the same, Fig. 38-89. A depth micrometer may

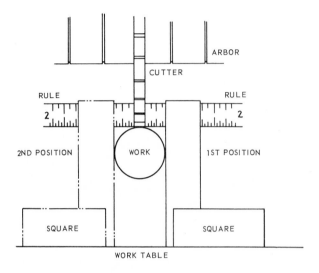

Fig. 38-89. Centering a cutter on round stock with a steel rule.

be used for more accurate positioning.

2. Short pieces cannot always be centered by the above method. For this situation, the work is positioned under and lightly

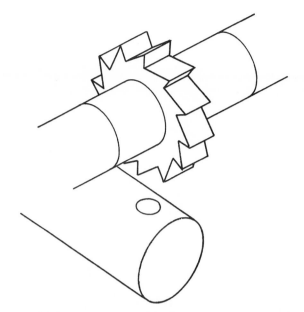

Fig. 38-90. Positioning cutter on center using an oval cut into the work as a guide.

sition the cutter on the oval, Fig. 38-90.

3. The previously mentioned paper strip method may also be used to locate the cutter precisely, Fig. 38-91. After the cutter has been brought up against the stock, the table must be lowered for the cutter to clear the top of the work. Move the cutter in one-half the diameter PLUS one-half the cutter thickness PLUS the

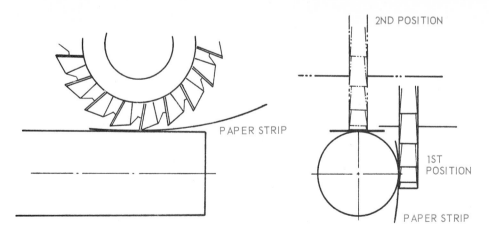

Fig. 38-91. Using paper strip to position the cutter on round stock.

brought into contact with the rotating cutter. Traverse (in-out) feed is used to pass the work under the cutter. An oval-shaped cut will result, and the location of the cut will be perfectly centered. Po-

thickness of the paper. The same technique is used to center a Woodruff keyseat cutter, Fig. 38-92.

Lock the saddle to prevent table movement after the cutter has been centered.

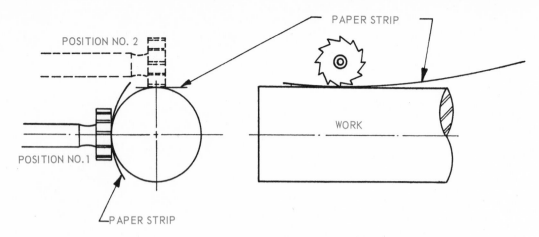

Fig. 38-92. The technique shown in Fig. 38-91, can also be used to center a Woodruff cutter.

SLITTING (HOW TO SAW IN THE MILLING MACHINE)

Slitting or sawing thin stock into various widths, Fig. 38-93, is a fairly common operation performed on the milling machine.

A slitting saw of the smallest diameter that

Fig. 38-93. Using slitting saw to cut a piece to length.

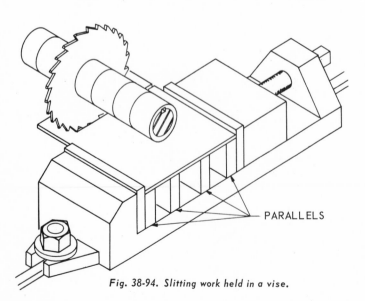

Fig. 38-94. Slitting work held in a vise.

permits adequate clearance should be used. It must be keyed to the arbor and the key should pass into the spacers on either side of the cutter.

If the section is narrow enough, the piece can be clamped in a vise for slitting, Fig. 38-94. It must be well supported with parallels. DO NOT PERMIT THE PARALLELS TO PROJECT OUT INTO THE PATH OF THE CUTTER.

Long strips must be clamped to the worktable. The clamp shown in Fig. 38-95, is made

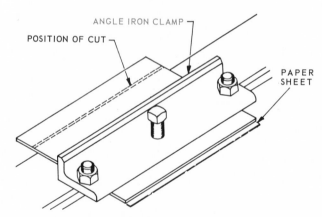

Fig. 38-95. A table clamp made from angle iron.

from a piece of angle iron. The work is aligned with the column face and must be positioned to permit the saw to make the cut over the center of a table slot, Fig. 38-96. A piece of paper between the work and the table will prevent slippage during the slitting operation. The cutter is set to a depth equal to the thickness of the material plus 1/16 in. USE A SHARP CUTTER.

SLOTTING

Slotting, Fig. 38-97, is very similar to slitting except that the cut is made only part way through the work. The slot in the head of a screw is an example of slotting.

HOW TO DRILL AND BORE
ON A PLAIN MILLING MACHINE

The toolmaker often finds it necessary to produce precision holes in jigs, fixtures and machine parts. The milling machine offers a convenient way to drill and bore holes in alignment with one another.

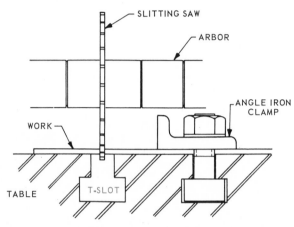

Fig. 38-96. Position the work so that the cut can be made over a T-slot.

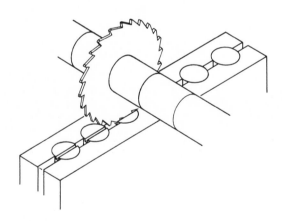

Fig. 38-97. Slotting screw heads with a slitting saw.

Fig. 38-98. Drilling on the mill.

Fig. 38-99. Drill with a tapered shank fitted in spindle.

Small drills are held in a standard Jacobs chuck mounted in the machine spindle, Fig. 38-98. Taper shank drills are held in a sleeve, Fig. 38-99.

Boring is done with a single point cutting tool mounted in a BORING HEAD, Fig. 38-100.

Fig. 38-100. Boring permits large holes to be machined to close tolerances.

The boring tool is held in the spindle by a collet.

A WIGGLER, Fig. 38-101, is used to align the machine if holes are to be drilled prior to

Fig. 38-101. Wiggler being used to locate hole for drilling.

reaming or boring. A DIAL INDICATOR must be used to realign existing holes for boring, Fig. 38-102.

THE VERTICAL MILLING MACHINE

The vertical milling machine, Fig. 38-103, is a highly useful and versatile machine tool for milling, drilling, reaming and boring. It

Fig. 38-102. Dial indicator permits existing holes to be aligned accurately.

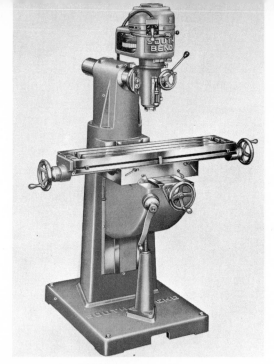

Fig. 38-103. Vertical milling machine. (South Bend Lathe)

differs from the conventional mill in that the spindle is normally in a vertical position. The SPINDLE HEAD, Fig. 38-104, swivels 90 deg. left or right for angular work, Fig. 38-105. The ram on which it is mounted can be adjusted in and out and, on many vertical mills, revolves

Fig. 38-104. Spindle head assembly. A—Spindle draw bar. B—Spindle feed lever. C—Spindle stop-brake lever. D—Micrometer spindle feed crank. E—Micrometer depth stop. F—Spindle. G—Spindle clamping lever. H—Feed Clutch lever. I—Spindle power down-feed engagement lever. J—Swiveling adjustment bolt. K—Spindle feed rate lever. L—Infinitely variable down-feed unit. M—Directional power feed lever. N—Motor.
(George Gorton Machine Co.)

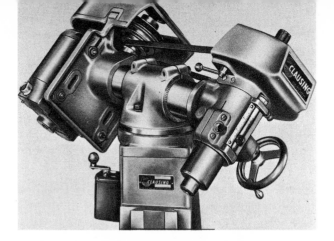

180 deg. on a horizontal plane. Both swivels are graduated with a Vernier scale to assure accurate angular settings, Fig. 38-105.

CUTTERS FOR THE VERTICAL MILLING MACHINE

Although adapters are available that permit side and angular cutters to be used on the vertical mill, Fig. 38-106, face mills and end mills are the normally used cutters.

Taper shank end mills too small to fit directly into the spindle are fitted into a sleeve for mounting, Fig. 38-107(A). Taper shanks that are large enough are mounted directly into the spindle, Fig. 38-107(B). Straight shank end mills are held in a collet chuck, 38-107(C), or in an adapter, Fig. 38-107(D). Small drills and reamers are held in a Jacobs chuck.

Fig. 38-106. Adapter which permits arbor-type cutters to be used on a vertical mill.

Fig. 38-107. Four of the more common methods used to mount end mills in a vertical mill.

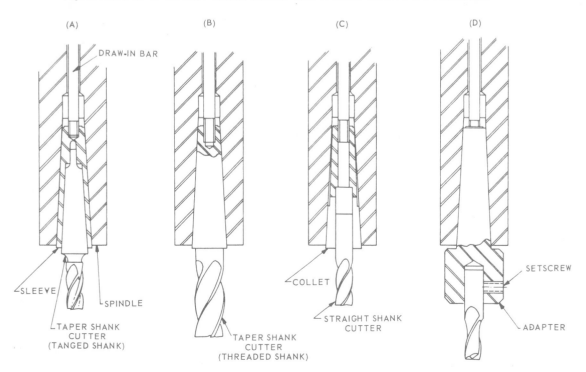

HOW TO MACHINE ANGULAR SURFACES

Angular surfaces (bevels, chamfers and tapers) may be milled by tilting the spindle head, Fig. 38-108, at the required angle, or by setting the work at an angle in the vise, Fig. 38-109.

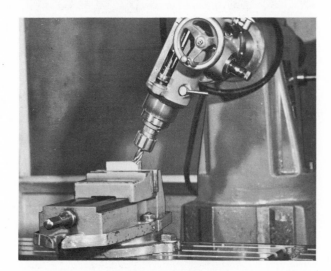

Fig. 38-108. Cutting an angular surface with the spindle head set to the desired angle.

Fig. 38-109. Angular surface may also be cut by positioning the work at the desired angle.

When the pivoted spindle head assembly is used, it is essential that the vise be aligned with a dial indicator. Make a layout of the re-

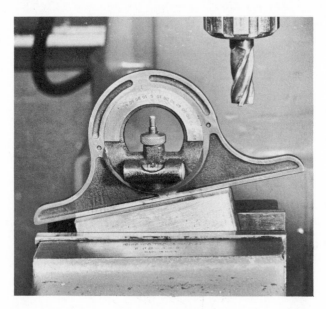

Fig. 38-110. The desired angle is set using a spirit level in a protractor head.

quired angle on the piece and clamp it in the vise. Position the cutter and cut to the line.

Work held at an angle in the vise for machining the angle must be set up very carefully. Alignment may be made with a PROTRACTOR, Fig. 38-110, fitted with a spirit level, or with a SURFACE GAUGE, Fig. 38-111.

HOW TO MILL A SLOT OR KEYWAY

An end mill may be used to cut a keyway or slot. The work is clamped in the vise and a cutter equal in diameter to the width of the cut is

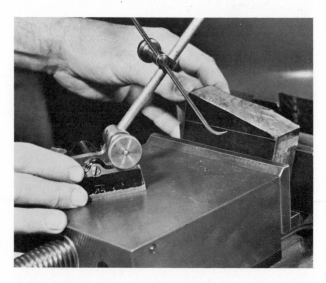

Fig. 38-111. Using a surface gauge to position the work.

selected. A two-flute end mill is used when a blind keyway must be cut, Fig. 38-112; otherwise, a four-flute end mill is used.

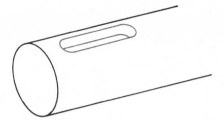

Fig. 38-112. Blind slot.

The end mill is centered in the same manner as a side milling cutter would be for the same operation, Fig. 38-91.

HOW TO MACHINE AN INTERNAL OPENING

Internal openings, Fig. 38-113, are easily machined on a vertical mill. A two-fluted end mill must be used if the cutter is to start the opening as it can be fed directly into the metal like a drill.

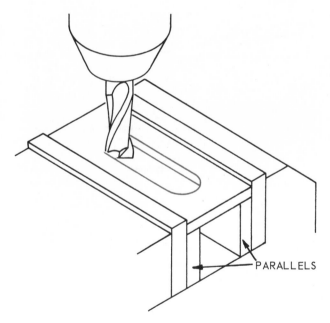

PARALLELS

Fig. 38-113. Milling an internal opening with an end mill.

When the slot is wider than the cutter diameter, it is important that the proper direction of feed, in relation to cutter rotation, be observed. THE DIRECTION OF FEED IS ALWAYS AGAINST CUTTER ROTATION, Fig. 38-114, and applies only when the cutter is removing material from one side of the opening.

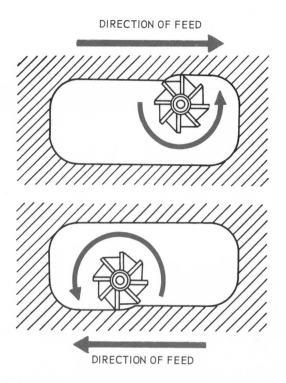

DIRECTION OF FEED

DIRECTION OF FEED

Fig. 38-114. The direction of feed is always against the rotation of the cutter.

HOW TO MACHINE MULTI-LEVEL SURFACES

Milling multi-level surfaces, Fig. 38-115, is probably the easiest of the milling operations. A layout of the various levels is made on the work surfaces and cuts are made until the layout lines are reached. For accuracy, the depth of the cut must be checked with a micrometer and table adjustments made accordingly.

Fig. 38-115. Machining a step surface.

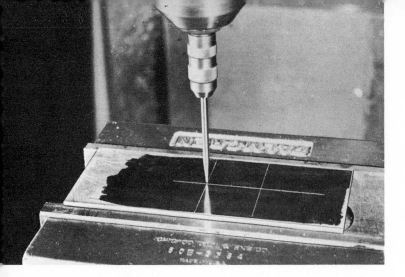

Fig. 38-116. The first hole is aligned by using a "wiggler."

HOW TO DRILL AND BORE ON A VERTICAL MILLING MACHINE

Holes may be located for drilling, reaming and boring to very close tolerances on the vertical mill. After the first hole has been located using the "wiggler," Fig. 38-116, and machined, it is possible to locate the remaining holes by using the micrometer feed dials on the table movement screws.

Boring, Fig. 38-117, permits holes of any

Fig. 38-117. Boring on the vertical mill.
(Lido Tools)

diameter to be machined accurately with fine surface finishes. A single point tool is fitted to the BORING HEAD which is, in turn, mounted in the spindle, Fig. 38-118. Hole diameter is

controlled by off-setting the tool point from center. The adjustment screw is graduated for direct reading.

Fig. 38-118. An offset boring head. Note the graduated adjusting screw. (Lido Tools)

CARE OF THE MILLING MACHINE

Many of the problems encountered in the operation of the milling machine will not occur if careful thought is given to preplanning the job:

1. Check and lubricate the machine with the recommended lubricants.
2. Clean the machine thoroughly after each job. Use a brush to remove chips, Fig. 38-119, NEVER USE YOUR HANDS AND STOP THE MACHINE BEFORE ATTEMPTING TO DO ANY CLEANING.

Fig. 38-119. Use a brush to remove metal chips--NEVER your hand.

3. Keep the machine clear of tools.
4. Check each setup for adequate clearance, Fig. 38-120.
5. Clean the spindle opening and arbor taper before inserting the arbor.

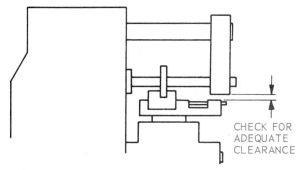

Fig. 38-120. Check for clearance before starting the cut.

6. Never force a cutter on an arbor.

7. No attempt should be made to loosen or tighten the arbor nut without proper arbor support. Make it a habit to tighten the nut as the last step in a setup, and loosening

Fig. 38-121a. An aft head of a solid propellant rocket chamber is contoured on a template controlled three-dimensional milling machine. The template (located at top of worktable) is used to guide the cutting tool. Three-dimensional milling eliminates much welding that would otherwise be necessary.
(Avco Corp., Lycoming Div.)

Fig. 38-121b. The duplex type fixed bed milling machine makes use of two cutting heads. These machines are frequently programmed to go through the cutting cycles automatically.
(Kearney & Trecker Corp.)

Fig. 38-121c. Another type of fixed bed milling machine. Machine movement is controlled from the cabinet to the left of the machinist. Note the variety of cutting tools.
(Portage Machine Co.)

it the first step in the tear down.

8. Use a wrench of the correct size and type to tighten the arbor nut.

9. Never use a dull cutter.

10. Check the machine to determine whether it is level. This should be done at regular intervals.

11. Speed and feed changes should be made according to the manufacturer's recommendations.

12. Never operate a machine until all guards are in place.

13. Check the level and condition of the coolant if the reservoir is built in. Change when it becomes contaminated.

14. Do not operate the machine until you are sure that everything is in satisfactory working condition. Ask for help if you are not sure how an operation should be performed.

INDUSTRIAL APPLICATIONS

The milling machines used by industry operate on the same basic principle as those in the school shop. However, it is possible to program these machines, by the use of automatic feeds and a series of trip dogs, through an automatic machining cycle. Many of the most recently designed fixed bed milling machines are fitted with controls that can be activated and controlled by tapes or punch cards. Fig. 38-121, illustrates a number of fixed bed-type milling machines. They are all production type machines.

TEST YOUR KNOWLEDGE, Unit 38

1. The_____ and _____are the two basic milling machine families.
2. The worktable has three movements: _____, _____and _____.
3. The vertical milling machine is best suited for operations done with an _____ _____ and a_____ _____cutter.
4. What are the two basic types of milling cutters?
   a._____.
   b._____.
5. Cutters are also classified by the method used to mount them in the machine. List them:
   a._____.
   b._____.
   c._____.
6. The slab milling cutter is a member of the _____milling cutter family.
7. The_____fluted end mill is used when the cutter must be fed into the work like a twist drill.
8. Make a sketch showing the difference between conventional milling and climb milling.
9. In general, the shortest arbor suitable for the job should be used. True or false?
10. The draw-in bar goes through the spindle and helps to hold the arbor in the spindle. True or false?
11. The flanged vise has a swivel base that permits it to be pivoted to any desired angle. True or false?
12. Cutting fluids have three functions:
    a._____.
    b._____.
    c._____.
13. The dividing head is used to:
    a. Locate the center of round stock.
    b. Divide the circumference of a workpiece into any number of equal parts.
    c. Locate hole positions for drilling.
    d. None of the above.
14. Gang milling means:
    a. Several cutters used to do the job.
    b. One or more cutters straddling the job.
    c. Two or more cutters cutting at the same time.
    d. None of the above.
15. Explain how to center a side cutter on round stock for the purpose of machining a keyway. Use the paper strip technique.
16. The_____ _____is the most accurate tool to be used to align a vise.
17. Milling cutters should be handled with_____ _____to prevent hand injuries.
18. Blind or closed keyways are made with a _____end mill.
19. Small drills and reamers are held in a_____ _____in the vertical milling machine.
20. List two ways of machining a bevel, chamfer or taper on a vertical milling machine:
    a._____.
    b._____.
21. Calculate the cutting speed (RPM) of a 6-in. diameter side mill (HSS) to machine aluminum.
22. Calculate the cutting speed (RPM) of a 1-in. diameter end mill (HSS) to machine mild steel.
23. The_____tooth side milling cutter is used to machine deep slots.
24. The_____is used for cuttoff operations.
25. End mills are available with_____and _____shanks.
26. An_____is used to support a slab milling cutter.
27. Flat surfaces are machined with_____or _____tooth_____milling cutter.
28. Accurate holes may be machined on a vertical milling machine with the aid of a_____head.
29. Chips are removed with the hands. True or false?
30. Stop the machine before making measurements. True or false?
31. Make adjustments while the cutter is rotating. True or false?
32. Get help to move heavy milling vises. True or false?

RESEARCH AND DEVELOPMENT

1. The milling machine and its inventor, Eli Whitney, played an important part in early attempts at mass-production. Prepare a term paper on Whitney's project of producing 10,000 muskets, with interchangeable parts, for the federal government in 1798, and how it lead to the invention of the milling machine.

2. Make a series of 35 mm slides illustrating the safety precautions that must be followed when operating the milling machine.

3. Cutting fluids play an important part in any machining operation. Secure samples of cutting fluids used by industries in the community, and conduct a series of experiments to show the quality of surfaces machined dry and with the various cutting compounds. Your experiment should show the best cutting fluid for use with steel, aluminum and brass.

4. Contact a shop that uses milling machines and secure cutters that have been ruined by different means. Make a panel to display them with an explanation of how they were ruined.

5. Present a demonstration on the proper way to center a cutter to machine a keyway in a shaft. Use the paper strip technique.

6. Milling machines were the first machines automated. Do a research project on automated milling machines. Secure samples of the perforated tapes and punch cards used to control them, and some small products made on a tape programmed machine.

Photo of model of the first practical milling
machine, invented by Eli Whitney in 1818.
(DoAll Co.)

Unit 39

SPECIAL PURPOSE MACHINES

In the study of the field of metalworking, mention must be made of the many special purpose machine tools used by industry. These machines have been designed for a specific but limited operation or job. Machines with such limited applications are only practical when

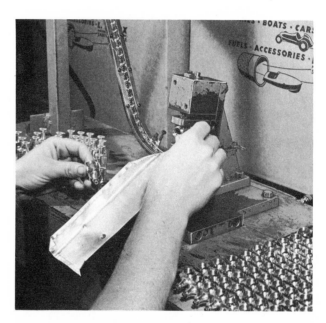

Fig. 39-2. A small special purpose machine designed to press the propeller drive plate onto the crankshaft.

production is of sufficient quantity to justify designing and manufacturing costs. Some machines have such limited uses that when the part they produce or the operation they per-

Fig. 39-1. A machine specially designed to drive four screws simultaneously joining the fuel tank assembly to the crankcase of a miniature internal combustion engine.
(L. M. Cox Manufacturing Co.)

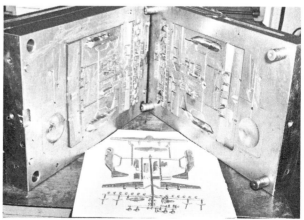

Fig. 39-3. The machine tool that made these dies for molding plastic model airplanes has a metal finger that touches the surface of a model of the finished die and controls the movement of the cutting tool to duplicate the surface in this finished die.
(Revell Inc.)

Fig. 39-4. *This machine is designed for low cost production of split molds for glass and plastic bottles and other similar work. Action of the machine is automatic, rapid and efficient. The mold sections are machined simultaneously from a single master, so that the cost of producing any required number of complete molds is substantially reduced.* (Pratt and Whitney Co.)

Fig. 39-5. *Another view of the Automatic Duplicating Machine for bottle molds.*

Fig. 39-6. *This Turbine Blade Airfoil Grinder produces a profile section by copying an airfoil master cam. Stock is removed from the work by a high speed abrasive belt. The entire cycle is automatic and rapid. The operator has only to remove the finished blades, load a new blank and restart the cycle.* (Pratt and Whitney Co.)

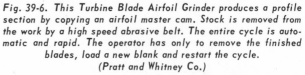

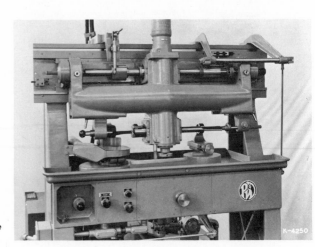

Fig. 39-7. *A close-up of the working area of the Turbine Blade Airfoil Grinder.* (Pratt and Whitney Co.)

form becomes unnecessary the machines are junked rather than modifying them for other work.

Illustrated are but a few of the many special purpose machines. Several are of but one of a kind.

Fig. 39-8. A close-up of the cutting head and follower of the machine described in Fig. 3. However, in this case a die for producing jet turbine blades is being machined instead of a model plane die. The master is to the left. The die being machined to the right. (Pratt and Whitney Co.)

Fig. 39-9. A special purpose machine designed to cut large gears. (National Machine Tool Builders Association)

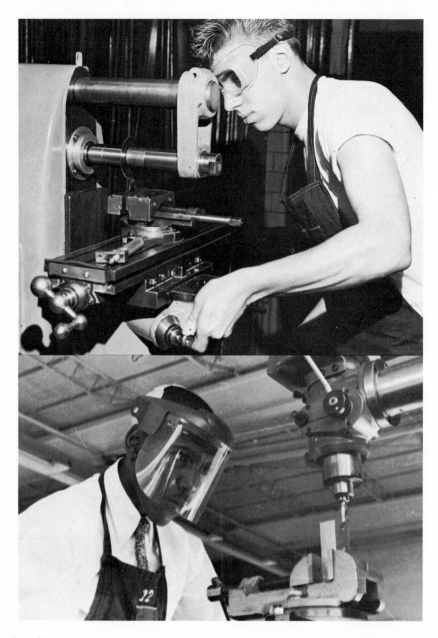

A "*must*" in the school shop, as well as in industry--Wear approved type safety glasses, goggles, or shields, where there is possibility of eye injury by flying chips.

Unit 40

METAL SPINNING

Metal spinning is a method of working metal sheet into three-dimensional shapes. It involves, in its simplest form, rotating a metal disc with a forming block (chuck) made to the dimensions

The pressure is applied by a simple lever consisting of a forming tool, Fig. 40-2. The spinner rests the forming tool on a tool rest and begins to apply pressure at the center of the

Fig. 40-1a. Sheet metal disc and the forming block revolving on spinning lathe.
(Phoenix Products Co.)

specified for the inside of the finished object. As the lathe rotates the metal disc and forming block, pressure is applied and the metal is gradually worked around the form until it assumes its size and shape, Figs. 40-1a to 40-1d incl.

disc which responds by starting to form itself over the forming block.

Most metals can be spun. However, aluminum, copper, brass, pewter and silver are best suited for spinning in the school shop. They

Fig. 40-1b. Pressure is applied and disc begins to assume the shape of the forming chuck.

Fig. 40-1c. As metal disc begins to assume its final shape it may have to be removed from the lathe and annealed (softened) before it can be completed.

must be in the annealed state and may have to be annealed from time to time as they become workhardened during the spinning operation.

EQUIPMENT

LATHE

Any lathe with heavy-duty head spindle bearings and an adequate speed range can be used for spinning. For best results, the tailstock

Fig. 40-1d. The finished product. In this case a lighting fixture.

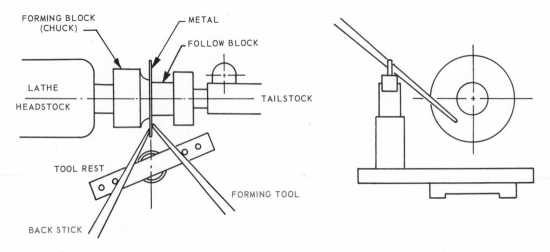

Fig. 40-2. A typical spinning setup for hand operation. Pressure is applied with the forming tool. The back stick prevents the disc from buckling.

Spinning

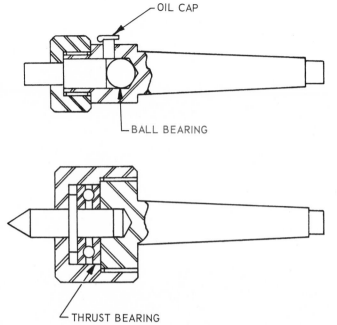

Fig. 40-3. Typical ball bearing centers.

should be fitted with a ball bearing center, Fig. 40-3. The conventional tool rest or tool post is replaced with a tool rest fitted with movable steel pins, Fig. 40-4. The pins act as fulcrum points for applying pressure to the spinning tools.

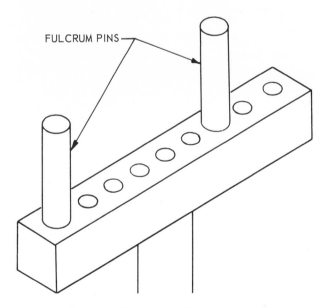

Fig. 40-4. Tool post used for spinning.

TOOLS

Spinning tools may be made from hickory hammer handles (18-24 in. long) or commercially made from steel, Fig. 40-5.

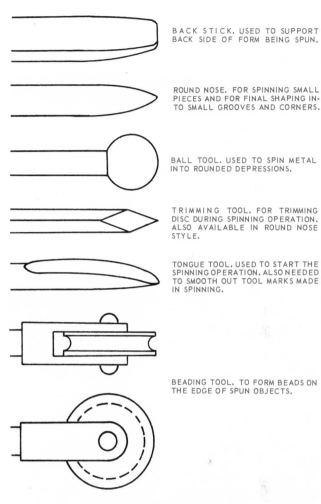

BACK STICK. USED TO SUPPORT BACK SIDE OF FORM BEING SPUN.

ROUND NOSE. FOR SPINNING SMALL PIECES AND FOR FINAL SHAPING INTO SMALL GROOVES AND CORNERS.

BALL TOOL. USED TO SPIN METAL INTO ROUNDED DEPRESSIONS.

TRIMMING TOOL. FOR TRIMMING DISC DURING SPINNING OPERATION. ALSO AVAILABLE IN ROUND NOSE STYLE.

TONGUE TOOL. USED TO START THE SPINNING OPERATION. ALSO NEEDED TO SMOOTH OUT TOOL MARKS MADE IN SPINNING.

BEADING TOOL. TO FORM BEADS ON THE EDGE OF SPUN OBJECTS.

Fig. 40-5. Spinning Tools.

CHUCKS

Chucks are the forms over which the metal disc is shaped. Most of them are made from birch, maple or cherry woods. Metal chucks

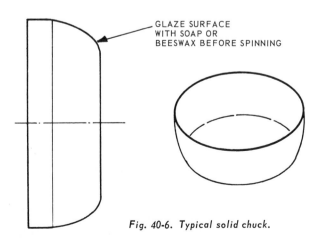

GLAZE SURFACE WITH SOAP OR BEESWAX BEFORE SPINNING

Fig. 40-6. Typical solid chuck.

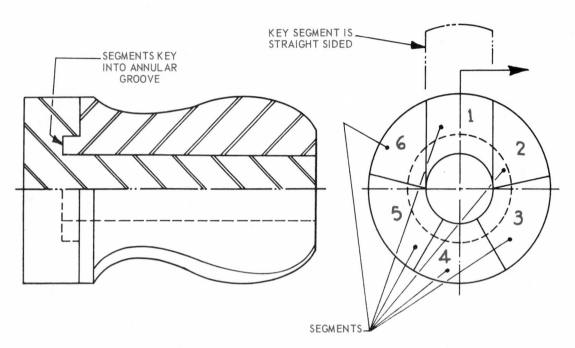

SEGMENTS KEY
INTO ANNULAR
GROOVE

KEY SEGMENT IS
STRAIGHT SIDED

SEGMENTS

Fig. 40-7. Segmented chuck for spinning tankard.

are used, if great accuracy or long production runs are required. The SOLID CHUCK, Fig. 40-6, is used for spinning simple forms while the SEGMENTED CHUCK, Fig. 40-7, must be used for more complex shapes like the tankard in Fig. 40-8. The chuck is made in segments

SAFETY

1. Beware of sharp-pointed metal edges when cutting the metal disc to size and when getting it ready for spinning.
2. Check over the spinning lathe to be certain that it is in a safe condition for spinning.
3. Be sure the tool post is securely tightened in place before attempting to spin.
4. Wear goggles when trimming the disc.
5. Remove all burrs formed during the trimming operation with a file.
6. Make certain the spinning tools are fitted solidly to the handle.
7. Never stand in line with the disc during the centering operation.
8. Always double check the condition of the follow block on the disc. Remember to re-tighten the tailstock after the disc has been centered.
9. Use care when handling a disc that has been annealed and may still burn you if you do not use tongs or wear gloves.
10. Do not attempt to do spinning unless you are positive of what must be done and how it is to be done. Seek help if you are in doubt or do not know a specific operation.

Fig. 40-8. A pewter tankard made by the spinning process.
(Henry J. Kauffman)

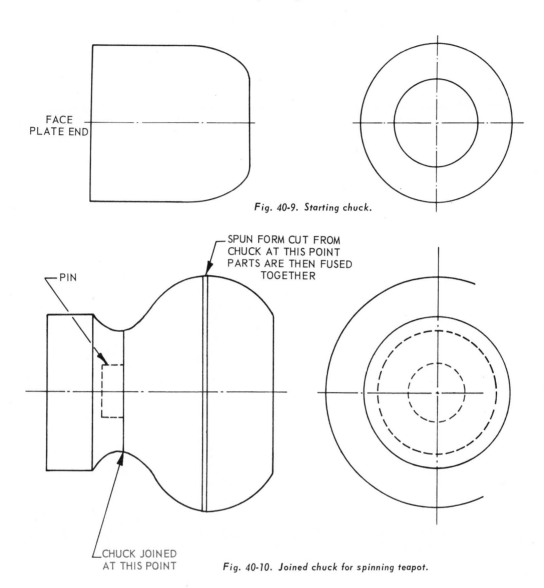

FACE
PLATE END

Fig. 40-9. Starting chuck.

PIN

SPUN FORM CUT FROM
CHUCK AT THIS POINT
PARTS ARE THEN FUSED
TOGETHER

CHUCK JOINED
AT THIS POINT

Fig. 40-10. Joined chuck for spinning teapot.

that are disassembled after the form has been spun. A STARTING CHUCK, Fig. 40-9, is used for the initial shaping of the metal after which it is fitted on the segmented chuck. A JOINED CHUCK, Fig. 40-10, is used when a bulged form like the teapot, Fig. 40-11, is spun. The form spun on the joined chuck cannot be made on a segmented chuck. After spinning, the form is cut at its largest diameter, the chuck sections removed, and the metal pieces are fused or soldered back together.

FOLLOW BLOCK

The follow block, Fig. 40-12, is a wooden block that fits over the tailstock center and applies the pressure needed to hold the work on the chuck.

Fig. 40-11. The body of this pewter teapot was spun
on a joined chuck.

position the circles on the follow block, Fig. 40-14.

b. Turn the lathe over by hand and tap the blank on the high side until it runs true.

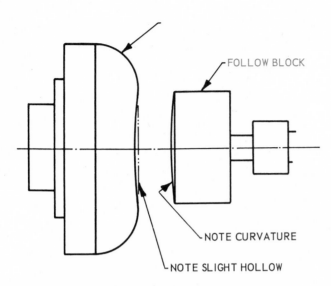

FOLLOW BLOCK

NOTE CURVATURE

NOTE SLIGHT HOLLOW

Fig. 40-12. Follow block.

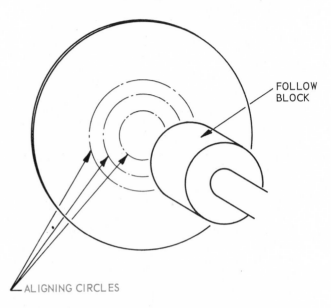

FOLLOW BLOCK

ALIGNING CIRCLES

Fig. 40-14. Centering disc on spinning lathe.

LUBRICANT

A lubricant such as yellow bar soap or beeswax is applied to the metal disc to prevent the forming tool from gauling the surface of the metal during the spinning operation.

SPINNING

HOW TO SPIN A SIMPLE FORM

1. Secure or turn a chuck of the desired shape.
2. Cut a metal disc to size. Fig. 40-13, shows how the diameter is determined.

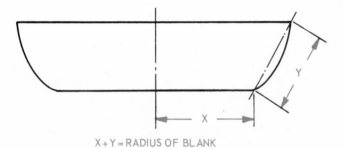

X + Y = RADIUS OF BLANK

Fig. 40-13. How to determine disc size.

3. Insert the disc between the chuck and follow block. Turn up the tailstock until the follow block holds the disc snugly to the chuck. Center the disc on the chuck by one of the following methods:

a. Draw a series of circles on the blank and

c. Run the lathe at a very slow speed and hold the back stick between the tool rest and the disc. Loosen the tailstock slightly and apply light pressure to the edge of the rotating disc until it runs true, Fig. 40-15. Retighten the tailstock after the piece has been centered.

CAUTION: Do not stand directly behind the revolving disc while it is being centered.

Fig. 40-15. Centering disc with back stick. (Stieff Silver Co.)

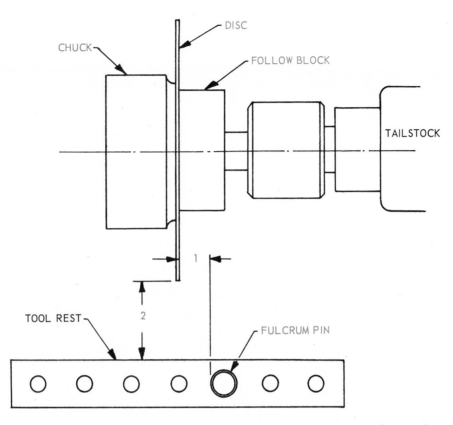

Fig. 40-16. Typical spinning setup.

4. Adjust the lathe to run at 1000-1500 rpm. Position the tool rest about 2 in. away from the edge of the disc with the fulcrum pin about 1 in. in front, Fig. 40-16.

5. Turn on the power and apply lubricant to the disc face. Do not apply too much as it will fly off when the disc heats up during the spinning operation.

6. Use a round nose tool positioned slightly below center, and, with body pressure, move the tool nose down and to the left to hook the disc on the blank, Fig. 40-17.

7. After the disc has been hooked to the chuck, reposition the tool rest until it is about 1/2 in. away from the disc edge and trim the edge until the disc runs true. Use a file to remove any burrs formed during the trimming operation.
   CAUTION: Wear goggles and keep your hands away from the rotating disc edge at all times.

8. Move the tool rest back far enough to permit the forming tool to have room to move freely. Insert one pin about 1-1/2 in. in front and another the same distance in back

of the disc. Be sure the rest is securely clamped.

9. Place the forming tool over the rest with point about 1/4 in. outside and below the

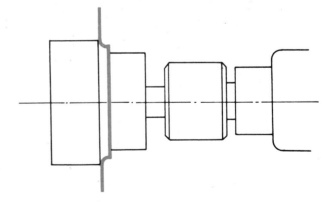

Fig. 40-17. A disc hooked on chuck.

base just formed. Apply pressure in the direction of the chuck forcing the metal to flow against the chuck. Work the tool so that the metal is gradually forced down on the chuck. Constant pressure to the left has a

tendency to thin the metal, often to the breaking point. To prevent this, reverse the tool
movement towards the base to flow the metal
back to normal thickness, Fig. 40-18.

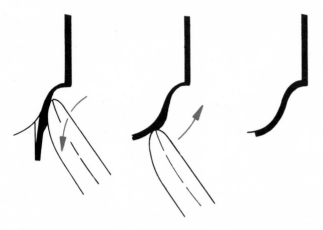

Fig. 40-18. Reverse tool travel to keep metal thickness uniform
and to prevent disc from tearing.

If the work starts to buckle or wrinkle
on the edge, place the back stick against the
left side of the disc and force the metal to
pass between the back tool and the forming
tool, Fig. 40-19. Work too b u c k l e d to

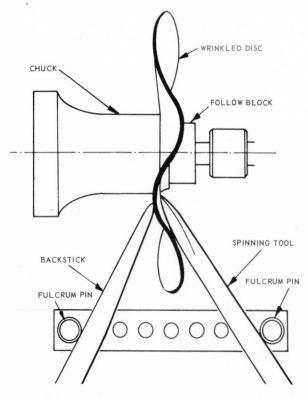

Fig. 40-19. Straightening wrinkled or buckled disc.

Fig. 40-20. Spinning a tankard body by the conventional spinning
technique.   (Stieff Silver Co.)

straighten by this method must be removed
from the chuck and flattened with a mallet.
Force the metal tightly to the chuck and move
the forming tool back and forth along the surface to remove ridges and distribute the
metal evenly, Fig. 40-20.

10. Trim the edge if needed and remove any
    burr that may have formed. Remove all
    traces of the lubricant with a cloth and a sol-
    vent or soap and water.

11. Increase the lathe speed and polish the work
    with fine steel wool (3/0) or aluminum oxide
    cloth (300). Buff if a high polish is desired.

Fig. 40-21. Typical bead on spun object.

HOW TO FORM A BEAD ON THE EDGE OF A SPUN SHAPE

The edge of a spun piece is often turned back
to form a bead, Fig. 40-21. This operation can
be performed with the beading tool as shown in
Fig. 40-22, or it may be done with conventional
spinning tools and a back stick as shown in
Fig. 40-23.

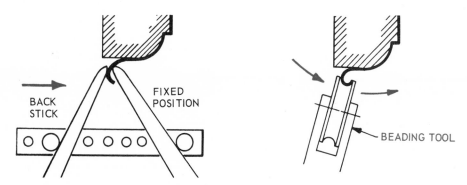

Fig. 40-22. Making bead with beading tool.

BACK STICK

FIXED POSITION

BEADING TOOL

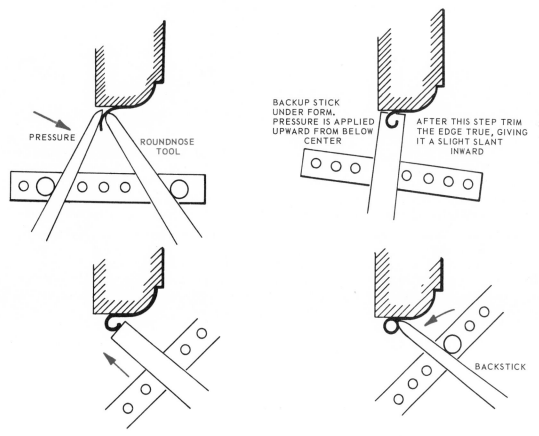

PRESSURE

ROUNDNOSE TOOL

BACKUP STICK UNDER FORM. PRESSURE IS APPLIED UPWARD FROM BELOW CENTER

AFTER THIS STEP TRIM THE EDGE TRUE, GIVING IT A SLIGHT SLANT INWARD

BACKSTICK

Fig. 40-23. Making a bead with conventional spinning tools.

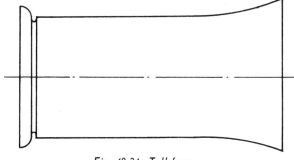

Fig. 40-24. Tall form.

HOW TO SPIN DEEP FORMS

Objects that are rather tall with straight sides, Fig. 40-24, require a slightly different spinning technique to maintain uniform metal thickness along their entire length.

The constant application of pressure often causes the metal to tear before it can be worked down on the chuck. This can often be avoided if a BREAKDOWN CHUCK, Fig. 40-25, is used first. This chuck has a base that is the same

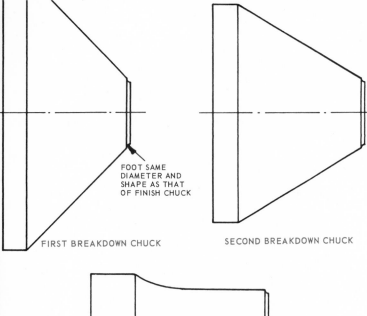

FOOT SAME
DIAMETER AND
SHAPE AS THAT
OF FINISH CHUCK

FIRST BREAKDOWN CHUCK   SECOND BREAKDOWN CHUCK

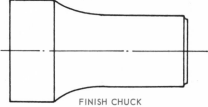

FINISH CHUCK

Fig. 40-25. Breakdown chucks and finish chuck for tall form.

diameter and shape as the final chuck. The steps in spinning a deep form are shown in Fig. 40-26.

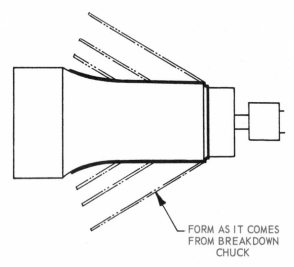

FORM AS IT COMES
FROM BREAKDOWN
CHUCK

Fig. 40-26. Spinning a tall form.

INDUSTRIAL APPLICATIONS

Modern spinning practices have gained wide acceptance as a method of forming metal sheet into shapes that cannot be done physically or economically by stamping or drawing.

The size and gauge of metal spun manually

Fig. 40-27. The compound tool multiplies the spinner's muscular power for large, heavy work.
(Phoenix Products Co.)

is limited by the skilled craftsman's muscle power. The desire to increase the spinner's power to form larger and thicker diameters has lead to the development of a COMPOUND LEVER TOOL, Fig. 40-27. This tool resembles a large nutcracker with a steel roller near the fulcrum. The tool pivots on a lever and permits changes of fulcrum to give the operator maximum leverage in forming heavy metals.

Although the manual methods are still used when the operation is economical and efficient, they are still not adequate for most modern needs. Today, thanks to lathes with tremendous power and hydraulically powered forming tools, Fig. 40-28, that not only duplicate manual movement, but also gives the operator a sense of "feel" that is so sensitive that the metal thickness can be controlled on the most intricate forms. They are so powerful, that diameters upwards of 200 in. and thicknesses over 2 in. can be formed to close tolerances.

For certain ranges of conical shapes, especially used in the missile field, automatic machinery, Fig. 40-29, has been developed. These machines are capable of spinning heavy sections of the "exotic" metals in quantities to close tolerances.

THE ADVANTAGES OF SPINNING

Spinning has many advantages over certain other types of metal forming:

1. The forms over which the metal is shaped can be made quickly and inexpensively of wood. They cost only a fraction of the investment involved in making tools and dies for other processes.

2. The forms can be made in days, and in some instances in hours, compared to the weeks

Fig. 40-28. *Hydraulic power with built-in "feel" enables the craftsman to shape extremely large, up to 200 in. in diameter, and heavy, aluminum up to 2 in. thick, into intricately shaped products.*

Fig. 40-29. *Automatic spinning machines are used to shape missile sections.*

Fig. 40-30. *A silver teapot made by the spinning process. (Henry J. Kauffman)*

and months when tools and dies have to be made.

3. Working the metal cold improves its physical characteristics.

4. Spinning is ideal for pilot production or product development. As an example, experimental missile nose cones can be made for a few hundred dollars instead of several thousand dollars that the next most economical method of metal forming would have cost. Changes were made quickly and easily.

USES FOR SPUN OBJECTS

While many inexpensive novelty items such as ash trays, flower pots and lamp shades are made by spinning, the majority of the items spun are used as components of major products like missiles, radar units, jet planes, tank trucks, air conditioning units and heating plants. The process is also used to produce some of the finer things of life--church goods, silver and pewter hollow ware, Fig. 40-30.

SHEAR SPINNING

Shear spinning is a metalworking technique that is similar to conventional spinning in outward appearance only. It is a cold extrusion process where the parts are shaped by rollers that exert tremendous pressures on a starting blank or preform and displace the metal parallel to the centerline of the workpiece. The metal is taken from the thickness of the blank, whereas in spinning, the metal is taken from the diameter of the blank, Fig. 40-31a and 40-31b. Instead of displacing the metal as in the shear spin technique, spinning folds it over and places it on or close to the spinning form.

The process, known commercially as FLO-TURN and HYDROSPIN, is well adapted for manu-

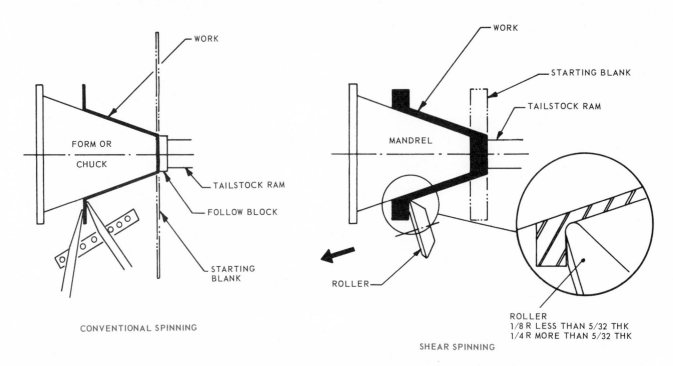

CONVENTIONAL SPINNING

SHEAR SPINNING

ROLLER
1/8 R LESS THAN 5/32 THK
1/4 R MORE THAN 5/32 THK

Fig. 40-31a. The difference between conventional spinning and shear spinning.

Fig. 40-31b. A 42-in. by 50-in. shear spinning machine producing a head for a missile motor case. When completely formed it will be 13-1/2 in. deep and 40 in. in diameter.
(Meta-Dynamics Div., Cincinnati Milling Machine Co.)

facturing parts for jet planes and missiles, Fig. 40-32a and 40-32b. Shear spinning is widely used because it has made it feasible to shape from a

Fig. 40-32a. Using the shear spinning technique to shape tail cone for the B-58 Hustler.
(Lodge & Shipley Co.)

single blank of metal parts that formerly had to be welded up of several pieces. The tolerances attained make it possible to eliminate much unwanted weight. Fine surface finishes that require little or no additional work can be obtained.

Templates are needed to guide the rollers and they maintain the proper relationship between the tool and mandrel making it possible to hold tolerances as close as 0.005 in. on diameters. Preforms, workpieces that have been partially shaped by forging, machining or one of the other metalworking processes, are used for increased economy.

Fig. 40-32b. *The B-58 Hustler. The tail cone (circled) was manufactured by the shear spin technique.*
(U. S. Air Force)

TEST YOUR KNOWLEDGE, Unit 40

1. Metal spinning is a method of working metal sheet into _____ _____ shapes.
2. The forming tool is positioned on a _____ _____ with a pin as the fulcrum point.
3. The metal disc may have to be annealed because _____ _____ _____ _____ during the spinning operation.
4. When a piece of metal is annealed it is _____.
5. The _____ chuck is used for spinning simple shapes.
6. The _____ _____ fits between the tail-stock center and the metal disc.
7. A lubricant is used to _____ _____ _____.
8. A bead is added to a spun object for appearance and to add strength. True or false?
9. Buckled or wrinkled pieces can often be straightened on the lathe. True or false?

10. A segmented chuck is used to spin deep forms. True or false?
11. Spinning makes it possible to form metal sheet into shapes that cannot be done economically by other methods. True or false?
12. Spinning can only be done by manual methods. True or false?
13. Only small items can be produced by spinning. True or false?
14. Shear spinning is a metalworking technique that is:
    a. Similar to spinning.
    b. Accomplished by using great pressures applied by rollers to displace the metal over the form.
    c. Accomplished by folding the metal back over the form with tremendous pressures.
    d. None of the above.

RESEARCH AND DEVELOPMENT

1. Develop a unit on spinning for your school shop if there is not one already in operation.
2. Prepare a display board showing the steps in spinning a simple coaster. Demonstrate to the class how you went about spinning it.
3. Secure samples of objects that were produced by spinning. Select novelty items, items used in the home or by industry and an item spun in pewter or silver.
4. Contact a firm that does spinning and inquire

what the term "spinning on air" means.
5. Present a motion picture on spinning to the class.
6. Prepare a series of slides on the spinning process. Emphasize the safety aspects.
7. Design a project that must be spun on a segmented chuck. Make the chuck and other necessary tools to spin the job. Prepare a display that will show the step-by-step procedures you followed to produce the item.

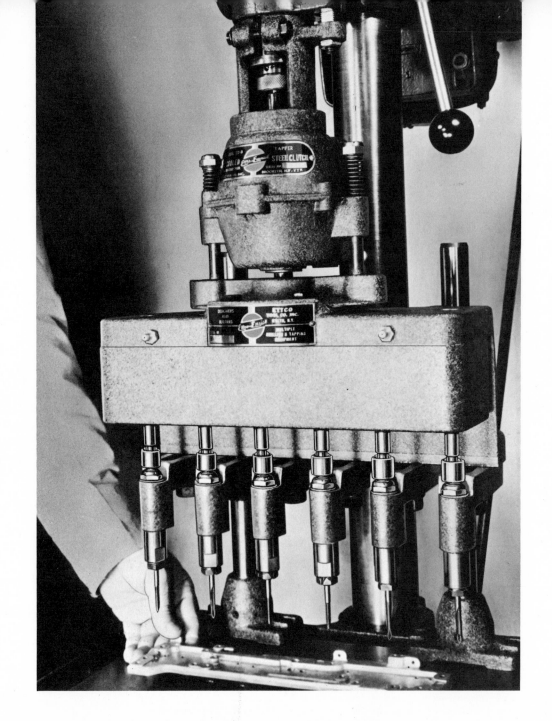

Industry photo--Multiple-spindle tapping attachment fitted to a drill press, is being used to tap small parts. (Ettco Tool & Machine Co.)

Unit 41

EXTRUSION PROCESSES

Two extrusion processes used to shape metal are HYDRAULIC EXTRUSION and IMPACT EXTRUSION.

Hydraulic Extrusion is employed to manufacture irregular shapes, both solid and hollow that cannot be made economically by any other process because of the design, Fig. 41-1. The second method which is known as IMPACT EXTRUSION, was used originally to form collapsible tubes--tooth paste, shaving cream, etc.,

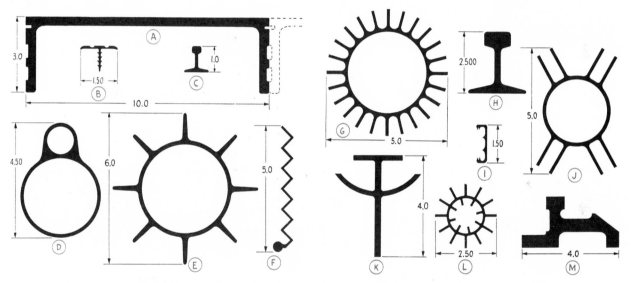

Fig. 41-1. The wide scope of extrusion applications is illustrated by this group of aluminum sections; (A) Diving board; (B) Table edge trim molding; (C) Rail for miniature railroad; (D) Milk bottle warmer; (E) Heat exchanger; (F) Window jalousy section; (G) Shape for pencil vending machine; (H) Mine track rail; (I) Price tag holder for grocery store shelves; (J) Hinge section for clothes drier; (K) Drip catcher for roofs of textile mills; (L) Heat exchanger; (M) Track rail for woolen mill.   (Reynolds Metals Co.)

Fig. 41-2. A large extrusion press. Notice how it compares in size to the operator.
(Reynolds Metals Co.)

Fig. 41-3. An extrusion die. Fitted into extrusion presses, dies shape aluminum and other metals into a wide variety of cross sections.

HYDRAULIC EXTRUSION of metal may be compared to the squeezing of frosting from a "cake frosting tube" when decorating a cake. The frosting as it comes from the tube assumes the shape of the nozzle on the end of the tube. In hydraulic extrusion metal is substituted for the frosting. A press actuated by hydraulic pressure is used in place of the tube and a die is employed to shape the metal. See Figs. 41-2, and 41-3.

The metal, known as an ingot or billet, is heated to a plastic (but not molten) state and is inserted in the press. Tremendous pressures are exerted on the metal and literally squeeze it through the die, Fig. 41-4. After forming the piece is cut to length and straightened. Some alloys require heat treatment to develop their maximum strength.

The extrusion process is an economical method of producing complex shapes.

The size of the extruded shape is limited by the press capacity. A press recently put into operation by the Air Force has made it possible to shape sections that will fit into a 24-in. circle, have a cross section area up to 75 square inches

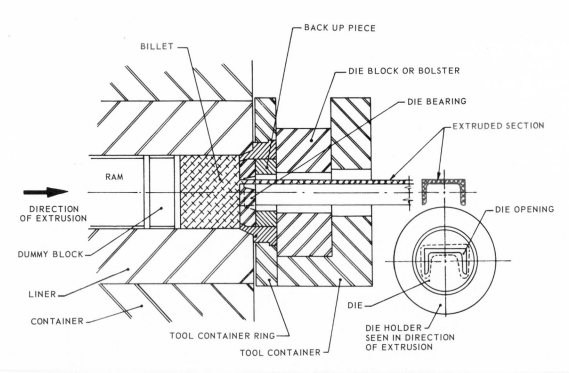

Fig. 41-4. A sectional view of an extrusion press showing the metal (billet) being extruded in the shape of a channel.

from tin and other soft metals. Today it has been developed to such a point that items weighing up to 100 lbs. have been formed by the impact extrusion process.

and weigh 25 lbs. per foot. Fig. 41-5, illustrates how sections wider than 24 in. can be made.

Extruded shapes are widely used in bus, truck and trailer body construction, aircraft

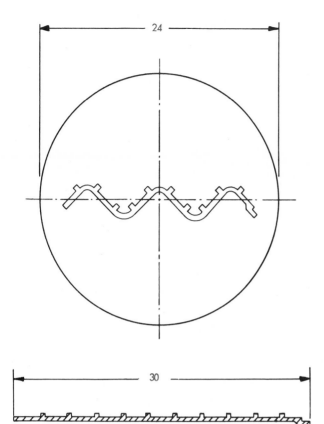

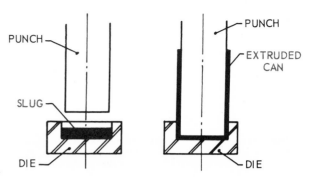

Fig. 41-6. A diagram of the impact extrusion process. A slug is placed in the die and the pressure is applied. The cycle occurs in 1/50 to 1/100 of a second.

Fig. 41-5. This drawing illustrates how sections larger than the diameter of the die may be formed. After extrusion the section is flattened as shown in the lower drawing. A floor section for a trailer truck is shown.

Fig. 41-7. A sampling of the large variety of sizes and shapes that can be formed by the impact extrusion process.

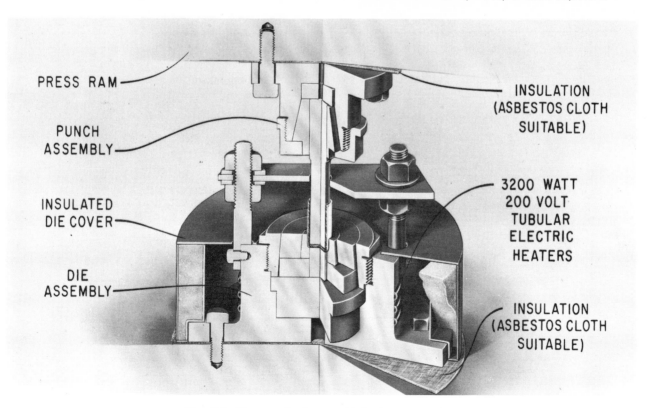

Fig. 41-8. Close-up of a die assembly for impact extrusion.
(Dow Chemical Co.)

and missile work, machine parts, bridge rails, storm windows, store fronts and other architectural applications.

The IMPACT EXTRUSION, Fig 41-6 process was introduced to the United States shortly after World War I. The process makes it possible to produce parts that can be round, square, oval or a combination of these shapes. The part can be solid or hollow, and vary in size from a thimble to an item several feet high and up to a foot in diameter, Fig. 41-7.

The process can be described as the making of a part by placing a disc or slug of metal into a die cavity and applying pressure with a punch, Fig. 41-8. The pressure (cycle occurs in 1/50 to 1/100 of a second) causes the metal to "squirt" up the side of the punch, the wall thickness of the part being determined by the clearance between the punch and the die.

The automatic extrusion press, Fig. 41-9, can produce 75 to 100 parts per minute.

Fig. 41-9. A Bliss 95 ton tube extruding press with a heating device to bring the metal slugs to the proper forming temperature.

TEST YOUR KNOWLEDGE, Unit 41

1. In the extrusion process, metal is heated to the plastic stage and literally_____ through a die of the required shape.
2. The size of the extrusion is governed by the _____of the extrusion press.
3. The_____extrusion process is used to produce the familiar tooth paste tube.

4. In the above process a disc or slug of metal is placed into a die cavity. When pressure is applied the metal:
   a. Squirts up the side of the punch.
   b. Is punched to shape.
   c. Is forced into a mold.
   d. None of the above.

RESEARCH AND DEVELOPMENT

1. Demonstrate the hydraulic extrusion process by using a tube of tooth paste as the press and supply of material. Cut different shaped openings in several caps to vary the cross section of the extruded material. The demonstration can also be performed with a cake frosting tube and plaster of Paris. CAUTION: Clean the tube before the plaster sets.

2. Develop a simple method to demonstrate the impact extrusion process. Modeling clay may be used in place of the metal slug.
3. Design a panel that illustrates samples of metal formed by the extrusion process. Use thin cross sections.
4. Make transparencies of the extrusion processes for use on the overhead projector.

Unit 42

FLAME SPRAYING

FLAME SPRAYING is the term that has been adopted to describe any process where a metal is brought to its melting point and sprayed onto a surface to produce a coating. These processes now include:

1. METALLIZING
2. THERMO SPRAY
3. PLASMA FLAME

The term METALLIZING describes the flame-spraying process that involves the use of metal in wire form. The wire is drawn through a special spray gun by a pair of powered feed rolls. The wire is melted in the gas flame and atomized by a blast of compressed air which also carries it to the previously prepared work surface, Fig. 42-1. Upon striking the surface the particles interlock or mesh to produce a coating of the desired metal. The surface must be cleaned and roughened before spraying, or the metal will not bond to it and build up to the desired thickness. Theoretically, there is no limit to the thickness that can be sprayed.

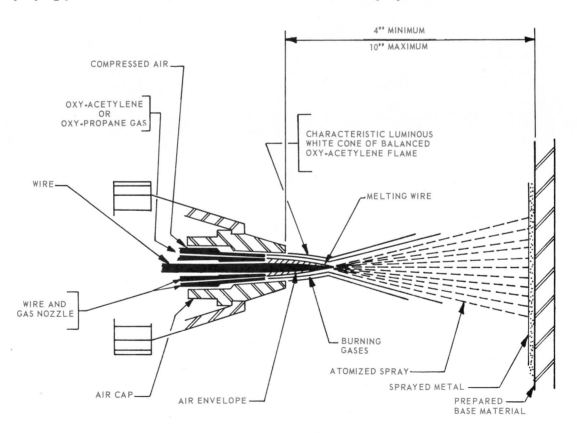

Fig. 42-1. The metallizing process. Wire is fed through a special spray gun, melted by a gas flame and atomized and sprayed onto the work by compressed air.

Since the air blast also acts to keep the sprayed surface cool, the process can be used to spray metal on wood and plastic either for decorative purposes or for protection.

Fig. 42-2. Two flame-spray guns applying stainless steel on a destroyer rudder post. Until the advent of this process this large expensive item would have had to be scrapped.
(Metco Inc.)

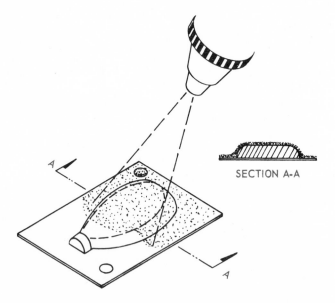

SECTION A-A

Fig. 42-3. Molds used to produce familiar plastic squeeze bottles are made by the flame-spray process. Inexpensive wood patterns are made and mounted onto a plate. The patterns are sprayed with a suitable parting compound to prevent the sprayed metal from adhering to it. The metal is sprayed onto a suitable thickness. The shells are s t r i p p e d from the patterns and are then backed with additional metal and a supporting frame to be mounted in molding machine.

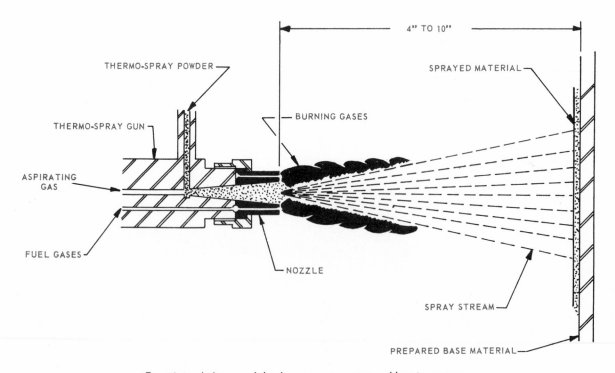

Fig. 42-4a. A diagram of the thermo-spray process and how it operates.

Any metal that can be drawn into wire form can be sprayed by this process.

Metallizing has been used for more than a quarter of a century and was used originally for repair and maintenance of machine parts. Today, it is used to apply protective corrosion resistant coatings of zinc and aluminum to steel surfaces; to build up worn bearings and shafts, Fig. 42-2, that might otherwise have to be discarded. The process is being used to apply a tough, wear resistant surface on the cylinder liners of lightweight gasoline engines. It is also being used to make molds for forming plastics and low melting temperature metals, Fig. 42-3. The electrical and electronic industry makes wide use of the metallizing process to prepare non-metallic materials for soldering.

The term THERMO SPRAY is used to describe the type of flame-spraying equipment which involves the application of metals, and other materials in powder form. The equipment makes it possible to flame-spray materials in powder form that cannot be drawn into wire, Fig. 42-4a and 42-4b. These special alloys are ideal for hard facing critical areas of parts that operate under severe conditions. They also can be used to spray high temperature refractories which are chemically inert in the highly corrosive conditions of the petrochemical industries.

In the PLASMA FLAME SPRAY PROCESS the spray gun utilizes an electric arc that is contained within a water-cooled jacket. An inert gas, passed through the arc, is "excited" to temperatures up to 30,000 deg. F. The plasma of ionized gas resembles an open oxyacetylene

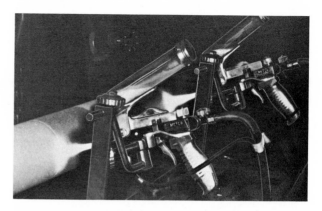

Fig. 42-4b. In this photo alumina powder is being applied to steel sheet mill carrier rolls. The purpose was to eliminate scale pick-up which was causing a production problem.
(Metco Inc.)

flame in shape and appearance. See Figs. 42-5a and 42-5b.

In general, most inorganic materials that can be melted without decomposition can be applied. The coatings applied by this process are, in many cases, superior to conventional flame-sprayed coatings.

Application of the process includes the spraying of rocket nozzles and nose cones with high melting point materials. The electronic and chemical industries make considerable use of the process.

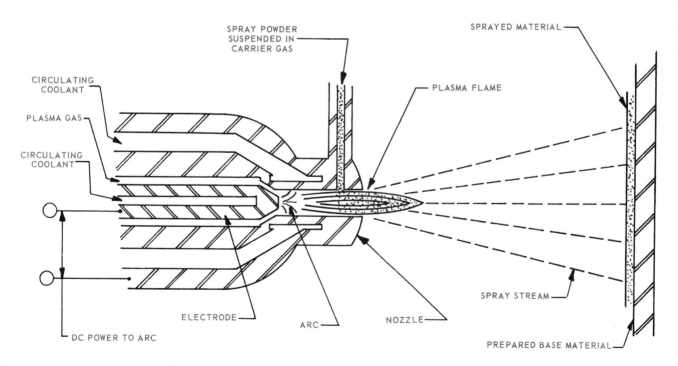

Fig. 42-5a. The plasma flame process, capable of temperatures up to 30,000 deg. F. can spray any material that will melt without decomposing.

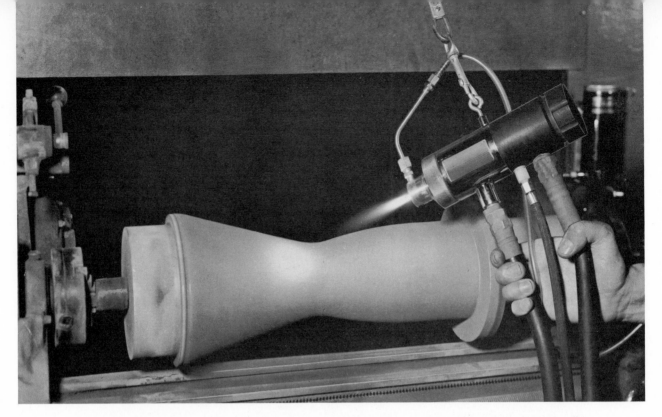

Fig. 42-5b. A missile cone being made by spraying metallic tungsten on a split mandrel using the plasma flame process. Salt is used as a separation coating and is then leached out with water. (Metco Inc.)

TEST YOUR KNOWLEDGE, Unit 42

1. Flame spray is the term used to describe the process that:
   a. Is an inexpensive way to remove old paint.
   b. Brings metal wire to its melting point whereupon it is sprayed onto a surface to produce a coating.
   c. Both of the above.
   d. None of the above.
2. _____describes the flame-spraying process that involves the use of metal in wire form.
3. The surface must be roughened but not necessarily cleaned before it is sprayed. True or false?
4. The surface must be cleaned and roughened before it is sprayed. True or false?
5. The surface does not have to be cleaned or roughened before it is sprayed. True or false?
6. Metallizing is used to:
   a. Apply corrosion resistant coatings of zinc and aluminum to steel surfaces.
   b. Build up worn bearings and shafts.
   c. Prepare non-metallic surfaces for soldering.
   d. None of the above.
   e. All of the above.

RESEARCH AND DEVELOPMENT

1. Secure an example of metal that has received a coating by the metallizing process. Examine a cross section of it under a microscope. Make a sketch or a transparency for use on the overhead projector of what was observed.
2. Make transparencies for use on the overhead projector on the three basic techniques of flame spraying. These can be used for future demonstrations and class discussions on the basic metalworking processes.
3. Demonstrate the flame spray process to the class. Roughen a piece of steel rod while it is in the lathe. Spray it with aluminum paint

from a spray can until a 1/32 in. thick covering has been built up. Machine it until it is true.

CAUTION: Cover the lathe to protect it from the spray.

4. Plan a visit to a local industry that uses the flame spray process. Use a portable tape recorder, if one is available, to record the sound of the various processes. Use the recording with the transparencies described in #2 above.

Unit 43

ELECTRICAL DISCHARGE MACHINING

Electrical Machining, Electro Erosion or Electrical Discharge Machining is a process where hard, tough, fragile and heat sensitive metals that are difficult or impossible to machine by conventional processes can be worked. Die blanks can be worked in heat treated condi-

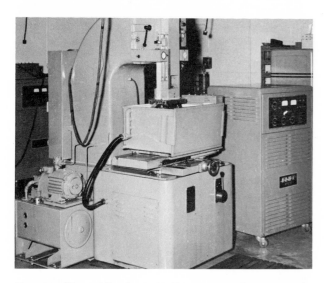

Fig. 43-1. Electric Discharge Machining unit and power supply. The electrode or tool is fitted to the vertical arm and the work is enclosed in the trough. (Elox Corp. of Mich.)

tion eliminating warpage and distortion that frequently occurs during the heat treating process. Superhard metals that previously could not be worked, are readily worked to tolerances as small as 0.0005 in. with very fine surface finishes.

HOW IT WORKS. Almost everyone is familiar with the sparking and arcing that takes place when an electrical switch is turned on or off. "Pitting" or "burning" such as occurs on the switch contacts, is the basis of electric discharge machining, Fig. 43-1.

An electrical discharge unit, Fig. 43-2 is composed of a power supply to provide direct current and a method to control voltage and

frequency; an electrode of the proper configuration - the electrode, usually yellow brass, can be compared with the cutting tool in conventional machining; a servo mechanism to accurately control the movement of the electrode to maintain the correct distance between it and the work as the machining is done; a coolant, usually a light oil, that forms a dielectric barrier between the electrode, and the work at the arc gap.

The servomechanism maintains a very thin gas (about 0.001 in.) between the electrode and the work. These are submerged in a fluid (dielectric) that is a non-conductor. When the voltage across the gap reaches a point sufficient to cause the dielectric to break down, an arc occurs. Each spark erodes a minute piece of metal, but as the sparking occurs 20,000 to 30,000 times per second, appreciable quantities

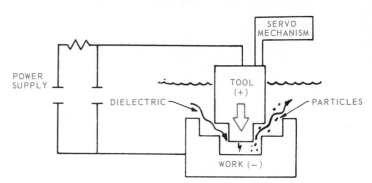

Fig. 43-2. A diagram showing the principle used by the Electric Discharge Machining process.

of metal are removed. The dielectric fluid also flushes the particles from the gap, and keeps the tool and work cool.

The process is used for shaping and sharpening carbide cutting tools, machining the very hard metals used in missile construction, and other applications where the physical characteristics of the metal or its use makes it impossible, or very expensive, to machine by conventional methods.

TEST YOUR KNOWLEDGE, Unit 43

1. Electrical discharge machining makes it possible to machine:
   a. Hard materials.
   b. Fragile materials.
   c. Materials that are difficult or impossible to machine by any other process.
   d. All of the above.
   e. None of the above.
2. The electrical machine is made up of the following units:
   a._____.
   b._____.
   c._____.
   d._____.
   e._____.
3. The_____also helps to flush the particles from between the tool and work.
4. The servomechanism does the following:
   a. Provides the power for the arcing.
   b. Keeps the work and electrode cool.
   c. Controls the movement of the electrode.
   d. All of the above.

RESEARCH AND DEVELOPMENT

1. Secure samples of superhard and/or fragile metals. (Examples - carbide cutting tools, stainless steel or aluminum honeycomb, etc.) Try to work them with conventional hand tools. What difficulties did you encounter? Prepare a short report on your success or failure in working these materials.
2. Some of the larger tool and metalworking machinery supply houses have demonstration models of electrical discharge machining units. Contact such firms and try to borrow samples of metals worked by this process along with the electrodes used.
3. Make a collection of material on this machining technique for the shop industrial process file.
4. Demonstrate the process to the class by using an electric pencil (tool used to burn or etch identifying information on tools).
   CAUTION: Do not use a dielectric fluid with this pencil. Follow the manufacturer's instructions on how to use the tool.

Unit 44

EXPLOSIVE FORMING

An advanced industrial technique of exploding sheet metal into a shaped, finished part has been developed by the missile industry.

Because of their sheer size, up to 8 by 15 ft. many missile components cannot be formed on existing presses. The presses are either too small, or are not powerful enough to provide the pressure required to fabricate high-strength space age metals.

The main advantage of the explosive forming process is that it eliminates many of the welds which, until its introduction, were required to form certain parts. The welds, always possible trouble spots in a structure, reduce reliability and economy.

Fig. 44-2. Welding the preform of a torus (donut) shape tank for explosive forming. This is the first step in the process. Formed conventionally it would require forty sections rather than twelve and would require 60 per cent more weld footage.
(Martin Co.)

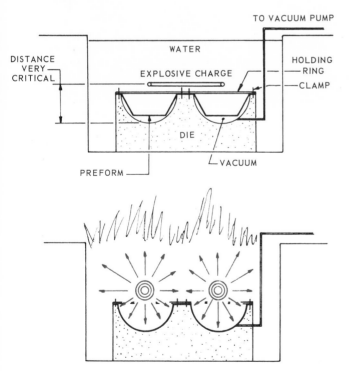

Fig. 44-1. Diagram which shows principle of the Explosive Forming process. Fifty cents worth of explosives, in some applications, will do the work of a press that costs thousands of dollars.

Explosive forming utilizes the pressure wave generated by an explosion in a fluid to force the stock being formed against the walls of the die, Fig. 44-1. The fluid has the effect of rounding off the pressure pulse generated by the detonation. The piece is fabricated to a shape determined by the contours of the finished piece Fig. 44-2. It is placed in a die, filled with water and an explosive charge is suspended in it. A large holding ring, clamped over the outer edge of the work assures the necessary seal for drawing a vacuum in the die.

When detonated, the explosion forces the walls of the piece against the walls of the die, Fig. 44-3.

The nature of the explosive charge was among the most difficult problems to solve in perfecting the new process. It can range from a blasting cap to several pounds of high explosives. It can

Fig. 44-3. Once resembling a cake pan, the exploded metal now is torus, or donut-shaped. Engineers examine the inner contour of the formed part, removed from the die underneath. Metal clamps around the edge of the die secured a holding ring which assured the necessary tight seal for drawing a vacuum into the die during explosion. (Martin Co.)

be shaped in many different ways including a tube, rod, ball or sheet.

The distance between the charge and the metal preform also is of critical importance. When the charge is too far away portions of the work piece may be stretched beyond their limitations.

TEST YOUR KNOWLEDGE, Unit 44

1. List two of the main advantages of explosive forming:
   a._____.
   b._____.
2. Explosive forming:
   a. Utilizes the pressure wave generated by an explosion in a fluid to force the metal into the die.
   b. Utilizes the power of an explosion in a die to form the metal to shape.
   c. Neither of the above.
   d. Both of the above.

RESEARCH AND DEVELOPMENT

1. Because of the nature of explosive forming, it is not recommended that students experiment with this metalworking process.

2. See if explosive forming is done by manufacturers in your area. If so, arrange for a visit, and report your findings to your class.

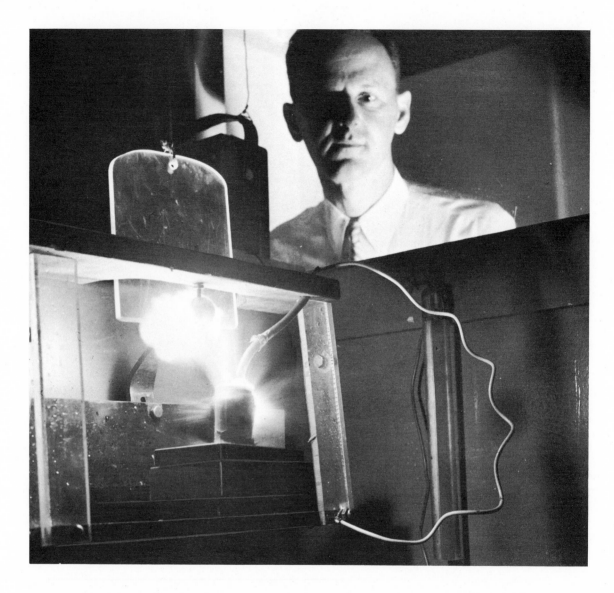

The mechanical engineer designs and develops new machines, devices, manufacturing and fabricating techniques. Here the engineer is developing a technique for forming space-age metals by explosive forming. (Republic Aviation Corp.)

Unit 45

CHEMICAL MILLING

Chemical milling, chem-milling or contour etching is a recognized and accepted technique for controlled removal of metals by chemicals rather than by conventional machine milling.

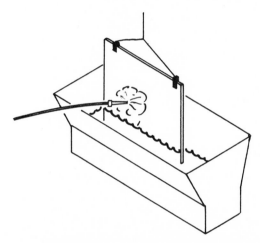

Fig. 45-1. CLEANING. *The entire part is cleaned to remove all grease or dirt that will affect the etching process.*

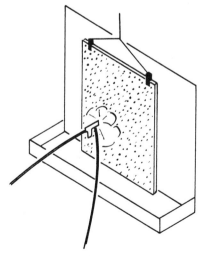

Fig. 45-2. MASKING. *After cleaning and drying, the entire part is coated with a maskant material. This can be applied by brushing, dipping, spraying or roller coating.*

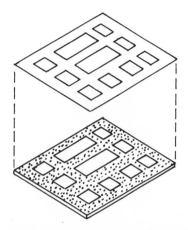

Fig. 45-3. SCRIBING and STRIPPING. *A template is placed over the part and areas to be exposed to the etch are circumscribed and the masking material stripped away.*

This process is used to remove metal to exacting tolerances, on parts that are shaped in such a manner that conventional machining methods would be extremely difficult. Chem-milling is not a rival to conventional milling; both processes should be considered complimentary.

Basically, chem-milling is a process in which the part is immersed in an etchant (usually a strong alkaline solution) where the resulting chemical action removes the desired metal. The immersion time must be carefully controlled. Areas that are not to be subjected to metal removal must be protected by materials (masks) which do not react to the etching solution.

STEPS IN THE PROCESS:

The principal steps in chem-milling are shown in Figs. 45-1 to 45-6.

ADVANTAGES OF CHEM-MILLING:

1. Tooling costs are low.
2. Tolerances of plus or minus 0.003 in. are

obtainable on cuts of 0.125 in. or less. On deeper cuts the tolerances are plus or minus 0.005 in.

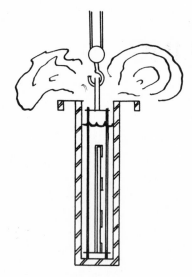

Fig. 45-4. ETCHING. *The parts are racked and lowered into the etchant for the milling operation.*

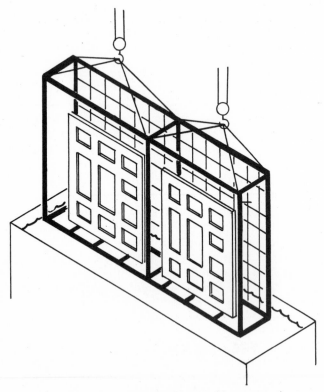

Fig. 45-5. RINSING *and* SOLVENT STRIP. *After rinsing, the parts are lowered into the solvent tank which releases the maskant bond and the residue of the maskant is stripped from the part.*

3. The only size limitations imposed is by the size of the immersion tanks available.

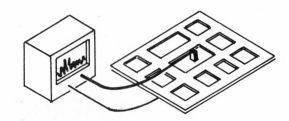

Fig. 45-6. INSPECTION. *The accuracy of depth of chemical milling cut is measured with the aid of an ultrasonic thickness gauge.*

4. Warping is negligible.
5. Contoured or shaped parts can be etched after they have been formed, Fig. 45-7.
6. Many parts can be produced simultaneously.
7. Sections as thin as 0.0005 in. can be machined without danger of buckling.

DISADVANTAGES:

1. Process is slow and takes considerable time to remove large quantities of metal.
2. All surface imperfections must be re-

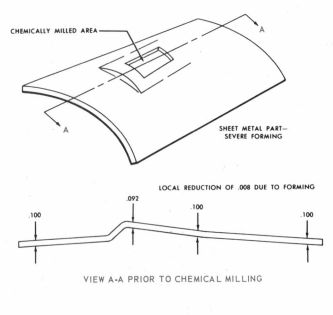

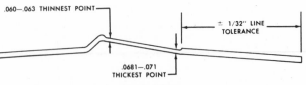

Fig. 45-7. *This aircraft part was chem-milled after it was formed. Pieces more severely formed than this part have been milled economically.*
(Grumman Aircraft Engineering Corp.)

moved before etching. These areas etch at a different rate and are amplified on the finished surface.

3. A l u m i n u m castings cannot be chem-milled.
4. Not recommended for etching holes.
5. Surface finishes on deep etches are not comparable with machined surfaces.

PRESENT USES IN INDUSTRY

Chemical milling is becoming increasingly more important in the manufacture of high speed aircraft and missiles. The supertough metals used on these items are very difficult to machine by conventional methods. Most of these metals can be machined by this process.

TEST YOUR KNOWLEDGE, Unit 45

1. Chemical milling is the process that:
   a. Removes metal chemically rather than by conventional machining.
   b. Is arrival to conventional milling.
   c. Immerses metal into a liquid. The liquid is heated to remove the metal.
   d. None of the above.
   e. All of the above.

2. The_____ _____ must be controlled carefully or too much metal will be removed.
3. A mask must be used to protect the portion of the job that is:
   a. Not to be etched.
   b. To be etched.
   c. To be cleaned.
   d. None of the above.

RESEARCH AND DEVELOPMENT

1. Prepare a series of transparencies for use with the overhead projector that shows the chemical milling sequence.
2. Secure information on the subject from tech-

nical magazines and prepare a short paper, duplicate it for the class if possible, on the latest developments in this area. Make drawings of several parts machined by the process.

Safety Precaution--DO NOT attempt to operate the metal lathe (or any other machine) until all guards are in place.

Unit 46

POWDER METALLURGY
(Sintering)

The technique of fabricating parts from metal powders, usually known as SINTERINGS or POWDER METALLURGY, Fig. 46-1, was developed in the late twenties by the automotive industry. While the process is relatively unknown to the average person it is widely used by industry for applications such as:

1. Self-lubricating bearings and bearing materials.
2. Precision finished machine parts, gears,

jet and missile applications that require the heat resistance of ceramics and the heat transfer qualities of metals and special cutting tools (Cermets).

d. High density counterweights for missile instruments that require maximum weight concentrated in a minimum space.

The first phase in the manufacture of powder metal products is the careful mixing of high

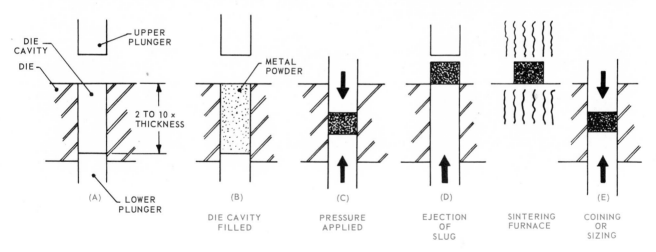

Fig. 46-1. Steps in fabricating an article by the powder metallurgy process: (A) Cross section of die and die cavity. Depth of cavity is determined by thickness of required part, and amount of pressure that will be applied. (B) Die cavity is filled with proper metal powder mixture. (C) Pressure as high as 50 tons per square inch is applied. (D) Briquette is pushed from the die cavity. (E) Pieces are then passed through a sintering furnace to convert them into a strong useful product. (F) Some pieces can be used as they come from the furnace. Others, may require a coining or sizing operation to bring them to exact size and to improve their surface finish.

cams, ratchets, etc., with tolerances as close as $\pm$ .0005 in.
3. Permanent metal filters.
4. Fabricating materials that are very difficult to work by other methods:
    a. Tough cutting tools (Tungsten Carbide).
    b. Supermagnets (Aluminum-Nickel Alloys-Alnico).
    c. Mixtures of metals and ceramics for

purity metal powder. The powders are carefully weighed and thoroughly mixed into a blend of correct proportions. Many materials - iron, steel, stainless steel, brass, bronze, nickel, chromium and combinations of these metals and non-metals, can be used for sinterings.

The powder blend is then fed into a precision die with a cavity that is the shape, and several times deeper than the thickness, of the desired

Fig. 46-2. Briquetting presses in operation.
(American Sinterings)

Fig. 46-2a. Close-up of the briquetting press showing "green compacts" moving to the furnace.
(Delco Moraine, Div. of General Motors Corp.)

Fig. 46-3. This sintering furnace permits continuous operation. Atmosphere within the furnace is carefully controlled to prevent oxidation or contamination of the sinterings. (Delco Moraine, Div. General Motors Corp.)

piece and is compressed by a lower and upper punch, Fig. 46-2. Pressures applied range from 15 to 50 tons per square inch. This portion of the operation is known as BRIQUETTING. See Fig. 46-2 and 46-2a.

The piece as ejected from the die appears to be solid metal; however, it is quite brittle and fragile and will crumble if not handled carefully.

To transform the briquette or "green compact" into a strong useful unit it must be "sintered" at 1500 to 2300 deg. F. from 30 minutes to 2 hours, depending upon the metals, in a carefully controlled atmosphere furnace, Fig. 46-3.

Many parts can be used as they come from the furnace, Fig. 46-4, however, because of shrinkage and distortion caused by the heating

Fig. 46-4. The finished pieces emerging from the sintering furnace. They may be used as is, or they may require additional operations to make them usable.

Powder Metallurgy
(Sintering)

operation the pieces are subjected to a sizing or coining operation. This consists of pressing the sintered pieces into accurate dies to obtain precision finish dimensions, higher densities and smoother surface finishes.

The tool cost is moderate and the process is best suited to quantity production. If production quantities exceed several thousand units, the finished piece can frequently be produced at less than the cost of rough sand castings.

Powder metal parts can be drilled, tapped, plated, heat treated, ground and machined.

TEST YOUR KNOWLEDGE, Unit 46

1. The technique of fabricating parts from metal powders is known as sintering or_____
   _____.
2. The process is used to make:
   a. Self-lubricating bearings.
   b. Precision finished machine parts.
   c. Permanent metal filters.
   d. All of the above.
   e. None of the above.
3. List the steps in making an object by the sintering process.
   a._____.
   b._____.
   c._____.
   d._____.
4. Metal parts made by the sintering process can be machined like other metal. True or false?
5. The process is not suited for quantity production. True or false?

RESEARCH AND DEVELOPMENT

1. Secure a bearing made by the sintering process, and a filter made by the same process. The filters on the fuel lines of some automobiles are made by this process. Such a filter has the ability to separate water from gasoline.) Examine filters under a microscope. Make a sketch, with details exaggerated, reproduce it on a duplicator. Distribute the copies to the class.
2. Contact a firm that makes metal products by the sintering process and request samples of the various sintering stages. Prepare a display panel using these samples for the class bulletin board.

In the cold metal forming process, flat strip is passed
through a series of rolls that form it into its final shape.
(Yoder Co.)

Unit 47

COLD FORMING
METAL SHEET

STAMPING is the term used for many press forming operations. The process can be divided into two separate classifications: CUTTING and FORMING. Both operations, although separate and distinct, can be done on the same machine with only minor modifications.

CUTTING OPERATIONS

CUTTING is a process where the metal is cut or sheared by the action of the tool. Two cutting techniques have been developed for volume production:

Fig. 47-1a. Powered shears used for blanking. (Cincinnati Shaper Co.)

Fig. 47-1b. Straight shearing of polished stainless steel sheet. Felt under the hold down protects the finished surface. (Allegheny Ludlum Steel Corp.)

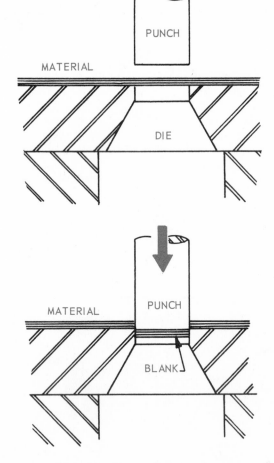

Fig. 47-2a. The punching operation.

BLANKING

Blanking, Fig. 47-1a and 1b, involves cutting flat sheet metal to the shape and size of the finished part. Subsequent forming operations may follow.

PUNCHING

Punching, Fig. 47-2, is a partial blanking process. It is used in progressive die work, Fig. 47-3a and 3b, where each stage of the operation cuts a portion of the blank, but leaves small connections so the piece can be transferred to the next stage.

Fig. 47-2b. CUTTING TO OUTLINE – Flat rolled blanks are fed to a machine which punches out the piece close to its final shape. Note safety device on operator's right hand that will not permit the machine to operate when he is placing the blank into position.

Fig. 47-2c. BLANKING – Blanking is the first operation in making spoons and forks. This operation produces a blank of the required size and shape as required to manufacture a piece of flatware. (International Silver Co.)

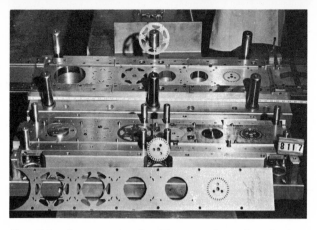

Fig. 47-3a. A progressive die. The strip of metal in the foreground shows the various steps in punching the electric motor part in the background. (Lamina Dies and Tools, Inc.)

Fig. 47-3b. Punch and die for a progressive punching operation. (Allegheny Ludlum Steel Corp.)

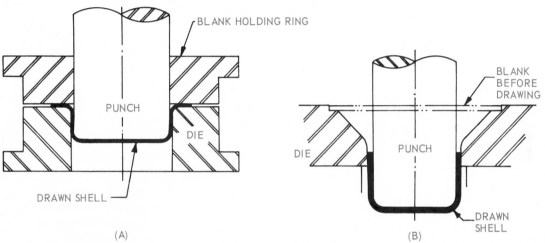

(A)

BLANK HOLDING RING

PUNCH

DIE

DRAWN SHELL

BLANK BEFORE DRAWING

DIE

PUNCH

DRAWN SHELL

(B)

Fig. 47-4a. The drawing process.

Fig. 47-4b. A draw press. (Niagara Machine and Tool Works)

FORMING

FORMING is a process where flat metal blanks are utilized to form the piece. It requires the use of presses and dies. A few of the more widely used forming techniques are:

DRAW PRESS

The draw press operation, Fig. 47-4a, 4b, and 4c, is the drawing operation performed on either mechanical or hydraulic presses employing a matched punch and die set.

Fig. 47-4c. A sequence of drawing operations as required in forming a pen cap. (Allegheny Ludlum Steel Corp.)

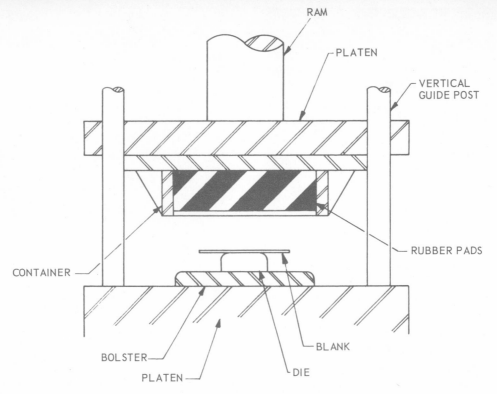

Fig. 47-5a. A diagram of the Guerin process. The rubber pad forms the female die.

GUERIN PROCESS

The Guerin process, Fig. 47-5a and 5b, is used for forming shallow parts in rubber dies rather than metal dies. Several thin rubber mats are mounted in a container attached to the ram. The rubber form compresses as the ram is lowered and forces the metal blank to assume the shape of the form block.

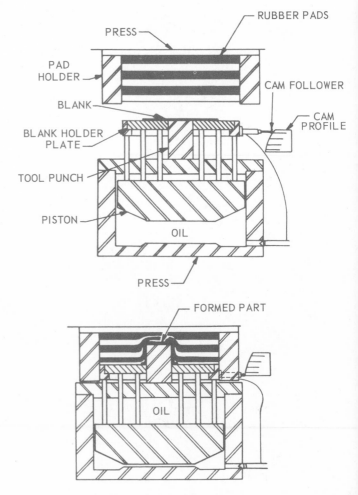

Fig. 47-6a. The Marform process.

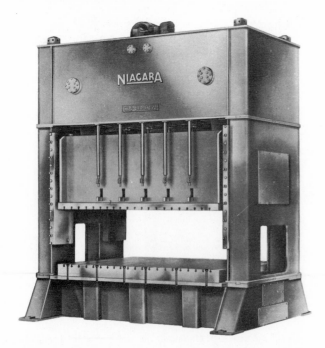

Fig. 47-5b. Press used to form metal sheet by the Guerin process.

MARFORM PROCESS

Marform, Fig. 47-6, is similar to the Guerin process but is used for deep drawing. The rubber pad is forced down against a flat blank which

Fig. 47-7a. Production type Hydroform machine. This can be rapidly converted to a conventional press. (Meta-Dynamics Div., Cincinnati Milling Machine Co.)

rests on the BLANK SUPPORT PLATE. As downward pressure mounts, the blank support plate is slowly lowered forcing the metal blank to take the shape of the male die.

The Marform process is a development of the Martin-Marietta Co.

HYDROFORMING

Hydroforming, Fig. 47-7a and 7b, differs from the Guerin and Marform processes in that a rubber diaphram, backed up by hydraulic pres-

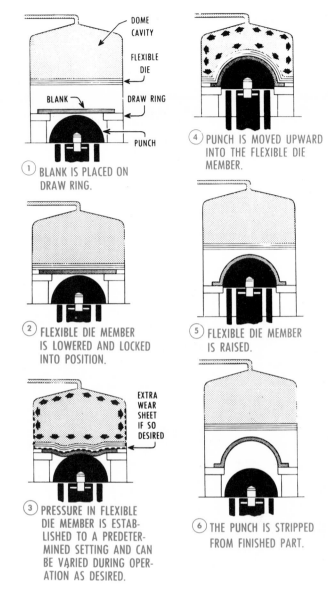

① BLANK IS PLACED ON DRAW RING.

② FLEXIBLE DIE MEMBER IS LOWERED AND LOCKED INTO POSITION.

③ PRESSURE IN FLEXIBLE DIE MEMBER IS ESTABLISHED TO A PREDETERMINED SETTING AND CAN BE VARIED DURING OPERATION AS DESIRED.

④ PUNCH IS MOVED UPWARD INTO THE FLEXIBLE DIE MEMBER.

⑤ FLEXIBLE DIE MEMBER IS RAISED.

⑥ THE PUNCH IS STRIPPED FROM FINISHED PART.

Fig. 47-7b. A diagram of the Hydroform process. (Allegheny Ludlum Steel Corp.)

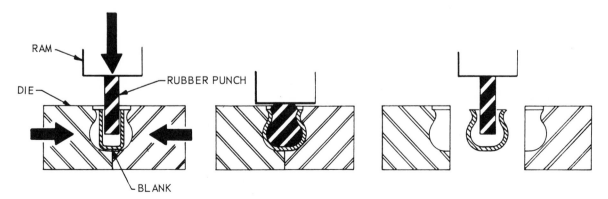

Fig. 47-8a. Bulging or entrapped rubber forming process.

sure, replaces the solid rubber pad. Deeper draws can be made by this process and only two

Fig. 47-8b. Hub caps produced by the bulging or entrapped rubber forming process. (Allegheny Ludlum Steel Corp.)

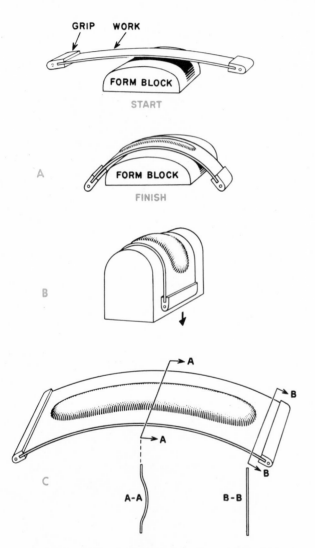

Fig. 47-9. A. Relative positions of work. Form block and clamps at start and finish of a typical stretch forming operation produce a raised rib. B. A typical shape produced by stretch forming over a form block. C. A stretch-formed shape similar to that of the bottom of a canoe. (Allegheny Ludlum Steel Corp.)

parts, the punch and draw ring, are needed for the tool. The Hydroform process is a product of the Cincinnati Milling Machine Co.

BULGING

Bulging, Fig. 47-8a and 8b, is sometimes referred to as entrapped rubber forming. The illustrations are self-explanatory.

STRETCH FORMING

Stretch forming, Fig. 47-9, is a process where a metal blank is gripped by inserting opposite edges in clamps and subjecting it to a light pull in such a way as to cause it to hug or to wrap around a form block of the desired shape. The piece is trimmed to final shape after

Fig. 47-10. Forming brake. (Niagara Machine and Tool Works)

Fig. 47-11. Typical bending operations possible on press brake equipment. (Allegheny Ludlum Steel Corp.)

Fig. 47-12. Bending operation being performed on press brake equipment.

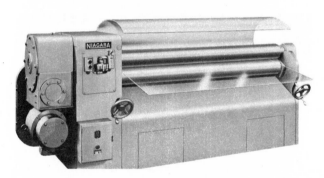

Fig. 47-13. Forming rolls.

the forming operation is completed. The technique is used to form the leading edge of aircraft wings and tail surfaces.

BENDING

Bending is the operation in which the surface area of the work is not appreciably changed. Types of conventional bending include the BRAKE, Fig. 47-10. (Figs. 47-11, 47-12, includes a few typical bending operations that are possible on press brake equipment.) FORMING ROLLS, Fig. 47-13, and TUBE BENDERS, Fig. 47-14a, 14b and 14c.

COLD ROLL FORMING

Cold roll forming, Fig. 47-15a and 15b, is a process in which flat strip is passed through a

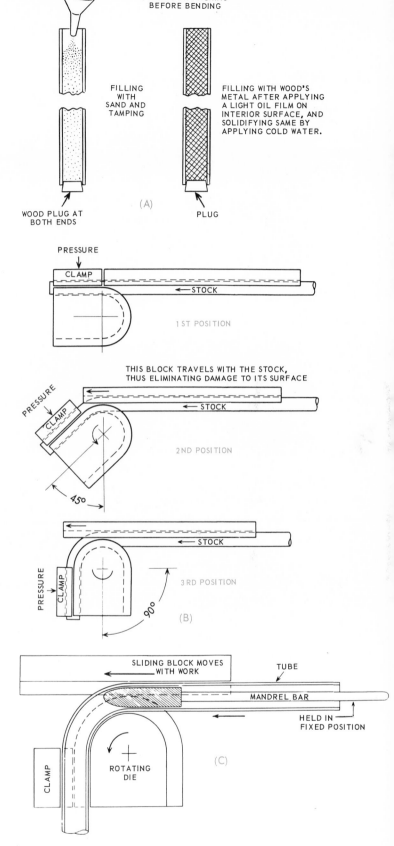

Fig. 47-14. Diagrammatic layout of the rotating die tubing bending technique. (A) Preparing the tube for bending. The filler material prevents the tube from collapsing during the forming operation. (B) Steps in bending a tube. (C) It is not necessary to fill the tube before bending if the reinforcing mandrel is used.
(Allegheny Ludlum Steel Corp.)

Fig. 47-15a. A roll forming machine. Note how the rolls progressively form the sheet. (Yoder Co.)

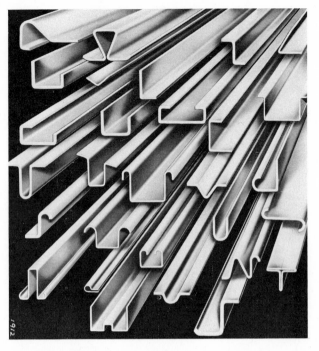

Fig. 47-15b. Typical shapes made by the roll forming process.

series of rolls that progressively form it into its final shape. The process is extremely rapid and almost any desired configuration is possible.

TEST YOUR KNOWLEDGE, Unit 47

1. Cold forming may be classified into two separate classifications:
   a._____.
   b._____.
2. Both operations can be done on the same machine. True or false?
3. Blanking involves:
   a. Cutting flat sheet metal to shape and size.
   b. Cutting a portion of the blank but leaves small connections so that the piece can be transferred to the next stage.
   c. Rolling the metal to form.
   d. None of the above.
   e. All of the above.

4. Punching involves:
   a. Cutting flat sheet metal to shape and size.
   b. Cutting a portion of the blank but leaves small connections so that the piece can be transferred to the next stage.
   c. Rolling the metal to form.
   d. None of the above.
   e. All of the above.
5. The drawing operation employs a matched _____ and _____ set.
6. Bulging is used to form hub caps. True or false?
7. Cold forming is the process in which _____ _____.

RESEARCH AND DEVELOPMENT

1. Design a simple blanking die to make tool checks.
2. Secure samples of progressive die products from a local manufacturer. Try to get sections showing the various stages of the operation.

3. Secure samples of the drawing process at various stages of the draw. Mount them on a panel in sequence.
4. Develop a simple design, a small tray, coaster, etc., and produce it by the Guerin

process. Use an arbor press for pressure. If this is not suitable, design a hydraulic press that makes use of a hydraulic auto jack.

5. Use the same equipment and demonstrate the bulging process.
6. Design simple equipment to demonstrate stretch forming, use offset printing plates or heavy gauge aluminum foil for material. Produce a wing section for a model airplane.
7. Make the equipment to demonstrate tube bending. Use hardwood dies.
8. Secure samples of products made by the various cold forming processes. Mount them according to family - cutting and forming.

Industry photo--A cylindrical grind-
er. This model is tape controlled.
(Covel Mfg. Co.)

Unit 48

AUTOMATION

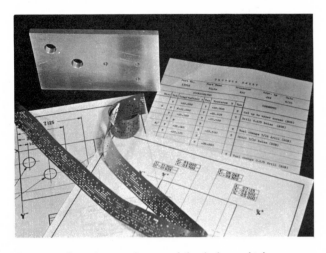

Fig. 48-1. Aircraft part shown at left of photo which was produced on a tape-controlled machine tool, tape, process sheet and drawings which indicate locations of holes in the part.

The trend in recent years has been the development and adaptation by industry of fantastic and excitingly new methods of producing goods.

NUMERICAL CONTROL (N/C) is one such development. This facet of AUTOMATION can be described as a method of operating machine tools with electronic devices activated by numbers in the form of holes punched in a paper or plastic tape, Fig. 48-1. The machine shown in Fig. 48-2, is numerically controlled in the X, Y and Z axes, Fig. 48-2a, and receives its instructions from such a tape rather than from the operator.

To perform cutting operations on a conventional machine, the machinist studies the blueprint, mounts the work and positions it for machining, by moving one or more lead screws. He then selects the proper cutting speeds and

Fig. 48-2. Numerically controlled machine tool is being used to shape complex helicopter gear box. At left, programmer studies statements describing surfaces of the part. Only 180 such statements were needed to produce more than 8,000 detailed instructions for the tool to follow in milling the part. (IBM)

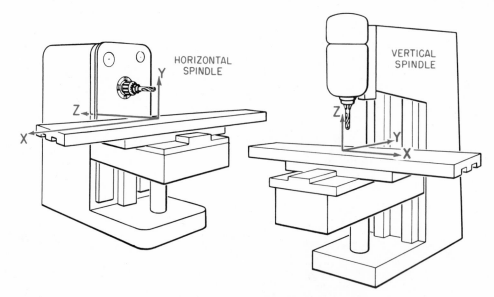

Fig. 48-2a. Axes of machine tool movement. (IBM)

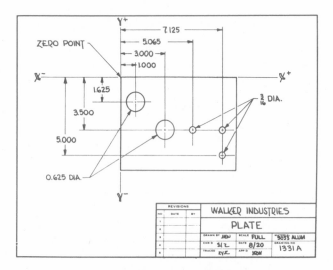

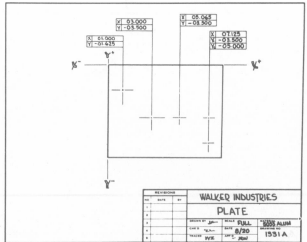

Fig. 48-3. Operations required to machine the aircraft part shown in Fig. 48-1, have been converted into a series of numbers and symbols.

feeds the cutter into the work. He does all these things according to the specifications indicated on the blueprint.

In NUMERICAL CONTROL, all of these movements are controlled automatically by electric motors connected to the lead and feed screws of the machine. They provide the power that positions the work and feeds the cutter. The punched tape controls the current to the motors and tells them when to start, how far to turn, and exactly where to stop. The unit that controls the feed, speed and in some instances the type of cutter, is also activated by the tape.

In principle, the purpose served by a perforated tape on a machine tool, is comparable to that of a perforated paper roll used on a player piano. On a player piano, each hole across the roll width matches a key on the piano keyboard. When the hole in the roll aligns with a corresponding hole in the air supply, a jet of air activates that key (makes it play). By arranging the holes in proper sequence, the piano can play almost any musical selection.

The same applies when positioning a piece by N/C. The information is PROGRAMMED into the tape by converting each machining operation into a series of numbers and symbols which corresponds to the COORDINATES or path the cutting tool must follow, Fig. 48-3. The coordinates are transferred to a PROCESS SHEET, Fig. 48-4. This material is then coded and punched in the tape on the TAPE PUNCH MACHINE, Fig. 48-5. These operations correspond to the positioning that would be done by a human operator.

As the tape is fed through the TAPE READER,

PROCESS SHEET

PART NO.		PART NAME		PROCESSOR	APPR. BY	DATE.	
COORDINATES					COMMENTS		
M I S C	T A B	LONGITUDINAL X	T A B	TRANSVERSE Y	T A B		
	T	+00.000	T	+00.000	T	SET UP TO UPPER CORNER	
%	T	%+01.000	T	−01.625	T	DRILL 0.625 HOLES (EOB)	
	T	+03.000	T	−03.500			
	T	¢	T		T	TOOL CHANGE 3/16 DRILL (EOB)	
¢/	T	+05.065	T	−03.500	T	DRILL 3/16 HOLES (EOB)	
	T	+07.125	T				
			T	−05.000			
		¢/	T		T	TOOL CHANGE 0.625 DRILL (EOB)	

PROCESS SHEET

		Part No. 1331A		Part Name Plate		Processor KJC		Appr. by JRW		Date 8/20
COORDINATES								COMMENTS		
Misc	Tab	Longitudinal X	Tab	Traverse Y	Tab					
	T	+00.000	T	+00.000	T	Set up to upper corner (EOB)				
%	T	%+01.000	T	−01.625	T	Drill 0.625 holes (EOB)				
	T	+03.000	T	−03.500						
	T	&	T		T	Tool change 3/16 drill (EOB)				
&/	T	+05.065	T	−03.500	T	Drill 3/16 holes (EOB)				
	T	+07.125	T							
			T	−05.000						
		&/	T		T	Tool change 0.625 drill (EOB)				

Fig. 48-4. Information given in Fig. 48-3, is transferred to process sheet.

it passes under a series of stiff wire fingers (compressed air or a photo electric cell may also be used to trigger the circuit). Each time a hole appears a finger drops through and pushes a small key. The key is connected to an elec-

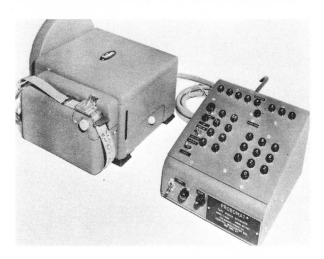

Fig. 48-5. Device that punches on tape which guides the machine through its machining cycle.
(Warner Swasey Co.)

tronic circuit. When it is pushed an electrical pulse is transmitted to a sensing device on the controls which "tells" the worktable when to move, in what direction and how far. Pulses also

Electronic equipment as used to control delivery of ingots, Fairless Works, U. S. Steel Corp.

control other machine functions. Pulse combinations and frequency does the positioning with great accuracy. Fig. 48-6, illustrates one such

drilling, spot welding, straight-line milling, etc.) is the simpler of the two. Unless it is less expensive or the accuracy is adversely affected,

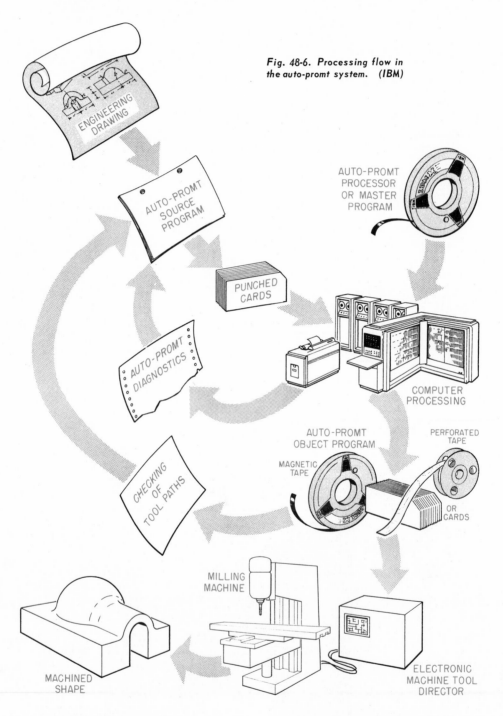

Fig. 48-6. Processing flow in the auto-promt system. (IBM)

sequence from plans to finished part.

There are two major categories of N/C:
1. Point-to-Point system.
2. Contour Path or Continuous Path system.

The point-to-point system (usually used for

the table moving from point A to point B does not have to follow any specific path, Fig. 48-7, because the machine will be performing no productive operation until it gets to point B. Point-to-point programming rarely requires the use

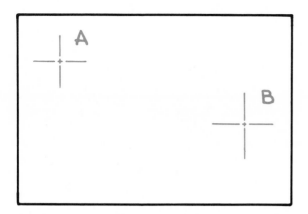

Fig. 48-7. *Point-to-point. No specific path need be followed from point A to point B.*

of a computer.

However, in the case of the continuous path system, it *is* important what path the tool takes because the tool is continuously cutting as it moves along the prescribed shape, Fig. 48-8. Each movement must be monitored and adjusted through a feed-back mechanism to the tape sensing unit, to maintain correct position and the correct speed and feed.

Cutter shape and other machining variables

must be taken into consideration when programming the cutter path.

A computer is mandatory for continuous path programming, because the time required to determine the almost infinite number of coordinates needed for the continuous path system would become prohibitive. The complex shapes shown in Fig. 48-9, can be produced economically without the need for expensive jigs, fixtures and templates, by the continuous path system.

Machines that can be adapted to N/C range from the drill press, to the huge machine that loads rough engine block castings into one end, transfers them from station to station through a definite machining sequence, and unloads the finished pieces automatically at the other end, Fig. 48-10. Some of the machines are composed of units of special design while others are essentially units of standard manufacture equipped with special tools and controls. Included in most designs are more powerful drives. Motors of 50 to 100 HP are common and cutting speeds have been increased to such a degree that it has become necessary to incorporate chip conveyor belts into the basic machine design to handle the large volume of chips that are

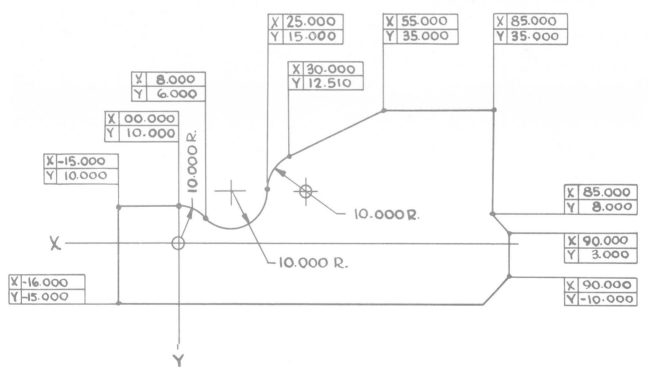

Fig. 48-8. *Contour Path or Continuous Path system. The machine slides must be moved certain definite distances synchronously with each other, in definite directions. When planning these movements, the coordinate positions of all points where changes in direction occur, must be known. For example: the points where two different curves become tangent to each other are shown. By adding a Z axis, three-dimensional machining is possible.*

produced during the machining operation.

N/C applications have been adapted to operations other than the removal of metal. It has been applied to material applications (filament winding); material transfer or positioning (assembly); and material forming (tube bending).

N/C drafting machines which will produce accurate engineering drawings from a tape now make it possible for a designer of machine parts to describe a new design mathematically, communicate this description through N/C language to a computer, and end up with a prototype part, although it has never been bluprinted. This is a great saving of time and money and reduction of human error.

Only time will tell what impact automation will have on our society. Some workers, mostly semiskilled and unskilled, will lose their jobs. This has happened many times in history. Consider the home craftsman during the Industrial Revolution. The carriage maker, blacksmith and feed dealer when Henry Ford started to mass-produce the automobile to make it a necessity rather than a curiosity, or the introduction of the dial telephone system. Both developments were decried during their inception as automation is condemned today. They eventually employed (directly or indirectly) many more people than the number they originally displaced. Better jobs, with higher pay and improved working conditions, were created.

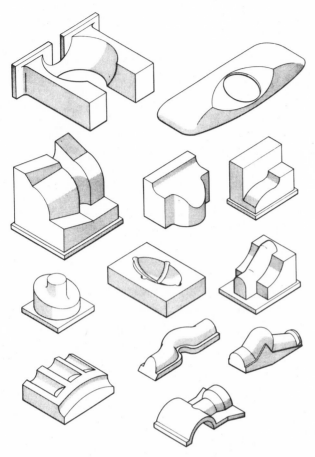

Fig. 48-9. These examples indicate the wide range of shapes which may be contoured by numerical control methods. (IBM)

Fig. 48-10. A large machine tool used for automated production. At one time 104, V-8 cylinder blocks are having some machining operation performed on them. The machine is almost two city blocks long and performs 555 operations; including 265 drilling, 6 milling, 21 boring, 56 reaming, 101 countersinking, 106 tapping and 133 inspections. It produces 100 pieces per hour at high efficiency. (Cross Co.)

TEST YOUR KNOWLEDGE, Unit 48

1. Some_____and_____workers will loose their jobs because automated machines can do the work more rapidly with human error minimized.
2. Numerical control can be described as a method of operating machines by_____.
3. Stiff wire fingers push buttons that are attached to electric motors that move the work into position. True or false?
4. One disadvantage of automated machine tools is that they require expensive jigs, fixtures and complex setups. True or false?
5. List four advantages of numerically con-
trolled machines.
   a._____.
   b._____.
   c._____.
   d._____.
6. Numerical controlled machines can only be used when large numbers of parts must be machined. True or false?
7. Programmed machines can receive their instructions by what three methods?
   a._____.
   b._____.
   c._____.

RESEARCH AND DEVELOPMENT

1. The advent of automation is frequently thought of as the start of the second Industrial Revolution. Prepare a research paper on the first Industrial Revolution with emphasis on wages, working conditions and how the people lived. Are there any similarities between the problems the average worker encountered then and what the worker is running into today? If so, what are they and what was the eventual outcome?

2. Arrange a visit to a plant that uses automated machinery.
3. If visiting a plant is impractical, book a motion picture that illustrates automation.
4. Secure samples of tapes and cards.
5. Prepare a book report on a text that deals with automation and present it to the class. Include a discussion period.
6. Develop a simple machine that will illustrate how automation works.

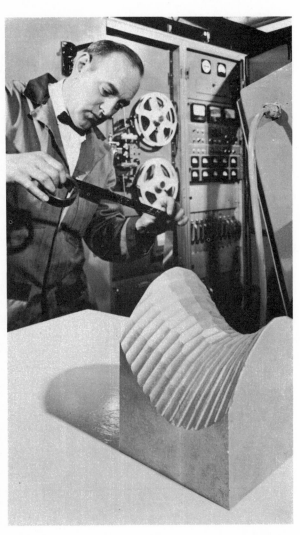

Industry photo--Left. Finished piece which is complex in shape shown in photo at the right, is being machined by a tape-controlled cutter. Such a machine can automatically generate tool paths while maintaining tolerances within a few millionths of an inch. (IBM)

Unit 49

QUALITY CONTROL

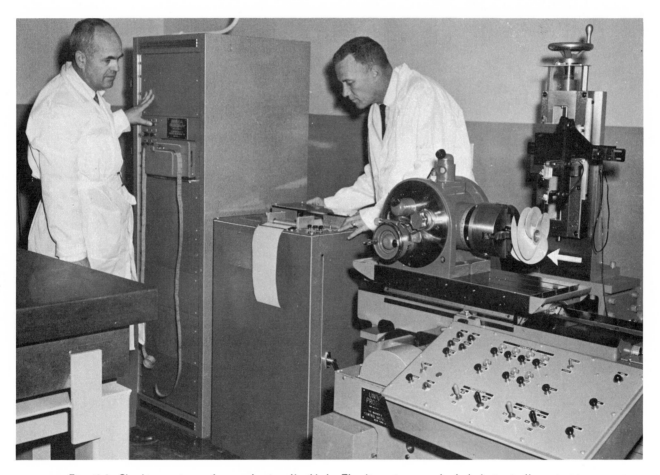

Fig. 49-1. Checking contours of a complex impeller blade. The dimensions are checked electronically against information stored on the perforated tape. (Warner & Swasey Co.)

The primary purpose of QUALITY CONTROL is to seek out potential product defects before they can cause damage and to prevent their occurence in the manufacturing process.

Quality control can be divided into two classifications:

1. DESTRUCTIVE TESTING. The part is destroyed during the test period.
2. NON-DESTRUCTIVE TESTING. This testing procedure does not damage the

material to such an extent that it cannot be used for the purpose for which it was originally intended.

DESTRUCTIVE TESTING

Destructive testing is a costly time consuming and unreliable testing technique. It is an indirect process whereby the specimen is selected at random from a given number of

Fig. 49-2. *Checking the shape of a turbine blade for a jet engine with a Guillotine type gauge.* (Westinghouse Electric Corp.)

pieces, and statistically at least, indicates the characteristics of the undestroyed, and untested, remaining pieces.

NON-DESTRUCTIVE TESTING

Non-destructive testing programs are well adapted to electronic and space vehicles where the performance of each of the thousands of parts is critical. Each piece can be tested and compared for its conformity to specifications.

METHODS OF NON-DESTRUCTIVE TESTING

You are familiar with many forms of nondestructive testing; measuring, weighing, and visual observation. This type of quality control is satisfactory for many products, for others it leaves much to be desired. Industry has developed many testing techniques to eliminate these shortcomings.

MEASURING

The shape of some products is so complex that conventional measuring tools cannot be used to give accurate measurements. Tools that measure electronically and check thousands of individual reference points on the object against specifications have been devised, Fig. 49-1. In

other situations, tremendous numbers of the product must be checked for accuracy and it must be done rapidly. Special measuring fixtures are used in this case, Fig. 49-2.

X-RAY

X-ray examination, Fig. 49-3, has become a routine step in the acceptance of parts and materials. Internal defects are readily detected and located.

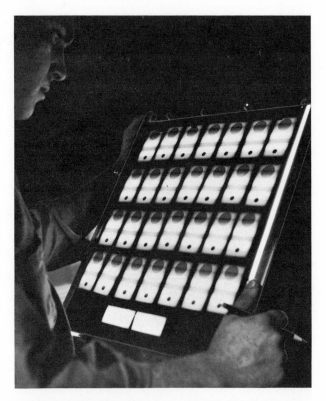

Fig. 49-3. *X-ray examination of a number of parts. Hidden flaws are easily detected.* (Westinghouse Electric Corp.)

ULTRASONIC TESTING

Ultrasonic techniques, Fig. 49-4, utilize a high frequency sound beam to detect cracks and flaws in the product. The defects reflect and attenuate the beam and locate the depth of the flaw by a gauge on the trace screen.

FLUORESCENT PENETRANT INSPECTION

The theory of Fluorescent Penetrant Inspection, Fig. 49-5, is based on capillary action. The penetrant solution is applied to a part surface by dipping, spraying or brushing. Capillary

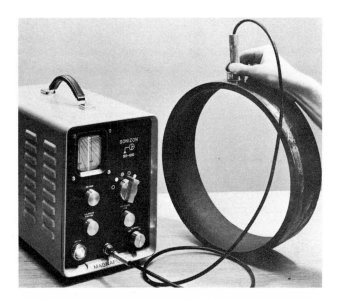

Fig. 49-4. The Ultrasonic testing device is often called a "one arm micrometer." It makes thickness measurements as quickly as the probe can be moved over the surface - and "reports" its findings on a direct reading scale on the face of the cathode ray tube. (Magnaflux Corp.)

Fig. 49-5. Three ways to inspect a kingpin for a truck front axle. At left, it is as it appeared under visual inspection, apparently sound and safe for service. In the middle you see what inspection with Magnaflux revealed. Excessive heating during grinding caused dangerous cracks. At right, the same kingpin and the same cracks, this time it was treated with a fluorescent penetrant testing material and photographed under black light. (Magnaflux Corp.)

action literally pulls the solution into the defect. The surface is rinsed clean, and before or after drying, a wet or dry developer is applied. This acts like a blotter, and draws the penetrant back to the surface.

When inspected under black light, every defect glows with fluorescent brilliance. This glowing line or spot marks each defect, right on the part itself.

SPOTCHECK (Trademark: Magnaflux Corp.)

Spotcheck, Fig. 49-6, is another of the penetrant type inspection devices. It is easy to use, accurate, economical and does not require a black light to bring out the flaws. Application procedure is similar to that described for the fluorescent type penetrant.

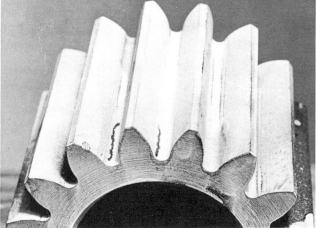

Fig. 49-6. SPOTCHECK penetrant inspection technique. 1. Apply cleaner to loosen grease and dirt. 2. Remove grease and dirt loosened by cleaner. 3. Left photo. Spray on penetrant. 4. Apply developer. 5. Right photo. Inspect for flaws. Flaws not seen in photo number 1 now stand out sufficiently to be seen by the naked eye. (Magnaflux Corp.)

MAGNAFLUX (Trademark: Magnaflux Corp.)

Magnaflux, Figs. 49-7, and 49-8, is a method of non-destructive testing of magnetic materials, by magnet particle inspection. The technique is rapid, but shows only serious defects, not scratches nor minor visual flaws. A magnetic field is set up electrically within the part. Fine

Fig. 49-7. Magnafluxing a large crankshaft to determine whether any flaws developed during use.

particles of magnetic iron are blown (dry method) or flowed in liquid suspension (wet method) on the part, many of them are attracted and cling to the fracture and form a definite indication of its exact location, extent and shape.

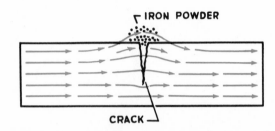

Fig. 49-8. HERE IS A MAGNAFLUX INDICATION BY MEANS OF LONGITUDINAL MAGNETIZATION. The crack in a steel bar makes a magnetic field outside the part, to hold iron powder and build up an indication of the crack.

In addition to the above mentioned techniques, industry makes wide use of highly specialized test devices. Now that we are well into the space age more and more highly specialized and sophisticated test devices will have to be designed because of the terrific cost of just one space vehicle.

TEST YOUR KNOWLEDGE, Unit 49

1. Quality control falls into two classifications:
   a. _____ testing where the piece is destroyed during the test period.
   b. _____ testing where the test piece is not damaged to the point where it cannot be used.
2. List three familiar forms of testing that would fall under "b" above:
   a. _____.
   b. _____.
   c. _____.
3. Quality control is important because:
   a. It is inexpensive.
   b. It is quickly and easily accomplished.
   c. It guarantees that the parts being manufactured maintain predetermined standards and specifications.
   d. None of the above.
4. Ultrasonic inspection makes use of:
   a. Accurately made measuring fixtures.
   b. A high frequency sound beam.
   c. X-rays.
   d. Flaws and defects in the material.
5. Fluorescent inspection must be made under _____ to make the flaw or defect glow with fluorescent brilliance.
6. Name three hardness testers.
   a. _____.
   b. _____.
   c. _____.

RESEARCH AND DEVELOPMENT

1. Devise a quality control system for your school shop.
2. Ask for a demonstration of the Magnaflux technique the next time you take a field trip to a plant that uses the system.
3. Select a machine part and examine it care-
fully. What points on this piece come under the quality control system in the plant that made it? What points must be checked against specifications if the piece is to be interchangeable with similar pieces?
4. Design a project and develop simple measur-

ing fixtures to check it against the plans.

5. Investigate the possibilities of having a plant in your area demonstrate the Rockwell or Brinell hardness testers.

6. The penetrants described in the text are simple and easy to use. Their cost is within reach of many shop budgets. Carefully analyze the needs of your shop, and if the need is there present your analysis to the instructor requesting that they be purchased.

7. Show a film on quality control to your group. Preview it before showing it and prepare an outline on the more significant parts. If time permits, prepare a short test on the film.

Industry photo--Investment casting;
stripping a wax pattern from the mold.
(Westinghouse Electric Corp.)

Unit 50

OCCUPATIONS IN METALWORKING INDUSTRIES

Considering its scope, there is an excellent possibility that you will be employed in an occupation that has been made possible, either directly or indirectly, by the metalworking industries.

Whether your choice of employment is classed as SEMI-SKILLED, SKILLED, TECHNICAL or PROFESSIONAL, one of its basic requirements, if you want to be successful and ad-

Fig. 50-1. The inspection of manufactured products is often classified as a semi-skilled job. Here the landing gear of an aircraft is being inspected. (Cessna Aircraft Co.)

vance in it, is a continuing educational program. As jobs become more and more complex, persons with higher levels of education and specialized training will have a better opportunity for securing and retaining employment.

With jobs that require little or no skill in a steady decline, the person who leaves school, or who does not plan his high school program with

care, will find it more and more difficult to secure employment in coming years, because employers prefer workers who have completed high school and who have acquired a salable skill.

Jobs in the metalworking industries fall into the four general categories mentioned previously:
1. SEMI-SKILLED
2. SKILLED
3. TECHNICAL
4. PROFESSIONAL

SEMI-SKILLED WORKERS

SEMI-SKILLED WORKERS, Fig. 50-1, are those who perform operations that do not require a high degree of skill or training. Most of the work done by the semi-skilled worker is routine and may be classified by the following general types:
1. Those who serve as helpers to skilled workers.
2. Those who operate machines and equipment used in making things.
3. Those who assemble the various manufactured parts into a single final product.
4. Those who inspect and test the manufactured items to determine whether they are made correctly and operate satisfactorily.

There is little chance for advancement out of semi-skilled jobs without additional study and training. Most semi-skilled work is found in production shops where there are great numbers of repeat operations.

SKILLED WORKERS

The most common method of becoming a skilled worker is through an APPRENTICESHIP PROGRAM which involves several years of study with an experienced craftsman. During this period of training, usually four years, the APPRENTICE, Fig. 50-2, spends part of the time working in the shop, and part of the time

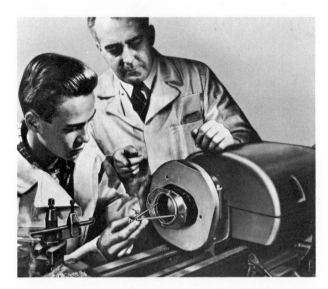

Fig. 50-2. The apprentice studies under an experienced craftsman for a period of four or more years. The training program includes study of related subjects - math, English, science, etc. (L. S. Starrett Co.)

studying related subjects (math, science, English, etc.). Upon the successful completion of the apprentice program, the worker is capable of performing the exacting work and skills of the trade.

Because a major portion of the text involves the machining of metal, the various skilled jobs

of that trade will be used for examples.

ALL-AROUND MACHINIST, Fig. 50-3,--a competent person who can set up and operate most types of machine tools. He is expected to plan and carry out all of the operations needed to machine a particular job.

Fig. 50-3. The all-around machinist can set up and operate most types of machine tools. (Greaves Div., J. A. Fay & Eagan Co.)

TOOL AND DIE MAKER, Fig. 50-4, -- a skilled person who specializes in producing the tools, dies, jigs and fixtures needed to manufacture various products. He has a

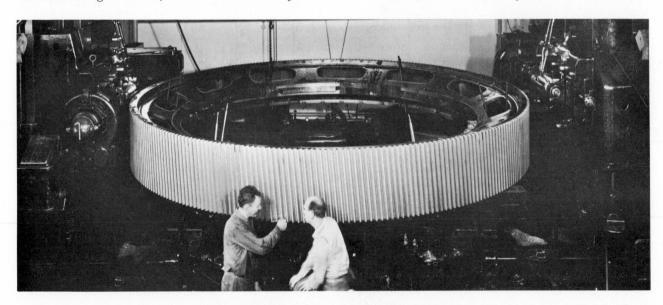

Machinists inspecting precision gear 24-ft. in diameter. (Falk Co.)

Fig. 50-4. This jig, used for the assembly of wing panel of a light plane, was made by tool and die makers. (Cessna Aircraft Co.)

broader background of machining operations and mathematics than other skilled workers in the trade. He also normally works to closer tolerances.

SETUP MAN, Fig. 50-5, -- a person whose job it is to set up machine tools for the machine operator. He is often expected to ex-

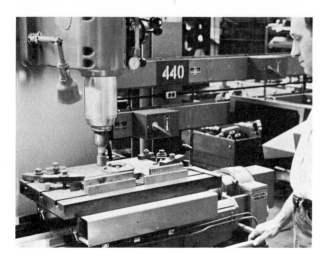

Fig. 50-5. A machining cycle being checked out by a setup man. (Warner & Swasey Co.)

plain to the machine operator how to do the job and how to check the accuracy of the finished pieces. The setup man is a skilled machinist.

LAYOUT MAN, Fig. 50-6, -- the specialist who interprets the drawings and, with precision measuring tools, locates and marks off where and how much material must be removed from forgings, castings or metal

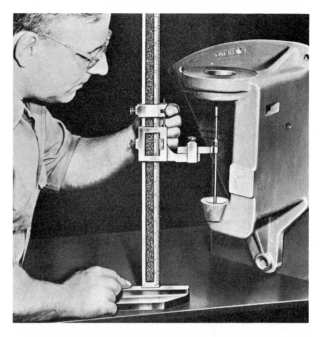

Fig. 50-6. The layout man is the specialist who interprets the drawings and, with precision measuring tools, locates and marks off where and how much material must be removed from forgings, castings or metal stock. (L. S. Starrett Co.)

stock. He is a skilled machinist who is familiar with the operations and capabilities of standard machine tools, and well trained in mathematics and print reading.

Fig. 50-7. The foreman or supervisor of the production department works very closely with the engineering and metallurgical staff to be positive that customer specifications are met. (Lindberg Steel Treating Co.)

SUPERVISOR OR FOREMAN, Fig. 50-7, -- usually a skilled machinist who has been promoted to a position with more responsibility. He directs the work of the other men in the

Fig. 50-8. The technician has many responsibilities. One group is responsible for the repair and maintenance of tape controlled equipment. (Warner & Swasey Co.)

shop and is responsible for meeting production "deadlines" and for keeping "rejects" (work that does not meet specifications) to a minimum.

TECHNICIANS

TECHNICIAN, Fig. 50-8, -- a relatively new member of the production team and operates in the realm between the shop and the engineering department. His position is an outgrowth of today's highly technological and scientific world. The job usually requires at least two years of college with a program centered on math, science, English and manufacturing and production processes.

The technician assists the engineer by testing various experimental devices and machines, compiling statistics, making cost estimates, and preparing technical reports. In some manufacturing plants, the person who programs the part for production by numerically controlled machines (production by machines controlled by tapes or perforated cards) is classified as a technician as well as the craftsman who repairs and maintains the numerically controlled equipment.

THE PROFESSIONS

The professions offer many excellent opportunities in the field of metal working:

TEACHING, Fig. 50-9, -- one of the most satisfying of the professions is in a field that

Fig. 50-9. The teaching profession is too often overlooked by the student. There will be a great demand for teachers in the coming years. (Greaves Div., J. A. Fay & Eagan Co.)

the student too often overlooks. The teacher of Industrial Arts, Industrial, Vocational, and Technical Education is in a most fortunate position. It is a challenging profession that offers a freedom not found in most other professions. It is not an overcrowded profession and with the anticipated school population increase, there will be a demand for several thousand additional teachers each year for many years to come.

Four years of college training is required, and while industrial experience is ordinarily not a prerequisite, it will prove helpful.
ENGINEERING is the second largest professional occupation. A bachelor's degree in engineering is usually the minimum requirement for entering the profession. However, some have been able to enter the profession without a degree after experience as draftsmen or engineering technicians. They were required to take some college level training.
INDUSTRIAL ENGINEER, Fig. 50-10,--he is primarily concerned with the safest and

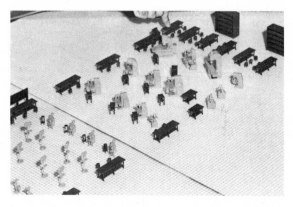

Fig. 50-10. The industrial engineer is responsible for the safest and most efficient use of machines, materials and personnel. One phase of this job is planning plant layout. (Republic Aviation Corp.)

most efficient use of machines, materials and personnel. He may, in some instances, be responsible for the design of special machinery and equipment to be used in manufacturing operations.
MECHANICAL ENGINEER, Fig. 50-11, -- usually responsible for the design and development of new machines, devices and ideas, and with the redesign and improvement of existing equipment. In many cases the mechanical engineer is responsible for the installation and maintenance of industrial equipment.

Fig. 50-11. Here the engineer is preparing an experiment that will give more information on a welding technique that makes use of an electron beam to join the metals. (Republic Aviation Corp.)

TOOL AND MANUFACTURING ENGINEER, Fig. 50-12, -- the mechanical engineer is concerned with the design and development of the original or prototype model. When this model has been thoroughly tested, and it has been proven that it will meet design requirements, the product is turned over to the TOOL AND MANUFACTURING ENGINEER to devise the methods and means to manufacture and assemble the item in the quantities desired by the customer.

able from junior or community colleges. Many of them offer programs in a number of the technical areas.

WHAT INDUSTRY EXPECTS OF YOU

The primary reason for attending high school is to help to prepare for a job, hold that job and advance in it. With this in mind, it is well to establish what industry expects from those it employs.

Fig. 50-12. The tool and manufacturing engineer devises the methods and means of producing a product such as this fighter-bomber. He must also plan methods that will enable major changes and modifications to be made while the plane is in production.

WHERE TO OBTAIN INFORMATION ON METALWORKING OCCUPATIONS

There are many sources of occupational information. No doubt the closest is the school's guidance office, or the teachers of industrial education, who can often give information about occupations related to the subjects they teach.

The State Employment Office is an excellent source of information on local employment opportunities, as are the various trade unions that are concerned with the metalworking trades.

Information on technical occupations is avail-

You will encounter quite a disappointment if you think that graduation means the end of training. Advanced technology is constantly developing new ideas, materials, processes and manufacturing techniques that are creating occupations that did not previously exist. If a person wants to hold his job and advance in it, he must study, almost continuously, to keep pace with these new developments. There are very few skilled positions that do not require in-plant studies or advanced studies on a college level to maintain the required job proficiencies.

Industry also expects a fair day's work for

a fair day's pay. High manufacturing costs make this a real necessity.

Do your assigned work and never knowingly turn out a piece of substandard work. Take pride in what you do.

Equipment and tools are very expensive. Develop a sense of responsibility for the equipment under your control. Production makes teamwork essential; any breakdown may put many out of work until repairs can be made. This causes a serious loss of salary to all concerned.

Finally, look for new ways to do and improve your job. An idea that would reduce the production time for an automobile by a minute or two, could result in several hundreds of thousands of dollars in savings in a year's time.

Industry always has a place for a young person with ideas, who is not afraid to work.

TEST YOUR KNOWLEDGE, Unit 50

1. List the four categories of the metalworking occupations:
    a._____.
    b._____.
    c._____.
    d._____.
2. _____workers are those who perform operations that do not require a high degree of skill or training.
3. The skilled worker usually starts as an _____.
4. This period of training is frequently_____

5. The_____assists the engineer.
6. His training program involves considerable _____, _____science and manufacturing and production processes.
7. _____is the second largest professional occupation.
8. List three sources of information on metalworking occupations.
    a._____.
    b._____.
    c._____.

RESEARCH AND DEVELOPMENT

1. Invite a spokesman from the State Employment Office to discuss with your shop class, employment opportunities in the local metalworking industries.
2. Make a study of the HELP WANTED COLUMNS in the daily papers for a period of two weeks. Prepare a list of the metalworking positions available, the salaries offered and the minimum requirements for securing the jobs. How often are additional benefits like insurance, hospitalization, etc., mentioned?
3. Summarize the information on the metalworking occupations given in the OCCUPATIONAL OUTLOOK HANDBOOK (a Government publication) and make it available to the class.
4. Contact the local office of the International Association of Machinists for information on machinist trades apprentice programs.
5. Contact engineering societies and make arrangements to borrow a few of the excellent films they have on the engineering profession.

Unit 51

GLOSSARY OF TERMS

ABRASIVE: A material that penetrates and cuts a material that is softer than itself. It may be natural (emery, corundum and diamonds) or man-made (silicon carbide, aluminum oxide).

ACCURATE: Made within the tolerance allowed.

ACME THREAD: Similar in form to the square thread in that the top and bottom of the thread is flat, however, the sides have a 29 deg. included angle. The Acme thread is used for feed and adjusting screws on machine tools.

ACUTE ANGLE: An angle of less than 90 deg.

ADDENDUM: That portion of the gear tooth that projects above or outside of the pitch circle.

ALIGN: Adjusting to given points.

ALLOWANCE: The limits permitted for satisfactory performance of the machined parts.

ALLOY: A mixture of two or more metals fused or melted together to form a new metal.

ANGLE PLATE: A precisely made tool of cast iron, steel or granite that is used to hold work in a vertical position for layout or machining. Faces are at right angles (90 deg.) and may have slotted openings for easier mounting of the work or clamping to the machine tool table.

ANNEALING: The process of heating metal to a given temperature (the exact temperature and the period the temperature is held depends upon the composition of the metal being annealed) and cooling it slowly to remove stresses and induce softness.

ANODIZING: A process for applying an oxide coating to aluminum. It is done electrolytically in an acid solution with equipment similar to that used for electroplating. The technique can be varied to produce a light colored, porous coating that can be dyed in a variety of colors to a harder and non-porous coating for protection against corrosion.

APRON: A covering plate or casting that encloses and protects a mechanism. The portion of the lathe carriage that contains the gears, clutches and levers for moving the carriage by hand and power feed.

ARBOR: A shaft or spindle for holding cutting tools.

ASSEMBLY: A unit fitted together from manufactured parts. A machine tool may comprise several assemblies.

AUTOMATION: An industrial technique whereby mechanical labor and mechanical control are substituted for human labor and human control. Basically an extension and a refinement of mass-production.

AXIS: The center line, real or imaginary, passing through an object about which it could rotate. A point of reference.

BACK GEARS: Gears fitted to belt driven machine tools to increase the number of spindle speeds. Used to slow the spindle speed of the lathe for cutting threads, knurling and for making heavy roughing cuts.

BACKLASH: Lost motion (play) in moving parts, such as thread in a nut or in the teeth of meshing gears.

BED: One of the principal parts of a machine tool. It contains ways or bearing surfaces that support and guide the work or cutting tool.

BERYLLIUM: A metal that weighs almost 80 percent less than steel, yet offers virtually equal strength characteristics. It is easy to machine but is brittle. Used in missiles and aircraft where weight is critical and in nuclear reactors. One of the "exotic" metals.

BEVEL: The angle formed by a line or a surface that is not at right angles to another line or surface.

BLANKING: A stamping operation in which a die is used to shear or cut a desired shape from flat sheets or strips of metal.

BLOWHOLE: A hole produced in a casting when gases are entrapped during the pouring operation.

BRAZING: Joining metals by the fusion of non-ferrous alloys that have melting temperatures above 800 deg. F. but lower than the metals being joined.

BRITTLENESS: In some respects the opposite of toughness. The characteristics that cause metal to break easily.

BUFFING: The process of bringing out the luster of metal. Buffing is accomplished by using cloth wheels, usually cotton or muslin disks sewed together, and a tripoli compound. Proper wheel speed depends on the size of the wheel.

BURNISHING: The process of finishing a metal surface by compressing its surface. Often done by tumbling the work with steel balls.

BURR: The sharp edge remaining on the metal after cutting, stamping or machining. The burr can be dangerous if not removed.

BUSHING: A bearing for a revolving shaft. A hardened steel tube used on jigs to guide drills and reamers.

CAM: A rotating or sliding element that, because of the curvature of its driving surface, imparts complicated motions to the followers or driven elements of the machine tool.

CARBURIZING: A process that introduces carbon to the surface of steel by heating the metal below its melting temperature in contact with carbonaceous solids, liquids or gases and holding at that temperature for a predetermined time after which the piece is quenched.

CASEHARDENING: A process of surface hardening iron base alloys so that the surface layer or case is made substantially harder than the interior or core. Typical casehardening processes are carburizing, cyaniding and nitriding.

CASTING: An object made by pouring molten metal into a mold.

CAT HEAD: A sleeve or collar which fits over out-of-round or irregular shaped work permitting it to be supported in a steady rest. The work is centered in the cat head by using the adjusting screws located around its circumference.

CENTER, DEAD: A stationary center.

CENTER LINE: A line used to indicate an axis of a symmetrical part. The center line consists of a series of long and short dashes.

CENTER, LIVE: A rotating center.

CENTRIFUGAL CASTING: A casting technique in which the mold is rotated during pouring and solidification of the metal. It produces a casting with certain desirable characteristics.

CERMETS: A combination of ceramics and metals that is finding increased use for high temperature applications. Resistance to high temperatures and wear indicates great promise as a super high-speed cutting tool.

CHASER: A thread cutting tool that fits into a die head used on a turret lathe or screw machine. Usually a hardened steel plate with several teeth of the correct pitch cut into it. Three or four chasers are used in a die head.

CHASING THREADS: Cutting threads on a machine tool.

CHATTER: Vibrations caused by the cutting tool springing away from the work. It produces small ridges on the machined surface.

CHEMICAL MILLING: Controlled removal of metal by chemicals rather than by conventional machining methods.

CHIP BREAKER: A small groove ground on the top of the cutting tool, near the cutting edge, to break the chips into small sections.

CHUCK: A device to hold work or cutting tools on a machine tool.

CIRCULAR PITCH: The distance from the center of one gear tooth to the center of the next tooth measured on the pitch circle.

CLEARANCE: The distance by which one object clears another object.

CLIMB MILLING: Feeding work into the milling cutter in the same direction it rotates.

CLOCKWISE: From left to right in a circular motion. The direction clock hands move.

COINING: The process that impresses the image or characters on the die and punch onto a plain metal surface.

COLD HEADING: An operation in which metal is worked cold.

COLOR HARDEN: A hardening technique usually done for appearance only.

COLOR TEMPER: Using the color range steel passes through when heated to determine the proper degree of hardness.

CONCAVE SURFACE: A curved depression in the surface of an object.

CONCENTRIC: Having a common center.

CONE PULLEY: A one piece pulley having two or more diameters.

CONTINUOUS CASTING: A casting technique in which the ingot is continuously solidified while it is being poured. The length of the casting is not determined by mold dimensions.

CONTOUR: The outline of an object.

CONVENTIONAL: Not original; customary, or traditional.

CONVEX SURFACE: A rounded surface on an object.

COOLANT: A fluid or gas used to cool the cutting

edge of a tool to prevent it from burning up during the machining operation.

CORE: A body of sand or other material that is formed to a desired shape and placed in a mold to produce a cavity or opening in a casting.

COUNTERBORE: Enlarging a hole to a given depth and diameter.

COUNTERCLOCKWISE: From right to left in a circular motion.

COUNTERSINK: Chamfering a hole to receive a flat-head screw.

CUTTING FLUID: A liquid used to cool and lubricate the cutting tool to improve the quality of the surface finish.

CYANIDING: A process of casehardening a ferrous alloy by heating in molten cyanide causing the metal to absorb carbon.

DECARBURIZING: The process of removing carbon from metals.

DEDENDUM: The portion of the gear tooth between the pitch circle and the root circle and is equal to the addendum plus the clearance.

DEMAGNETIZING: The removal of magnetism from a piece held in a magnet chuck.

DIE: A tool used to cut external threads. Also, a tool used to impart a desired shape to a piece of metal.

DIE CASTING: A method of casting metal under pressure by injecting it into the metal dies of a die casting machine.

DIE CAVITY: A hollow space inside a die where metal solidifies to form a casting.

DIE CHASERS: See CHASER.

DIE STOCK: The handle for holding a threading die.

DIVIDING HEAD: A machine tool attachment for accurate spacing of holes, slots, gear teeth and flutes. When geared to the table lead screw it can be used to machine spirals.

DOG: A projecting piece on the side of a machine tool worktable to trip the automatic feed mechanism off or for reverse travel.

DOG, LATHE: A device for clamping work so that it can be machined between centers.

DRAFT: The clearance on a pattern that allows easy withdrawal of the pattern from the mold.

DRIFT: A tapered piece of flat steel used to separate tapered shank tools from sleeves, sockets or machine tool spindles.

DRILLING: Cutting round holes by use of a cutting tool sharpened on its point.

DRILL ROD: A carbon steel rod accurately and smoothly ground to size. Available in a large range of sizes.

DRIVE FIT: Using force or pressure to fit two pieces together. One of several classes of fits.

DROP FORGING: A forming operation, usually done under impact, that compresses the metal in dies designed to produce the desired shape.

DUCTILITY: The property of a metal that permits permanent deformation by hammering, rolling and drawing without breaking or fracturing.

ECCENTRIC: Not on a common center. A device that converts rotary motion into a reciprocating (back and forth) motion.

ELECTROPLATING: A plating process accomplished by passing an electric current from an anode (usually made of the plating material) to the work, through an electrolyte containing salts of the plating metal in solution.

EMERY: A natural abrasive.

EXPANSION FIT: The reverse of shrink fit. The piece to be fitted is placed in liquid nitrogen or dry ice until it shrinks enough to fit into the mating piece. Interference develops between the fitted pieces as the cooled piece expands.

EZY-OUT: A tool for removing broken bolts and studs from a hole. It is made in several sizes.

FACE: To make a flat surface by machining.

FACEPLATE: A circular plate that fits to the headstock spindle and drives or carries work to be machined.

FATIGUE: The tendency for metal to break or fracture under repeated or fluctuating stresses.

FERROUS: Denotes family of metals in which iron is the major ingredient.

FILLET: The curved surface that connects two surfaces that form an angle.

FIT: The clearance or interference between two mating parts. There are several classes of fits.

FIXTURE: A device for holding work in a machine tool. IT DOES NOT GUIDE THE CUTTING TOOL.

FLAME HARDEN: A method of surface hardening steel by rapidly heating the surface with the flame of an oxyacetylene torch, and quenching.

FLASH: A thin fin of metal formed at the parting line of a forging or casting where a small portion of metal is forced out between the edges of the die.

FLASK: A wooden or metal form consisting of a cope (the top portion) and a drag (the bottom portion) used to hold the sand that forms the mold.

FLOTURN PROCESS: Another term for shear spinning.

FLUORESCENT PENETRANT INSPECTION: A

nondestructive testing technique. An oil base penetrant is sprayed on the work and is drawn into every crack and flaw. The surface is rinsed with solvent to remove excess penetrant. After developing the surface is viewed under a "black light." Defects glow with fluorescent brilliance.

FLUTE: A groove machined in a cutting tool to facilitate easy chip removal and to permit cutting fluid to reach the cutting point.

FLUX: The fusible material used in brazing and welding to dissolve and facilitate removal of oxides and other undesirable substances.

FLY CUTTER: A single point tool fitted in an arbor. Inexpensive to make but is relatively inefficient because only one point does the cutting.

FORCE FIT: The interference between the two mating parts is sufficient to require force to press the pieces together. The parts are considered permanently assembled.

FORGE: To form metal with heat and/or pressure.

FORMING: The operations or steps necessary to shape metal to a desired form. The change does not intentionally change the thickness of the metal.

FREE FIT: Used when tolerances are liberal. Clearance is sufficient to permit a shaft to run freely without binding or overheating when properly lubricated.

GANG MILLING: Using two or more milling cutters to machine several surfaces at one time.

GATE: The point where molten metal enters the mold cavity.

GAUGE: A tool used for checking metal parts to determine whether they are made within specified limits.

GEARS: Toothed wheels that transmit rotary motion from one shaft to another shaft without slippage.

GIB: A wedge-shaped strip that can be adjusted to maintain a proper fit of movable surfaces of a machine tool.

GRADUATE: To divide into equal parts by engraving or cutting lines or graduations into the metal.

GRADUATIONS: The lines that indicate points of measurement on measuring tools and machine dials.

GUERIN PROCESS: A method of forming metal sheet in which the metal is forced to conform to the shape of a male die by the application of force to a confined rubber pad.

HALF-NUTS: The mechanism that locks the lathe carriage to the lead screw for the purpose of cutting threads.

HARDENING: The heating and quenching of certain iron-base alloys for the purpose of producing a hardness superior to that of the untreated material.

HARDNESS TESTING: Techniques used to determine the degree of hardness of heat-treated material.

HEAT TREATMENT: The careful application of a combination of heating and cooling cycles to a metal or alloy in the solid state to bring about certain desirable conditions such as hardness and toughness.

HELICAL GEARS: Gears with the teeth cut at some angle other than at right angles to the gear face permitting two or more teeth to be engaged at all times. Their operation is smoother and not as noisy as the operation of spur gears.

HELIX: The path a point generates as it moves at a fixed rate of advance on the surface of a cylinder, such as screw threads or the flutes on a twist drill.

HIGH ENERGY FORMING: A metal forming technique involving the release of a source of high energy such as explosives, electrical or pneumatic-mechanical.

HOB: A special type gear cutter designed to cut gear teeth on a continuous basis.

HOBBING: Cutting gear teeth with a hob. The gear blank and hob rotate together as in mesh during the cutting operation.

HONING: A process used to produce an extremely fine surface finish on an object after the grinding operation. Honing permits a closer fit on critical parts. Abrasive blocks are forced against the work surface under very light spring pressure in a rotary motion and at the same time moved back and forth. The area is flooded with cutting fluid. Honing is an expensive operation.

HYDROFORM: A method of forming parts in rubber under accurately controlled fluid pressure. The metal is formed over a movable male die in a flexible diaphragm.

HYDROSPIN: Another name for shear spinning.

ID: Abbreviation for inside diameter.

IDLER GEAR: A gear or gears placed between two other gears to transfer motion from one to the other without changing the direction of rotation or the ratio between them.

INDEPENDENT CHUCK: A chuck in which each jaw can be moved independently of the other jaws.

INDEXING: The term used to describe the correct spacing of holes, slots, etc., on the periphery of a cylindrical piece using a dividing or indexing head.

INDICATOR: A sensitive instrument capable of measuring slight variations when testing the trueness of work, machines or machine attachments.

INSERTED TOOTH CUTTER: A milling cutter with teeth that can be replaced when they become damaged or worn rather than replacing the entire cutter.

INSPECTION: The measuring and checking of finished parts to determine whether they have been made to specifications.

INTERCHANGEABLE: Refers to a part that has been made to specific dimensions and tolerances and is capable of being fitted in a mechanism in place of a similarly made part.

INVESTMENT CASTING: A process that involves making a wax, plastic, or even a frozen mercury pattern, surrounding it with a wet refractory material, melting or burning the pattern after the investment material has dried and set, and finally pouring metal (usually under air or centrifugal pressure) into the cavity.

JARNO TAPER: A standard taper of 0.600 in. per foot. Used on machine tools.

JIG: A device that holds the work in position and positions and guides the cutting tool.

JO BLOCK: Precisely made steel blocks used by industry as a standard of measurement. They are made in a range of sizes and with a dimensional accuracy of ± 0.000002 (two millionth) inch, with a flatness and parallelism of ± 0.000003 (three millionth) inch.

KEY: A small piece of metal imbedded partially in the shaft and partially in the hub to prevent rotation of the gear or pulley on the shaft.

KEYWAY: The slot or recess in the shaft that holds the key.

KNEE: The unit that supports the saddle and table of a column and knee-type milling machine.

KNURLING: The operation that presses grooved, hardened steel wheels (knurls) into the surface of cylindrical work, rotating in the lathe, to produce rows of uniformly spaced serrations which provide a better grip, or, for decorative purposes.

LAND: Metal left between flutes or grooves in drills, reamers, taps and other cutting tools.

LAPPING: The process of finishing surfaces with a very fine abrasive like diamond dust or abrasive flours.

LARD OIL: A cutting oil made from animal fats. It is often mixed with mineral oils that improve the lubricating qualities.

LAY OUT: To locate and scribe points for machining and forming operations.

LEAD: The distance a nut will advance on a screw in one revolution.

LEAD SCREW: The long precision screw on the front of the lathe bed that is geared to the spindle to transmit motion to the carriage for thread cutting.

LONGITUDINAL MOVEMENT: Lengthwise movement.

MACHINABILITY: The characteristic of a material that describes the ease or difficulty of machining it.

MACHINABILITY INDEX: The table that indicates the degree of ease or difficulty of machining a material. It is based on the machining characteristics of a common steel (AISI B1112 = 100). Magnesium alloy (Machinability Index = 500 to 2000) is relatively easy to machine. Tool steel (Machinability Index = 34) is difficult to machine.

MACHINE TOOL: The name given to that class of machines which, taken as a group, can reproduce themselves.

MACHINIST: A person who is skilled in the use of machine tools and is capable of making complex machine setups.

MAGNAFLUX: A nondestructive inspection technique that makes use of a magnetic field and magnetic particles to locate flaws in materials.

MAGNAGLO: See FLUORESCENT PENETRANT INSPECTION. For use on magnetic materials only.

MAGNETIC CHUCK: A work-holding device that uses magnetic fields to hold work for machining (grinding).

MAJOR DIAMETER: The largest diameter of a thread measured perpendicular to the axis.

MALLEABILITY: The property of metal that determines its ease in being shaped when subjected to mechanical working (forging, rolling, etc.).

MANDREL: A slightly tapered, hardened steel shaft that supports work that cannot be held by any other method for machining between centers.

MARFORM: A drawing process that forms metal sheet by using a movable steel punch and a rubber headed ram.

Modern Metalworking

MATCH PLATE: Production type of pattern equipment usually made of metal. Consists of a plate on each side of which is mounted the matching halves of the pattern.

MESH: To engage gears to a working contact.

MILL: To remove metal with a rotating cutter on a milling machine.

MILLING MACHINE: A machine that removes metal from the work by means of a rotary cutter.

MINOR DIAMETER: The smallest diameter of a screw thread measured across the roots and perpendicular to the axis. Also known as the "root diameter."

MITER GEARS: Right angle bevel gears having the same number of teeth. Used to transmit power through shafts at right angles to each other.

MORSE TAPER: A standard taper of approximately 5/8 in. per foot. Used on lathe centers, drill shanks, etc.

MUSIC WIRE: A carbon steel wire used to manufacture springs.

NC: Abbreviation for the National Coarse series of screw threads.

NECKING: Machining a groove around a cylindrical shaft.

NF: Abbreviation for the National Fine series of screw threads.

NITRIDING: A casehardening technique in which a ferrous alloy is heated in an atmosphere of ammonia or in contact with a nitrogenous material to produce surface hardness by the absorbtion of nitrogen. Quenching is not necessary.

NONFERROUS: Metals containing no iron.

NORMALIZING: A process in which ferrous alloys are heated to approximately 100 deg. F. above the critical temperature range and cooled slowly in still air at room temperature to relieve stresses that may have developed during machining, welding or forming operations.

OBTUSE ANGLE: An angle of more than 90 deg.

OD: Abbreviation for outside diameter.

OFF CENTER: Eccentric, not accurate.

OIL HARDENING: Using a mineral oil as a quenching medium in the heat treatment of certain alloys.

OUT OF TRUE: Not on center, eccentric, out of alignment.

PEENING: An operation that involves the mechanical working of metal by means of hammerlike blows.

PERMANENT MOLD: A mold ordinarily made of metal that is used for the repeated production of similar castings.

PICKLING: A technique employed in the removal of stains and oxide scales from metal surfaces by immersion in acid baths.

PINION: The smaller of two mating gears.

PITCH: The distance from a point on one thread to a corresponding point on the next thread.

PITCH DIAMETER: The diameter of an imaginary cylinder that would pass through the threads at such points as to make the width of the thread and width of the space equal at the point where they are cut by the cylinder. It is equal to the major diameter of the thread minus the depth of one thread. In gearing - the diameter of the pitch circle which is an imaginary circle located at about mid-point on the teeth, where the teeth of both gears contact each other.

PLASTER MOLD CASTING: A casting process which uses plaster molds in place of sand molds. The castings produced in a plaster mold have a much better surface finish than those cast in sand. Used primarily with aluminum.

PRESS FIT: A class of fit where the interference between the mating parts is sufficient to require force to press the pieces together. The assembly is considered permanent.

PYROMETER: A device for measuring high temperatures. Temperatures are determined by measuring the electric current generated in the thermocouple as it heats up.

QUENCHING: The process of rapid cooling from an elevated temperature by contact with fluids or gases.

QUICK RETURN: The mechanism on some machine tools that can be engaged to return the worktable rapidly to its starting point during the noncutting cycle.

QUILL: The steel tube in the head of some machine tools that encloses the bearings and rotating spindle on which are mounted the cutting tools. It is geared to a handwheel and/or lever that is used to raise or lower the rotating cutting tool on the work surface. The quill can be locked in position.

RACK: A flat strip with teeth designed to mesh with teeth on a gear. Used to change rotary motion to reciprocating motion.

RAM: The part of the shaper that moves back and forth and carries the cutting tool.

RAPID TRAVERS: Used to bring the work on the milling table rapidly into cutting position and return the table quickly to the starting position for the next cut.

Glossary

REAM: To finish a drilled hole to exact size with a reamer.

REAMER: A cutting tool used to produce a smooth, accurate hole by removing a small amount of metal from a drilled hole.

RELIEF: An undercut of offset surface to provide clearance.

RIGHT ANGLE: An angle of 90 deg.

RISER: A reservoir of molten metal provided to compensate for the contraction of cast metals as they solidify.

ROLLING: A process of forming and shaping metal by passing it through a series of driven rolls.

ROOT DIAMETER: The smallest or "minor diameter" of a thread.

ROTARY TABLE: A milling attachment that gives a rotary motion to the piece. It consists of a circular worktable rotated by a handwheel through a worm and worm gear. The hub of the handwheel is graduated in degrees permitting precise spacing of holes, slots, grooves, etc., around the piece.

ROUGHING: The rapid removal of stock without regard for the quality of the surface finish.

RUNNER: The channel of a gating system through which molten metal flows from the sprue to the casting and risers.

SAE: Abbreviation for the Society of Automotive Engineers.

SAFE EDGE: The edge of a file on which no teeth have been cut.

SANDBLAST: The process of cleaning castings and metals by blowing sand at them under very high air pressure.

SAND MOLD CASTING: A process which involves pouring molten metal into a cavity that has been formed in a sand mold.

SCALE: Surface oxidation caused on metal by heating them in air.

SCRAPING: The process of removing an exceedingly small portion of the wearing surfaces of machinery by means of scrapers, in order to bring such surfaces to a precision fit and finish not attainable by ordinary filing techniques.

SCRIBE: To draw a line with a scriber or other sharp pointed tool.

SET-OVER: The distance a lathe tailstock has been offset from the normal center line of the machine. Used in one method of taper turning.

SET UP: The term used to describe the positioning of the workpiece, attachments and cutting tools on a machine tool.

SHEAR SPINNING: A process whereby a metal blank, which may be flat or preformed to some shape, is clamped between the tailstock of the shear spinning machine and a power driven spinning mandrel. The mandrel is the same shape and size as the inside of the finished part, and the metal is forced to flow onto the mandrel by action of the forming rollers.

SHIM: Pieces of sheet metal, available in many thicknesses, that are used between mating parts to provide the proper clearance.

SHRINK FIT: A fit in which the outer member is expanded by heating to permit insertion of the inner member and a tight fit is obtained as the outer member shrinks as it cools. A very tight fit is made and must be considered permanent.

SINE SPINNING: Another name for shear spinning.

SINTERING: A method of bonding metal powders that have been compacted by heating them to a predetermined temperature.

SOLDERING: A method of joining metals by means of a nonferrous filler metal, without fusion of the base metals, and is normally carried out at temperatures lower than 800 deg. F.

SPINNING: A process that involves making a sheet metal disk into hollow shape by pressing a tool against it forcing it against a rotating form (chuck).

SPLINE: A series of grooves, cut lengthwise, around a shaft or hole.

SPOTFACE: To machine a circular spot on the surface of a part to furnish a flat bearing surface for the head of a bolt or nut.

SPRUE HOLE: The opening in a mold into which the molten metal is poured.

SPUR GEAR: A gear having straight teeth that are cut parallel to the direction of rotation. The most commonly used gears.

STAKING: The joining of two parts by upsetting the metal at their junction.

STANDARD: An accepted base for a uniform system of measurement and quality.

STELLITE: An alloy of cobalt, chromium and tungsten used to make high speed cutting tools.

STOPS: Projections on the side of the work table to disengage automatic power feed. Also known as a dog.

STRADDLE MILL: Using two or more milling cutters to perform several milling operations simultaneously.

STRAIGHTEDGE: A precision tool for checking the accuracy of flat surfaces.

STRAIN: A measure of the change in shape or size of a body, compared to the original shape or size.

STRESS: The intensity, at a point in a body, of the internal forces.

STRETCH FORM: A process of forming parts and shapes with large curvatures by stretching the sheet over a form of the desired shape.

SUPER FINISH: A surface finish where surface irregularities have been reduced to a few millionths of an inch to produce an exceptionally smooth and long-wearing surface.

SURFACE PLATE: A plate of iron or granite that has been ground, and sometimes lapped, to a smooth flat surface. It is used to give a base for layout measurements and inspection.

SURFACE ROUGHNESS SCALE: A series of small plates visualizing the degree of roughness for a particular surface. They establish a standard permitting a machinist or an inspector to compare specified finishes visually and by feel.

TANG: The flats or tongue machined on the end of tapered shanks. The tang fits into a slot in the mating part and prevents the taper from rotating in the mating part.

TANTALUM: A metal that is capable of withstanding temperatures in the 2500-4000 deg. F. range. A metal finding more and more use in the space age.

TAP: The tool used to cut internal threads.

TAPER: A piece that increases or decreases in size at a uniform rate to assume a wedge or conical shape.

TAPPING: The operation of producing internal threads with a tap. May be done by hand or machine. Also, the process of removing molten metal from a furnace.

TEMPERING: A sequence in heat treating consisting of reheating quench hardened or normalized parts to a temperature below the transformation range and holding it for a sufficient time to produce the desired properties.

TEMPLATE: A pattern or guide.

TENSILE STRENGTH: The maximum load a piece can support in tension without breaking or failing.

TENSION: The stress due to forces that tend to make a body longer.

THREAD: The act of cutting a screw thread.

THREAD ROLLING: A technique for applying a thread to a bolt or screw by rolling it between two grooved die plates, one of which is in motion, or between rotating circular rolls.

TITANIUM: A metal used for applications that require the properties of lightweight, high strength, and good temperature and corrosion resistance. It weighs only about half as much as steel yet is almost as strong as some commonly used steels.

TOLERANCE: The permissible deviation from a basic dimension.

TOOL CRIB: A room or area in a machine shop where tools and supplies are stored and dispensed as needed.

TOOLROOM: The area or department where tools, jigs, fixtures and dies are manufactured.

TRAIN: A series of meshed gears.

TRUE: On center.

TUMBLER GEARS: Gears in a gear train that can be adjusted to reverse the direction of rotation of the driven gear.

UNIFIED THREADS: A series of screw threads that have been adopted by the United States, Canada, and Great Britain to attain interchangeability of certain screw threads. The revised standard provides greater strength, easier assembly and longer tool life.

UNIVERSAL CHUCK: A chuck on which all jaws move simultaneously at a uniform rate to center round or hexagonal stock automatically.

V-BLOCK: Square or rectangular shaped steel blocks with a 90 deg. V accurately machined through its center. It is provided with a clamp for holding round stock for drilling, milling and laying out operations. The blocks are furnished as pairs and are frequently hardened and ground for additional accuracy.

VENTS: Narrow openings in molds that permit gases generated during pouring to escape.

VERTICAL MILLING ATTACHMENT: A mechanism that can be attached to some milling machines to convert them into vertical milling machines.

V-WAYS: The raised portion on machine tool beds that act as bearing surfaces and guide and align the movable portion of the machine that rides on them. They are shaped like an inverted V.

WAYS: The flat or V-shaped bearing surfaces on a machine that aligns and guides the movable part of the machine that rides on them.

WHEEL DRESSER: A device to true the face of a grinding wheel.

WORK HARDNESS: The name applied to the increase in hardness that develops in metal as a result of cold forming.

WORKING DRAWING: A drawing or drawings that give the machinist the necessary information to make and assemble a mechanism.

Glossary

WRINGING FIT: A fit that is practically metal to metal. It is a selective rather than interchangeable and requires a twisting motion to assemble.

X-RAY: A nondestructive inspection technique that has become a routine step in the acceptance of parts and materials.

ZYGLO: A fluorescent penetrant inspection technique for detecting flaws in nonmagnetic metals and solids.

ACKNOWLEDGEMENTS

While it would indeed be a pleasant task, it would be impossible for one person to develop the material included in a text of this nature by visiting the industries that use the many metalworking techniques and processes described and observing, studying and taking the photos first hand.

My sincere thanks to those who helped in the gathering of the necessary material, information and photographs. Their cooperation was heart warming.

We have endeavored to give credit where due. Any omission was purely accidental.

John R. Walker

FOR FURTHER STUDY

BENCH WORK, Delmar Publishers Inc., Albany, New York.

DRILL PRESS WORK, Delmar Publishers Inc., Albany, New York.

HEAT TREATMENT OF METALS, Delmar Publishers Inc., Albany, New York.

HOW TO RUN A DRILL PRESS, South Bend Lathe Inc., South Bend, Indiana.

HOW TO RUN A SHAPER, South Bend Lathe Inc., South Bend, Indiana.

HOW TO RUN A LATHE, South Bend Lathe Inc., South Bend, Indiana.

LATHE WORK, Delmar Publishers Inc., Albany, New York.

LECTURES IN GRINDING, Norton Company, Worcester, Massachusetts.

MILLING MACHINE WORK, Delmar Publishers Inc., Albany, New York.

MODERN STEELS AND THEIR PRODUCTION, Bethlehem Steel Company, Bethlehem, Pennsylvania.

PRECISION MEASUREMENT, Delmar Publishers Inc., Albany, New York.

SHAPER WORK, Delmar Publishers Inc., Albany, New York.

SHOP THEORY, McGraw-Hill Book Co., Inc., New York, New York.

PROCEDURE HANDBOOK OF ARC WELDING DESIGN AND PRACTICE, The Lincoln Electric Co., Cleveland, Ohio.

WELDING HANDBOOK (Section Two): American Welding Society, New York, New York.

Joseph J. Almon: VISUALIZED BASIC SHEET METAL DRAFTING, The Bruce Publishing Co., Milwaukee, Wisconsin.

A. D. Althouse and C. H. Turnquist: MODERN WELDING PRACTICE, Goodheart-Willcox Co., Inc., Homewood, Illinois.

Arthur C. Ansley: MANUFACTURING METHODS AND PROCESSES, Chilton Company, Philadelphia, Pennsylvania.

T. Gardner Boyd: METALWORKING, Goodheart-Willcox Co., Inc., Homewood, Illinois.

Leroy F. Bruce: SHEET METAL SHOP PRACTICE, American Technical Society, Chicago, Illinois.

Henry D. Burghardt: MACHINE TOOL OPERATIONS - Parts I and II, McGraw-Hill Book Company, Inc., New York, New York.

John L. Ferier: GENERAL METALS, McGraw-Hill Book Co., Inc., New York, New York.

John L. Ferier and Earl E. Tatro: MACHINE TOOL METALWORKING, McGraw-Hill Book Co., Inc., New York, New York.

Roland R. Frazer and Earl L. Bedell: GENERAL METAL, Prentice-Hall, Inc., Englewood Cliffs, New Jersey.

Giachino, Weeks and Brune: WELDING SKILLS AND PRACTICES, American Technical Society, Chicago, Illinois.

Carl Gerbacht and Frank E. Robinson: UNDERSTANDING AMERICA'S INDUSTRIES, McKnight and McKnight, Bloomington, Illinois.

Everett R. Glazner: BASIC METALWORK, The Steck Company, Austin, Texas.

Charles F. Kettering and Allen Orth: AMERICAN BATTLE FOR ABUNDANCE, General Motors Corp., Detroit, Michigan.

Emil F. Kronquist: ART METALWORK, McGraw-Hill Book Company, Inc., New York, New York.

Rupert LeGrand, Editor: THE NEW AMERICAN

Reference

MACHINIST'S HANDBOOK, McGraw-Hill Book Company, Inc., New York, New York.

Oswald A. Ludwig: METALWORKING TECHNOLOGY AND PRACTICE, McKnight and McKnight Publishing Co., Bloomington, Illinois.

Harvey D. Miner and John G. Miller: EXPLORING PATTERNMAKING AND FOUNDRY, D. Van Nostrand Co., Inc., Princeton, New Jersey.

Eric Oberg and F. D. Jones: MACHINERY'S HANDBOOK, The Industrial Press, New York, New York.

S. E. Rusinoff: AUTOMATION IN PRACTICE, American Technical Society, Chicago, Illinois.

S. E. Rusinoff: MANUFACTURING PROCESSES - MATERIALS AND PRODUCTION, American Technical Society, Chicago, Illinois.

John T. Shuman: MACHINE SHOP WORK, American Technical Society, Chicago, Illinois.

Robert E. Smith: UNITS IN ETCHING, SPINNING, RAISING AND TOOLING METAL, McKnight and McKnight Publishing Co., Bloomington, Illinois.

Robert E. Smith: FORGING AND WELDING, McKnight and McKnight Publishing Co., Bloomington, Illinois.

Robert E. Smith: MACHINING OF METAL, McKnight and McKnight Publishing Co., Bloomington, Illinois.

Robert E. Smith: SHEET METAL WORK, McKnight and McKnight Publishing Co., Bloomington, Illinois.

Emanuele Stieri: FUNDAMENTALS OF MACHINE SHOP PRACTICE, Prentice-Hall, Inc., Englewood Cliffs, New Jersey.

Tustison, Kranzusch and Blide: METALWORK ESSENTIALS, The Bruce Publishing Co., Milwaukee, Wisconsin.

Albert M. Wagener and Harlan R. Arthur: MACHINE SHOP THEORY AND PRACTICE, D. Van Nostrand Co., Inc., New York, New York.

PROJECT BOOKS

Henry J. Kauffman: MACHINE SHOP AND FOUNDRY PROJECTS, McKnight and McKnight Publishing Co., Bloomington, Illinois.

Roy E. Knight: MACHINE SHOP PROJECTS, McKnight and McKnight Publishing Co., Bloomington, Illinois.

John R. Walker: PROJECTS FOR METALS, Goodheart-Willcox Co., Inc., Homewood, Illinois.

MACHINE SCREW AND CAP SCREW HEADS

FILLISTER HEAD

SIZE	A	B	C	D
#8	.260	.141	.042	.060
#10	.302	.164	.048	.072
1/4	3/8	.205	.064	.087
5/16	7/16	.242	.077	.102
3/8	9/16	.300	.086	.125
1/2	3/4	.394	.102	.168
5/8	7/8	.500	.128	.215
3/4	1	.590	.144	.258
1	1 5/16	.774	.182	.352

FLAT HEAD

SIZE	A	B	C	D
#8	.320	.092	.043	.037
#10	.372	.107	.048	.044
1/4	1/2	.146	.064	.063
5/16	5/8	.183	.072	.078
3/8	3/4	.220	.081	.095
1/2	7/8	.220	.102	.090
5/8	1 1/8	.293	.128	.125
3/4	1 3/8	.366	.144	.153

ROUND HEAD

SIZE	A	B	C	D
#8	.297	.113	.044	.067
#10	.346	.130	.048	.073
1/4	7/16	.1831	.064	.107
5/16	9/16	.236	.072	.150
3/8	5/8	.262	.081	.160
1/2	13/16	.340	.102	.200
5/8	1	.422	.128	.255
3/4	1 1/4	.526	.144	.320

HEXAGON HEAD

SIZE	A	B	C
1/4	.494	.170	7/16
5/16	.564	.215	1/2
3/8	.635	.246	9/16
1/2	.846	.333	3/4
5/8	1.058	.411	15/16
3/4	1.270	.490	1 1/8
7/8	1.482	.566	1 5/16
1	1.693	.640	1 1/2

SOCKET HEAD

SIZE	A	B	C
#8	.265	.164	1/8
#10	5/16	.190	5/32
1/4	3/8	1/4	3/16
5/16	7/16	5/16	7/32
3/8	9/16	3/8	5/16
7/16	5/8	7/16	5/16
1/2	3/4	1/2	3/8
5/8	7/8	5/8	1/2
3/4	1	3/4	9/16
7/8	1 1/8	7/8	9/16
1	1 5/16	1	5/8

DECIMAL EQUIVALENTS OF PARTS OF AN INCH

Fraction	Decimal	Fraction	Decimal
1/64	0.015625	33/64	0.515625
1/32	0.03125	17/32	0.53125
3/64	0.046875	35/64	0.546875
1/16	0.0625	9/16	0.5625
5/64	0.078125	37/64	0.578125
3/32	0.09375	19/32	0.59375
7/64	0.109375	39/64	0.609375
1/8	0.125	5/8	0.625
9/64	0.140625	41/64	0.640625
5/32	0.15625	21/32	0.65625
11/64	0.171875	43/64	0.671875
3/16	0.1875	11/16	0.6875
13/64	0.203125	45/64	0.703125
7/32	0.21875	23/32	0.71875
15/64	0.234375	47/64	0.734375
1/4	0.25	3/4	0.75
17/64	0.265625	49/64	0.765625
9/32	0.28125	25/32	0.78125
19/64	0.296875	51/64	0.796875
5/16	0.3125	13/16	0.8125
21/64	0.328125	53/64	0.828125
11/32	0.34375	27/32	0.84375
23/64	0.359375	55/64	0.859375
3/8	0.375	7/8	0.875
25/64	0.390625	57/64	0.890625
13/32	0.40625	29/32	0.90625
27/64	0.421875	59/64	0.921875
7/16	0.4375	15/16	0.9375
29/64	0.453125	61/64	0.953125
15/32	0.46875	31/32	0.96875
31/64	0.484375	63/64	0.984375
1/2	0.500	1	1.000

DECIMAL EQUIVALENTS — NUMBER SIZE DRILLS

No.	Size of Drill in Inches	No.	Size of Drill in Inches	No.	Size of Drill in Inches	No.	Size of Drill in Inches
1	.2280	21	.1590	41	.0960	61	.0390
2	.2210	22	.1570	42	.0935	62	.0380
3	.2130	23	.1540	43	.0890	63	.0370
4	.2090	24	.1520	44	.0860	64	.0360
5	.2055	25	.1495	45	.0820	65	.0350
6	.2040	26	.1470	46	.0810	66	.0330
7	.2010	27	.1440	47	.0785	67	.0320
8	.1990	28	.1405	48	.0760	68	.0310
9	.1960	29	.1360	49	.0730	69	.0292
10	.1935	30	.1285	50	.0700	70	.0280
11	.1910	31	.1200	51	.0670	71	.0260
12	.1890	32	.1160	52	.0635	72	.0250
13	.1850	33	.1130	53	.0595	73	.0240
14	.1820	34	.1110	54	.0550	74	.0225
15	.1800	35	.1100	55	.0520	75	.0210
16	.1770	36	.1065	56	.0465	76	.0200
17	.1730	37	.1040	57	.0430	77	.0180
18	.1695	38	.1015	58	.0420	78	.0160
19	.1660	39	.0995	59	.0410	79	.0145
20	.1610	40	.0980	60	.0400	80	.0135

LETTER SIZE DRILLS

Letter	Inches	Letter	Inches
A	0.234	N	0.302
B	0.238	O	0.316
C	0.242	P	0.323
D	0.246	Q	0.332
E	0.250	R	0.339
F	0.257	S	0.348
G	0.261	T	0.358
H	0.266	U	0.368
I	0.272	V	0.377
J	0.277	W	0.386
K	0.281	X	0.397
L	0.290	Y	0.404
M	0.295	Z	0.413

Probable Percentage of Full Thread Produced in Tapped Hole Using Stock Sizes of Drill

Tap	Tap Drill	Decimal Equiv. of Tap Drill	Theoretical % of Thread	Probable Oversize (Mean)	Probable Hole Size	Percentage of Thread	Tap	Tap Drill	Decimal Equiv. of Tap Drill	Theoretical % of Thread	Probable Oversize (Mean)	Probable Hole Size	Percentage of Thread
0-80	56	.0465	83	.0015	.0480	74	8-32	29	.1360	69	.0029	.1389	62
	3/64	.0469	81	.0015	.0484	71		28	.1405	58	.0029	.1434	51
1-64	54	.0550	89	.0015	.0565	81	8-36	29	.1360	78	.0029	.1389	70
	53	.0595	67	.0015	.0610	59		28	.1405	68	.0029	.1434	57
1-72	53	.0595	75	.0015	.0610	67		9/64	.1406	68	.0029	.1435	57
	1/16	.0625	58	.0015	.0640	50	10-24	27	.1440	85	.0032	.1472	79
2-56	51	.0670	82	.0017	.0687	74		26	.1470	79	.0032	.1502	74
	50	.0700	69	.0017	.0717	62		25	.1495	75	.0032	.1527	69
	49	.0730	56	.0017	.0747	49		24	.1520	70	.0032	.1552	64
2-64	50	.0700	79	.0017	.0717	70		23	.1540	67	.0032	.1572	61
	49	.0730	64	.0017	.0747	56		5/32	.1563	62	.0032	.1595	56
3-48	48	.0760	85	.0019	.0779	78		22	.1570	61	.0032	.1602	55
	5/64	.0781	77	.0019	.0800	70	10-32	5/32	.1563	83	.0032	.1595	75
	47	.0785	76	.0019	.0804	69		22	.1570	81	.0032	.1602	73
	46	.0810	67	.0019	.0829	60		21	.1590	76	.0032	.1622	68
	45	.0820	63	.0019	.0839	56		20	.1610	71	.0032	.1642	64
3-56	46	.0810	78	.0019	.0829	69		19	.1660	59	.0032	.1692	51
	45	.0820	73	.0019	.0839	65	12-24	11/64	.1719	82	.0035	.1754	75
	44	.0860	56	.0019	.0879	48		17	.1730	79	.0035	.1765	73
4-40	44	.0860	80	.0020	.0880	74		16	.1770	72	.0035	.1805	66
	43	.0890	71	.0020	.0910	65		15	.1800	67	.0035	.1835	60
	42	.0935	57	.0020	.0955	51		14	.1820	63	.0035	.1855	56
	3/32	.0938	56	.0020	.0958	50	12-28	16	.1770	84	.0035	.1805	77
4-48	42	.0935	68	.0020	.0955	61		15	.1800	78	.0035	.1835	70
	3/32	.0938	68	.0020	.0958	60		14	.1820	73	.0035	.1855	66
	41	.0960	59	.0020	.0980	52		13	.1850	67	.0035	.1885	59
5-40	40	.0980	83	.0023	.1003	76		3/16	.1875	61	.0035	.1910	54
	39	.0995	79	.0023	.1018	71	1/4-20	9	.1960	83	.0038	.1998	77
	38	.1015	72	.0023	.1038	65		8	.1990	79	.0038	.2028	73
	37	.1040	65	.0023	.1063	58		7	.2010	75	.0038	.2048	70
5-44	38	.1015	79	.0023	.1038	72		13/64	.2031	72	.0038	.2069	66
	37	.1040	71	.0023	.1063	63		6	.2040	71	.0038	.2078	65
	36	.1065	63	.0023	.1088	55		5	.2055	69	.0038	.2093	63
6-32	37	.1040	84	.0023	.1063	78		4	.2090	63	.0038	.2128	57
	36	.1065	78	.0026	.1091	71	1/4-28	3	.2130	80	.0038	.2168	72
	7/64	.1094	70	.0026	.1120	64		7/32	.2188	67	.0038	.2226	59
	35	.1100	69	.0026	.1126	63		2	.2210	63	.0038	.2248	55
	34	.1110	67	.0026	.1136	60	5/16-18	F	.2570	77	.0038	.2608	72
	33	.1130	62	.0026	.1156	55		G	.2610	71	.0041	.2651	66
6-40	34	.1110	83	.0026	.1136	75		17/64	.2656	65	.0041	.2697	59
	33	.1130	77	.0026	.1156	69		H	.2660	64	.0041	.2701	59
	32	.1160	68	.0026	.1186	60							

(Concluded on following page)   *(Standard Tool Co.)*

Probable Percentage of Full Thread Produced in Tapped Hole Using Stock Sizes of Drill

Tap	Tap Drill	Decimal Equiv. of Tap Drill	Theoretical % of Thread	Probable Oversize (Mean)	Probable Hole Size	Percentage of Thread
5/16-24	H	.2660	86	.0041	.2701	78
	I	.2720	75	.0041	.2761	67
	J	.2770	66	.0041	.2811	58
3/8-16	5/16	.3125	77	.0044	.3169	72
	O	.3160	73	.0044	.3204	68
	P	.3230	64	.0044	.3274	59
3/8-24	21/64	.3281	87	.0044	.3325	79
	Q	.3320	79	.0044	.3364	71
	R	.3390	67	.0044	.3434	58
7/16-14	T	.3580	86	.0046	.3626	81
	23/64	.3594	84	.0046	.3640	79
	U	.3680	75	.0046	.3726	70
	3/8	.3750	67	.0046	.3796	62
	V	.3770	65	.0046	.3816	60
7/16-20	W	.3860	79	.0046	.3906	72
	25/64	.3906	72	.0046	.3952	65
	X	.3970	62	.0046	.4016	55
1/2-13	27/64	.4219	78	.0047	.4266	73
	7/16	.4375	63	.0047	.4422	58
1/2-20	29/64	.4531	72	.0047	.4578	65
9/16-12	15/32	.4688	87	.0048	.4736	82
	31/64	.4844	72	.0048	.4892	68
9/16-18	1/2	.5000	87	.0048	.5048	80
	33/64	.5156	65	.0048	.5204	58
5/8-11	17/32	.5313	79	.0049	.5362	75
	35/64	.5469	66	.0049	.5518	62
5/8-18	9/16	.5625	87	.0049	.5674	80
	37/64	.5781	65	.0049	.5831	58
3/4-10	41/64	.6406	84	.0050	.6456	80
	21/32	.6563	72	.0050	.6613	68
3/4-16	11/16	.6875	77	.0050	.6925	71
7/8-9	49/64	.7656	76	.0052	.7708	72
	25/32	.7812	65	.0052	.7864	61
7/8-14	51/64	.7969	84	.0052	.8021	79
	13/16	.8125	67	.0052	.8177	62
1"-8	55/64	.8594	87	.0059	.8653	83
	7/8	.8750	77	.0059	.8809	73
	57/64	.8906	67	.0059	.8965	64
	29/32	.9063	58	.0059	.9122	54
1"-12	29/32	.9063	87	.0060	.9123	81
	59/64	.9219	72	.0060	.9279	67
	15/16	.9375	58	.0060	.9435	52

Tap	Tap Drill	Decimal Equiv. of Tap Drill	Theoretical % of Thread	Probable Oversize (Mean)	Probable Hole Size	Percentage of Thread
1"-14	59/64	.9219	84	.0060	.9279	78
	15/16	.9375	67	.0060	.9435	61
1 1/8-7	31/32	.9688	84	.0062	.9750	81
	63/64	.9844	76	.0067	.9911	72
	1"	1.0000	67	.0070	1.0070	64
	1 1/64	1.0156	59	.0070	1.0226	55
1 1/8-12	1 1/32	1.0313	87	.0071	1.0384	80
	1 3/64	1.0469	72	.0072	1.0541	66
1 1/4-7	1 3/32	1.0938	84			
	1 7/64	1.1094	76			
	1 1/8	1.1250	67			
1 1/4-12	1 5/32	1.1563	87			
	1 11/64	1.1719	72			
1 3/8-6	1 3/16	1.1875	87			
	1 13/64	1.2031	79		No	
	1 7/32	1.2188	72		Test Results	
	1 15/64	1.2344	65		Available	
1 3/8-12	1 9/32	1.2813	87			
	1 19/64	1.2969	72		Reaming	
1 1/2-6	1 5/16	1.3125	87		Recommended	
	1 21/64	1.3281	79			
	1 11/32	1.3438	72			
	1 23/64	1.3594	65			
1 1/2-12	1 13/32	1.4063	87			
	1 27/64	1.4219	72			

Taper Pipe		Straight Pipe	
Thread	Drill	Thread	Drill
1/8-27	R	1/8-27	S
1/4-18	7/16	1/4-18	29/64
3/8-18	37/64	3/8-18	19/32
1/2-14	23/32	1/2-14	47/64
3/4-14	59/64	3/4-14	15/16
1-11 1/2	1 5/32	1-11 1/2	1 3/16
1 1/4-11 1/2	1 1/2	1 1/4-11 1/2	1 33/64
1 1/2-11 1/2	1 47/64	1 1/2-11 1/2	1 3/4
2-11 1/2	2 7/32	2-11 1/2	2 7/32
2 1/2-8	2 5/8	2 1/2-8	2 21/32
3-8	3 1/4	3-8	3 9/32
3 1/2-8	3 3/4	3 1/2-8	3 25/32
4-8	4 1/4	4-8	4 9/32

SCREW THREAD ELEMENTS FOR UNIFIED AND NATIONAL FORM OF THREAD

Threads per Inch (n)	Pitch (p) $p = \frac{1}{n}$	Single Height — Subtract from Basic Major Diameter to Get Basic Pitch Diam.	Double Height — Subtract from Basic Major Diameter to Get Basic Minor Diam.	83⅓% Double Height — Subtract from Basic Major Diam. to Get Minor Diam. of Ring Gage	Basic Width of Crest and Root Flat $\frac{p}{8}$	Constant for Best Size Wire also Single Height of 60° V-Thread	Diameter of Best Size Wire
3	.333333	.216506	.43301	.36084	.0417	.28868	.19245
3¼	.307692	.199852	.39970	.33309	.0385	.26647	.17765
3½	.285714	.185577	.37115	.30929	.0357	.24744	.16496
4	.250000	.162379	.32476	.27063	.0312	.21651	.14434
4½	.222222	.144337	.28867	.24056	.0278	.19245	.12830
5	.200000	.129903	.25981	.21650	.0250	.17321	.11547
5½	.181818	.118093	.23619	.19682	.0227	.15746	.10497
6	.166666	.108253	.21651	.18042	.0208	.14434	.09623
7	.142857	.092788	.18558	.15465	.0179	.12372	.08248
8	.125000	.081189	.16238	.13531	.0156	.10825	.07217
9	.111111	.072168	.14434	.12028	.0139	.09623	.06415
10	.100000	.064952	.12990	.10825	.0125	.08660	.05774
11	.090909	.059046	.11809	.09841	.0114	.07873	.05249
11½	.086956	.056480	.11296	.09413	.0109	.07531	.05020
12	.083333	.054127	.10826	.09021	.0104	.07217	.04811
13	.076923	.049963	.09993	.08327	.0096	.06662	.04441
14	.071428	.046394	.09279	.07732	.0089	.06186	.04124
16	.062500	.040595	.08119	.06766	.0078	.05413	.03608
18	.055555	.036086	.07217	.06014	.0069	.04811	.03208
20	.050000	.032475	.06495	.05412	.0062	.04330	.02887
22	.045454	.029523	.05905	.04920	.0057	.03936	.02624
24	.041666	.027063	.05413	.04510	.0052	.03608	.02406
27	.037037	.024056	.04811	.04009	.0046	.03208	.02138
28	.035714	.023197	.04639	.03866	.0045	.03093	.02062
30	.033333	.021651	.04330	.03608	.0042	.02887	.01925
32	.031250	.020297	.04059	.03383	.0039	.02706	.01804
36	.027777	.018042	.03608	.03007	.0035	.02406	.01604
40	.025000	.016237	.03247	.02706	.0031	.02165	.01443
44	.022727	.014761	.02952	.02460	.0028	.01968	.01312
48	.020833	.013531	.02706	.02255	.0026	.01804	.01203
50	.020000	.012990	.02598	.02165	.0025	.01732	.01155
56	.017857	.011598	.02320	.01933	.0022	.01546	.01031
60	.016666	.010825	.02165	.01804	.0021	.01443	.00962
64	.015625	.010148	.02030	.01691	.0020	.01353	.00902
72	.013888	.009021	.01804	.01503	.0017	.01203	.00802
80	.012500	.008118	.01624	.01353	.0016	.01083	.00722
90	.011111	.007217	.01443	.01202	.0014	.00962	.00642
96	.010417	.006766	.01353	.01127	.0013	.00902	.00601
100	.010000	.006495	.01299	.01082	.0012	.00866	.00577
120	.008333	.005413	.01083	.00902	.0010	.00722	.00481

Using the Best Size Wires, the measurement over three wires minus the Constant for Best Size Wire equals the Pitch Diameter.

STANDARD SYSTEM OF MARKING

GENERAL

Taps, dies, and other threading tools will be marked with the nominal size, number of threads per inch, and the proper symbol to identify the thread form. These symbols are in agreement with the A.S.A. B1-7-1949 Standard on Nomenclature, Definitions and Letter Symbols for Screw Threads.

The markings for the British Threads are the fully abbreviated form based on the data in the British Standard Institute, Specification No. 84-1940.

SYMBOLS USED FOR AMERICAN THREADS ARE:

Symbol	Reference
NC	American National Coarse Thread Series
NF	American National Fine Thread Series
NEF	American National Extra Fine Thread Series
N	American National 8, 12 and 16 Thread Series (8N, 12N, 16N)
NH	American (National) Hose Coupling and Fire Hose Coupling Threads
NM	National Miniature Screw Thread
NGO	American (National) Gas Outlet Thread
NS	American Special Thread (60° Thread Form)
NPT	American (National) Taper Pipe Thread
NPTF	Dryseal American (National) Taper Pipe Thread
PTF	Dryseal SAE Short Internal Taper Pipe Thread
ANPT	Military Aeronautical Pipe Thread Specification MIL-P-7105
NPS	American (National) Straight Pipe Thread
NPSC	American (National) Straight Pipe Thread in Pipe Couplings
NPSF	Dryseal American (National) Fuel Internal Straight Pipe Thread
NPSH	American (Standard) Straight Pipe Thread for Hose Couplings and Nipples
NPSI	Dryseal American (National) Intermediate Internal Straight Pipe Thread
NPSL	American (National) Internal Straight Pipe Thread for Locknut Connections (Loose Fitting Mechanical Joints)
NPSM	American (National) Internal Straight Pipe Thread for Mechanical Joints (Free Fitting)
NPTR	American (National) Internal Taper Pipe Thread for Railing Joints (Mechanical Joints)
AMO	American Standard Microscope Objective Thread
ACME C	Acme Screw Thread — Centralizing Type
ACME G	Acme Screw Thread — General Purpose Type
STUB ACME	Stub Acme Threads
N. BUTT	National Buttress Screw Thread
V	A 60° "V" Thread with Truncated Crests and Roots. The Theoretical "V" Form is usually flatted several thousandths of an inch to the user's specifications.
SB	Manufacturers Stovebolt Standard Thread
STI	Special Threads for Helical Coil Wire Screw Thread Inserts

SYMBOLS USED FOR BRITISH THREADS ARE:

Symbol	Reference
BSW	British Standard Whitworth Coarse Thread Series
BSF	British Standard Fine Thread Series
BSP	British Standard Taper Pipe Thread
BSPP	British Standard Pipe (Parallel) Thread
WHIT	Whitworth Standard Special Thread
BA	British Association Standard Thread

BENT SHANK TAPPER TAPS

In addition to the regular marking, bent shank tapper taps will be marked with the table number to which they are made.

GROUND THREAD TAPS — LIMIT NUMBERS

All standard Ground Thread Taps made to Tables 327 and 329 will be marked with the letter G to designate Ground Thread. The letter G will be followed by the letter H to designate above basic (L below basic) and a numeral to designate the Pitch Diameter limits.

Example: G H3 Indicates a Ground Thread Tap with Pitch Diameter limits .0010 to .0015 over basic.

Pitch Diameter limits for Taps to 1″ diameter inclusive.

L1 = Basis to Basic minus .0005
H1 = Basic to Basic plus .0005
H2 = Basic plus .0005 to Basic plus .0010
H3 = Basic plus .0010 to Basic plus .0015
H4 = Basic plus .0015 to Basic plus .0020
H5 = Basic plus .0020 to Basic plus .0025
H6 = Basic plus .0025 to Basic plus .0030

(Morse Twist Drill & Machine Co.)

DRILL SIZES FOR TAPER PINS

TAPER PIN AND REAMER SIZE*

Length of Pins	6/0	5/0	4/0	3/0	2/0	0	1	2	3	4	5	6	7	8	9	10
*3/8	50	44	38	32	29											
*1/2	51	45	39	33	30							P				
*5/8	52	46	41	34	30	27						O				
*3/4	1/16	47	42	7/64	1/8	27	21					5/16	W			
*1		49	44	37	31	9/64	5/32	16	13/64	15/64		N	V			
*1 1/4					32	29	25	11/64	9	1	I	N	V			
*1 1/2						30	26	19	10	2	H	M	U	21/64	35/64	43/64
*1 3/4						*1/8	*9/64	20	3/16	7/32	G	M	U	21/64	35/64	21/32
*2						*31	*29	*5/32	14	3	F	L	23/64	21/64	35/64	21/32
*2 1/4						*33	*30	*25	*16	4	E	9/32	T	7/16	17/32	21/32
*2 1/2						*7/64	*31	*26	*11/64	*13/64	D	J	S	7/16	17/32	41/64
*2 3/4						*37	*33	*28	*19	*8	C	*I	11/32	7/16	17/32	41/64
*3						*40	*35	*29	*21	*11	*B	*H	R	27/64	33/64	41/64
*3 1/4						*42		*30	*5/32	*3/16	*1	*G	Q	27/64	33/64	5/8
*3 1/2									*24	*14	*2	*F	*Q	27/64	33/64	5/8
*3 3/4									*26	*16	*2	*1/4	*P	Z	1/2	5/8
*4										*17	*3	*D	*O	Z	1/2	39/64
*4 1/4										*19	*4	*C	*O	13/32	1/2	39/64
*4 1/2											*5	*B	*5/16	Y	31/64	39/64
*4 3/4													*N	X	31/64	19/32
*5														*25/64	31/64	19/32
*5 1/4														*W	15/32	19/32
*5 1/2															*15/32	37/64
*5 3/4															*15/32	37/64
*6															*29/64	37/64

* Hole sizes too small to admit taper pin reamers of standard length. Special, extra length reamers are required for these cases.

FEEDS AND SPEEDS FOR HIGH SPEED STEEL
DRILLS, REAMERS AND TAPS

Material	Brinell	Drills			Reamers		Taps — S.F.M.			
		S.F.M.	Point	Feed	S.F.M.	Feed	Threads per Inch			
							3-7½	8-15	16-24	25-Up
Aluminum	99–101	200–250	118°	M	150–160	M	50	100	150	200
Aluminum bronze	170–187	60	118°	M	40–45	M	12	25	45	60
Bakelite	....	80	60°–90°	M	50–60	M	50	100	150	200
Brass	192–202	200–250	118°	H	150–160	H	50	100	150	200
Bronze, common	166–183	200–250	118°	H	150–160	H	40	80	100	150
Bronze, phosphor, ½ hard	187–202	175–180	118°	M	130–140	M	25	40	50	80
Bronze, phosphor, soft	149–163	200–250	118°	H	150–160	H	40	80	100	150
Cast iron, soft	126	140–150	90°	H	100–110	H	30	60	90	140
Cast iron, medium soft	196	80–110	118°	M	50–65	M	25	40	50	80
Cast iron, hard	293–302	45–50	118°	L	67–75	L	10	20	30	40
Cast iron, chilled*	402	15	150°	L	8–10	L	5	5	10	10
Cast steel	286–302	40–50*	118°	L	70–75	L	20	30	40	50
Celluloid	....	100	90°	M	75–80	M	50	100	150	200
Copper	80–85	70	100°	L	45–55	L	40	80	100	150
Drop forgings (steel)	170–196	60	118°	M	40–45	M	12	25	45	60
Duralumin	90–104	200	118°	M	150–160	M	50	100	150	200
Everdur	179–207	60	118°	L	40–45	L	20	30	40	50
Machinery steel	170–196	110	118°	H	67–75	H	35	50	60	85
Magnet steel, soft	241–302	35–40	118°	M	20–25	M	20	40	50	75
Magnet steel, hard*	321–512	15	150°	L	10	L	5	10	15	25
Manganese steel, 7–13%*	187–217	15	150°	L	10	L	15	20	25	30
Manganese copper, 30% Mn.*	134	15	150°	L	10–12	L	..	..	..	..
Malleable iron	112–126	85–90	118°	H	....	H	20	30	40	50
Mild steel, .20–.30 C	170–202	110–120	118°	H	75–85	H	40	55	70	90
Molybdenum steel	196–235	55	125°	M	35–45	M	20	30	35	45
Monel metal	149–170	50	118°	M	35–38	M	8	10	15	20
Nickel, pure*	187–202	75	118°	L	40	L	25	40	50	80
Nickel steel, 3½%	196–241	60	118°	L	40–45	L	8	10	15	20
Rubber, hard	....	100	60°–90°	L	70–80	L	50	100	150	200
Screw stock, C.R.	170–196	110	118°	H	75	H	20	30	40	50
Spring steel	402	20	150°	L	12–15	L	10	10	15	15
Stainless steel	146–149	50	118°	M	30	M	8	10	15	20
Stainless steel, C.R.*	460–477	20	118°	L	15	L	8	10	15	20
Steel, .40 to .50 C	170–196	80	118°	M	8–10	M	20	30	40	50
Tool, S.A.E., and Forging steel	149	75	118°	H	35–40	H	25	35	45	55
Tool, S.A.E., and Forging steel	241	50	125°	M	12	M	15	15	25	25
Tool, S.A.E., and Forging steel*	402	15	150°	L	10	L	8	10	15	20
Zinc alloy	112–126	200–250	118°	M	150–175	M	50	100	150	200

*Use specially constructed heavy duty drills.
Carbon Steel Tools should be run at speeds 40% to 50% of those recommended for High Speed.
Spiral Point Taps may be run at speeds 15% to 20% faster than regular Taps.
See pages 50 through 65 for tables of Surface Feet per Minute (S.F.M.) vs. Revolutions per Minute (R.P.M.).

DRILL FEED PER REVOLUTION IN INCHES   REAMER FEED

Reference Symbol	Diameter of Drill — Inches					All Diameters
	Under ⅛	⅛ to ¼	¼ to ½	½ to 1	Over 1" Diameter	
L — Light	.001	.002	.003	.005	.006	Use a feed equal to two or three times that recommended for Drills.
M — Medium	.0015	.003	.006	.010	.012	
H — Heavy	.0025	.005	.010	.020	.025	

INDEX

Index

Index

Index

Wheels, grinding, 33-10
Wilkinson, John, 4-26
Wired edge, 19-14
Work mounting in lathe, 36-18
Wrench safety, 15-5
Wrenches, unit on, 15-1 to 15-5

Wrought iron,
 finishing, 27-13
 work, assembling, 27-10
Wrought metal,
 bending, 27-4
 bending and shaping, 27-2

 safety, 27-3
 unit on, 27-1 to 27-14
X
X-ray testing, 49-2
Z
Zinc, 1-14